A MANUAL OF
ELEMENTARY ZOOLOGY

Members of a snow fauna.

An example of the possession, by a group of different animals living in the same
locality of common features, which enable them to support life there (see p.
662). Note the thick, white clothing, which keeps them warm and renders
them inconspicuous. The animals shown, which are drawn from an exhibit in
the British Museum (Natural History), are the Arctic fox, Stoat or Ermine,
Weasel, Mountain hare, Willow grouse and Ptarmigan. They come from the
south of Norway, and assume this covering in winter. Others, such as the
Polar bear, Snowy owl, and Greenland falcon, living amid perpetual snows, are
clad in the same way all the year round.

OXFORD MEDICAL PUBLICATIONS

A MANUAL OF ELEMENTARY ZOOLOGY

BY

L. A. BORRADAILE, Sc.D.

FELLOW OF SELWYN COLLEGE, CAMBRIDGE, AND
SOMETIME LECTURER IN ZOOLOGY IN THE UNIVERSITY

ELEVENTH EDITION

OXFORD UNIVERSITY PRESS

LONDON   NEW YORK   TORONTO

1945

OXFORD UNIVERSITY PRESS
AMEN HOUSE, E.C.4
London Edinburgh Glasgow New York
Toronto Melbourne Capetown Bombay
Calcutta Madras
HUMPHREY MILFORD
PUBLISHER TO THE UNIVERSITY

First Edition 1912
Second ,, ... 1918
Third ,, ... 1920
Fourth ,, ... 1923
    Second Impression . . . 1924
Fifth Edition 1926
Sixth ,, ... 1928
    Second Impression Revised . 1930
    Third Impression 1931
Seventh Edition 1932
    Second Impression . . . 1933
Eighth Edition 1935
Ninth ,, ... 1938
    Second Impression . . . 1939
Tenth Edition 1941
    Second Impression 1943
Eleventh Edition 1945

BOOK
PRODUCTION
WAR ECONOMY
STANDARD

THE PAPER AND BINDING OF
THIS BOOK CONFORM TO THE
AUTHORIZED ECONOMY STANDARDS

PRINTED IN GREAT BRITAIN BY
MORRISON AND GIBB LTD., LONDON AND EDINBURGH

CHAPTER XXVIII

TO THE STUDENT

1. *If you are using this book only in preparation for a preliminary medical or some similar examination,* you should begin by reading the first chapter ; then read the large print of those chapters which deal with the animals specified in the schedule of your examination, and section A of the Appendix ; then by means of the Index find and re-read the passages on the various general topics which come within the scope of the examination. At a later stage in your medical studies you may find useful those pages which deal with parasites of man.

2. *If you are taking a general course in Zoology,* read straight through the book.

3. *In any case* (*a*) read at least twice, once to get a general view of the subject, and a second time to learn its details ; (*b*) do not omit to look up the references given from one page to another ; (*c*) make full use of the figures, identifying each detail they contain as you come to it in the text, and afterwards studying each figure by itself with the aid of the explanation attached to it. Note that some of the figures needed for certain chapters are placed with the corresponding paragraphs of the Appendix.

4. Note also that discussions of various general topics (such as digestion, the functions of the blood, the lay-out of the vertebrate skeleton, the general features of joints and muscles, histology, etc.), are to be found in the earlier chapters, particularly in those on the frog, and are not repeated in those which treat of other animals when mention is made of special features of the latter. Therefore if, for instance, the dogfish or the rabbit is the animal which is treated in most detail in your course of study, in reading for it you must look up these topics in the earlier chapters. A number of references are given to help you in this.

5. You will find the Index of use not only in searching for particular pieces of information, but also in getting a connected view of all that you have read on any subject.

from the disintegration of substances in itself. But life differs from the other processes, and from all processes that go on in lifeless things, in that its energy is liberated in such a way as to tend to the preservation and increase of the thing in which it goes on—that is, of the living being.

The mode in which the living body avails itself of energy contained in its own substance depends upon the following facts. Whenever atoms unite to form molecules, energy is set free, and the stabler the molecules formed, the greater, almost invariably, is the amount of energy liberated at their formation. The same amount of energy must be used to break up a molecule as was set free when it was formed. The molecules that compose the substances from which the body obtains its energy contain carbon, hydrogen, oxygen, and sometimes nitrogen and other elements, and are complex and relatively unstable and rich in energy. The body breaks down these molecules so as to form smaller and more stable molecules. The energy which is freed in the formation of the stabler molecules is so much greater than that which is required to break down those that are less stable that a large balance of energy is set free, and becomes available for the work of life. Usually the breaking-down process is continued until the carbon and hydrogen atoms are in the very small and stable molecules of carbon dioxide and water—that is to say, it is a complete oxidation. But it is not always so. The substances which are broken down never contain enough oxygen to combine with all the carbon and hydrogen in their molecules, and therefore many animals and plants which live in surroundings from which they cannot obtain additional oxygen are unable to complete the process of disintegration. Thus the fungus known as Yeast, living in solutions which contain no dissolved oxygen, breaks down the sugar glucose according to the following equation :

$$C_6H_{12}O_6 = 2C_2H_6O + 2CO_2$$
$$\text{(Glucose)} \qquad \text{(Alcohol)}$$

leaving, as an unoxidised residue, the alcohol, of whose production man avails himself in brewing. Similarly, many animals which are internal parasites, or otherwise live in situations which lack free oxygen, break down the substance glycogen (which is related to starch) so as to form lactic acid, according to the equation :

$$(C_6H_{10}O_5)n + nH_2O = 2nC_3H_6O_3$$
$$\text{(Glycogen)} \qquad\qquad \text{(Lactic acid)}$$

Animals and plants which carry out such processes as these are said to be *anaerobic*. Their mode of obtaining energy, since it leaves a residue containing energy of which they have not availed themselves, is wasteful as compared with that of the majority of living beings, which are *aerobic*, that is, draw from their surroundings—air or water (see p. 5)—free oxygen, and with it complete the oxidation of the substances from which they obtain their energy. The obtaining of free energy by the disintegration of complex substances is familiar to us in various processes employed by man. Thus the energy imparted to a bullet by an explosive is liberated, like the energy of anaerobic animals and plants, by a decomposition without importing oxygen, while the energy of a petrol or steam engine or the light of a candle is obtained by the use of oxygen from the air in combustion, like the energy of aerobic beings.

It is not difficult to prove that this disintegration is taking place in the body. The breaking down of the molecules which are destroyed forms, as we have seen, carbon dioxide and water. Since many of the disintegrated molecules contain nitrogen, there are formed also certain fairly simple nitrogenous compounds, such as urea, $CO(NH_2)_2$. (1) The intake of oxygen and loss of carbon dioxide during life are easily demonstrated. Men or animals enclosed in a vessel to which air has not access are unable to live for more than a short time. The animals are stifled, just as a fire or the flame of a candle may be stifled, by want of air, and subsequent examination of the gases in the vessel will show that the oxygen has been depleted and replaced by carbon dioxide, just as it would be if a candle had been burnt in it. This loss of carbon dioxide and the intake of oxygen which usually accompanies it are characteristic of living animals and are known as *Respiration*.[1] In man and animals like him, they take place through the lungs, in breathing. If the breath be tested, it will be found to have undergone the same changes as the air in a vessel in which an animal has been stifled. Fishes and other aquatic animals use the oxygen which is held in solution in the water in which they live. They usually respire by means of structures known as gills, which offer to the water a large surface upon which gases can be exchanged ; of these we shall consider examples when we study the crayfish and dog-fish. The necessity for renewing by aeration the dissolved oxygen in the water of an aquarium is due to the respiration of the inhabitants. (2) The nitrogenous waste matters may be identified by chemical analysis in excreta such as the urine of man. (3) The formation of water is less easily demonstrated, because the bulk of the water lost to the body has been taken in as such through the mouth to perform certain indispensable functions, one of which is the washing out of nitrogenous waste substances, which are harmful, but a careful comparison of the quantities of water which enter and leave the body shows that more goes out than has entered.

While the chemical processes by which energy is liberated in the body are all of the general character which we have just outlined, they are nevertheless varied in detail and extremely complicated. Oxidation takes place, not by single reactions between oxygen and the substances which are ultimately oxidised, but by chains of reactions. These cannot here be described **Complications : Wear and Tear.** more fully. It must, however, be mentioned that, besides those processes in which by the disintegration of certain substances energy is liberated, there is involved a considerable loss of material by wear and tear of the more permanent part of the living matter in which the oxidised substances are contained.

The energy freed in the disintegration of the body-

[1] The student is apt to be puzzled by the fact that this term is used in different senses. In modern Botany it denotes the oxidations by which the energy of the processes of life is liberated. In Medicine and Zoology it retains its original meaning, and is applied to that exchange of gases with the surroundings which is necessitated by the oxidations in the body.

substance appears, as we have seen, in various processes. The most characteristic and important of these are contraction, chemical work, excretion, secretion, and the conduction of impulses. *Contraction* is the process by which mechanical movements are carried out. In it a portion of the living substance changes in shape but not in size, growing shorter in one direction but thicker in others. This may easily be felt in the working of any of the great muscles of the human body, as when the well-known " biceps," in shortening to pull up the forearm, grows at the same time thicker. Instances of *chemical activity* are seen in the formation of the constituents of the many juices which are used for various purposes in the body. Thus the " gastric juice," by which food is digested and disinfected in the stomach, contains among other substances hydrochloric acid, whose formation in face of the alkalinity of the blood involves very considerable chemical work. Other examples of liquids formed for special purposes are the spittle or saliva which helps in the swallowing and digestion of food, tears which wash clean the surface of the eyes, and so forth. The regions in which materials are thus formed are known as *glands*. Again, a part of the energy liberated in the body is used in the discharge of materials from the substance of the body. We have seen that in the process of disintegration there arise waste products of which the body gets rid ; with these it casts out poisonous or excessive materials absorbed from the food. We have just seen also that certain activities of the body consist in the chemical manufacture of materials which are not purely waste but have their uses to the body. The casting out from the substance of the glands of the materials of these two classes, and of the water in which they are dissolved, is a necessary part of the working of the bodily machine. The harmful or excessive products are got rid of because they are injurious, and the products of chemical manufacture are removed in order to be of use elsewhere. Both kinds of material are accordingly shed, sometimes upon the surface of the body, but usually into tubes known as *ducts*, in which they flow to the required locality. This shedding out is a

Appearance of the liberated energy in various forms.

distinct process, carried on by an exercise of the activity of the living substance of the body. No real distinction can be drawn between the two cases, but the process is called *excretion* when the substances cast out are purely waste, as in the urine, and *secretion* when they are of some further use to the body, as in the gastric juice. Finally, an expenditure of energy is involved in the conveyance of impulses which bring about events in the body from the localities where the impulses are started by stimuli (p. 8) to the localities in which the events take place. Thus, when a drop of water which has fallen upon the skin is brushed off, an impulse is started in the skin and conveyed along those tracts of the body which we know as nerves till it causes such movements of the muscles of the arms as are necessary to brush off the drop. This property in living matter of conveying impulses is known as *con-ductivity*, and it involves the evolution of energy by disintegration in the conducting substance.

It should be noted that the forms in which the energy of the body is used in these and other processes are very different. Besides mechanical movement, the exhibition of *molar* energy, it may bring about *chemical* changes, or become *heat*, as is shown by its warming the human body, or *light*, as in the glow-worm, or *electricity*, as in the well-known electric eel, and less conspicuously in many events in the human and other living bodies ; and there are other processes, such as secretion, its action in which has not yet been certainly compared with any event in the lifeless world.

That all this expenditure of energy is so directed as to be of service to the creature in which it takes place is due to two properties of the living being which **Irritability.** are known as *Irritability* and *Automatism*. These properties reside, of course, in the living substance (protoplasm) which usually forms only a part of a body which is alive. Irritability is the property of acting in response to external events. Thus, in various animals, the coming into sight of an enemy will cause action in the form of flight or preparation for defence ; the smell of food sets the mouth watering ; a sound will wake a sleeper ; and so forth. The events external to a living being which directly affect it so that it responds by action are known as *stimuli*. Two things must be noted concerning the activity started by them. Firstly, that its energy is derived, as we have seen, not from without, as when a change is brought about in water by heating it, but from within, as when a change is brought about in gunpowder by heating it. Secondly, that the extent of the internal change bears no relation to that of the external one which acts as its stimulus. Thus, when, in response to a command, a man lifts a heavy load, the energy of the sound-waves which call forth this reaction is immeasurably smaller than that of the work done by the man, and either may be greater or less without a corresponding alteration in the other.

Activity, however, is not necessarily associated with **Automatism.** irritability. The activity of living animals is characterised by a feature which is sometimes held to be in its essence the very opposite of irritability. This feature is called *automatism*. Automatism is the occurrence in the body of activity which is not the direct result of any stimulus from without. The simplest instance of this is the beating of the heart. In view of the great number of stimuli which the body is always receiving, and of the fact that one internal event can act as a stimulus to bring about another, it is necessary to be cautious in attributing an automatic character to any action, but much activity is at least not due to any stimuli that we can trace, and numerous happenings which follow stimuli are rather the modifying of processes that are already going on than the initiation of entirely new action. Indeed the response to external events which is so conspicuous in the living being is set against a background of automatic procedure. In any case, the processes that we are next to study are not direct responses to external events.

It is, as we have seen, characteristic of the living body **Incorporation** to be continually wasting its substance by **of Food :** disintegration in producing energy for its **(a) Foodstuffs** activity. Clearly this could not go on in- **and Digestion.** definitely without some compensating repair. The waste is made good by the *incorporation* of food. Two distinct processes may be recognised in incorporation

—absorption and assimilation. Before it can be absorbed the food of animals has generally to undergo a preliminary process of *digestion*, whereby solid or indiffusible nutriment which it contains is made soluble and diffusible. The food must always contain the following materials : (1) *water*, which is of the highest importance both as an essential constituent of the living matter (protoplasm) and also because it is used in the body for transporting substances in solution, as in the blood and urine, (2) certain *inorganic salts*, such as the chlorides and phosphates of sodium, potassium, and calcium, (3) the very complex compounds known as *proteins*. A protein is a colloid substance consisting of carbon, hydrogen, nitrogen, and oxygen, with small quantities of sulphur and sometimes phosphorus. A familiar example is the " albumin " which, mixed with water, forms white of egg. Proteins are very complex linkages of amino-acids.

An amino-acid is a compound which contains both the basic radicle NH_2 and the acid group COOH. A simple example is Amino-acetic acid or Glycine, $CH_2.NH_2.COOH$.

Thus in the complicated chemistry of the body proteins are able to exercise the power, which amino-acids have, of uniting either with acids or with bases ; and on final disintegration they always yield their nitrogen in a form related to ammonia. The proteins of the body are many, and even those of similar parts in different animals are slightly different. That the food does not consist of proteins identical with those of the body it is entering does not matter, since in digestion proteins are resolved into the amino-acids of which they are composed and the animal so recombines these as to meet its own needs. The food must, however, supply the right amino-acids in sufficient quantities. It is found, for instance, that mice fed upon a diet in which the only protein present is zein, the protein of maize, which does not contain the important constituent tryptophane, are unable to support life. Proteins are the one indispensable organic item in the food of all animals, because, while, like other substances that we shall mention below, they can be oxidised to provide energy, it is they alone that can make good the protein matter that every living body contains and loses by wear and tear (p. 5) and also that can provide such material for growth. When they are used for fuel the nitrogen is discharged from their molecules as ammonia. This is *deamination* ; it is the ultimate source of most of the nitrogenous compounds which we mentioned above as forming part of the excreta. Besides these substances the food usually contains (4) *carbohydrates* (sugars, starches, and related substances), (5) *fats*. It is chiefly these two classes of substances that are oxidised to provide energy. Both contain carbon, hydrogen, and oxygen. In carbohydrates the oxygen is present in exactly the proportions to oxidise the hydrogen, as in cane sugar and malt sugar or maltose, which both have the formula $C_{12}H_{22}O_{11}$, grape sugar or glucose, $C_6H_{12}O_6$, and starch $(C_6H_{10}O_5)n$. In fats there is relatively less oxygen ; therefore they require for complete combustion more of that element than is needed to oxidise the carbon, and their potential energy is greater than that of carbohydrates. In digestion, insoluble carbohydrates, such as starch, are dissolved by conversion into glucose, and fats are split into soluble components—fatty acids and glycerine.

Both these processes, and also the digestion of protein, are *hydrolyses*—decompositions into smaller molecules with the aid of water taken up. Thus :

$$2(C_6H_{10}O_5)n + nH_2O = nC_{12}H_{22}O_{11}$$
(Starch)   (Maltose)

$$C_{12}H_{22}O_{11} + H_2O = 2C_6H_{12}O_6$$
(Maltose)   (Glucose)

and again :

$$(C_{17}H_{35}COO)_3C_3H_5 + 3HO_2 = 3C_{17}H_{35}COOH + C_3H_5(OH)_3$$
(the fat Stearin)   (Stearic acid)   (Glycerine)

They are all brought about by organic catalysts (enzymes, p. 61). Starches and proteins pass through several intermediate stages before their digestion is completed.

Since proteins, carbohydrates, and fats are among the compounds known as " organic," which, in nature, are found only in the bodies of plants and animals and in their remains, all animals require for food such bodies. From these some if not all animals must also obtain (6) traces of the mysterious *vitamins*. These substances, originally manufactured by plants, are transmitted to herbivorous, and so to carnivorous, animals, and though in very small quantities, are essential to life. The nature of some of them and the mode of action of all are unknown, but they may be recognised by their effects. Thus two at least of them (vitamins A and B) must be present for normal growth to take place in the animals in which they have been investigated. When, for instance, young rats are fed upon an artificial liquid containing the protein, sugar, and fat of milk in the usual proportions, they fail to grow, but the addition to their diet of a very small quantity of fresh milk (which contains the vitamins) causes them to grow in a normal manner (Fig. 1). The absence of vitamin B from the diet of adults causes inflammation of the nerves and other disorders, which may be removed by adding to the diet wheatgerm, yeast, or other materials which contain the vitamin. About a dozen vitamins are known at present.

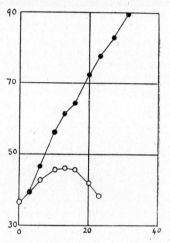

FIG. 1.—Curves showing the effect of vitamins on the growth of rats.—From Hopkins.

Lower curve (white circles), rats fed on artificial milk alone. Upper curve (black circles), rats fed on artificial milk and 2 c.c. of cow's milk daily. Average weight in grams, vertical. Time in days, horizontal.

The digested materials undergo *absorption* into the substance of the body, leaving the indigestible matter to be cast away as the *dung* or *fæces*. Incorporation, however, is not brought about simply by the absorption of digested matter. Neither before nor after digestion is the food of the same composition as the substance to which it is to be added. The flesh of a dead ox or sheep differs considerably in composition from that of a living man, and the difference is increased by its digestion. In the course

(b) Absorption and Assimilation.

of incorporation the food has therefore to undergo chemical changes by which it is converted into the substances which compose the body, and these changes it undergoes by the activity of the living matter itself. That is to say, the living substance has the power of making, out of unlike materials, additional matter of its own composition. The process by which this is done is known as *assimilation*. Both absorption and assimilation are processes in which work is done, and therefore involve the use of energy, but their net result is to add to the amount of material composed of complex molecules, and therefore to the amount of energy, in the body.

Metabolism. It will be seen that disintegration and its complementary assimilation constitute a series of chemical changes, continually taking place in the body, whereby there is kept up a continual evolution of energy. These changes, regarded as a whole, are known as *metabolism*, the disintegrative changes being known as *katabolism* and the assimilative as *anabolism*.

The reactions which take place in the living body are varied and immensely complicated. Practically all of them, however, belong to one or other of the following classes : (1) hydrolysis (p. 10) and dehydration, (2) deamination (p. 10 ; this is probably not a simple reaction), (3) reaction between an acid and a salt, (4) oxidation and reduction. Though the changes which fall into the first three of these classes are very important parts of the process as a whole, the liberation of energy during them is small, and it is by reactions of the fourth class that nearly all the energy of life is set free.

Repair and Growth. Part of the new complex material is used in the *repair* of the waste caused by disintegration, but the incorporation of new material has a further effect than the mere repair of waste. Throughout the body of a young animal, and in such parts as the roots of the hair and nails even in age, incorporation takes place in excess of waste, so that *growth* occurs. Both in repair and in growth the new material is not added in layers to a surface, like that which is taken up by a crystal, but is placed between the existing particles, as a substance is taken into solution. Growth, moreover, is a very complex architectural process in which the intricate structure of the body is built up out of many materials.

Growth is followed, sooner or later, by *reproduction.*
That is to say, a portion of the body breaks
off to form a new individual which leads an
independent existence. It will be convenient
to use the word " fission " to denote the actual breaking
away of the new body, for reproduction is more than a
mere act of separation. This will be seen if we consider
it a little more closely.

Reproduction.

(*a*) As has been said, *reproduction always involves the*
fission of an existing body. Life never starts anew, but is
always passed on from
one living being to
another which arises
from it. A living being
which divides to pro-
duce others is a
parent ; those which
it forms are *offspring.*

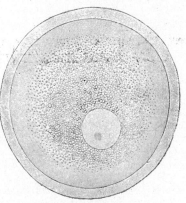

(*b*) *The offspring
are always at first
unlike the parent.*
There are, as we shall
see, certain creatures
in which the only evi-
dent difference be-
tween the offspring
and the individual by
whose division they
arose is the necessary
one of size. But in

FIG. 2.—The egg or " ovum " from which
a human being is developed, highly
magnified.

the great majority of cases there is also an obvious
difference in form, the offspring being at first very unlike
the parent in structure. This difference is obscured in
the case of man and some other animals, where the
offspring (Fig. 2) undergoes changes in the womb before
birth, but it is seen unmistakably in animals which are
born in the condition of an egg. In their immature
condition the offspring are known as *reproductive bodies.*

(*c*) In spite of this unlikeness at starting, *the offspring
become in time like the parent from which they arose,*
owing to a succession of changes which is sometimes

straightforward, or *direct* ; sometimes, as in the well-known case of the butterfly, very roundabout, or *indirect*. Thus the life of an animal or plant is a *cycle*, in which it passes through a series of stages, beginning with the small and simple reproductive body, and ending with the larger and usually more complex *adult*, ready to undergo fission again. Every individual goes through the same cycle of changes as its parent, resembling in each stage a similar stage passed through by the latter, till it reaches the likeness of the individual that produced it. This is due to the property known as *heredity*. Thus, in the strict sense of the word, reproduction includes the whole life cycle and consists of two distinct processes—*fission* and the *development* of the reproductive body into the adult—for until

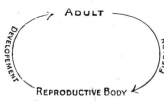

FIG. 3.—A diagram of the life-cycle of an animal.

this cycle has been completed the parent is not reproduced.[1] From this point of view, *growth* is that part of the process of development by which the reproductive body reaches the size of the adult. At the same time, in most cases, and perhaps in all, the growing individual is undergoing the *changes in structure* to which we have alluded.

Here must be mentioned a process which, though in itself it is not reproductive, is closely connected with reproduction. It is well known that in most animals reproduction is only possible by the co-operation of two individuals of different kinds known as the *sexes*. This is because in such animals the reproductive bodies are of two sorts, each produced only by one of the sexes, and neither sort can develop except after fusion with one of the other sort. That fusion is an example of the process known as a *syngamy*, union of two distinct living bodies, which occurs from time to time in nearly all species of animals and plants. The bodies which unite

Syngamy.

---

[1] Development may partly take place before fission, as in many cases of budding (Chap. XII.).

are known as *gametes*, and that which results from their fusion as a *zygote*. In some of the smallest living beings (Fig. 4) syngamy is the union of fully-grown adults and has no connection with reproduction. In other such creatures (Fig. 10), however, and in all large and complex animals and plants, syngamy takes place only between the reproductive bodies, which are generally unable to develop without it, so that it becomes a necessary part of the reproductive process. In these cases the reproductive bodies are of a kind known as *germs*, distinguished from other reproductive bodies (free buds, etc.) by their small size and the simplicity of their structure. The germs of such creatures are usually of two sizes which unite larger with smaller (Fig. 10 C). In all large and complex animals (and in some of the smallest) the gametes differ in form and behaviour as well as in size (Figs. 2 and 5). One is larger and passive, and is called the *female gamete*, or, in large animals, the *egg* or *ovum*. The other is smaller and active, and known as the *male gamete* or *spermatozoon*; it has usually a tail (flagellum) with which it swims in the fluid in which it is borne, and thus it moves to the egg and enters the latter (Fig. 6). This process is known as the *fertilisation of the ovum*. After it the

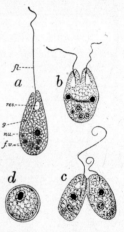

FIG. 4.—*Copromonas,* a minute inhabitant of dung.—After Dobell.

a, Adult individual ; *b,* the same in fission ; *c,* two adult individuals in syngamy ; *d,* the zygote, enclosed in a cyst.

f.v., Food vacuole; *fl.,* flagellum; *g.,* gullet; *nu.,* nucleus; *res.,* reservoir of contractile vacuole (see p. 140).

fertilised ovum or *oosperm* proceeds to develop. Ova and spermatozoa are usually formed by different adults, known respectively as *female* and *male*, but in some cases both kinds are formed by one individual, which is then known as a *hermaphrodite*. In some aquatic animals the gametes are set free, and syngamy takes place outside the body of the parent. In many cases, however, the ova are kept within the body of the mother, and the male gametes, known collectively as the *sperm*, are transferred in the *seminal fluid* by the male to the body of the female and there fertilise the ova. This transference is known as *coition*. Reproduction in which syngamy is necessary before the reproductive bodies can develop is known as *sexual reproduction*; that in which the reproductive bodies are not gametes is *asexual*.

As we shall see (p. 593) there is a kind of reproduction (parthenogenesis) in which a female germ (ovum) develops without syngamy. This kind is best regarded as an aberrant form of sexual reproduction.

The terminology of these processes is in some confusion. Syngamy is the fusion of two energids (p. 109), nucleus with nucleus and cytoplasm with cytoplasm, though one of the two may have little cytoplasm and possibly sometimes has none. The union of nuclei—which is by far more important than that of the cytoplasms—is *karyogamy*; the union of cytoplasm is *plasmogamy*. The term *conjugation* has been used as synonymous with syngamy and has also been used to designate the peculiar procedure by which syngamy is accomplished in the Ciliata (Chap. IX). The term *copulation* is used as synonymous with coition and also to denote syngamy in the lowest organisms (Protozoa other than Ciliata).

Summary of the Characteristics of Life. We are now in a position to sum up the characteristic features of the complex process which is known as life. In doing so we shall arrange them in a somewhat different order from that in which they have come under our notice, stating successively those that relate to the starting and stopping of the life processes, to the nature of these processes, and to the end to which they tend. We have found in life the following features : [1]—

FIG. 5.— Human spermatozoa, seen in face and in side view.—More highly magnified than Fig. 2.

[1] The process of respiration is not included in the following list because, though it is often rightly cited as a characteristic feature of

1. *Irritability*—the starting or stopping in the body of an activity of its own as the result of the receipt of a stimulus.

2. *Automatism*—the starting or stopping of activity without an immediate external stimulus.

3. *Disintegration with liberation of energy*, this energy appearing in various processes, of which the most conspicuous are :
    i. *Contraction*, or change of shape,
    ii. *Chemical work*,
    iii. *Excretion and Secretion*, the shedding out from the substance of the body of chemical products,
    iv. The *Conduction* of the impulses which start these processes from one part of the body to another.

4. *The Incorporation of food*, which involves (*a*) the *Absorption* of new material, (*b*) the conversion by *Assimilation* of unlike substances into the substance of the body.

5. *Purposiveness*—the direction of the activities of the body towards an end which concerns itself, namely, to its own preservation and that of its kind. This is shown :
    i. as regards the individual, in the *Struggle for Existence*—the obtaining of food, and the avoidance of overcoming of enemies and unfavourable circumstances ;
    ii. as regards the race, in *Reproduction*—the bringing into existence of new individuals, which involves (*a*) the breaking off by *Fission* of a part of the body, and (*b*) the process of growth and structural and chemical change known as the *Development* of the part broken off.

---

the life of animals, it is not a simple or distinct process. It consists in the excretion of carbon dioxide and the taking up of oxygen, which is not in its essence different from the incorporation of other materials. Syngamy is excluded because it is not a universal property of living matter.

Life is the only property which is peculiar to living
beings. All of them, however, present two
Three
Character- further characteristics which are found also in
istics. some other objects, though only in such as owe
their existence to living beings. One of these characteristics
is the presence in them of the substance known as *Proto-*
plasm. This they share with things that have been alive
and are now dead. The other is the existence in them of
Organisation. This they share not only with dead things
but with some others,
such as machines and
human societies, that have
been made by living
beings.

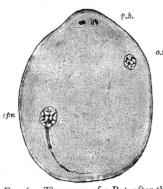

The life of animals and
plants is re-
Structure and
Function : flected in their
Organisation. structure. The
living body is a machine
which reacts to events in
the outer world in such a
way as to prolong its own
existence and that of its
kind. Like other machines
it consists of a number of
parts each of which does a
particular portion of the
work of the whole. Such
parts are called *organs.*
Thus there are *sense*

FIG. 6.—The ovum of a Bat, after the
entry of the spermatozoon.—
From F. H. A. Marshall, after
van der Stricht.

o.n., nucleus of the ovum ; *p.b.*, " polar
bodies " (see p. 122) ; *spn.*, spermatozoon.

organs, such as the eyes and ears, for the reception of
stimuli ; *nervous organs*, forming a *nervous system* (usually
provided with a central station such as the brain), for the
conduction of impulses set up by these and other stimuli,
to the organs which carry out the main part of the reaction ;
locomotive organs, such as legs and wings and fins, to carry
the body towards food or from danger ; *organs of offence*
and defence, such as teeth and claws, for procuring food and
resisting attack ; *organs of digestion*, such as the stomach
and bowels ; *organs of circulation*, such as the heart and
blood vessels, which distribute digested food, carry waste

matters to the *excretory organs*, such as the kidneys, and gases to and from *organs of respiration*, such as lungs and gills, and transport materials in general; and *organs of reproduction*. An organ may consist of subsidiary organs. Thus the leg is supported by *skeletal organs* known as bones, moved by *muscles*, and served by *blood vessels* and *nerves*. A complex of parts which work together is known as an *organism*, and this name is often applied to animals

H.c.

lac.

g.s.

FIG. 7.—A section of dry bone magnified. The dark spaces show where the living part of the tissue was lodged.

lac., Spaces known as "lacunæ." In these lay the cells into which the protoplasm was divided. *g.s.*, ground substance. This is traversed by numerous "canaliculi" in which processes of protoplasm united the cells into a meshwork. *H.c.*, "Haversian canals" in which minute blood vessels lay. The lacunæ are so arranged as to divide the ground-substance into concentric layers or "lamellæ" around the Haversian canals.

and to plants, for plants are also provided with organs, and also alive. The provision of separate organs for particular functions is called *organisation* or *differentiation*; the assignment of particular functions to separate organs which corresponds to organisation is called, by analogy with the similar separation of functions in modern industry, *the division of physiological labour*. Organisation exists to a very various extent among organisms, and of two organisms that which has the larger number of different organs is said to be the *more highly organised* or *more highly differentiated*, or simply the *higher*. Thus man is a higher organism than a jelly-fish. The higher the organism, the greater is its efficiency in coping with its surroundings, the greater the vicissitudes in them which it can survive. There are also great differences in form between the organs of animals of the same grade of organisation. Thus a butterfly is as highly organised as a fish, but its organs are utterly different in form. The differences in structure between animals correspond to differences in their modes of life. An animal which lives in water has, for instance, very different organs of loco-motion and respiration from one which lives on land ; the sense organs of an internal parasite are much less highly differentiated than those of an animal which has to seek food and avoid enemies from hour to hour ; and a car-nivorous animal has organs for seizing and eating its food which are different from those of one whose diet is vege-tarian. This correspondence between organisation and mode of life is known as *adaptation*.

Organisation involves more than the mere localising of
Tissues.   functions—more, that is, than the existence
in the body of regions where special functions are performed. It involves also a specialisation of each of these regions to fit it for its special functions. This specialisation is found partly in the shape of each organ, but also largely in its texture and composition. The sub-stance of the body is not alike throughout, but different portions of it have differences in texture and chemical composition which confer upon them different properties. Thus the outer layer of the skin is firm and hard to pene-trate, bone is rigid, blood is fluid, the substance known as " connective tissue " is tough and binds other tissues together,[1] nerve has the power of conduction highly developed, and muscle that of contraction, and so forth. Such a portion of the body-substance with particular properties, due to a particular texture and composition, is known as a *tissue*. An organ may consist of one tissue throughout, but is usually built up of several, upon the

---

[1] This may be seen in skinning any large animal. The tough, white material which holds down the skin and binds the muscles together is connective tissue.

nature and arrangement of which its powers depend. Thus a muscle contains, besides muscular tissue, connective tissue to bind it together and nervous tissue to conduct through it the impulses which cause it to contract.

The processes which go on in living organisms do not consist solely in action upon the outer world. **Regulation.** A great part of them is directed to keeping the machine in condition. The needs of the several organs in the way of food, oxygen, and the removal of waste, are very different, and vary from time to time with the activity of the organ. Often, too, the activity of one organ must be accompanied by an increase or depression of that of some other organ, as when heavy work by the muscles calls for a release by the liver of fuel in the form of sugar, or in an active gland or muscle the walls of the blood vessels relax their contraction and so allow a better flow of blood through the working tissue. Tasks of maintaining temperature also vary. Again, in growth the formation of the various parts of the body needs very strict adjustment. In all such respects the processes of the body are subject to *regulation*. This is effected in two ways, by the two systems of communication within the body—the blood vessels or other transporting system, and the nervous system. (*a*) Substances secreted into the blood by various organs affect the working of other organs which they reach in the course of the circulation. Some of these substances are not produced *ad hoc*. Thus the carbon dioxide passed into the blood by active organs as a result of the oxidation going on within them alters the degree of acidity or alkalinity of the blood, and this regulates the quantity and quality of the blood supply, the acidity causing small local blood vessels to dilate, so that the active organs are flushed with the blood they need, and stimulating the part of the brain which governs respiration, so that rapid breathing oxygenates the blood and removes the excess of carbon dioxide. But the most remarkable instances of regulation of this kind are effected by the secretion in small quantities of very powerful special agents known as " chemical messengers " or *hormones*. Various organs despatch these messengers, but the most conspicuous examples of their formation are afforded by the *ductless glands*. About these we shall have

more to say later on (see p. 62), and one example of their
functioning must suffice here. The *adrenal bodies*, little
glands which lie near the kidneys of backboned animals,
are, in moments of anger, fear, or other emotions which
forerun violent exertion, caused, by stimuli received through
the nerves, to discharge into the blood small quantities
of the substance *adrenalin*. This is carried round in the
circulation and tunes up the body for the crisis. It increases
the flow of blood in the muscles and brain by quickening
the heart beat and constricting the blood vessels of the
viscera, augments the supply of fuel for muscular action
by causing the liver to pour sugar into the blood, and in
other ways prepares the animal for action. The passing of
secreta into the blood instead of into tubes (ducts) to be
led to their destination is known as *internal secretion*.
(*b*) The nervous system is set into regulative action sometimes by the action of the blood upon the central nervous
organ, as in the case of breathing mentioned above ; but
more often messages sent in along nerves from organs are
translated at the centre into outgoing messages to other
organs, whose action they regulate appropriately. By them
the contraction of muscles, the secretion of glands, the
narrowing or dilatation of blood vessels, the beating of the
heart, to which the pressure of the blood is due, are all
affected, and thus the necessary co-ordination is brought
about.

We have hitherto spoken of the body as though it were
alive throughout. That, however, is rarely the
Protoplasm.   case. The living part of the body of all
organisms is a soft, slimy substance known as *protoplasm*.
In this the whole of the metabolism goes on. In composition, protoplasm is a solution in water of organic substances
and salts, especially characterised by the presence of
proteins. About its constituents and properties we shall
have more to say later on (p. 103). In a few cases the
protoplasm makes up the whole body, but in most it is
only a part. All tissues contain protoplasm, but many
contain also a framework of other substances known as
formed material, made and secreted by the protoplasm and
serving for its support. Thus in bone (Fig. 7) there is a
groundwork, consisting largely of salts of lime, to which

it owes its hardness, and this groundwork is penetrated by a meshwork of protoplasm. In many cases, as we shall see in a later chapter, the protoplasm is divided into minute units known as *cells* [1] (Fig. 8). In each cell a small protoplasmic body, the *nucleus*, acts as a regulative organ. Nuclei are also present in tissues and organisms whose protoplasm is not divided into cells.

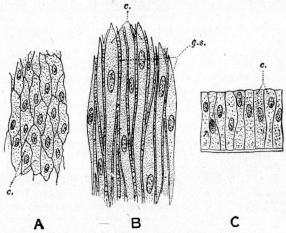

A   B   C

FIG. 8. —Portions of animal tissues, highly magnified, to show cells.

A, The lining of an artery; *B*, muscular tissue from the wall of the intestine; *C*, the lining of the intestine. *A* and *B* are shown in surface view, *C* in section.

c., Cells; *g.s.*, ground or intercellular substance, traversed by threads of protoplasm from cell to cell.

We have now to observe what are the differences between animals and the members of the other principal division of living beings, the plants. There is no fundamental difference in the composition of the protoplasm which is the essential part of all living things. Nor do they differ in the essentials of their life. This will be seen if we compare instances of the activities of plants with those which in the foregoing paragraphs we have drawn from the lives

[1] For the definition of this term, see pp. 103, 109.

of animals. That the protoplasm of plants is irritable we
see in such cases as the turning of a sunflower towards the
sun, or the stimulation by gravity of the stem to grow
upward and the root downward, or the folding of the leaves
of the Sensitive Plant (*Mimosa*) when they are touched.
That it is automatic appears in such facts as the slow
turning of the tendrils of climbing plants till they meet
with objects to which they can cling. That it has conductivity can be seen when a stimulus given to the leaf of
a mimosa causes distant leaflets to fold. That it can
execute movements may in many cases be seen under the
microscope, when it will be found to stream round the
cell. That it makes substances by chemical activity and
secretes them is illustrated by the long list of drugs and
other substances obtained from plants. That it grows and
reproduces need not be argued. In the sexual reproduction of the higher (or flowering) plants, the part of the
sperm is played by the pollen, that of the ova by " egg-
cells " which are contained in the flowers, in organs known
as carpels.

For all this agreement in essentials, however, there are
between animals and plants distinctions which
are both far-reaching and obvious. We may
take our start from familiar notions on the
subject. Any one who tried to state in words
the ideas which he had unconsciously formed of
animals and plants would probably find them to be somewhat as follows : An animal is a being that moves and
feeds ; a plant is a green thing that grows in the earth.
Let us examine these notions. It will be best to base our
analysis upon our definition of a plant. We find that the
information it implicitly contains is : (1) That the plant is
green, (2) that it does not swallow food, but draws nourishment from the earth (the fact that it also obtains food from
the air is less generally known), (3) that it is fixed in one
place and does not move about—usually, indeed, does not
move at all.

1. The green colour of plants is due to the presence of
the substance known as *chlorophyll*. This is contained in
protoplasmic structures known as *chloroplasts*, which in
the green cells of the higher plants are usually numerous

Differences between Animals and Plants.

and lens-shaped (Fig. 9). Chlorophyll is a complex compound of carbon, hydrogen, oxygen, and nitrogen, containing in the molecule an atom of magnesium. It is only found in those parts of plants which are exposed to sunlight, and is never found in animals, except in certain cases where minute green plants live embedded in the transparent protoplasm of animal bodies, as in the green *Hydra* (p. 217). At the same time it must be remembered that certain plants, such as the fungi, have no chlorophyll.

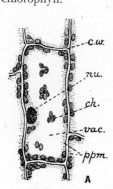

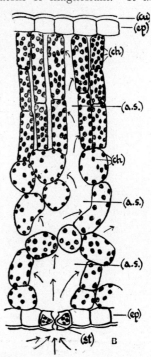

FIG. 9.—Plant cells.

A, A small portion of green tissue from a plant. *B*, Part of a section through a leaf.—From Godwin.

a.s., Air spaces between the cells; *ch.*, chloroplasts; *c.w.*, cell wall; *cu.*, cuticle; *ep.*, epidermis surface layer of cells; *nu.*, nucleus; *ppm.*, protoplasm; *st.*, stoma (opening through which air enters); *vac.*, vacuole (space containing fluid). The arrows show the paths of diffusion of carbon dioxide.

2. More important than the mere presence of chlorophyll is its function in the body, which is connected with the *nutrition* of the plant. This function is the obtaining of carbon from carbon dioxide by means of the energy of

the sun's rays, and the use of it in the manufacture of complex organic substances.   Absorbing certain rays of light, the chlorophyll, in some way not yet understood, enables the

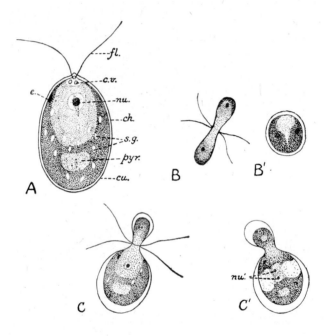

Fig. 10.—*Chlamydomonas*, a minute, motile plant.

A. Ordinary individual.   B, B', Two stages in the conjugation of gametes of equal size (isogamy) ;   C, C', Two stages in the conjugation of gametes of different sizes (anisogamy).   The conjugation is " head on " in each case.

c.v., Contractile vacuoles ;   *ch.,* chloroplast ;   *cu.,* cuticle of cellulose, *e,* eye spot ; *fl.,* flagellum ;   *nu.,* nucleus ;   *nu'.,* nuclei of two gametes about to fuse ;   *pyr.,* pyrenoid (a protoplasmic body which is concerned in starch formation) ;   *s.g.,* starch grains.

protoplasm to use the energy of the rays in breaking up molecules of carbon dioxide taken in from the surroundings —by land plants from the air, by water plants from the water, and by the green bodies of *Hydra* from the protoplasm of the animal. The carbon thus obtained is combined with the hydrogen and oxygen of water also absorbed to form sugar.[1] This process is known as *photosynthesis*. The oxygen of the carbon dioxide is set free. This can easily be shown in the case of water plants, from whose leaves in sunlight a stream of fine bubbles of oxygen may be seen to ascend. The sugar is used on the one hand for the manufacture of the more complex carbohydrates, such as starch, in which the plant body is usually very rich, and on the other hand for the formation of the various substances which the protoplasm of plants, like that of animals, requires for food, and in particular of proteins. The nitrogen, sulphur, and phosphorus for this purpose are obtained by the plants as salts in solution in the water which is taken in by their roots, or sometimes, as in seaweeds, by the whole surface of the body. From this peculiarity of nutrition arise several other features peculiar to the life of plants. (i) We have here the reason for the well-known fact that green plants cannot live in the dark. (ii) While animals, as we have seen, are always taking in oxygen and giving out carbon dioxide, green plants in the light are continually taking in carbon dioxide and giving out oxygen. Yet it must be remembered that the protoplasm of plants undergoes continually a true respiration like that of animals although this is obscured by the reverse process taking place to a greater extent during daylight. (iii) Though the food supplied to the protoplasm is similar in the two kinds of organisms, plants manufacture its organic components from simple substances, whereas animals obtain them from other organisms. Therefore, while the food of animals consists of complex organic substances, usually in the state of a solid or the viscous liquid protoplasm, and has to be swallowed through an opening, the materials taken in by green plants are simple inorganic substances which can be absorbed as gases or liquids through the surface of the body. It must be noticed, however, that plants which have no chlorophyll, such as fungi, and some animals which live as parasites or in decaying matter, absorb their nourishment through

[1] Probably carbonic acid, H_2CO_3, is reduced to formaldehyde, $H.COH$, which then polymerises into sugar.

the surface of the body, but take it in the form of organic substances, more or less complex in various cases, from the living or dead bodies of other organisms.

3. From the mode of nutrition of plants there follows the third character which we have marked in them. In the great majority of animals food must be either sought by locomotion or at least seized by other *active movements*, as it is, for instance, in a sea-anemone or *Hydra* (Chap. XII.). In plants, on the other hand, not only is this necessity absent, but, since it is desirable that they should expose as great a surface as possible to air and water for absorption— as they do, for example, in leaves and roots—the shape of their bodies is necessarily such as to be an actual hindrance to motion. Thus in most plants active motion is restricted or absent, and muscular and nervous tissues are not found in plant bodies. Certain microscopic aquatic organisms, however—members of the group known as *Flagellata*—are exceptions to the rule that locomotion accompanies the animal mode of nutrition only. Though they have one or more chloroplasts and nourish themselves like plants, their body (which is so small that it has only one nucleus) is compact, shaped like an egg or a spindle, and possesses one or two fine lashes of protoplasm (flagella), by the working of which it is rowed or drawn through the water, in search of sunlight of the needed strength. Many of them, including the example, *Chlamydomonas*, shown in Fig. 10, have a pigment spot which is a sense organ for the necessary appreciation of light, whose rays it absorbs. It is in such organisms as this that plant and animal meet.

4. The necessity for surface leads to a fourth character in plants. An extensive surface needs strong support. In correspondence with this need we find in plants a massive skeleton which forms a strong wall to each cell, so that the protoplasm is upheld by an intricate framework of compartments whose walls are thickest in the most woody parts of the body. Owing, no doubt, to the ample supply of starch at the command of the plant, this skeleton consists of a modified form of starch known as *cellulose*. Among plants, even including those like the fungi which have no chlorophyll, cellulose is almost invariably present ; among animals it is unknown. It happens, indeed that this com-

paratively unimportant character comes nearer than any other to giving an absolute distinction between the two kinds of organisms.

To sum up : we find between typical plants and typical animals the following distinctions :—

1. The presence in typical plants and not in animals of the green substance *chlorophyll*.

2. That while plants absorb through their surface simple inorganic compounds and from them *manufacture food-stuffs* for their protoplasm, animals swallow the complex substances of the bodies of plants and of other animals.

3. That while in all the familiar plants *motion is restricted* or absent, in animals it is conspicuous.

4. That plants have a skeleton of *cellulose*, which is absent from the bodies of animals.

The difference in nutrition between animals and plants has the important result that in their action **The Balance of Nature.** upon the inorganic world these two kinds of organisms bring about precisely opposite changes, and do so in such a way that each sets up conditions favourable to the activity of the other. The plant, absorbing the energy of the sun's rays, builds up with storage of that energy complex organic compounds from simple inorganic substances.[1] These manufactured substances it assimilates, partly in repairing the waste of its protoplasm, but mainly in adding to its substance by growth. Its construction of organic materials is in excess of its destruction of them, and the net result of its activity is to provide an accumulation of those complex substances which form a necessary part of the food of protoplasm. At the same time it sets free oxygen. The animal, on the other hand, obtains the organic food for its protoplasm in substances manufactured by plants, taking them either directly from plant bodies or after they have been incorporated in a somewhat altered form into the protoplasm of other animals. In the protoplasm of the animal these substances undergo destruction, in consequence of

---

[1] The storage of energy is, of course, due to the fact that more is taken up in splitting the stable inorganic molecules (p. 26) than is freed in forming the unstable organic molecules.

which there are set free carbon dioxide and simple nitrogen compounds. Thus plants provide food and oxygen for animals, while animals, destroying this food, provide simple nitrogen compounds [1] and carbon dioxide for the use of plants.

Zoology : Plan of Study. Biology comprises *Botany*, which deals with plants, and *Zoology*, which deals with animals. Now an organism may be regarded from two points of view according as attention is concentrated upon its structure or its functions, though of course these two are so closely connected that it is impossible to study structure intelligently or function at all without reference to the sister topic. The sciences of Zoology and Botany are correspondingly divided each into two subordinate sciences, *Anatomy* or *Morphology*, which deals with the structure of the bodies of organisms, and *Physiology*, which deals with their functions. In the following pages we shall of necessity approach Zoology in the first place from its anatomical side, but shall equally seek from Physiology light upon the meaning of the structures we find, endeavouring to trace in the bodies of the particular animals studied the provision which exists for carrying out all those functions which our survey in this chapter has revealed to us as taking place generally. With this purpose we shall first examine in considerable detail one of the higher animals, then study an exceedingly simple example, and afterwards survey, more briefly, a series of further examples. In these there will appear two phenomena that we have already noted (p. 19)—(*a*) that organisation exists in many grades of complexity (our examples will be taken roughly in an ascending order in this respect), and (*b*) that organisation differs not only in degree but in kind, and that its different kinds adapt animals to live in different surroundings, or to take advantage of different circumstances in the same surroundings. Finally, we shall discuss certain topics which concern animals in general, surveying the modes in which they reproduce their kind, and considering the relation of this reproduction to their immense variety, and the part which their multifarious activities play in the economy of Nature.

---

[1] These are not available for the use of most plants till they have been turned into nitrates by the action of bacteria.

CHAPTER II

THE FROG: EXTERNAL FEATURES AND BODY-WALL

Habits. THE Common Frog of Britain is the species known in Zoology as *Rana temporaria*. It is abundant in summer in damp places, but in winter is less easily found, owing to the fact that it is then in a torpid state, hidden in holes or buried in mud. In the spring the

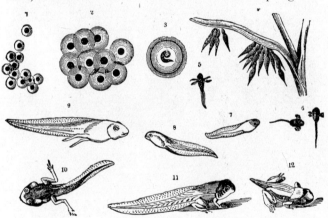

FIG. 11.—The life-history of a frog.—After Brehm.

1–3, Developing ova; 4, newly hatched forms hanging to water-weeds; 5, 6, stages with external gills; 7–10 tadpoles during emergence of limbs; 11, tadpoles with both pairs of limbs apparent; 12, metamorphosis to frog.

warmth wakes the frogs and they congregate, croaking loudly, and pair in the water, where the eggs are laid, enclosed in jelly as a mass of spawn and fertilised by the sperm which the male sheds over them as they pass out of the female. In about a fortnight there hatches from each egg a little, fish-like *tadpole*. This has no limbs, but a strong tail, which it uses for swimming, breathes wholly by

31

..., and is at first without a mouth. A young animal which like the tadpole differs markedly from the adults of its kind, but is capable of fending for itself, is known as a *larva*. The term *embryo* is applied to a young organism while it is helpless and is developing within the body of its parent or under shelter of an egg-shell or a jelly coat, like the young of man or a bird, or the early stages of the frog. In a few days the tadpole comes to possess a mouth and

FIG. 12.—The Common Frog.

begins to feed on vegetable matter. Gradually it changes, losing its gills and tail and gaining lungs and two pairs of limbs, till at the end of three months it becomes a small frog. Henceforward it lives principally on land, sometimes crawling about by means of both pairs of limbs, but generally jumping with the strong hinder pair and using the small fore pair to break its fall when it alights. From time to time, however, it takes to the water, and then it can swim strongly with its hind limbs. Its food, after it has left the water, consists of slugs, snails, insects, worms, and other small animals, the smaller prey being caught by a sticky tongue, the larger seized with the mouth.

In examining the body of a frog, we are struck, first by the fact that its mottled green and yellow skin **External Features.** is soft and slimy and without the covering of hairs, or scales, or feathers which we find in other animals, and next by its consisting only of head, trunk, and two pairs of limbs. There is no neck or tail. The *trunk* is flattened and bears the head at one end and the limbs of each pair opposite to one another on the narrow sides. In consequence of this symmetrical arrangement we may distinguish a *back* or *dorsal surface*, a *lower or ventral surface*, right and left sides, and fore and hind ends. Such a symmetry is called *bilateral*, and we shall see that in the frog it extends to the arrangement of nearly all the organs of the body. The *fore or anterior end* is that which is foremost when the animal moves, and is thus the first part to come into relation with objects in the world around it. At this end is placed the *head*, a distinct region of the body, smaller than the trunk, which bears the mouth with which food is taken and the three pairs of principal sense organs by which the animal becomes aware of the nature of its surroundings. The *eyes* are large, and have stout, almost immovable upper lids and thin, translucent, movable lower lids.[1] The *nostrils* or *external nares* are a pair of small openings on the top of the head in front of the eyes. Each of them leads into a chamber which communicates with the mouth. There is no flap to the *ear*, but the drum shows upon the surface at the side of the head behind and somewhat below the eye. If the drum be pierced, a bristle passed through it will be found to reach the mouth. On the lower side of the trunk there may be distinguished two regions—the large, soft-walled *belly* or *abdomen* behind, and the smaller stout-walled *breast region* in front.

The *limbs* of each pair resemble one another, and those of the two pairs correspond roughly in shape, each consisting of three successive parts, the first two slender and

---

[1] These do not represent the lower lids of man, which are wanting in the frog. The lower lid of the frog is the *third eyelid or nictitating membrane* found in many other animals (pp. 492, 518). All three eyelids are well developed in birds.

3

the third broad and adapted to be applied to the ground. In the *fore limb or arm* the segment nearest the body is known as the *upper arm or brachium*, the middle segment as the *forearm* or *antebrachium*, and the third segment as the *hand* or *manus*. In the hand may be distinguished a *wrist* or *carpus*, a *palm* or *metacarpus*, and *fingers* or *digits*, of which there are only four, that which corresponds to the thumb or pollex of man being absent. The first finger of the male frog bears at the breeding season a rough-skinned swelling, not unlike the ball of the human thumb. In the *hinder limb* or *leg*, which is longer than the arm, the first segment is known as the *thigh* or *femur*, the

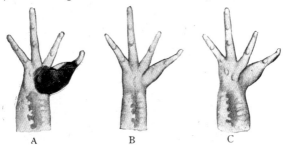

A   B   C

FIG. 13.—The right hand, *A* of a male frog at the breeding season, *B* of a female, *C* of a male out of the breeding season.

second as the *shank* or *crus*, the third as the *foot* or *pes*. The foot contains regions corresponding to those of the hand, and known respectively as the *ankle* or *tarsus*, *instep* or *metatarsus*, and *toes* or *digits*, but the ankle is much longer than the wrist, and all five toes are present and united by webs of skin, so that a wide surface is provided for use in swimming. The lower side of the foot is the *plantar surface* or *sole*, that of the hand the *palmar surface*.

Between the legs at the *hinder or posterior end* of the trunk is the *vent or cloacal opening*, through which are passed the fæces, urine, and eggs or sperm.

The skin of the frog is a thin, tough, protective covering.

Skin. Like that of many other animals it consists of a layer of connective tissue known as the *dermis* with a covering of cells called the *epidermis*.

The dermis contains pigment cells (Figs. 65, 72 B), and imbedded epidermal glands of several kinds which between them give a slimy liquid that possesses slightly the acrid property found in the secretion of the skin of toads and newts. The pigment in the cells is expanded and contracted in varying conditions of light, temperature, etc., and thus the colour of the frog changes (p. 64). Cold, dark, or wet surroundings cause expansion of the pigment and darkening of the skin. Warmth, light, or dryness cause contraction. From time to time the horny outer layer of the epidermis is shed and eaten by the frog.

General Arrangement of Internal Organs.

Immediately below the skin is a series of large spaces, the *subcutaneous lymph sacs*, containing a fluid known as lymph (p. 75). Between the lymph sacs the skin is bound down to the underlying flesh by tough, white connective tissue, but in consequence of the presence of the sacs it is

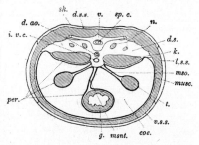

FIG. 14.—A diagram of a transverse section through the abdomen of a male frog.

coe., Cœlom ; *d.ao.*, dorsal aorta ; *d.s.*, dorsal lymph sac ; *d.s.s.*, dorsal subcutaneous lymph sac ; *g.*, gut ; *i.v.c.*, inferior vena cava ; *k.*, kidney ; *l.s.s.*, lateral subcutaneous lymph sac ; *msnt.*, mesentery ; *mso.*, mesorchium ; *musc.*, muscular body-wall ; *n.*, spinal nerves ; *per.*, peritoneum ; *sk.*, skin ; *sp.c.*, spinal cord ; *t.*, testis ; *v.*, vertebra ; *v.s.s.*, ventral subcutaneous lymph sac.

much looser than that of most animals. Below the sacs the body possesses a continuous layer of flesh, which consists, as the substance so-called always does, of muscles. There is thus a *body-wall*, composed of skin and muscles, with bones and a lining of peritoneum (to be mentioned shortly), and this wall encloses in the trunk a large space, the *body cavity* or *cœlom*, in which lie most of the principal *viscera*. The latter name is applied to the soft internal organs of the body, such as the stomach, bowels, liver, lungs, and heart. The viscera pretty well fill the body cavity, but it is easy for them to move in it because they are lubricated by a fluid—the *cœlomic fluid*. The frog is a backboned or " vertebrate " animal : that is, the body-wall of its back, which is much thicker than that of its belly, contains a structure known as the *backbone, spine*, or *vertebral column*. This consists of a row of ring-like bones, the *vertebræ*, placed end to end to form a tube, the *vertebral* or *spinal canal*, in which lies a part of the nervous system known as the *spinal marrow or cord*. The muscles of the ventral side are thicker at the ends of the trunk, where they contain bony hoops, the *shoulder girdle and hip girdle*, which, with the vertebræ between the upper ends of each of them, encircle the body. The cœlom is lined by a smooth membrane, the *peritoneum*, which is continued over the viscera, so that these are not truly exposed in the body cavity, but hang into it in folds of the peritoneum (Fig. 14). Each fold fits closely over the organ which it suspends, and above the organ the two sides of the fold come together to form a sheet which slings the organ from the body-wall. The largest of these suspensory sheets is that which holds the gut and is known as the *mesentery*. Between the peritoneum and the muscles of the back is on each side a large *dorsal lymph sac*, and in each dorsal lymph sac lies one of the pair of kidneys. In the head there is no body cavity, and the backbone is here continued by a large box of bone and cartilage known as the *skull*, while the spinal cord is prolonged into the skull by the *brain*. The limbs have neither body cavity nor viscera, and among their muscles lie the bones which support them.

The skeleton of the frog is composed chiefly of *bone*, but contains also a good deal of a gristly substance known as *cartilage*. There may be recognised in it an *axial part*, consisting of the skull, backbone, and breastbone, which supports the trunk and head, and an *appendicular part*, comprising the bones of the limbs and their girdles, which supports the arms and legs and anchors them to the trunk.

Skeleton : General Arrangement.

In the backbone there are nine vertebræ and a long bone, known as the *urostyle*, which represents several vertebræ fused together. The ninth is known as the *sacral vertebra*, and to it is attached the girdle

Backbone.

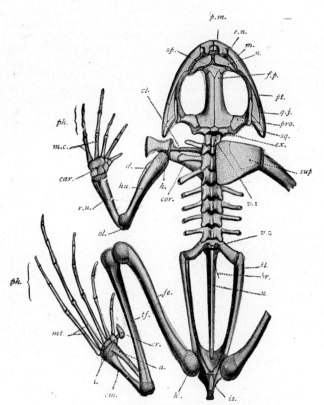

FIG. 15.—The skeleton of a frog, seen from above.

a., Astragalus ; *br.*, bristle passed into opening for last spinal nerve ; *car.*, carpal or wrist bones ; *cl.*, clavicle ; *cm.*, calcaneum ; *cor.*, coracoid ; *cr.*, calcar ; *d.*, deltoid ridge ; *e.n.*, external narial opening ; *ex.*, exoccipital ; *fe.*, femur ; *f.p.*, fronto-parietal ; *h., h'.*, heads of humerus and femur ; *hu.*, humerus ; *il.*, ilium ; *is.*, ischium ; *m.*, maxilla ; *m.c.*, metacarpals ; *mt.*, metatarsals ; *n.*, nasal bone ; *ol.*, olecranon process ; *ph.*, phalanges ; *p.m.*, premaxilla ; *pro.*, prootic ; *pt.*, pterygoid ; *q.j.*, quadratojugal ; *r.u.*, radioulna ; *sp.*, sphenethmoid ; *s.q.*, squamosal ; *sup.*, suprascapula ; *t.*, distal tarsals ; *tf.*, tibiofibula ; *u.*, urostyle ; *v.1*, first or atlas vertebra ; *v.9*, ninth or sacral vertebra.

The dotted regions consist of cartilage. The cartilage at the ends of the limb bones is the "articular" cartilage which caps the enlarged ends of the bones.

of the hind limbs. Each vertebra consists of a *body* or *centrum* and an arch, the *neural arch*, placed above the centrum so as to form a ring around the spinal cord. The hollow of each ring is a *vertebral foramen*, and the rings together form the vertebral canal. The roof of each arch is raised into a low ridge, the *neural spine* or *spinous process*, and in every vertebra except the first the arch bears on each side, a little above its junction with the centrum, a transverse process, which is especially large in the sacral vertebra. At the end of each transverse process is a small knob of cartilage which represents a *rib*. That part of the arch which lies between the transverse process of each side and the neural spine is known as a *lamina*, and the part between the centrum and the transverse process is a *radix* or *pedicle*. Each vertebra is jointed to those in front and behind it by projections, one on each side at each

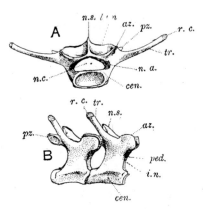

FIG. 16.—Vertebræ of a frog. *A*, fourth vertebra, seen from in front; *B*, sixth and seventh vertebræ from the right.

az., Prezygapophysis; *cen.*, centrum; *i.n.*, intervertebral notch; *lam.*, lamina of neural arch; *n.a.*, pedicle of same; *n.c.*, vertebral foramen; *n.s.*, neural spine; *ped.*, pedicle; *pz.*, postzygapophysis; *r.c.*, cartilage at end of transverse process; *tr.*, transverse process.

end of the arch, at the junction of transverse process and lamina, known as *zygapophyses*. The zygapophyses in front of the vertebra (*prezygapophyses* or *superior articular processes*) have each a flat surface facing upwards. Those behind (*postzygapophyses* or *inferior articular processes*) have flat surfaces facing downwards which fit on to the surfaces of the prezygapophyses and slide over them as the backbone bends. The front and hind edges of each pedicle are concave, forming thus *intervertebral notches*, and the adjoining notches of two vertebræ form an *intervertebral foramen*, through which a nerve passes from the spinal cord. Most of the centra are hollow in front and rounded behind and thus fit together by ball-and-socket joints, but the first vertebra has in front two hollows, which serve as sockets for two knobs, known as the occipital condyles, on the hinder end of the skull, while the eighth is hollow behind as well as in front, and the ninth projects in front, to articulate with the hollow of the eighth, and has behind two knobs which articulate with two hollows on the urostyle. The latter is a long, tapering bone with a ridge above, in the front part of which is a canal for the hinder part of the spinal cord.

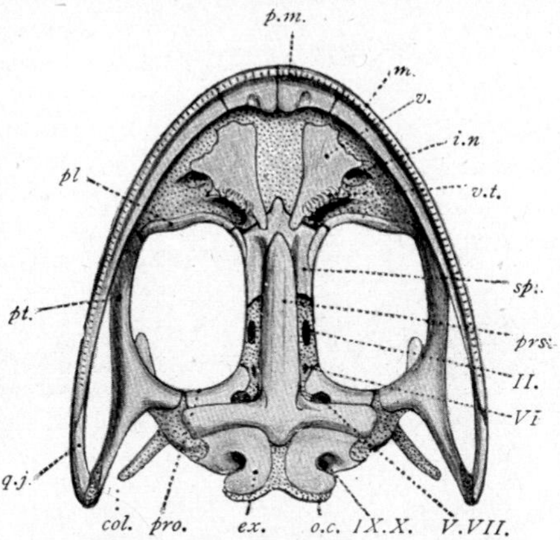

FIG. 17. —The skull of a frog, seen from below.

col., Columella; *ex.*, exoccipital; *i.n.*, internal nariai opening; *m.*, maxilla; *o.c.*, occipital condyle; *pl.*, palatine; *p.m.*, premaxilla; *pro.*, prootic; *prs.*, parasphenoid; *pt.*, pterygoid; *q.j.*, quadratojugal; *sp.*, sphenethmoid; *v.*, vomer (prevomer); *v.t.*, vomerine teeth; *II, V, VI, VII, IX, X*, foramina for cranial nerves.

In the skull, the following regions may be distinguished: (1) the *cranium* or *brain case*, (2) the *nasal capsules*, which enclose the organs of smell, (3) the *auditory capsules*, which enclose the inner part of the ear, (4) the *visceral arches*, an apparatus which lies below the cranium and is highly developed in a fish and in the tadpole, but in the adult frog is represented only by the jaws and by a structure in the floor of the mouth known as the hyoid.

The cranium is an oblong box, from which the nasal

capsules project in front and the auditory capsules at the sides of the hinder end, while the bones of the upper jaw form a scaffolding fixed to the capsules and supporting the sides of the head. Between the scaffolding and the cranium is on each side a large space known as the *orbit* in which lies the eye. The hinder part of the cranium, between the auditory capsules, is known as the *occipital region*, the middle part, between the orbits, is known as the *sphenoidal region*, and the front part, immediately behind the nasal capsules, is known as the *ethmoidal region*.

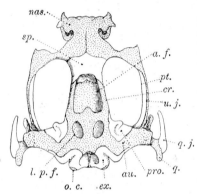

Fig. 18.—The cartilaginous skull of a frog, seen from above after the removal of most of the bones.

a.f., Anterior fontanelle ; *au.*, auditory capsule ; *cr.*, cranium ; *ex.*, exoccipital ; *l.p.f.*, left posterior fontanelle ; *nas.*, nasal capsule ; *o.c.*, occipital condyle ; *pro* , prootic : *pt.*, pterygoid ; *q.*, quadrate ; *q.j.*, quadratojugal ; *sp.*, sphenethmoid ; *u.j.*, upper jaw bar.

The skull consists of a foundation of cartilage taken over from the tadpole with certain bones which are formed while the tadpole is changing into a frog These bones may be divided into two sets according to the way in which they are formed. Those which arise by the replacement of parts of the original cartilaginous skull by bone are known as *replacing or cartilage bones*. Those which appear in development without being thus preformed in cartilage are known as *investing or membrane bones* on account of the membrane, consisting of a sort of connective tissue, which at first occupies the places in which they will appear. The cartilage bones are embedded in the cartilage of the skull and cannot be removed, but the membrane bones can easily be taken off.

At the hind end of the cranium is a large opening known as the *foramen magnum,* through which the spinal cord is

continuous with the brain. On each side of this is a cartilage bone called the *exoccipital*, which bears one of the
occipital condyles mentioned above, but the foramen
magnum is not completely bordered by the exoccipitals,
since these are separated above and below by cartilage.
The rest of the cranium is mainly composed of cartilage
covered by certain membrane bones, but the front end is
formed by a cartilage bone known as the *sphenethmoid*.
This has the form of a dice box divided across the narrowest
part by a transverse partition which closes the cranial cavity
in front. A longitudinal partition divides the front half of
the box into two. The roof of the cartilaginous cranium is
pierced by three large holes or *fontanelles*, but these are not
seen in an intact skull, since the whole roof is covered, from
the exoccipitals to the sphenethmoid, by two long bones, the
frontoparietals, placed side by side. The floor is complete,
and under it lies a large dagger-shaped bone, the *parasphenoid*, placed with the blade of the dagger forward
and the crosspiece of its hilt under the auditory capsules.

The wall of the cranium is pierced by certain openings
or *foramina*, for the passage of the nerves which arise from
the brain. These " cranial " nerves are ten in number on
each side. The *first nerve* of each side passes through a
foramen in the transverse partition of the sphenethmoid on
its way from the organ of smell in the nasal capsule. The
second-nerve, which serves the eye, enters the skull through
a conspicuous opening on each side in the middle of the
sphenoidal region. The *third and fourth nerves* have each
a minute foramen in the side of the same region. The *fifth
and seventh nerves* pass through a large common opening
on the under side of the skull, situated in a notch in the
prootic bone mentioned below. The foramen for the *sixth
nerve* is a small opening between those for the second and
for the fifth and seventh. The *eighth nerve* enters from
the inner part of the ear by an opening in the wall between
the cranium and the auditory capsule. A foramen for the
ninth and tenth nerves is situated in the exoccipital bone,
at the side of the occipital condyle.

The nasal capsules are a pair of irregular, mainly
cartilaginous enclosures continuous with the front end of
the cranium. Only their hinder part is ossified, and this

forms that part of the sphenethmoid which lies in front of the transverse partition of the latter. The wall between the two capsules is known as the *mesethmoid*. Through these capsules run the passages from the nostrils to the mouth, and each of them has therefore an opening above and below. Each bears two membrane bones, one on its upper side and one beneath. The upper bone is known as the *nasal*, and is shaped like the outline of a pear, with the stalk directed outwards. The lower is the *vomer (pre-vomer)*. It is of irregular shape and carries a patch of teeth which project through the skin of the roof of the mouth.

The auditory capsules are blocks of cartilage continuous with that of the cranium. Each contains a complicated space, the *cartilaginous labyrinth*, which lodges a structure known as "the membranous labyrinth of the ear." Part of the front of the capsule is ossified to form the *prootic* bone.

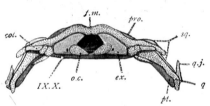

FIG. 19.—The skull of a frog, seen from behind.

col., Columella; *ex.*, exoccipital; *f.m.*, foramen magnum; *o.c.*, occipital condyle; *pro.*, prootic; *pt.*, pterygoid; *q.*, quadrate; *q.j.*, quadratojugal; *sq.*, squamosal; *IX.X.*, foramen for ninth and tenth cranial nerves.

Above, there abuts in its outer side a T-shaped membrane bone known as the *squamosal*, which touches it by one limb of the cross-piece of the T, the main limb being directed outwards and downwards. At one spot on the outer side of the capsule the cartilage fails and the labyrinth is covered only by membrane. This gap is known as the *fenestra ovalis*, and from it a slender rod of bone and cartilage, the *columella auris*, runs to the drum of the ear, so that when the latter is thrown into vibrations by sound waves its movements are transferred by the columella to the labyrinth through the membrane.

The framework of the upper jaw is composed of two series of structures, an outer, which borders the opening of the mouth, and an inner, which supports the outer.

The inner series is known as the *palato-pterygo-quadrate* on account of the parts of which it is composed. These are as follows. From the junction of the cranium with the nasal capsules there projects outwards a bar of cartilage, against the hinder, or orbital, side of which lies a membrane bone known as the *palatine*.[1] At its outer end the cartilaginous bar turns backwards, and here another membrane bone, the *pterygoid*,[1] fits against its inner side. The pterygoid is Y-shaped, with the fork directed backwards, the inner branch of the Y abutting on the auditory capsule. The outer branch underlies the main branch of the squamosal, and between these two bony rods there projects outwards from the auditory capsule a rod of cartilage, the *quadrate*, continuous with the longitudinal bar. With the quadrate held firm as it is by

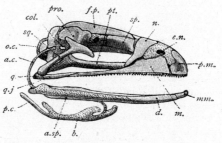

FIG. 20.—The skull of a frog, seen from the right side.

a.c., Anterior cornu of hyoid ; *a.sp.,* angulo-splenial ; *b.,* body of hyoid ; *col.,* columella ; *d.,* dentary ; *e.n.,* external narial opening ; *f.p.,* fronto-parietal ; *m.,* maxilla ; *mm.,* mentomeckelian , *n.,* nasal ; *o.c.,* occipital condyle ; *p.c.,* posterior cornu of hyoid ; *p.m.,* premaxilla ; *pro.,* prootic ; *pt.,* pterygoid ; *q.,* quadrate ; *q.j,* quadratojugal ; *sp,* sphenethmoid ; *sq.,* squamosal.

processes of the squamosal and pterygoid, articulates the lower jaw, for which the structures in question are said to form the *suspensorium*. The outer series of bones of the upper jaw begins with the *premaxilla*, a small membrane bone applied to the front of the nasal capsule, on to whose upper surface it sends a process. The two premaxillæ meet in the middle line, forming the tip of the upper jaw, and each of them

[1] The palatine and pterygoid are cartilage bones in certain of the animals in which they occur. In the frog the cartilage bone is replaced in development by membrane bone.

bears a row of teeth. Behind the premaxilla, on each side, another membrane bone, the *maxilla*, continues the edge of the jaw. The maxilla is a long slender bone which bears a row of teeth. Along the greater part of its length it is supported by the nasal capsule and pterygoid, but the hinder part lies free till it meets a small membrane bone, the *quadratojugal*, which connects it with the quadrate.

The lower jaw or *mandible* consists of two halves united in front by a ligament. Each half is a curved rod of cartilage, known as *Meckel's cartilage*, ossified at the end to form the small *mentomeckelian* bone, and almost completely ensheathed by a couple of membrane bones, the *angulo-splenial* within, and the *dentary* without. The latter does not, as its name would imply, bear teeth, the frog having no teeth in the lower jaw. At the near end or *angle* of the jaw the dentary bears a small knob or *condyle*, which fits into a hollow, known as the *mandibular fossa*, on the end of the quadrate.

The hyoid is a flat structure in the floor of the mouth. It consists of a wide *body* with two short processes on each side and two longer processes, the *cornua*, at each end. The *anterior cornua* are very long and slender and curve backwards at the sides of the body and then upwards to be attached to the sides of the auditory capsules. The *posterior cornua* are shorter and stouter and project backwards at the sides of the windpipe. They are the only ossified parts of the hyoid, the remainder consisting of cartilage.

The following table represents in a summary form the architecture of the skull :

Regions of skull.	Cartilage bones.	Membrane bones.
Cranium	{ Exoccipitals { Sphenethmoid (part)	Fronto-parietals. Parasphenoid.
Nasal Capsules	{ Sphenethmoid (part) { Mesethmoid	Nasals. Vomers.
Auditory Capsules	Prootics	Squamosals.[1]
Visceral Arches—		
Upper jaw	{ (Palatines) { { (Pterygoids)	Premaxillæ. Maxillæ. Quadratojugals.
Lower jaw	Mentomeckelians	{ Angulo-splenials. { Dentaries.
Hyoid	Posterior cornua	None.

[1] Attached to auditory capsules but not belonging to them.

The *shoulder girdle or pectoral arch* is a flat structure
Limb Girdles. of cartilage and bone embedded in the body-
wall of the forepart of the trunk, which it
almost encircles. It consists of two similar halves, one
on each side of the body, united below but separate
above, where they are bound by muscles to the backbone. Each half is composed of an upper *scapular
portion* or *shoulder blade*
and a lower *coracoid
portion*. The uppermost
part is a broad, flat plate
lying on the back known
as the *suprascapula*. A
great part of this consists
of cartilage stiffened by
calcareous matter, but it
has a narrow rim of plain
cartilage and a patch of
true bone [1] lies upon it,
where it joins the *scapula*,
a narrower but stouter
bone placed at the side of
the body. A forward pro-

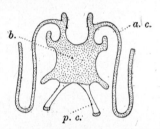

FIG. 21.—The hyoid apparatus
of a frog.

a.c., Anterior cornua; *b.*, body;
p.c., posterior cornua.

jection from this bone is known as the *acromion process.*
To the lower end of the scapula is attached the coracoid
portion of the girdle. This is a plate of cartilage and
bone lying on the under side of the body in the breast
region and pierced by a wide oval space called the *coracoid fontanelle*. Behind the fontanelle lies the stout
coracoid bone; in front is a narrow strip of calcified
cartilage, the *precoracoid*, continuous with another strip
known as the *epicoracoid* which forms the inner border
of its half of the girdle and lies against its fellow in the
middle line. This junction of the two halves of the
girdle is known as its *symphysis*. Scapula and coracoid
are cartilage bones. A pair of slender membrane bones,
the *clavicles*, overlie the precoracoid cartilages. Each

---

[1] The structure of bone has already been alluded to. It will be
more fully described together with that of cartilage in a later chapter.
Bone differs from cartilage not in the mere presence of calcareous
matter, but in structure and composition.

sends forward a prolongation beside the acromion process. At the junction of the scapula and coracoid bones is the *glenoid cavity*, a hollow, lined by cartilage, on the hinder edge of the girdle, into which fits the head of the humerus or bone of the upper arm.

To the ends of the epicoracoids, before and behind the girdle, are attached certain structures which correspond to the *breastbone* or *sternum* of other animals. In front is a bone known as the *omosternum*, bearing at its

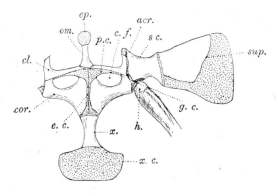

FIG. 22. —The shoulder girdle of a frog, seen from below, with the right scapula removed.

acr., Acromion process ; *c.f.*, coracoid fontanelle ; *cl.*, clavicle ; *cor.*, coracoid ; *e.c.*, epicoracoid ; *ep.*, episternum ; *g.c.*, glenoid cavity ; *h.*, head of humerus ; *om.*, omosternum ; *p.c.*, precoracoid ; *sc.*, scapula ; *sup.*, suprascapula ; *x.*, xiphisternum ; *x.c.*, xiphoid cartilage.

end a small plate of cartilage, the *episternum*. Behind is the larger *xiphisternum*, bearing the broad, flat *xiphoid cartilage*.

The *hip girdle* or *pelvic arch* lies at the hinder end of the trunk in a position similar to that occupied in front by the shoulder girdle, which it also resembles in consisting of two halves, each composed of several pieces, joined below in a symphysis. Its shape, however, is very different ; it is connected with the backbone not solely by muscles, but also by joints or articulations with the large transverse processes of the sacral vertebra ; it bears no bone comparable with the clavicle, and there are in connection with it no unpaired structures such as the sternum. The greater part of each half consists of a long slender bone, the *hip-bone* or *ilium*, corresponding in position to the scapular part of the shoulder girdle, which runs downwards and backwards from the sacral vertebra, curving inwards on the under side of the body to join its fellow. The junction is enlarged into a flattened mass by the addition of several elements which are more distinct while they are being formed in development than they are in the adult. Behind lies a ridge of bone known as the *ischium*, which consists at first of two parts, one belonging to each half of the girdle. A slight groove marks the limits of this bone. In front a similar ridge, not marked off from the ilium, is known as the *pubis*, and represents a pair of pubic bones found in certain other animals, though its relation to the bones so called in man is uncertain. Ventrally, between the pubis and the ischium, lies a triangular piece of calcified cartilage, the *postpubic cartilage*. In each of the flat sides of the mass formed by the union of these structures is a round hollow, the *leg-socket* or *acetabulum*, into which fits the head of the thigh-bone.

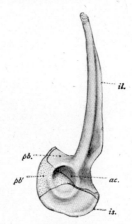

FIG. 23.—The hip girdle of a frog, seen from the left side.

ac., Acetabulum; *il.*, ilium; *is.*, ischium; *pb.*, pubic region of ilium; *pb'.*, post-pubic cartilage

Limbs. The upper arm contains a single bone, the *upper arm bone* or *humerus*. This consists of a stout shaft, swollen at each end, and bearing on its inner side a ridge known as the *deltoid ridge*. The swelling at the upper end is the *head*, and fits into the glenoid cavity of the shoulder girdle. That at the lower end, the *trochlea*, is more irregular in shape and serves for the articulation of the *forearm bone* or *radio-ulna*. In man, and in most animals whose limbs are built upon the same plan as those

of the frog, the forearm contains two bones, the *radius* and
the *ulna*, and traces of the fusion of these can clearly be
seen in the frog. The radius is the inner of the two components of the bone, but its upper end lies partly in front of
the ulna.[1] The upper end of the radio-ulna is hollowed to
receive the humerus at the elbow-joint, behind which it
projects as the *elbow-bone* or *olecranon process*. The wrist
consists of six small *carpal bones* arranged in two rows
across the limb. Those of the first row are named according
to their position *radiale, intermedium,* and *ulnare*.[2] The

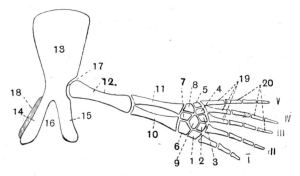

FIG. 24. —A diagram to illustrate the structure of the limbs and
girdles of pentadactyle animals.

1–5, Distal carpals or tarsals; 6, radiale or tibiale; 7, intermedium . 8,
ulnare or fibulare; 9, centrale; 10, radius or tibia; 11, ulna or fibula :
12, humerus or femur; 13, scapula or ilium; 14, precoracoid or pubis ,
15, coracoid or ischium; 16, coracoid fontanelle or obturator foramen;
17, glenoid cavity or acetabulum; 18, clavicle; 19, metacarpals or
metatarsals; 20, phalanges; I.-V., digits.

second row contains in the early stages of its development
five bones, called *distal carpals*, corresponding to five digits,
but in the adult frog the third, fourth, and fifth of these
have fused.[3] The palm contains five *metacarpal bones*.
The first digit is wanting, but the second and third have
each two bones and the fourth and fifth three, according

[1] See p. 536.
[1] For the names of the corresponding bones in the rabbit and man,
see p. 536.
[1] In many animals (but not in man) a bone known as the *central*
or *os centrale* lies between the two rows of bones of the wrist.

to the number of their joints. These bones are called *phalanges*.

The bones of the leg correspond closely to those of the arm. The *thigh-bone or femur* has a long, slender, slightly curved shaft with a rounded *head* to fit into the acetabulum and a wide *condyle* for articulation with the *shank-bone, os cruris, or tibio-fibula*. The latter, like the radio-ulna, corresponds to two bones in man and many other animals, showing traces of being formed by the fusion of an inner or anterior *shin-bone or tibia* and an outer or posterior *fibula*. The ankle, like the wrist, consists of two rows of bones, which are here called *tarsals*. The first row contains two bones, the *tibiale, astragalus, or talus* and the *heel-bone, fibulare, or calcaneum*. These bones are joined at each end by a piece of cartilage. The second row consists of two small *distal tarsals*. The metatarsus contains six *metatarsals*, one minute and corresponding to a small extra toe, the *prehallux or calcar*, which lies inside the first toe or hallux, but does not project from the foot. The calcar has one phalanx, the first two toes have each two, the third and fifth toes three, and the fourth toe, which is the longest, has four.

It will be seen that the fore- and hind-limbs and girdles are built upon a common plan. The skeleton of this is shown in Fig. 24. It may be traced in all animals which are *pentadactyle*—that is, have fingers and toes. Neither of the limbs of the frog conforms to it exactly.

The movements of the body and of its organs are brought about by means of a tissue known as *muscle*.

Muscles. This tissue is classed according to its function as *voluntary* when it is under the direct control of the will and *involuntary* when it is not under such control. Between voluntary and involuntary muscle there is, generally speaking, a difference in fine structure: of this we shall speak later (p. 117). Involuntary muscle usually forms part of the wall of some internal organ such as the stomach, bowel, bladder, or heart, and by its contraction brings about changes in the width of this organ and thus movement of the fluid it contains. Voluntary muscle is usually found in the form of distinct organs or *muscles*, which are attached at their ends to two parts of the skeleton

4

and, by their contraction moving one of these lever-wise upon the other, change the relative position of the regions of the body which they support. Sometimes the end of a muscle may be attached by a stout band or *aponeurosis* of connective tissue to another muscle. A muscle has a *belly* of muscular tissue which is attached by *tendons* of a peculiar kind of connective tissue. One of the two attachments is called the *origin*, and this is made to a relatively fixed part ; the other, called the *insertion*, is made to a more movable part. Parts of the skeleton which are

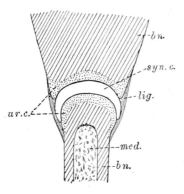

Fig. 25. — A diagram to illustrate the structure of " perfect " joints.

ar.c., Articular cartilage ; *bn.*, bone ; *lig.*, ligament ; *med.*, medulla or marrow ; *syn.c.*, synovial capsule.

thus movable upon one another must be provided with *joints*. When the amount of movement which is possible is small, the joint consists of an intervening layer of cartilage or ligament, and is said to be *imperfect*. This kind of joint is found, for instance, between the bones of the frog's shoulder girdle. When free movement is possible there is a *perfect joint*. Here a convex surface of one structure plays within a concave surface of another, the two surfaces being separated by a fibrous bag, the *synovial capsule*, which contains a watery fluid, the *synovia*, and serves as a cushion. Outside the joint, ligaments hold the movable pieces together. The muscular system of the frog is complicated, and we shall therefore only give an outline of its general arrangement and mention a few of the more important muscles.

The following table sets forth the *general arrangement of the muscular system* :

A. MUSCLES OF THE TRUNK.

1. *Muscles of the lower side.*
   a. *Muscles of the Belly.*
      e.g. *Rectus abdominis,* a wide band running along the belly, divided lengthwise down the middle by the connective tissue *linea alba* and transversely by *tendinous intersections.*

      Obliquus externus, a broad sheet at each side of the body, arising from an aponeurosis known as the *dorsal fascia* which covers the muscles of the back, and inserted into the linea alba above the rectus abdominis.

      Obliquus internus and *transversus,* muscular sheets within the external oblique.

      By their contraction all these muscles lessen the size of the body cavity and compress the organs within it.
   b. *Muscles of the Breast Region.*
      e.g. *Pectoralis,* large and fan-shaped, inserted into the deltoid ridge of the humerus and consisting of a *sternal portion,* arising from the pectoral girdle, which draws down the arm, and an *abdominal portion,* arising from the aponeurosis at the side of the rectus abdominis, which draws the arm backwards.

      Coraco-radialis, arising from the coracoid and inserted into the upper end of the radius. It bends the arm.
2. *Muscles of the Back.*
   a. *Muscle inserted into the Lower Jaw.*
      Depressor mandibulæ, triangular, arising from the suprascapula and inserted into the angle of the lower jaw, which it draws downwards and backwards, thus opening the mouth.
   b. *Muscles inserted on the Fore-Limb.*
      e.g. *Latissimus dorsi,* triangular, arising from the dorsal fascia and inserted into the deltoid ridge. It draws back the arm.

      Dorsalis scapulæ, in front of and similar to the latissimus dorsi. It raises the arm.
   c. *Muscles inserted into the Shoulder Girdle.*
      e.g. *Levator scapulæ,* arising from the skull and inserted into the under side of the suprascapula, which it draws forward.

      Serratus, arising from the little knobs which

represent ribs on the ends of the transverse processes of the vertebræ. This muscle is inserted
into the under side of the suprascapula which it
draws backwards, outwards, or inwards according
to the division which is contracted.

d. *Muscles inserted into the Hind-Limb.*

e.g. *Iliacus externus*, arising from the ilium and inserted into the femur, which it rotates inwards.

Obturator internus, arising from the ischium and
pubis and inserted into the head of the femur,
which it rotates outwards.

e. *Muscles inserted into the Hip Girdle.*

e.g. *Coccygeo-iliacus*, arising from the urostyle and
inserted into the ilium, which it holds firm as a
fulcrum for the movements of the hind-limb.

f. *Muscles of the Backbone.*

e.g. *Longissimus dorsi*, a band running the whole
length of the back, divided by tendinous inter-
sections, which are attached to the transverse
processes, and inserted in front into the skull. It
straightens the back.

B. MUSCLES OF THE HEAD.

1. *Muscles underneath the Head.*

e.g. *Sternohyoid* from hyoid to pectoral girdle.

Geniohyoid from hyoid to chin.

Hyoglossus from hyoid to tongue.

Petrohyoid from hyoid to auditory capsule.

Mylohyoid, submandibular, or submaxillaris, a sheet of
muscle running from side to side of the lower jaw.

These muscles alter the position of the floor of the
mouth.

2. *Muscles of the Lower Jaw.*

e.g. *Temporalis and masseter*, arising from the skull and inserted into the lower jaw, which they raise.

3. *Muscles of the Eyeball.*

Rectus superior, r. inferior, r. externus (or *lateralis*), *r.
internus* (or *medialis*), arising from the skull in the
hinder part of the orbit and inserted into the eyeball.

Obliquus superior and o. inferior, arising from the skull
in the front part of the orbit and inserted into the
eyeball.

These muscles will be more fully described in the chapter
on the dogfish.

C. MUSCLES OF THE FORE-LIMB.

1. *Muscles for the Upper Arm.*

e.g. *Deltoideus*, arising from the scapula and episternum
and inserted into the humerus. It raises and pulls
forward the arm.

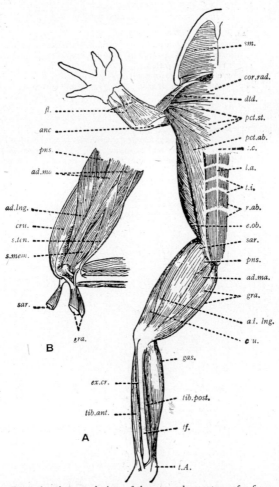

FIG. 26.—A ventral view of the muscular system of a frog.

ad. lng., *ad.ma.*, Adductores longus and magnus; *anc.*, anconæus; *cor.rad.*, cor-aco-radialis; *cru.*, crureus; *dtd.*, deltoid; *e.ob.*, external oblique; *ex.cr.*, extensor cruris brevis; *fl.*, flexors of hand; *gas.*, gastrocnemius; *gra.*, graciles; *l.a.*, linea alba; *pct.ab.*, *pct.st.*, abdominal and sternal parts of pectoral; *pns.*, pectinæus; *r.ab.*, rectus abdominis; *s.mem.*, semimembranosus; *s.ten.*, semitendinosus; *sar.*, sartorius; *sm.*, submaxillaris; *t.A.*, tendo Achillis; *t.i.*, tendinous inter-sections; *tf.*, tibiofibula; *tib.ant.*, *tib.post.* tibiales anticus and posticus; *x.c.*, xiphoid cartilage.

B is a ventral view of the thigh after removal of certain muscles.

2. *Muscles for the Fore-Arm.*

> *Triceps brachii or anconæus*, arising from the scapula and humerus, and inserted into the upper end of the ulna. It straightens the arm.
>
> There is no *Biceps* muscle in the arm of the frog.

3. The *muscles of the Wrist and Fingers* are numerous and complicated.

D. MUSCLES OF THE HIND-LIMB.

1. *Muscles of the Thigh.*

> e.g. *Adductores magnus* and *longus*, large muscles arising from the pubis and ischium, lying on the front of the thigh, and inserted into the femur near its lower end. They draw the thigh towards the body.

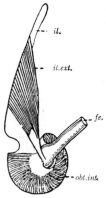

FIG. 27.—A dissection showing the muscles which rotate the femur of a frog.—After Ecker.

fe., Femur ; *il.*, ilium ; *il.ext.*, iliacus externus ; *obt.int.*, obturator internus.

> *Iliacus internus*, arising from the base of the ilium and inserted into the femur. It draws the thigh away from the flank.
>
> *Pectineus*, arising from the pubis and inserted into the femur. It draws the thigh away from the flank.
>
> *Sartorius*, a long, narrow band arising from the lower end of the ilium, lying obliquely upon the adductor magnus, and inserted into the tibia on its inner side near the end. It bends the knee and helps to draw the thigh to the flank.

Graciles major and minor, muscles arising from the ischium, lying along the inner side of the adductor magnus, and inserted into the inner side of the head of the tibia. They bend the knee.

Semimembranosus, a stout muscle arising from the ischium, lying on the back of the thigh, and inserted into the back of the head of the tibia. It bends the knee.

Semitendinosus, a long, thin muscle arising by two heads from the ischium and inserted into the proximal end of the tibia. Its action is like that of the semimembranosus.

Triceps extensor cruris or *t. femoris*, a very large muscle inserted into the front of the tibia just below the head of the latter, but arising from the pelvic girdle as three separate muscles, the *rectus femoris*, the *vastus lateralis* or *glutæus magnus*, and the *vastus medialis* or *crureus*. All these lie on the front of the thigh, and their action is to straighten the leg.

2. *Muscles of the Shank.*

e.g. *Peronæus*, a long muscle, which arises from the end of the femur, lies along the side of the tibio-fibula, and is inserted into the end of the tibia and the calcaneum. It straightens the leg.

Gastrocnemius, a large, spindle-shaped muscle which forms the " calf." It arises from the hinder side of the end of the femur and tapers into the long *tendo Achillis* (or *t. calcaneus*), which passes under the ankle joint and ends in the sole. It straightens the foot on the shank.

Tibialis anticus, arising from the front of the femur by a long tendon, lying in front of the shank, and dividing into two bellies, which are respectively inserted into the astragalus and calcaneus. It bends the foot on the shank.

3. The *muscles of the Ankle and Toes* are numerous and complicated.

It should be noted that the muscles which move the limbs are so arranged that to those which produce any movement there are opposed others which reverse it.

Thus, in the hind limb:

The *thigh* is *abducted* (drawn away from the flank) by the iliacus externus and pectineus, *adducted* by the adductores, graciles, semimembranosus and semitendinosus, *rotated inwards* on its axis by the iliacus externus and *rotated outwards* by the obturator internus.

The *shank* is *flexed* by the sartorius, graciles, semimembranosus, and semitendinosus, and *extended* by the triceps femoris and peronæus.

The *ankle* is *flexed* by the tibialis anticus and peronæus. and *extended* by the gastrocnemius and extensores eruris.

In the fore limb :

The *upper arm* is *abducted* by the deltoid, *adducted* by the abdominal part of the pectoral, *drawn down* by the latissimus dorsi and the sternal part of the pectoral, and *raised* by the dorsalis scapulæ (with other muscles).

The *forearm* is *flexed* by the coraco-radialis and *extended* by the anconæus.

No muscle has precisely the same action as any other, and by the combined use of muscles very various and complicated movements are executed.

Muscles ordinarily contract because stimuli reach them as impulses along nerves (p. 93). The irritability which makes them responsive to these stimuli is also

FIG. 28.—(*From left to right*) Successive postures of a toad during crawling.—After Gray.

shown by their contraction when artificial stimuli are directly applied to them by pinching, heating, electric shocks, etc. (see p. 738).

It would not be possible here to describe the various **Locomotion.** modes of locomotion of the frog (p. 32), even if they were at present thoroughly understood. Something must, however, be said about crawling, in which the frog practises what is the primary mode of loco-motion of four-footed animals. In it the body is levered forwards over the ground by the limbs, which are used in diagonal pairs, the left hind-limb immediately after, or practically with, the right fore-limb, and similarly the right hind-limb with the left fore-limb. Fig. 28 shows a toad moving in this way.

CHAPTER III

THE FROG: VISCERA AND VASCULAR SYSTEM

THE food of the frog is received and digested by a winding tube, known as the *gut or alimentary canal*, **Alimentary System.** which runs from mouth to cloacal opening and has a muscular wall lined by a soft, glandular *mucous membrane* (p. 111). The *gape* of the mouth lies between two *jaws*, of which the upper is not movable, but the lower is hinged. There are no *teeth* in the lower jaw, but the upper bears a row of maxillary teeth, and a patch of vomerine teeth is found on each side of the roof of the mouth. The teeth are small, sharp-pointed structures, consisting of a *base* and a spike or *crown*. The greater part of the crown is composed of *ivory or dentine*, but the base is formed of bone, and the crown is covered by a cap of very hard substance known as *enamel*, and both are pierced by a core of soft tissue called the *pulp* (Fig. 30). The teeth are all alike, and all fused to the surface of the bones that carry them. As they are destroyed by use they fall out and are replaced one by one.

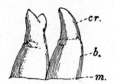

FIG. 29.—Two of the maxillary teeth of a frog, seen from the outside of the jaw.

b., Base of the tooth; *cr.*, crown; *m.*, edge of the maxilla.

On the front part of the roof, beside the vomerine teeth, open the *internal nares* (p. 102). The tongue is a muscular structure arising from the front part of the floor of the mouth and forked at its free end, which is directed backwards when it is at rest. In taking food the tongue is turned over and its free end thrown out of the mouth, wiping up, as it goes, a sticky substance secreted by glands in the roof of the mouth so that the prey adhere to it. Behind the angle of the jaw is a region known as the *pharynx*, into which open, at the sides of its roof, the pair of *Eustachian tubes* which lead to the drums of the ears, and below, in the male, a pair of *vocal sacs* which are inflated and act as resonators during croaking. In the middle of the floor of the pharynx is a slit-like opening, the *glottis*, which leads into the wind-pipe (Figs. 31 and 537).

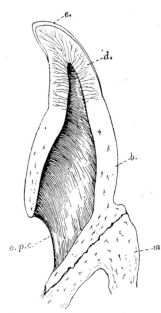

From the pharynx a tube known as the *gullet or œsophagus* leads backwards in the body cavity to the *maw or stomach*, which is spindle-shaped and separated by a slight constriction, the *pylorus*, from the *bowel or intestine*. The first part of the intestine, known as the *duodenum*, is narrow and turns forward so as to lie parallel with the stomach. It is succeeded by another narrow tube, the *ileum*, which runs backwards in several coils. Duodenum and ileum are together known as the *small intestine* : at its hinder end this region opens suddenly into a much wider tube, the *rectum*. The length of the small intestine is from 4 to 5 inches ; that of the rectum is about an inch and a quarter. The internal surface of the intestine is increased by folds of its lining. These are transverse in the duodenum and longitudinal in the ileum. The rectum passes without distinct *anus* into a *cloaca*, which receives ventrally a thin

FIG. 30.—A vertical section through a tooth and part of the maxilla of a frog.

b., Base of the tooth, composed of bone (cement); *d.*, dentine ; *e.*, enamel ; *m.*, maxilla ; *o.p.c.*, opening of the pulp cavity.

walled, bilobed sac, the *urinary bladder*, and dorsally the ducts of the kidneys and in the female those which bear the eggs.

Besides numerous small *glands* in the mucous membrane, the alimentary canal receives the secretions of two large glands, the liver and the pancreas. The *liver* is a large, reddish-brown structure in the forepart of the belly. It

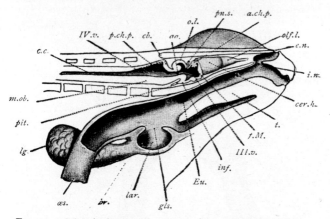

FIG. 31.—A longitudinal median section through the head of a frog.

aq., Aquaeductus cerebri ; *a.ch.p.*, anterior choroid plexus ; *br.*, bronchus ; *c.c.*, central canal of spinal cord ; *cb.*, cerebellum ; *cer.h.*, left cerebral hemisphere ; *e.n.*, nostril ; *Eu.*, Eustachian tube ; *f.M.*, foramen of Monro ; *gls.*, glottis ; *i.n.*, internal narial opening ; *inf.*, infundibulum ; *lar.*, larynx ; *lg.*, left lung ; *m.ob.*, medulla oblongata ; *o.l.*, optic lobe ; *œs.*, œsophagus ; *olf.l.*, olfactory lobe ; *p.ch.p.*, posterior choroid plexus ; *pit.*, pituitary body ; *pn.s.*, pineal stalk ; *III.v.*, third ventricle ; *IV.v.*, fourth ventricle.

consists of a right and a left lobe and a small median lobe which unites them. The left lobe is the larger and is itself deeply cleft into two. Between the right and left lobes lies the *gall-bladder*, which receives the green bile secreted by the liver and passes it by the *bile-duct* into the duodenum. The *pancreas* is an oblong, creamy-white structure lying between the stomach and duodenum. It is traversed by the bile-duct, into which it passes the pancreatic juice which it secretes.

The food is not chewed, but is swallowed whole, the

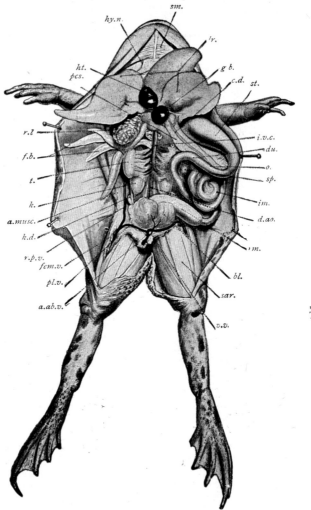

FIG. 32.—A male frog dissected from the ventral side.

a.ab. v., Anterior abdominal vein, cut short, ligatured, and turned back ; *a.musc.*, cut edge of abdominal muscles ; *bl.*, urinary bladder ; *c.d.*, common duct of gall-bladder and pancreas ; *d.ao.*, dorsal aorta ; *du.*, duodenum ; *f.b.*, fat body ; *fem.v.*, femoral vein ; *g.b.*, gall-bladder ; *ht.*, heart ; *hy.n.*, hypoglossal nerve ; *im.*, ileum ; *i.v.c.*, inferior vena cava ; *k.*, kidney ; *k.d.*, kidney duct with vesicula seminalis ; *lr.*, liver ; *o.*, point at which *c.d.* enters the duodenum ; *pcs.*, pancreas ; *pl.v.*, pelvic vein ; *r.l.*, right lung ; *rm.*, rectum ; *r.p.v.*, renal portal vein ; *sar.*, sartorius muscle ; *sm.*, mylohyoid muscle ; *sp.*, spleen ; *st.*, stomach ; *t.*, testis *v.v.*, vesical vein.

Digestion. only use of the teeth being to prevent the escape of the prey, which they can the better do because they slant backwards. In the stomach the food meets the *gastric juice*, secreted by the glands of the mucous membrane of the stomach (p. 111). The important contents of this watery juice are free hydrochloric acid and the organic substance *pepsin*, which starts the digestion of protein, turning it into a more soluble form (peptone). Mixed with the juice, the food is churned by rhythmical contraction of muscle-layers in the stomach wall, and thus is killed, disinfected of bacteria by the acid, softened, partly dissolved by the action of the pepsin, and broken up. Pepsin is one of a very important class of substances, found in living bodies, which are organic catalysts, having the power of bringing about changes in other substances without themselves undergoing change, and of doing this even though they be present in very small quantities in a large mass of the substance acted upon. These agents are called *ferments or enzymes*.

Enzymes. Enzymes act not only in digestion but also in many chemical events in the cells of the body. Oxidation, the preparation of excreta, and other processes take place with their aid. The classes of enzymes are known by names derived from those of the substances upon which they act, with the termination *-ase*. Thus pepsin is a *protease*. The protease of pancreatic juice (see below), is *trypsin*, the carbohydrase is *amylase*, the fat-splitting enzyme is *lipase*.

From time to time a ring of muscle known as the *pyloric sphincter*, which guards the opening of the duodenum, relaxes and lets through partly digested food into the intestine, where it meets three alkaline juices, the *bile*, the *pancreatic juice*, and a juice known as the *succus entericus*, which is secreted by the intestinal wall. Of these the pancreatic juice is the most powerful, turning all three classes of organic food-stuffs, each by means of a distinct enzyme, into the soluble substances mentioned on pp. 9, 10. The action of the bile and succus entericus is subsidiary to that of the pancreatic juice, and the bile is also partly an excretion. The food thus rendered diffusible is absorbed by the activity of the intestinal lining. The movement of the food along the alimentary canal is brought about by the working of a muscular layer in the wall of the latter (see Fig. 58), down which waves of contraction pass, pressing the contents before them. This process is called *peristalsis*. Finally the undigested portion of the food is driven out through the rectum and cloaca to the exterior.

FIG 35.—Two individuals of the same age from the same batch of frog's eggs. The one on the right has changed normally into a frog; that on the left had the rudiment of its thyroid removed and has not become adult but has grown into a giant tadpole.—From Haldane and Huxley.

The secretion of bile is not the only function of the liver.

Functions of the Liver. That organ is the great chemical workshop and storehouse of the body. In it a part of the excess of carbohydrate and fatty food taken during the summer is stored for use during the winter sleep and the breeding season. The fat is stored in droplets, the carbohydrate in the form of *glycogen* or animal starch, which, when it is to be transferred to other parts of the body, is converted into sugar and cast into the blood. In the liver also the ammonia which results from the decomposition of proteins is converted into urea ready for excretion by the kidneys, and various other chemical changes take place.

We must here mention the organs known as the *ductless*

Ductless Glands. *glands* or *endocrine organs*, which, while they manufacture substances of importance to the body, discharge these products not through a duct but into the blood or lymph by the process known as *internal secretion*. Substances are, of course, continually being passed into the blood by every organ, but among these it is important to distinguish between (*a*) the waste products of metabolism, (*b*) substances which are used in bulk, such as the sugar discharged by the liver, and (*c*) the " chemical messengers " or *hormones* (p. 21), of which minute quantities are secreted as a stimulant or inhibiting agent to the action of other organs. It is to this latter class that the characteristic products of the ductless glands belong.

The *thyroid glands* of the frog are a pair of small, rounded, pinkish bodies lying on the external jugular veins. Their secretion, which contains an organic compound of iodine (*thyroxin*), has an important, but not well understood, action in maintaining the normal working of various parts of the body. The change from tadpole to adult is

FIG. 34.—Two frogs nineteen days after operation. From that on the left only the anterior lobe of the pituitary body has been removed ; from that on the right both anterior and posterior lobes. Lack of the hormone from the posterior lobe has caused in the right-hand frog pallor due to non-expansion of the pigment in the pigment cells.—From Hogben.

brought on by it. In man, the thyroid is a single, median body (as it is in the embryo of the frog) ; and defect of its secretion has very serious consequences both for the young and for adults, in whom the lack of it produces both mental dullness and physical disorder (see p. 673).

The *adrenal bodies* (so-called *suprarenal glands*) are small yellowish masses lying on the ventral surface of the kidneys. They consist of two kinds of tissue, which in the frog are mixed, while in man one, the *cortex*, is a layer around the other, the *medulla*. The secretion of the cortex is essential to the maintenance of life, but its mode of action is unknown. The medulla secretes a substance (*adrenalin*) whose effects resemble those of the activity of the sympathetic nervous system (p. 92), influencing, positively or negatively according to the organ affected and its condition, the " tone " of muscle and the activity of glands. At times of excitement and exertion its discharge tunes up the body for action (see p. 22).

The *thymus* is a small body which lies behind and above the angle of the jaw on each side. Its functions are unknown.

The *pituitary body* lies in the skull below the brain (see p. 87). It is a gland of many hormones. It consists of an anterior and a posterior lobe, of different function. The anterior lobe arises solely from an ingrowth, known as the *hypophysis*, from the roof of the mouth. Its secretion acts not only directly, by means of hormones which stimulate growth, particularly that of bone, and sexual processes, but also indirectly by hormones which stimulate the thyroid and the cortex of the adrenal body. The posterior lobe is partly hypophysial, partly a ventral appendage of the brain (the *infundibulum*). Its secretion is the means of dilating the pigment cells in the frog's skin (p. 35), increases blood pressure by contracting vessels, and has various other effects.

Hormones are also secreted by ordinary glands. Thus the production at the right moment of large quantities of gastric and pancreatic juice is brought about by the stimulation of their glands, partly by impulses through the nervous system during feeding, and partly by hormones, known as *secretins*, formed in the wall of the alimentary canal under the influence of substances in the food and carried by the blood to the glands. *Insulin*, whose defect causes diabetes, is produced by certain cells (*islets of Langerhans*) in the pancreas. The testes and ovaries not only form spermatozoa and ova but also liberate hormones, of which some influence the development of secondary sexual characters in the growing individual, and others bring about events in the process of reproduction.

The *spleen* is a small, round, dark red body, lying in the mesentery opposite to the beginning of the rectum. Its cells remove and destroy effete " red corpuscles " (cells, see p. 122) of the blood, and certain minute parasites. It is also concerned in the preparation of nitrogenous waste matter for excretion. In some animals at least, including man, it acts as a reservoir of blood. Its removal is not fatal.

The *fat bodies* are two orange-coloured tufts of flattened processes, attached in front of the ovary or testis to the dorsal wall of the body cavity. They consist of fatty tissue (see p. 120) which, like the reserves in the liver, increases during the summer and decreases during the winter sleep, when it is being drawn upon for nourishment, particularly in the preparation of germ cells for breeding in the spring.

The *heart* of the frog is a hollow, conical, muscular organ,
which lies, with the apex backwards, in the body
Vascular System: Heart. cavity, between the breast-bone and the gullet.
It is enclosed in a thin sac, the *pericardium*,
whose cavity is a part of the body cavity (cœlom) separated
from the rest during development, the heart having the
same relation to it that the alimentary canal has to the
pleuroperitoneal or
general body cavity—
that is, being covered
by a continuation of
the pericardial mem-
brane as the gut is by
the peritoneum. The
heart contains five
chambers. Of these
the most conspicuous
is the *ventricle*, a
large, conical struc-
ture, with thick, mus-
cular walls, from
which arises in front,
on the right side of the
ventral surface, the
much smaller, tubular
truncus arteriosus.
The *right and left
auricles* or *atria* are
relatively thin walled
chambers, the right
larger than the left,
separated by a septum
and lying in front of

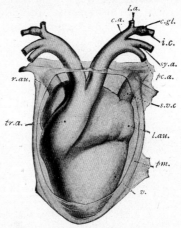

FIG. 35 —The heart of a frog, seen from
the ventral side.

c.a., Carotid arch; *c.gl.,* carotid gland; *i.c.,*
internal carotid artery; *l.a.,* lingual artery;
pc.a., pulmocutaneous arch; *p.m.,* pericardium; *r.au., l.au.,* right and left
auricles; *s.v.c.,* superior vena cava; *sy.a.,*
systemic arch; *tr.a.,* truncus arteriosus;
v., ventricle.

the ventricle, into which each opens. On the dorsal surface
of the heart, opening into the right auricle, lies the still
thinner walled, triangular *sinus venosus*; into the left auricle
opens the pulmonary vein (p. 71).

The openings between these chambers are guarded by
certain *valves* or folds of the lining of the heart. Two
simple lips of the opening between the sinus and right
auricle are the *sinu-auricular valves*; these allow blood to

5

flow into the auricle; but when it tends to flow the other way fold over and meet to oppose it. The edge of the auricular septum is cleft and projects into the ventricle as two flaps, the *auriculo-ventricular valves.* Each of these is connected with the walls of the ventricle by fine cords, the *chordæ tendineæ,* and thus, while blood can pass from auricles to ventricle, its reflux is prevented by its raising the valves, which are kept from turning back into the auricle by the chordæ tendineæ.

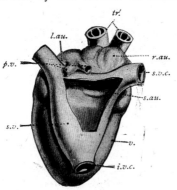

FIG. 36. —The heart of a frog, removed from the pericardium and seen from the back with the sinus venosus opened.

i.v.c., Inferior vena cava ; *p.v.,* pulmonary veins ; *r.au., l.au.,* right and left auricles; *s.au.,* opening from sinus to right auricle ; *s.v.c.,* superior vena cava ; *s.v.,* sinus venosus ; *tr′.*; branches of truncus cut across ; *v.,* ventricle.

The opening from ventricle to truncus is guarded by three *semilunar valves,* shaped like watch-pockets, which are spread out by any reflux of blood, so that by meeting one another they stop it. The truncus arteriosus is divided internally by a *second ring of semilunar valves* into two unequal parts, a long *conus arteriosus* or *pylangium* next the ventricle, and a short *ventral aorta* or *synangium.* The conus is incompletely divided longitudinally by a *spiral valve* into a *cavum aorticum,* which begins dorsal and curves round by the right to become ventral, and a *cavum pulmocutaneum,* which begins ventral and curves round by the left to become dorsal. The synangium is completely divided into a dorsal and a ventral chamber.[1]

---

[1] The septum which makes this division ends towards the heart by cutting across the hollow of one of the second row of semilunar valves. It is from the outer side of this valve that the spiral valve starts. Thus it comes about that the outer ends of the cavum aorticum and cavum pulmocutaneum are each guarded by one and a half valves.

The dorsal chamber communicates behind with the cavum pulmocutaneum and in front with the blood vessel to the lungs

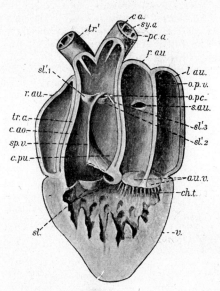

FIG. 37. —A ventral view of the heart of a frog, opened to show the internal structure. The ventral wall of the truncus, ventricle, and auricles has been removed, with part of the spiral valve.

au.r., Auriculo-ventricular valves ; *c.a.*, carotid arch ; *c.ao.*, cavum aorticum ; *c.pu.*, cavum pulmocutaneum ; *ch.t.*, chordæ tendineæ ; *l.au.*, left auricle ; *o.p.v.*, opening of pulmonary vein ; *o.pc.*, opening of dorsal division of synangium, by which blood passes from the cavum pulmocutaneum to the pulmocutaneous arch ; *pc.a.*, pulmocutaneous arch ; *r.au.*, right auricle ; *s.au.*, sinu-auricular opening with valves ; *sl.*, first row of semilunar valves ; *sl'.*, semilunar valves of second row ; *sl'.*1, the semilunar valve from which the spiral valve starts ; *sl'.*2, small semilunar valve at end of cavum pulmocutaneum ; *sl'.*3, a small part of a large semilunar valve, of which the rest extends across that portion of the front wall of the truncus which has been removed ; *sp.v.*, spiral valve ; *sy.a.*, systemic arch ; *tr.a.*, wall of truncus arteriosus ; *tr'.*, one of the two bundles of arteries into which the truncus divides ; *v.*, ventricle.

(pulmocutaneous arch) ; the ventral chamber communicates behind with the cavum aorticum and in front with the blood vessels known as the systemic and carotid arches.

The function of the heart is, by the contractions of its
Heart-beat. muscular wall which are known as its *beat*, to
drive blood through the vascular system to
all parts of the body. The contraction starts in the sinus
venosus, driving the contained blood into the right auricle.
Meanwhile the left auricle is filling by the inflow of blood
from the lungs through the pulmonary vein. The auricles
now contract simultaneously, driving the blood into the
ventricle. The sinus is beginning to relax, but the reflux
of blood into it is prevented by the sinu-auricular valves.
The right-hand side of the ventricle receives the blood
from the right auricle and the left-hand side that from the
left auricle, and these por-
tions of blood mix slowly
because a great part of the
hollow of the ventricle is
spongy, owing to the presence of muscular projections
known as *columnæ carneæ.*
The ventricle contracts immediately after the auricles,
the   auriculo - ventricular
valves preventing the passage of blood back into the
latter. The effect of the
contraction of the ventricle
is therefore to drive the
blood onward into the
truncus arteriosus. Since this is on the right side of
the ventricle, it will receive first the blood from the
right auricle. Both cavum aorticum and cavum pulmocutaneum are filled, but since the pressure in the
carotid and systemic arches is higher than that in the
pulmocutaneous arch, blood is first driven into the latter.
As the ventricle continues to contract, the pressure of the
blood rises until it is high enough to overcome the resistance
in the systemic and finally in the carotid arches. At the
same time the contraction of the truncus arteriosus brings
the spiral valve into a position in which it shuts off the
cavum pulmocutaneum. Thus the blood from the left
auricle (and therefore from the lungs), which is the last to

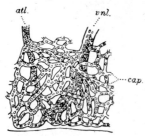

FIG. 38.—Capillaries in the web
of a frog's foot.—After Allen
Thomson.

atl., Arteriole ; *cap.*, capillaries ;
vnl., venule.

enter the truncus, passes along the cavum aorticum into the systemic and carotid arches. The blood in the systemic arch is a mixture of that from the right and left auricles ; the final portion which passes into the carotid comes only from the left auricle. The meaning of this separation of the blood will be seen later.

To and from the heart leads a complicated system of **Circulation of the Blood.** *blood vessels*, through which the red blood is driven by the heart-beat. The vessels which lead from the heart are called *arteries* ; those which lead to the heart are *veins*. The arteries have thick, muscular walls, and after many subdivisions become small vessels known as *arterioles*.

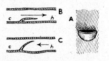

These in turn divide into minute, very thin-walled vessels called *capillaries*, that lie among the tissues in the form of a meshwork, which in active tissues, such as glands and muscles, is exceedingly fine, so that the blood is brought close to every part. From the capillaries the blood is collected into small *venules* which join to form the veins. The walls of the veins are thinner and less muscular but more elastic than those of the arteries, and many of them contain small watch-pocket valves, placed with the opening of the pockets towards the heart so as

FIG. 39.—Diagrams of a valve in a vein.

A, Part of the wall of the vein from within ; *B*, longitudinal section of the vein, showing the position of the valve when blood flows from the direction of the capillaries; (*c*) towards the heart (*h*) ; *C*, similar section showing how reflux is prevented by the valve.

to prevent the blood from being driven in the wrong direction when the vessels are compressed by the movements of the body. Through heart, arteries, capillaries, and veins there takes place a *circulation of the blood*, which can be seen under the microscope in the capillaries of the thin web between the toes of the frog's foot. In the arteries the blood flows fast and with jerks, which are caused by the beating of the heart and known as the *pulse*. In the arterioles the increased friction owing to the increased surface of the numerous branches obliterates the pulse. In the capillaries the increased area lessens the rate of flow. In the veins the blood is flowing back to the heart evenly and less fast than in the arteries, though faster than in the capillaries.

The supply of blood which an organ receives depends on two factors : (1) the width of the small blood vessels in the organ, (2) the pressure under which the blood is flowing.

Regulation of the Circulation.

When an organ such as a muscle is active, its small vessels are caused to dilate by the presence of carbonic acid (p. 21) and other products of the activity of its tissues, and also by the action of the nervous system. Now any dilatation of blood vessels, by enlarging the bed of the blood stream, tends to lower the general blood pressure, and thus both to diminish the local effect of enlarging the vessels, and also to have injurious results in other organs. These tendencies, however, if they be on a sufficient scale, are counteracted through the nervous system in two ways—by an acceleration of the rate of the heart-beat, and by the contraction of vessels in other parts of the body (in this case, of the alimentary canal and of the spleen), so that the total capacity of the vascular system is not increased.

From the truncus arteriosus there arise on each side three arteries, which are for some distance bound together, so that they seem to be a single vessel.

Blood Vessels.

The hindermost of these is the *pulmocutaneous arch*, the middle the *systemic arch*, the foremost the *carotid arch* or *common carotid artery*. After separating, the three arches continue to run outwards, diverging as they go. The pulmocutaneous arch divides into the *pulmonary artery* for the lung and the *cutaneous artery* for the skin and mouth. The carotid arch gives a *lingual* or *external carotid artery* to the muscles of the tongue and hyoid, and then becomes the *internal carotid artery* which bears a round swelling due to the fact that it here breaks up into a number of small vessels which reunite. This swelling is the *carotid labyrinth*, often inappropriately called the *carotid gland*. The friction of the blood against the large surface provided by its numerous small vessels is the cause of the high pressure in the carotid arch. Beyond the carotid gland the artery runs forwards and upwards towards the head, where, after an *orbital* (*stapedial*) branch to the orbit and roof of the mouth, it passes into the skull and supplies the brain. The systemic arch curves upwards and backwards round the œsophagus to join its fellow in the middle line below the backbone. On its way it gives off an *œsophageal artery* to the œsophagus, an *occipito-vertebral artery* to the head and backbone, and a large *subclavian artery* to the arm. Just before joining its fellow, the left systemic arch gives off backwards the large *cœliaco-mesenteric artery*. This divides into an *anterior mesenteric,* to bowel and spleen, and a *cœliac,* which supplies the stomach after giving a *hepatic* branch to the liver. The vessel formed by the junction of the systemic arches is the *dorsal aorta.* It runs backwards immediately below the backbone, giving off paired *renal arteries* to the kidneys, *ovarian or spermatic* arteries to the generative organs, and a small median *posterior mesenteric artery* to the rectum, after which it divides into two *iliac arteries* to the legs and abdominal muscles.

The blood from the lungs is returned by the *right and left pulmonary veins,* through a short *common pulmonary*

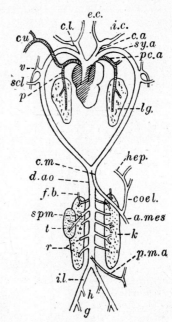

FIG. 40.—A diagram of the arterial system of the frog, seen from the ventral side.

The lungs (*lg.*), kidneys (*k.*), and right testis (*t.*), are shown. The course of the venous blood is shaded.

Arteries : *a.mes.,* anterior mesenteric ; *c.a.,* carotid arch ; *c.l.,* carotid labyrinth ; *c.m.,* cœliaco-mesenteric ; *cœl.,* cœliac ; *cu.,* cutaneous ; *d.ao.,* dorsal aorta ; *e.c.,* external carotid ; *f.b.,* to fat body ; *g.,* gluteal ; *h.,* hæmorrhoidal ; *hep.,* hepatic ; *i.c.,* internal carotid ; *il.,* common iliac ; *p.,* pulmonary ; *p.m.a.,* posterior mesenteric ; *pc.a.,* pulmocutaneous arch ; *r.,* renals ; *scl.,* subclavian ; *spm.,* spermatic ; *sy.a.,* systemic arch ; *v.,* occipitto-vertebral.

vein to the left auricle. From the rest of the body the blood is returned to the sinus venosus by three large veins, the right and left superior venæ cavæ or precaval veins in front, and the median inferior vena cava or post-caval vein behind. Each precaval is formed by the junction of three veins, the external jugular, innominate, and subclavian. The external jugular is fed by a lingual vein from the floor of the mouth and a mandibular from the lower jaw. The innominate arises by the junction of an internal jugular from the head and a subscapular from the shoulder and back of the arm. The subclavian receives the brachial from the arm and the great musculocutaneous from the skin, the mucous membrane of the mouth, and

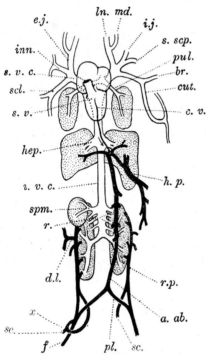

Fig. 41.—A diagram of the venous system of the frog.

a.ab., Anterior abdominal vein; *br.*, brachial; *c.v.*, cardiac (conducts *backward* from wall of heart): *cut.*, cutaneous; *d.l.*, dorsolumbar; *e.j.*, external jugular; *f.*, femoral; *h.p.*, hepatic portal; *hep.*, hepatic; *i.j.*, internal jugular; *i.v.c.*, inferior vena cava; *inn.*, innominate; *l.*, lingual; *md.*, mandibular; *pl.*, pelvic; *pul.*, pulmonary; *r.*, renals; *r.p.*, renal portal; *sc.*, sciatic; *s.scp.*, subscapular; *s.v.*, sinus venosus (seen through ventricle); *s.v.c.*, superior vena cava; *scl.*, subclavian; *spm.*, right spermatic; *x.*, vessel joining sciatic to femoral.

many head and trunk muscles. The inferior vena cava arises by the junction of several *renal veins* from the kidneys and *ovarian* or *spermatic veins* from the generative organs, and, just before it enters the sinus, is joined by two *hepatic veins* from the liver. Blood is returned from the legs by a *femoral vein* on the outside and a *sciatic* on the inside of each limb. Each femoral vein divides on reaching the trunk into a *renal portal* and a *pelvic*. The former receives the sciatic and runs to the kidney, just before entering which it receives the *dorsolumbar vein* from some of the muscles of the back. In the kidney the vein breaks up into capillaries, which are collected, with those of the renal artery, to give rise to the renal veins. Thus it comes about that much of the blood in the renal veins has passed through two sets of capillaries, one in the leg and another in the kidney. Such an arrangement, in which the blood having passed through one set of capillaries is then sent through a second, is called a *portal system*. The pelvic veins of the two sides lie in the abdominal wall and join to form the *anterior abdominal vein* which runs forwards above the linea alba in the middle of the belly (see p. 51). This vessel receives a small *vesical vein* from the bladder, several pairs of vessels from the recti muscles of the abdomen, and a little backward vessel from the heart-wall. It ends in front by passing into the liver and there breaking up into capillaries again. The blood from the stomach, bowel, pancreas, and spleen is gathered up into a great *hepatic portal vein*, which also breaks up in the liver. Thus the liver has a portal system, which is fed with blood (*a*) from the dorsal aorta, (*b*) from the anterior abdominal vein, (*c*) from the hepatic portal vein, and discharges by the hepatic veins into the inferior vena cava.

The general course of the circulation in the frog is

Course of the Circulation. summed up in the table on p. 74. The thick lines indicate " venous " blood the narrow, lines " arterial " blood (see p. 76).

Function of the Blood. The elaborate arrangements whereby the blood circulates through all parts of the body point to the fact that it is a universal means of transport between them. It conveys nourishment from the gut to the rest of the body, oxygen and carbon dioxide between the organs of respiration and the tissues (p. 76), the waste products of metabolism from the tissues to the organs of excretion, and various substances secreted into it by the liver and other organs to the regions of the body where they are made use of. It distributes hormones (p. 62). It also conveys heat—which, inside as outside the body, is set free by most chemical changes—from the organs where there is much chemical activity, such as the muscles and glands, to those where there is little, such as the

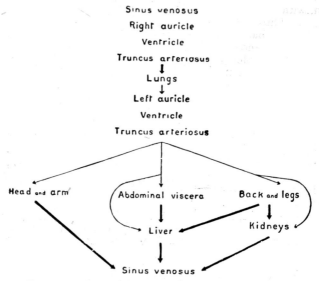

FIG. 42. —A diagram of the circulation of the blood in the frog. Thick lines indicate venous blood, narrow lines arterial.

skeleton and nervous system, and to the surface of the body, where what is excessive is lost. In some animals, as in the rabbit (p. 557) and man, so much heat is produced that the body is kept constantly at a temperature which is a good deal higher than that of its normal surroundings, This does not happen in the frog, whose temperature is only a few tenths of a degree above that of the air or water, and varies with it. The frog is therefore said to be " cold-blooded." The blood is also an extremely important defence against the attacks of bacteria and other micro-organisms. In a later chapter (p. 123) we shall consider the warfare which its cells wage against these enemies.

Lymph. The preceding paragraph must not be taken to indicate that the blood comes itself into contact with the tissues. The blood vessels are completely closed, and the tissues are actually bathed by another fluid, known as *lymph*, which is produced by exudation through the capillary walls. This fluid is gathered by small *lymphatic vessels* into the big *lymph sacs* already mentioned, whence it is pumped back into the veins by two pairs of small contractile sacs known as *lymph hearts*. One pair of these lies below the scapulæ and opens into the sub-scapular veins ; the other lies at the end of the urostyle and opens into the femoral veins. The fluids in the cœlomic (pleuroperitoneal and pericardial) cavities are lymph. The pleuroperitoneal cavity communicates with the dorsal lymph sacs by minute openings (*stomata*) in the membrane which separates it from them.

Organs of Respiration. The *respiratory organs* of the frog are the *lungs*, the *skin*, and the mucous membrane of the *mouth*. The lungs communicate with the pharynx by way of the glottis, which leads into a short, wide *windpipe* consisting of the *larynx* or *voice organ* only, without the long trachea, or windpipe proper, which is found in animals with necks. The walls of this cavity are supported by a pair of flat *arytænoid cartilages* and a very irregular ring, the *cricoid cartilage*. The lining of the larynx is thrown into a pair of folds, the *vocal cords*. Between these is a narrow slit, the *rima glottidis*, through which the air must pass to and from the lungs. The cartilages are supplied with muscles, by which they can be moved, so as to tighten the vocal chords and bring them close together. In this condition the chords vibrate when air from the lungs is forced between them, and produce a sound which is the croaking of the frog. From the hinder part of the windpipe an opening leads on each side to a short tube known as the *bronchus*, which begins at once to expand into the lung. The latter is a wide, thin-walled, elastic, highly vascular sac, whose internal surface is increased by numerous folds. The lungs of the frog are not enclosed,

like those of man, in a " chest " shut off by a midriff, but lie
free in the fore-part of the common body cavity, and the
mode of breathing (air renewal) is correspondingly different
in the two cases.   In man, as in the rabbit (p. 547), it
consists in an enlargement of the chest, which draws air
into it, followed by a collapse which drives it out.   In the
frog, air is pumped into the lungs by the mouth.

Expiration is by collapse of the elastic lungs and pressure from
abdominal muscles.   In inspiration the mouth floor is raised by the
mylohyoid and jaw muscles, jaws and nostrils being closed and glottis
open.   Strangely, the air so forced in is not pure but a mixture of that
just expired into the mouth and fresh air previously " aspired " through
the nostrils by lowering the mouth floor by muscles of the hyoid.
Aspiration, expiration, inspiration, and discharge of air through the
nostrils occur in that order.   The jaws are closed throughout.

In the lungs an exchange of oxygen for carbon dioxide
takes place through the thin walls between
the air and the blood in the lung capillaries.
The same process goes on in the very vascular
mucous membrane of the mouth and in the skin.   Indeed,
when the frog is at rest respiration is performed more
through these organs than through the lungs.   In the
tissues of the body the blood undergoes a reverse change,
parting with its oxygen to the protoplasm and receiving
from it carbon dioxide formed there.   The blood which
has thus become poor in oxygen and rich in carbon dioxide
returns to the heart through the veins.   Such blood is
therefore known as *venous blood*.   It is of a dark red colour.
On reaching the heart, this blood is directed, as we have
seen, principally to the lungs, skin, and mucous membrane
of the mouth, there to be oxygenated again.   The blood
from the skin and mouth mingles on its way back to the
heart with the venous blood, but that from the lungs returns
separately to the heart and is then sent forth again to the
tissues through the arteries.   Oxygenated blood is therefore
called *arterial*.   It is of a bright red colour.   It will be
noted that the pulmonary artery contains venous blood, the
pulmonary vein arterial blood.   It will also be seen that
the course of the circulation contains two circuits, one
short, passing through the lungs, and the other long,
passing through the rest of the body, the blood returning to the heart between the two.   This is shown

**Arterial and
Venous Blood.**

on the diagram on p. 74. The two circuits are known respectively as the *lesser* or *pulmonary* and the *greater* or *systemic* circulations.

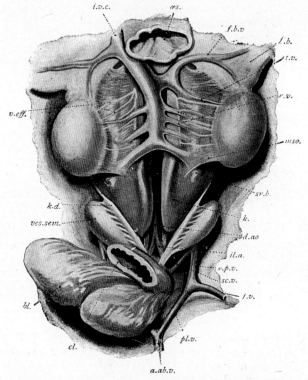

FIG. 43.—The urinary and generative organs of a male frog.

a.ab.v., Anterior abdominal vein, cut short and turned back; *bl.*, urinary bladder; *cl.*, cloaca; *d.ao.*, dorsal aorta: *f.b.*, base of fat body: *f.b.v.*, vein of fat body; *f.v.*, femoral vein; *il.a.*, iliac artery; *i.v.c.*, inferior vena cava; *k.*, kidney; *k.d.*, kidney duct; *mso.*, mesorchium; *œs.*, œsophagus; *pl.v.*, pelvic vein; *r.p.v.*, renal portal vein; *r.v.*, renal veins; *sc.v.*, sciatic vein; *sr.b.*, adrenal body; *t.v.*, spermatic vein; *v.eff.*, vasa efferentia; *ves.sem.*, vesicula seminalis. The testes are not labelled, nor are the sciatic plexuses, a portion of which may be seen beside the iliac arteries.

A diagram of these organs will be found on p. 82.

The respiratory organs are engaged, as we have seen, in ridding the body of carbon dioxide, and some water is also lost in the form of vapour through these organs. A further loss of water in a liquid form and the excretion of solids dissolved in it takes place through the *kidneys*. These are a pair of flattened, oblong,

Excretory Organs.

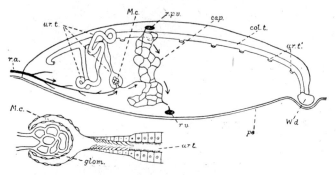

FIG. 44.—A diagram of a kidney of the frog, to show the arrangement of the tubules and blood vessels. One uriniferous tubule and a portion of the vascular meshwork are shown separately. In reality the blood vessels entangle the tubules.

cap., Capillaries ; *col.t.*, collecting tubule ; *glom.*, glomerulus ; *M.c.*, Malpighian capsule ; *pe.*, peritoneum ; *r.a.*, renal artery ; *r.p.v.*, branch of the renal portal vein ; *r.v.*, branch of a renal vein ; *ur.t.*, uriniferous tubule (somewhat unravelled ; note that its regions differ) ; *ur.t'.*, places where other uriniferous tubules open into the collecting duct ; *W.d.*, Wolffian or kidney duct.

dark red bodies which lie one on each side in the dorsal lymph sac above the cœlom and below the backbone. Each consists of a mass of twisted *uriniferous tubules*, held together by connective tissue and richly supplied with blood vessels. Each tubule begins blindly in the substance of the kidney as a thin-walled *Malpighian capsule*, whose side is indented by a cluster of blood vessels, the *glomerulus*, the rest of the tubule being glandular. The glomeruli receive blood only from the renal artery, the tubules also from the renal portal vein. The tubules open into *collecting tubes*, which run across the kidney to enter the main duct of the organ or *Wolffian duct*.[1] This lies along the outer edge of the organ and passes backward to open into the dorsal side of the cloaca. A watery fluid, containing some of the solids of the blood, but not the proteins, passes, under the blood pressure, through the thin wall of the glomerulus into the capsule and so down the tubules. In these it is deprived by reabsorption of some of its substances (sugars and certain salts) which would be a loss to the body and receives certain others, notably urea. It is then the urine, and is held in the bladder and voided at intervals.

In animals which are completely terrestrial, as in the rabbit and in man, the kidney tubules have a function which is little if at all exercised in the frog—that of reabsorbing some of the water lost in the glomerulus and so conserving for the body this liquid—which is immensely important, on land is inevitably lost more or less rapidly by evaporation, and can there only be replaced at the cost of a considerable expenditure of energy. In respect of the maintenance of the correct proportion of water in its body the frog, whose life is spent in or near water, is a fresh-water animal. For such animals there is danger not of defect but of excess of water in the body, because, the concentration of salts in the water they inhabit being less than that in their bodies, water tends to enter them by osmosis. That would cause swelling [2] and harmful dilution of the blood and other body fluids. This danger is met partly by excreting water, as in the urine, and partly by hindering its entry—in some animals by a thick cuticle over most of the surface and in all by the protoplasm of the surface tissues, which has the power of regulating, within limits, the passage of substances through itself. When it is on land the frog is losing water by evaporation from its skin, which, unlike that of a truly terrestrial animal, lets water through fairly readily ; this loss is made good by absorption through the skin when the animal is again in water. The absorption is regulated by the action of the tissues of the skin ; how that is done is not known, but it has been found to be influenced by the nervous system. The activity of the kidneys, described above, removes any excess of water. With this state of affairs in fresh-water animals we may contrast that in the lower (invertebrate) classes of marine animals. These, though their body walls are more permeable than those of fresh-water animals,

Water Regulation.

---

[1] Often called the ureter, although it does not correspond to the ureter of man.

[2] Swelling because the surface of the body of such animals is, broadly speaking, semipermeable—that is, lets water but does not let salts pass through it. If it were permeable, as is that of many marine animals, salts would pass out and the internal fluids would reach the same concentration as the surrounding water without swelling. But then the body fluids would be diluted more rapidly.

neither gain nor lose water to any dangerous extent, because the concentration of salts in the water is approximately that of their body fluids. About the way in which water is regulated in the bodies of fishes we shall have something to say later on (p. 448).

Besides urea, the urine of the frog contains smaller quantities of other nitrogenous excreta. Excretion of most of the nitrogen as urea is by no means universal among animals. Nitrogen leaves the protein molecule as ammonia, and in aquatic animals, from which compounds of ammonium are readily washed out or lost by diffusion, such substances form the bulk of the nitrogenous excreta. But these compounds are highly poisonous, and animals which have not facilities for immediately getting rid of them must convert the bulk of their nitrogenous waste into less noxious substances. The frog, turtles, mammals (including man), and some other animals change it into urea, which in small quantities is not harmful. Other land animals (birds, insects, many reptiles) excrete nitrogen in uric acid, which is both harmless and easily precipitated, so that it can be voided as a pasty mass and the loss of water thereby much reduced.

The organs in which the ova and spermatozoa of animals are formed are known as *gonads*.
Organs of Reproduction. Those in which spermatozoa arise are *testes*; those in which ova arise are *ovaries*. The male organs of reproduction of the frog are the testes and their ducts. The testes are a pair of ovoid bodies slung from the surface of the kidneys by a fold of the peritoneum known as the *mesorchium*. Each consists of a mass of *seminiferous tubules*, in which the spermatozoa are formed (Fig. 551). They communicate by about a dozen small ducts, the *vasa efferentia*, in the mesorchium, with the collecting tubules of the kidney, along which, and through the Wolffian ducts, the sperm passes to the cloaca, for the male frog has not separate ducts for sperm (*vasa deferentia*) and for urine, but passes these fluids to the exterior through the same passage. In the male each Wolffian duct has attached to it a sac, the *vesicula seminalis*, in which the sperm is stored until it is used for fertilising the eggs of the female. In the female, the ovaries correspond in position to the testes, the membrane by which each of them is slung being known as the *mesovarium*. They are pleated folds of peritoneum containing ova in various stages of ripeness, each ovum enclosed in a follicle of smaller cells (p. 114), and all held together by connective tissue. In the breeding season they enlarge and shed the ripe ova into the body cavity,

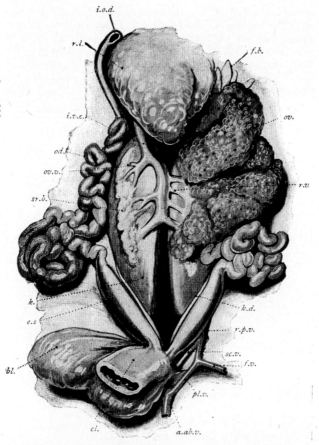

FIG. 45.—The urinary and genital organs of a female frog.

a.ab.v., Anterior abdominal vein, cut short and turned back ; *bl.*, urinary
bladder ; *cl.*, cloaca ; *e.s.*, egg sac ; *f.b.*, fat body ; *f.v.*, femoral vein ;
i.o.d., internal opening of oviduct ; *i.v.c.*, inferior vena cava ; *k.*, kidney ;
k.d., Wolffian or kidney duct ; *od.*, oviduct ; *ov.*, left ovary ; *ov.v.*,
ovarian vein ; *pl.v.*, pelvic vein ; *r.l.*, right lung ; *r.v.*, renal veins ;
r.p.v., renal portal vein ; *sc.v.*, sciatic vein ; *sr.b.*, adrenal body. The
ovary and fat body of the right side have been removed. A diagram of
these organs will be found on p. 82.

6

where, by ciliary action, the ova are carried to and into the internal openings of the *oviducts*. These are long twisted tubes, one on each side of the body, opening in front into the body cavity by a small aperture at the base of the lung, and behind into the cloaca just before the opening of the Wolffian ducts. The greater part of each tube is narrow and glandular and secretes a slimy substance, which

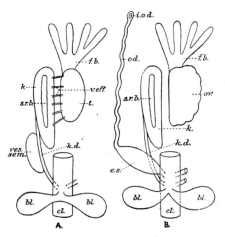

FIG. 46.—Diagrams of the urinary and generative organs of the frog.

A, Organs of the male ; *B*, those of the female ; *bl.*, bladder ; *cl.*, cloaca ; *e.s.*, egg sac ; *f.b.*, fat body ; *i.o.d.*, internal opening of oviduct ; *k.*, kidney ; *k.d.*, kidney duct (Wolffian duct) ; *od.*, oviduct ; *ov'.*, ovary ; *sr.b.*, adrenal body ; *t.*, testis : *v.eff.*, vasa efferentia ; *ves.sem.*, vesicula seminalis.

sets into a jelly on coming into contact with water, but at its hinder end the duct enlarges into a sac, which at the breeding season becomes distended with eggs and occupies a great part of the body cavity. At this season, which is in March, the male mounts upon the back of the female, clasping her behind the arms with his fore-limbs, which are provided for the purpose with the pads we have already mentioned. In this position the animals remain for days until the eggs are laid. As the spawn passes out, the male pours his sperm over it, the eggs are fertilised (p. 13), and the slimy coating that each of them has acquired in the oviduct swells up and sets in the water so as to form a protective layer of jelly. With their subsequent history we shall deal later (pp. 137, 616).

CHAPTER IV

THE FROG: NERVOUS SYSTEM AND SENSE ORGANS

IN the nervous system of the frog there may be recognised two main parts — *the cerebro-spinal system*, connected with the organs of sense and the voluntary muscles, and the *sympathetic system*, connected principally with the viscera and blood vessels. The cerebro-spinal system comprises the *central nervous system or cerebro-spinal axis*, composed of the brain and the spinal cord, and the *peripheral nervous system*, containing the *cerebro-spinal nerves* and certain knots of nerve cells upon them, known as their *ganglia*. The cerebro-spinal nerves are ten pairs of *cranial nerves* arising from the brain, and the same number of *spinal nerves*. The sympathetic system also consists of nerves and ganglia.[1]

Lay-out of the Nervous System.

The spinal cord is an elongated, subcylindrical structure, lying in the vertebral canal. It is somewhat flattened from above downward, tapers to a fine thread, the *filum terminale*, in the urostyle, and swells somewhat in the regions of the limbs. A transverse section (Fig. 49) shows that it is composed of nervous tissue of two kinds, a *grey matter* inside and a *white matter* outside (p. 116), enclosed in a connective tissue sheath, the *pia mater*, which along the dorsal and ventral middle lines passes in to some depth as the *dorsal and ventral fissures*. In the section the grey matter extends as *dorsal and ventral horns* on each side (Fig. 73). In the grey matter is a longitudinal *central canal*, which ends blindly behind, but in front is continuous with cavities in the brain.

Spinal Cord.

The ten pairs of spinal nerves pass out between the vertebræ to be distributed over the body. Each nerve

---

[1] The sympathetic system, together with some branches of certain cranial nerves (p. 90), constitutes the *visceral system* (see p. 93).

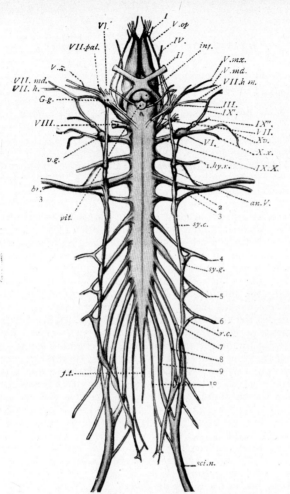

FIG. 47.—The central nervous system and principal nerves of a frog, seen from below.—Partly after Ecker.

I.-X., Cranial nerves; 1-10, spinal nerves (see footnote to p. 79); *V.md.*, *V.mx.*, *V.op.*, mandibular, maxillary, and ophthalmic branches of fifth cranial nerve; *V.x.*, a small twig from the undivided main branch of the same nerve; *VI'*, sixth cranial nerve after leaving the prootic ganglion; *VII.h.*, and *VII.md.*, hyoidean and mandibular branches of hyomandibular nerve; *VII.hm.*, *VII.pal.*, hyomandibular and palatine branches of seventh cranial nerve; *IX'*, branch from ninth cranial nerve to seventh; *IX''*., main branch of ninth cranial nerve; *X.v.*, tenth cranial nerve passing to viscera; *X.x.*, a branch from the vagus to certain muscles; *an.V.*, annulus of Vieussens, through which the subclavian artery passes; *br.*, brachial nerve; *f.t.*, filum terminale; *G.g.*, Gasserian-geniculate or prootic ganglion; *hy.n.*, hypoglossal (first spinal) nerve; *inf.*, infundibulum; *pit.*, pituitary body; *r.c.*, ramus communicans; *sci.n.*, sciatic nerve; *sy.c.*, longitudinal commissure of sympathetic chain; *sy.g.*, sympathetic ganglion; *v.g.*, vagus ganglion.

is surrounded as it issues by a soft, white *calcareous concre-
tion*. Every nerve arises by two *roots*, a dorsal
Spinal Nerves. and a ventral, and the dorsal root bears a
small swelling, the *dorsal root ganglion*. Just outside the
backbone the two roots join, and the nerve thus formed
proceeds at once to divide, giving rise to (*a*) a short *dorsal
branch* to the muscles and skin of the back, (*b*) a long
and conspicuous *ventral branch* to the muscles and skin of
the sides and ventral surface of the trunk, and in some
cases to the limbs, and (*c*) a small *ramus communicans* to
the sympathetic system. The dorsal root is also called
afferent or sensory because along it impulses pass inwards
to the spinal cord and produce, among other effects, sensation, and the ventral is called similarly *efferent or motor*
because along it impulses pass outward and produce,
among other effects, contraction of muscles and thus
movements. These functions are proved by the fact that
cutting the dorsal root deprives of sensation the parts
supplied by its nerve, while cutting the ventral root
paralyses the same parts. Each of the branches contains
elements derived from both dorsal and ventral roots. The
course of the dorsal branches and rami communicantes is
much the same in all cases, but that of the ventral branches
differs greatly in different nerves and must now be followed.

The *first spinal nerve* [1] is known as the *hypoglossal*.
It leaves the neural canal between the first and second
vertebræ, curves round the throat, turns forward below the
mouth (Fig. 537), and proceeds to the tongue. The *second
spinal nerve* is a large strand running straight outwards. It
receives branches from the first and third, forming thus the
brachial plexus, and proceeds as the *brachial nerve* to the
arm. The *third spinal nerve* is small, and beyond the
brachial plexus resembles the *fourth, fifth, and sixth spinal
nerves*. All these are small and run backwards to supply
the muscles and skin of the belly The *seventh, eighth,
ninth. and tenth spinal nerves* join to form a *sciatic plexus*,
from which arise several nerves to join the hind limb, the

---

[1] The nerve which is counted as the first spinal nerve in the frog is
in reality the second. The true first spinal nerve, which should issue
between the skull and the first vertebra, appears in the embryo, but is
lost later on.

principal being the very large *sciatic nerve*. The tenth nerve leaves the vertebral canal by a foramen in the side of the urostyle. The roots of the last four pairs of nerves do not issue from the spinal canal at once, but run backwards for some distance from their origin to reach their point of exit. Thus they form inside the vertebral canal a bundle known as the *cauda equina*.

The brain may be divided into three regions, known respectively as the *hind*, *mid*, *and fore brains*.

Brain.

The hind-brain consists of the *medulla oblongata* and the *cerebellum*. The medulla oblongata is the hindermost part of the brain. It is continuous behind with the spinal cord, which, as it is traced into the brain, widens, the central canal enlarging into a cavity in the medulla known as the *fourth ventricle* of the brain, the ventral side thickening, and the dorsal thinning out into a slight membrane over the fourth ventricle (Fig. 30). The pia mater above this membrane is very vascular and thrown into folds which project into the ventricle, forming thus a structure known as the *posterior choroid plexus*. The cerebellum is a narrow band across the roof of the front part of the fourth ventricle. In many other animals it is relatively much larger. The *mid-brain* is the region in front of the medulla. It has a thick floor formed by two longitudinal columns known as the *crura or pedunculi cerebri*, a roof consisting of a pair of rounded swellings known as *optic lobes*, and internally a narrow passage, the *aquæductus cerebri*, continuous behind with the fourth ventricle and above with cavities in the optic lobes. The fore-brain consists of the *thalamencephalon* and the *cerebral hemispheres*. The thalamencephalon lies immediately in front of the mid-brain. Its sides are thick and are known as the *thalami*; its roof and floor are thin. The floor is prolonged into a hollow structure known as the *infundibulum*, which, with a glandular, non-nervous mass called the *hypophysis*, makes up the *pituitary body*. The roof is prolonged into a short hollow stalk, which in the tadpole is connected with a structure known as the *pineal body*. In the adult this has become separated and lies outside the skull. In certain other animals the pineal body is much more highly developed and still connected with its stalk, and its structure shows that it is the remnant of a middle eye, though it is no longer functional. In front of the pineal stalk lies an *anterior choroid plexus*. The cavity of the thalamencephalon is deep but narrow, and is known as the

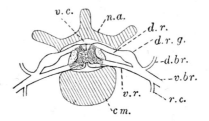

FIG. 48.—A diagram of the origin of the spinal nerves of the frog.

cm., Centrum ; *d.br.*, dorsal branch of the nerve ; *d.r.*, dorsal root ; *d.r.g.*, dorsal root ganglion ; *n.a.*, neural arch ; *r.c.*, ramus communicans ; *v.br.*, ventral branch ; *v.c.*, vertebral canal ; *v.r.*, ventral root.

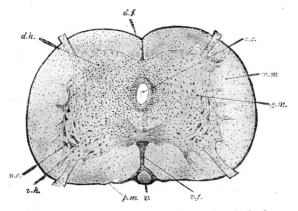

FIG. 49.—A transverse section of the spinal cord of a frog.

c.c., Central canal ; *d.f.*, dorsal fissure ; *d.h.*, dorsal horn ; *g.m.*, grey matter ; *n.c.*, large nerve cell ; *p.m.*, pia mater ; *v.*, vein ; *v.f.*, ventral fissure ; *v.h.*, ventral horn ; *w.m.*, white matter. The dorsal and ventral horns are better seen in the cord of man (Fig. 73).

third ventricle. It is bounded in front by a wall known as the *lamina terminalis.* Behind this on each side an opening known as the *foramen of Monro or foramen interventriculare* leads into the cavity or *lateral ventricle* of one of the cerebral hemispheres. These are oblong-oval bodies narrowing forwards to join a mass which is indistinctly separated into two *olfactory lobes.* The median walls of the cerebral hemispheres touch in front and behind, but for a consider-

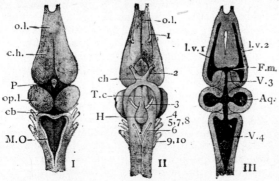

FIG. 50.—The brain of a frog.—After Wiedersheim.

I. DORSAL ASPECT.—*o.l.,* Olfactory lobes ; *c.h.,* cerebral hemispheres, *P.,* pineal stalk, rising from region of optic thalami ; *op.l.,* optic lobes ; *cb.,* rudimentary cerebellum ; *M.O.,* medulla oblongata.
II. VENTRAL ASPECT. — The numbers indicate the origins of the nerves. *ch.,* Optic chiasma ; *T.c.,* tuber cinereum (part of brain floor) ; *H.,* pituitary body.
III. HORIZONTAL SECTION.—*l.v.* 1 and 2, lateral ventricles of cerebrum ; *F.m.,* foramen of Monro ; *V.*3 and 4, third and fourth ventricles ; *Aq.,* cavities of optic lobes and aqueduct from third to fourth ventricle.

able distance they are quite separate. Two regions may be distinguished in the wall of each cerebral hemisphere— the ventrolateral region, which is thickened and is known as the *corpus striatum,* and the rest of the wall, which is the *pallium.* The brain, like the spinal cord, contains both white and grey matter. Most of the grey matter adjoins the ventricles as that of the spinal cord adjoins the central canal, but the grey layer or *cortex* which in higher animals overlies the white matter of the pallium (p. 560) is represented by a rudiment.

The *first or olfactory cranial nerve* of each side arises from the olfactory lobe and runs forward to the olfactory organ in the nostril. The *second or optic nerve* starts from the side of the mid-brain, curves round underneath the brain, running forwards and inwards, and crosses its fellow below the thalamencephalon on its way to the eyeball of the opposite side. Where the nerves cross they are fused, and the X-shaped structure thus formed is called the *optic chiasma*.[2] The *third or oculomotor nerve* supplies the eye muscles, with the exception of the superior oblique and external rectus. The small *fourth, pathetic, or trochlear nerve* arises between the optic lobe and cerebellum and supplies the superior oblique muscle. It is the only nerve which starts from the dorsal surface of the brain. The large *fifth or trigeminal nerve* arises from the side of the anterior part of the medulla. Just before it passes through its foramen it bears a large swelling, the *Gasserian-geniculate or prootic ganglion.* It then divides at once into an *ophthalmic branch*, which runs forwards along the inner wall of the orbit and supplies the skin of the forepart of the head, and a *main branch*, which runs outwards across the hinder part of the orbit and divides into a *maxillary branch* to the upper jaw and a *mandibular branch* to the lower jaw. The *sixth or abducent nerve* is very small. It arises from the ventral side of the medulla about the middle of the length of the latter, and supplies the external rectus muscle, after passing through the prootic ganglion. The *seventh or facial nerve* arises from the side of the medulla behind the fifth. It joins the prootic ganglion.[3] On leaving this it at once divides into a *palatine branch*, which runs forwards on the floor of the orbit to supply the roof of the mouth, and a *hyomandibular branch*, which runs outwards and forks into a *hyoidean*

Cranial Nerves.[1]

---

[1] For the foramina by which the cranial nerves leave the skull, see p. 41. These nerves can more easily be dissected in the dogfish, where their course is substantially the same (see pp. 452-454).

[2] The crossing is not complete, part of each nerve proceeding in that limb of the X which passes to the eye of the same side.

[3] This ganglion is formed by the fusion of two ganglia which are distinct in the tadpole. One is the *Gasserian ganglion* and belongs to the fifth nerve ; the other is the *geniculate ganglion* and belongs to the seventh.

branch, to the muscles of the hyoid, and a *mandibular or chorda tympani* to the lower jaw. The *eighth, auditory, or acoustic nerve* arises from the side of the medulla with the seventh, enters the auditory capsule, and ends in the membranous labyrinth of the ear. The *ninth or glossopharyngeal nerve* arises from the side of the medulla behind the eighth, immediately joins the tenth nerve, and passes through the ganglion of the latter. It then bears a small

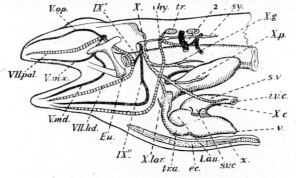

FIG. 51.—A diagram of a dissection, from the left side, of the forepart of the body of a frog. Compare Fig. 538.

V.-X., Cranial nerves ; *V.md., V.mx., V.op.*, mandibular, maxillary, and ophthalmic branches of fifth cranial nerve ; *VII.hd., VII.pal.*, hyomandibular and palatine branches of seventh cranial nerve ; *IX.*, branch joining ninth cranial nerve to seventh ; *IX″.*, main branch of ninth cranial nerve ; *X.c., X.g., X.lar., X.p.*, cardiac, gastric, laryngeal, and pulmonary branches of tenth cranial nerve ; 1, 2, spinal nerves ; *ec.*, epicoracoid ; *Eu.*, Eustachian tube ; *hy.*, hypoglossal ; *i.v.c.*, inferior vena cava ; *l.au.*, left auricle ; *s.v.*, sinus venosus ; *s.v.c.*, left superior vena cava ; *sy.*, sympathetic chain ; *tr.*, transverse process of second vertebra ; *tr.a.*, truncus arteriosus ; *v.*, ventricle ; *x.*, xiphisternum.

petrosal ganglion of its own, gives a branch to the hyomandibular nerve, and proceeds round the throat to turn forward and run along the floor of the mouth, supplying various structures there. The *tenth or vagus nerve* is large and very important. It arises by several roots adjoining the ninth, with which it is fused as far as the *jugular or vagus ganglion*. It then turns backward and downward round the throat and gives branches to the larynx, heart, lung, and stomach (Fig. 538). Through the branch which runs to the heart that organ receives from the central nervous system stimuli which raise or lower the strength and frequency of its automatic beat. The impulses which lower the beating arrive through the roots of the vagus from the brain : those which raise it come through a branch of the sympathetic system which joins the vagus (see below).

The cranial nerves do not, like the spinal nerves, arise each by a sensory and a motor root, but it is **Functions of** possible to distinguish among them a purely **the Cranial** sensory series, a purely motor series, and a series **Nerves.** of mixed function. The tenth, ninth, seventh, and fifth nerves are *mixed.* They correspond to the dorsal roots of spinal nerves with that part of the ventral root (the efferent visceral or *autonomic* part) which passes by the rami communicantes to the sympathetic system. This part in the cranial nerves passes direct to the viscera and vascular system. Each of the mixed nerves retains its dorsal root ganglion as a member of the series formed by the vagus, glosso-pharyngeal, auditory, geniculate, and Gasserian ganglia. The sixth, fourth, and third nerves are purely *motor* and correspond to the ventral roots of spinal nerves, the sixth being the ventral root of the seventh, the fourth that of the fifth, and the third that of a nerve whose dorsal root is contained in the ophthalmic branch of the fifth. The eighth is purely *sensory* and represents part of a dorsal root. Its ganglion is embedded in the labyrinth of the ear. The second and first nerves are also purely sensory, but are not comparable to the dorsal roots of spinal nerves.

The sympathetic system possesses a long nerve-cord on each side of the body below the backbone and **Sympathetic** alongside the aorta and systemic arch. It is **System.** connected by a ramus communicans with each spinal nerve. At the junction of each ramus communicans the sympathetic cord swells into a *ganglion.* Between the first two ganglia it is double, becoming thus a loop, the *annulus of Vieussens or ansa subclavia,* through which passes the subclavian artery. In front the longitudinal cord enters the skull with the ninth and tenth nerves, is connected with the tenth, and ends in the Gasserian ganglion. From the sympathetic ganglia small nerves are given off to those of the opposite cord and to the blood vessels and viscera. These nerves break up and rejoin to form networks or *plexuses*.

If any nerve be traced outward from the central nervous system, it is found, after dividing into finer **Functions of Nerves in General.** and finer branches, to end by entering some organ. Here the fine fibres of which every nerve is composed (see p. 115) end by coming into connection with cells in various tissues. Afferent fibres (*i.e.* those traced from the dorsal root or one of the sensory cranial nerves) are found to be in relation with cells, known as *receptor* cells, of various kinds, which are especially irritable by some kind of stimulus (as those of the lining of the eye by light), and their function is to conduct to the central nervous system impulses set up by these stimuli. Efferent fibres (*i.e.* those from the ventral root) join *effector* cells—muscular tissue, which the impulses they conduct will cause to contract, or glandular tissue, which their impulses will cause to secrete. Thus we may sum up the arrangement of the nervous system by saying that it consists of a central mass and a series of afferent and efferent paths along which impulses pass to and from it.

The nerves of the cerebrospinal and sympathetic systems are formed of components which fall into four primary categories **Nerve Components.** —the *somatic afferent*, which brings impulses from the organs of external sense and voluntary muscles ; the *somatic efferent*, which carries impulses to the same muscles ; the *visceral afferent*, which brings impulses from the viscera and other internal organs ; and the *visceral efferent*, which carries impulses to the blood vessels, the muscles and glands of the internal organs, and certain of those of the skin. As we have seen, each spinal nerve contains components from each of these categories and each cranial nerve from some of them only. The sympathetic system has visceral components only.

The components of the complete *Visceral Nervous System* of vertebrate animals may be tabulated as follows :

Visceral System	Efferent (autonomic)	Parasympathetic (cranial and sacral)	
		Sympathetic	Sympathetic System
	Afferent	Intrasympathetic	
		Extrasympathetic	

A nervous impulse is accompanied, and can be traced, along the nerve by a wave of electrical negativity. It appears to be an electrical event for which the energy is

Nervous Impulses.[1]

provided by a chemical process. Both of these are believed to take place on the surface of the axis cylinders (p. 115) of the nerve fibres. In the frog the average rate at which nervous impulses travel is 28 metres per second, in man and other warm-blooded animals it may rise to 120 metres. An impulse is normally originated at one end of a nerve fibre (as where an afferent fibre begins in a sense organ) and travels to the other end, but it can be caused to start at any other point, and then passes both ways. In either event it travels without hindrance as far as the points where the nerve fibre communicates with others (for instance where an afferent communicates with an efferent fibre) or, if it be an efferent fibre, with effector cells. The communication between fibres is made, not by continuity of the fibres, but by an interlocking of short branches which is called a *synapse* (Fig. 68). Through this impulses are able, if they can overcome a certain resistance which the synapse offers, to pass in one direction (axon to dendrites, see p. 115 ; for instance from afferent to efferent fibre) but cannot pass in the opposite direction. Thus an impulse passes along a track of fibres in one direction only. Even in that direction, however, the impulse will not always succeed in passing, since its ability to proceed depends upon its power of overcoming the resistance at synapses. This will bar the excitation generated by a weak stimulus when that of a stronger stimulus will get through. Actually, a single nervous impulse, like the contraction of a muscle fibre, is an " all-or-none " phenomenon—that is, if it be produced at all it has all the strength that it can have, whatever be the strength of the stimulus that started it. A stimulus, however, nearly always excites, not a single impulse, but a series of them, which are more frequent the stronger the stimulus is. Now as (within certain limits of frequency) impulses have a cumulative effect which is greater the more frequent they are, the series of impulses excited by a strong stimulus is more effective than that of a weak one. The overcoming of the resistance offered by a synapse is due to the secretion, by the end of the fibre along which

[1] The student is recommended before reading this paragraph to read pages 115–116.

impulses arrive, of a chemical whose function probably is, by stimulation, to restart impulses in the fibre on the other side of the synapse. The action of an impulse at a synapse is sometimes not to lessen but to increase the resistance. Thus impulses can *inhibit* one another. Lastly, it should be noted that, since nerve fibres branch, an impulse often has before it more tracks than one, and so, subject to the factors of resistance and inhibition, an afferent impulse may through several efferent fibres affect various organs.

It will be clear, from the arrangement of the nervous system which has been described above, that **Functions of** it is a complicated apparatus for conveying im-**the Central** **Nervous System.** pulses between the different parts of the body through the intervention of a central exchange. In it conductivity is highly developed, as irritability is in the sense organs ; its arrangement, however, is such that impulses are carried, not directly from organ to organ, but from each organ to the central nervous system, whence, if action is to take place, fresh impulses are directed to other organs. It is owing to connections and inhibitions in the central nervous system that there take place in an orderly manner the complex responses which the simplest stimuli evoke in the body of one of the higher animals. Even such slight and passing actions, for instance, as a leap from danger or the snapping up of an insect involve the harmonious action of numerous muscles in a manner which would be impossible without some mechanism which will co-ordinate their activity and inhibit that of muscles which might oppose them.

The actions which are excited through the nervous system are of two kinds, reflex and voluntary. A **Reflex and** *reflex action* is one in which stimulation of an **Voluntary** **Action.** afferent nerve brings about through an efferent nerve the production of activity in some tissue in an involuntary manner. Thus touching the eye brings about contraction of the muscle of the eyelid so that blinking takes place, but this happens without any effort of the will of the animal, which exercises no choice as to whether it shall take place or not. In a reflex action the same stimulus is always followed by the same response. In blinking the action is conscious, but many reflex actions

are purely unconscious, as when the passage of food over
the opening of the bile-duct causes through the central
nervous system a discharge of bile from the gall-bladder
without either the will or the knowledge of the animal.
For a reflex action three things are necessary : (1) an
afferent nerve, (2) a portion of the central nervous system,
known as the *centre* of the reflex, (3) an efferent nerve.
This apparatus is known as the *reflex arc*. For some reflex
actions the centre is in the brain, but for many it is only
necessary that a part of the spinal cord should be intact.
Thus a frog from which the brain has been removed will,

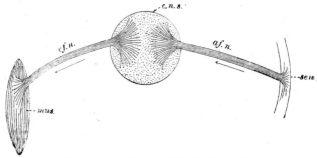

FIG. 52. —A diagram of the " reflex arc."

af.n., Afferent nerve ; *c.n.s.*, central nervous system ; *ef.n.*, efferent nerve ;
mus., muscle ; *sen.*, sensory surface.

if its spinal cord be uninjured, lift its leg to wipe off an
irritant, such as a drop of acid, from its flank. A *voluntary
action* is one in which the will intervenes, and a choice is
made, as when the animal decides between two directions
in which it can escape an enemy, or wanders to seek food
when it is hungry. Voluntary actions may or may not
follow immediately upon an external stimulus, but when
they do so the same stimulus is not always followed by
the same response. For nearly all, if not for all, voluntary
actions it is necessary that some part of the cerebral
hemispheres should be uninjured.

In the last paragraph we have had to mention *consciousness* as accompanying certain events in the nervous system.

A conscious being is one that is aware of events. The **Consciousness.** events which its consciousness immediately accompanies take place in its own nervous tissue. Awareness of other events, within or without the body, is of course due to nervous events which they cause.[1] A vast number of events in the human body are signalled in consciousness, always, of course, through the agency of the nervous system. On the other hand, innumerable events such as the opening of the bile-duct, which we mentioned above, take place in the viscera and elsewhere quite unconsciously, although they affect the nervous system. It is, of course, impossible for us to be certain that a frog possesses consciousness, but just as each of us infers from the behaviour of other men that they have a consciousness like his own, so it may be inferred from the behaviour of the frog that it possesses some dim counterpart of the consciousness of mankind. An unsolved and perhaps insoluble problem is presented by the relation of consciousness to the events which it accompanies. Is it caused by them? Does it affect their course? These are, of course, questions of the highest importance to philosophy. All that need be said here is that, though

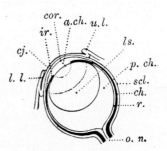

Fig. 53.—A diagram of a section through the eye of a frog.

a.ch., Anterior chamber; *ch.*, choroid; *cj.*, conjunctiva; *cor.*, cornea; *ir.*, iris; *ls.*, lens; *l.l.*, lower lid; *o.n.*, optic nerve; *p.ch.*, posterior chamber; *r.*, retina; *scl.*, sclerotic; *u.l.*, upper lid.

---

[1] This is not to say that the conscious being knows that the events of which it is aware are in the first place only events within itself. Ordinarily, the processes in sense organs and nervous system are not regarded, and consciousness is accepted as first-hand evidence of external things. Still less is it realised that consciousness does not necessarily present the likeness of things outside it, not even of the bodies with whose working it is linked, but rather signs which stand for such things, and that after this fashion alone does it know material things.

7

the consciousness of the living organism is probably
always accompanied with events in the nervous system,
the legitimate inference from this is, not that either
of them is the cause of the other, but rather that
between them there is some relation whose nature is
unknown to us.   We are here dealing with two things of
wholly different kinds, the events which happen in the
nervous system being physical[1] processes and consciousness a psychical process.   The difficulty in imagining any
interaction between them lies in the fact that such action
would apparently be contrary to the principle of the
conservation of energy, though this has been denied.
On the other hand, it seems equally clear that consciousness could not be talked or written about, or, if all
thinking be dependent upon processes in the brain, even
thought about, unless it affected the nervous system.

The *senses* of a backboned animal, such as a frog, are
more numerous than is generally realised.
Sense Organs : Besides the " five senses " of sight, hearing,
General State-
ments.   smell, taste, and touch, there are distinct kinds
of sensibility to heat, cold, and the movements
of the body, and an indefinite " general sensibility " which
when it is slight escapes attention, but when it becomes
excessive rises into pain.   Each of these senses has origin
in impulses derived from a special kind of nerve ending,
but only in the case of sight, hearing, and smell are these
endings situated in a highly specialised organ.   We shall
here consider only these organs.

The eyeball of the frog is roughly spherical, but flattened
on the front side.   It consists of the following
Eyes.
parts : (1) The *outer coat or sense capsule* corresponds to the auditory and nasal capsules, but fits closely to
the eye instead of forming a hollow capsule fused to the
skull.   Over the greater part of the eye it consists of dense
connective tissue with some cartilage and is known as the
sclerotic, but on the front side it is transparent and known
as the *cornea*.   (2) The skin over the cornea adheres to it
as a delicate, transparent covering, the *conjunctiva*, which
is kept moist by the secretion of *Harderian glands* below

---

[1] That is, processes which go on in material bodies ; not necessarily
" physical " in the sense in which that term is opposed to " chemical."

the eye. (3) Inside the sense capsule is the *choroid coat*, consisting of looser and highly vascular connective tissue containing numerous dark pigment cells. In front the choroid separates from the sclerotic and passes inwards, as a partition called the *iris*, across the hollow of the eyeball, which it thus divides into *anterior and posterior chambers*. The former is smaller and filled with a watery *aqueous humour*, the latter larger and filled with a gelatinous *vitreous humour*. In the middle of the iris is an opening, the *pupil*, and the iris contains muscular tissue by which the size of the pupil can be altered. (4) Immediately behind the iris lies a firm, transparent, sub-spherical body, the *lens*, which serves to focus upon the sensitive surface at the back of the eye the light which enters through the pupil. (5) The sensitive surface is provided by the *retina*, a delicate membrane containing two primary layers, an outer *pigment layer* of pigmented cells lining the choroid, and an inner *retina proper* which has at the back of the eye a very complicated structure (Fig. 61, B) and is connected with the optic nerve, by which the impulses which give rise to sight are conveyed to the brain. The fibres of the optic nerve pass right through the retina and spread out over its inner surface (that which is turned towards the hollow of the eyeball). The percipient cells are on the outer surface, against the pigment layer, so that light must pass through the layer of nerve fibres to reach them. In the front half of the eye the retina loses its complicated structure and becomes very thin, but it continues to line the posterior chamber up to the edge of the pupil.

For an object to be seen it is necessary that an image of it should be formed on the retina. The formation of such an image is due mainly to refraction of light by the lens, but refraction also takes place at the surfaces of all the other media (cornea, aqueous humour, vitreous humour) through which the light passes in the eye. In the diagram below (Fig. 54) these effects are combined and the refraction shown as taking place at a single surface (p) situated in the aqueous humour. Each point of the object may be considered as sending out a pencil of divergent rays which by refraction are made to converge again into a point in an image which is constituted by such points corresponding to those of the object. The diagram shows that the image is inverted—what is the upper part of the object is represented in the lower part of the image and what is on the right-hand side of the object by the left-hand side of the image. In the judgment which is based on the visual sensation, however, allowance is made for this—the left-hand side or the bottom of the image is taken as a token of the right-hand or top of the object.

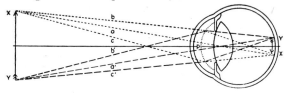

FIG. 54.—A diagram to show the formation of a retinal image.

a, b, c, Rays proceeding from the point X ; *a', b', c',* rays proceeding from the point Y ; *p,* theoretical " principal surface," at which the combined refraction caused by the several surfaces of the eye is supposed to take effect. The lens is shaped as in man and the rabbit.

The visual impulse originates in the retina, in the "layer of rods and cones" (p. 111). The rods, which are stimulated by a photochemical change in a substance known as *visual purple* that they contain, give vision in dimmer light than that which is necessary to stimulate the cones. The latter, owing to certain features of their nervous connections, are more acute in perceiving fine detail than the rods ; they also provide colour vision in those animals which possess it. The image is focussed in the frog and in fishes by moving the lens to and fro, in man and the rabbit by altering the convexity of the lens.

Ears.
The essential part of the ear is the *membranous labyrinth* which we have already mentioned (pp. 42, 91). It lies in the cavity of the auditory capsule. This cavity contains a fluid known as *perilymph,* and the membranous labyrinth contains a fluid known as *endolymph.* The labyrinth consists of the *vestibule* and the *semicircular canals.* The vestibule has an upper, larger division, the *utriculus,* and a lower, smaller *sacculus.* From the former arise the three semicircular canals, which are arched tubes opening into the utriculus at both ends. They are placed in planes at right angles to one another,

one of them being *horizontal*, another longitudinal-vertical (the *posterior vertical*), and another transverse vertical (the *anterior vertical*). One of the ends of each of them is enlarged to form a small, rounded *ampulla*. From the sacculus arises an offshoot known as the *lagena* which has three small dilatations; this represents the *cochlea* of higher animals. On the median side of the sacculus there starts a tube, the *ductus endolymphaticus*, which enters the cranial cavity and there expands into a thin-walled *saccus*. Be-tween the auditory capsules and the *membrane of the ear-drum* or *tympanic membrane* on the side of the head lies the *cavity of the ear-drum* or *tympanic cavity*, which, as we have seen, is crossed by the *columella* from the *fenestra ovalis* to the tympanic membrane and communicates with the pharynx by the *Eustachian tube*. This region is called the *middle ear*, the labyrinth being the *inner ear*. There is *no outer ear* in the frog.

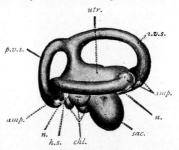

FIG. 55.—The labyrinth of the right ear of the frog, seen from the outer side.—Partly after Marshall.

a.v.s., Anterior vertical semicircular canal; *amp.*, ampullæ; *chl.*, small dilatations of the sacculus which represent the cochlea of higher animals; *h.s.*, horizontal semicircular canal; *n.*, branches of the auditory nerve to supply the ampullæ; *p.v.s.*, posterior vertical semicircular canal; *sac.*, sacculus; *utr.*, utriculus.

Functions of the Ears. The semicircular canals are not organs of hearing, but enable the animal to keep its balance by judging the position of its head. Placed as they are in three planes of space, the fluid in them is set in movement by any change in position, and the differences in pressure on their walls which are thus brought about start impulses which the auditory nerve conveys to the brain. When they are diseased or injured giddiness is caused. The true organ of hearing is the sacculus. The vibrations which constitute sound set the tympanic membrane in motion, and its movements are

transferred by the columella to the membrane of the
fenestra ovalis and thence through the perilymph and the
wall of the membranous labyrinth to the endolymph, where

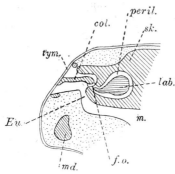

they stimulate the
endings of the audi-
tory nerve in the dilata-
tions of the saccule.

The organs of smell
are a pair
of irregu-
lar cham-
bers, enclosed by the
nasal capsules, separ-
ated by the *nasal
septum*, and com-
municating with the
exterior by the nostrils
and with the mouth
by the *internal nares*.
The lining of each is
connected with the
olfactory nerve of its

**Olfactory
Organs.**

FIG. 56.—A diagram of the ear of the frog.

col., Columella ; *f.o.*, fenestra ovalis ; *Eu.*, Eustachian tube ; *lab.*, part of the membranous
labyrinth, containing endolymph ; *m.*, mouth ;
md., mandible ; *peril.*, perilymph ; *sk.*, skull ;
tym., tympanic membrane.

side. Air is drawn through the chambers in the process
of breathing, and the odorous particles it contains affect
certain cells of the lining which are connected with fibres
of the nerve.

CHAPTER V

THE FROG: HISTOLOGY, THE GERM CELLS, DEATH

THE study of tissues is a branch of anatomy known as *Histology*. It was shown in the first chapter that the tissues of the animal body consist of *protoplasm* accompanied in many cases by a *ground-substance* which supports it. The differences between tissues depend upon differences in arrangement and composition both of the protoplasm and of the ground-substance. When protoplasm is stained with certain dyes, a portion of it colours more readily and deeply than the rest. This portion is usually collected into minute masses known as *nuclei*. The matter of which the nuclei are composed is known as *nucleoplasm*, the rest of the protoplasm as *cyto plasm*. In most tissues [1] the protoplasm is arranged in the little divisions, known as cells, to which we have already alluded, each cell containing a nucleus and being of a size and shape peculiar to the tissue to which it belongs. The cells may either lie side by side (Fig. 8, C) or be separated by ground-substance (Fig. 8, B) or by fluid, as in the tissue known as blood (Fig. 81). Every cell arises by fission from another cell, grows, and behaves to some extent as an independent individual, but in the majority of cases it remains in connection with its neighbours by fine strands of protoplasm. A cell-like unit with more than one nucleus is known as a *cænocyte*, or sometimes as

Histology. Cells.

Protoplasm itself has a fine *structure* which varies from tissue to tissue. Under high magnification it usually appears homogeneous, but sometimes —when killed, usually—it shows a meshwork composed of

Protoplasm.

[1] In all the tissues of the frog.

a denser substance known as *spongioplasm* with a more fluid *enchylema* or *hyaloplasm* in its interstices.[1]   Both these substances are liquids containing various substances in solution and others in suspension as granules and droplets.   Of the *chemical composition* of these solutions only the broad outlines are known, since it is not possible to analyse protoplasm without killing it and thereby bringing about in it chemical changes.   The solvent is water, and in dead protoplasm the dissolved substances are found to be in part inorganic salts, such as the phosphates and chlorides

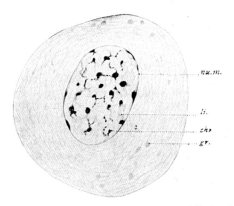

FIG. 57.—A diagram of a cell, after it has been killed and stained.

chr., Chromatin granules; *gr.*, granules in cytoplasm; *li.*, linin meshwork of nucleus; *nu.m.*, nuclear membrane.

of sodium, potassium, and calcium, but principally organic compounds, and those mainly colloidal.   Some of the organic bodies, such as glycogen and organic compounds

[1] This appearance has been interpreted in various ways. It is probably due, at least in many cases, to the fact that such protoplasm which exhibits it is a foam or emulsion, the walls of whose bubbles are formed by the spongioplasm while the enchylema fills them. These minute bubbles must not be confused with the larger spaces known as vacuoles.   The spongioplasm may contain threads or granules of still denser living substance.   Its ultimate framework probably consists of loosely interlacing linear protein molecules or molecule-chains.

of ammonia, are comparatively simple ; these were probably in course of assimilation or excretion by the living substance. The greater part, however, consists of proteins, which are peculiar to protoplasm and never found except in it or in substances manufactured by it. Metabolism never occurs without proteins, and its peculiar features certainly depend largely upon the nature of these substances, but it must not be overlooked that metabolism is exhibited only when the proteins form part of protoplasm, and only during the life of the latter.

Two physical facts are of great importance for an understanding of the properties of protoplasm. The first of these is *surface action*. Owing to the mutual attraction of its molecules, the surface layer of a body of liquid behaves like a stretched membrane. In this, for reasons into which we cannot enter, there occur various actions, chemical, physical, and mechanical, which take place less readily or not at all in the interior. One of the most important of these is *adsorption*, by which certain substances are attracted into the surface film, there to be retained, to enter into reactions with other substances, or to be passed into solution on the other side. In the living body, surface action takes place both on the surfaces of cells and on those of structures within the protoplasm, such as vacuoles ; and it is a factor in a vast number of processes, notably in the keeping in and excluding, taking up and casting away of substances by the protoplasm, in the formation of actual membranes, and perhaps in contraction. The second fact is the existence of certain *properties of colloid solutions*. Substances in solution are either " colloid " or " crystalloid " ; and those in the former of these conditions differ from those in the latter in that they do not readily crystallise, do not pass through membranes, and diffuse only very slowly. The size of their particles is responsible for these and other features of colloidal solutions. Though too small to sink, the particles are large enough to exhibit surface action of their own. Hence (*a*) in certain circumstances they abandon their condition of solution (known as a " sol ") by uniting into a more or less firm jelly or " gel," which may be reversible, as is that of gelatin by heating or cooling ; (*b*) they tend, when they are attracted into the surface film, there at times to unite into a true membrane such as that which forms upon hot milk when it cools ; (*c*) owing to adsorption by their surfaces, the solution as a whole has a great power of taking up substances. We have seen that protoplasm contains a great quantity of colloids. It is owing to these that it does not even when naked lose its identity by diffusion into the surrounding liquid, can form membranes upon its surfaces, can build internal structures by the formation of gels, and can take up and hold great quantities of materials from solutions around it.

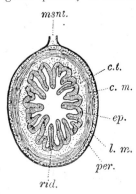

FIG. 5δ.— A diagram of a transverse section through the ileum of the frog.

c.m., Circular muscle layer; *c.t.,* connective tissue; *ep.,* epithelium which lines the gut ; *l.m.,* longitudinal muscle layer; *msnt.,* mesentery ; *per.,* peritoneum ; *rid.,* longitudinal ridges of ileum.

The granules and droplets suspended in protoplasm vary in composition and function. Some of them are truly alive. They are probably of the same nature as the spongioplasm but denser. Others, which may consist of proteins, carbohydrates, or fats, are to be regarded as material removed, for a time at least, from metabolism. Besides these bodies protoplasm often contains relatively large spaces filled with fluid known as *vacuoles*.

Protoplasm is extremely sensitive to the action of external agents, from which it is carefully screened **Reactions of Protoplasm.** in the bodies of most animals. Distilled water, solutions of salts, acids, alkalis, and narcotics all have characteristic effects upon it, stimulating, inhibiting, or killing it according to their nature and strength. It is also easily stimulated by electric shocks.

Changes of temperature have marked effects upon it. Moderate heat acts as a stimulus, causing increased activity of movements, etc. ; cold has a depressing effect. Heating above about 45° C. kills the protoplasm by causing its proteins to set into a solid mass or " coagulate." Cold below o° C. stops all exhibition of life, but unless it is extreme does not prevent the reappearance of vital processes if the temperature be raised.

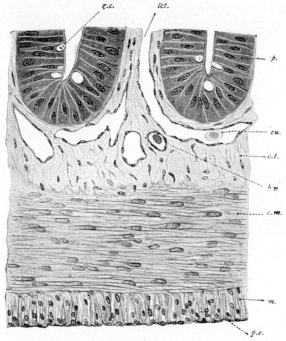

FIG. 59.—A portion of the section shown in Fig. 53, more highly magnified.

b.v., Blood vessel ; *c.t.*, connective tissue of mucous membrane ; *c.m.*, circular layer of muscle fibres ; *ep.*, epithelium ; *g.c.*, goblet cell ; *l.m.*, longitudinal layer of muscle fibres ; *lct.*, "lacteal" or lymph vessel of the intestine ; *leu.*, leucocyte of lymph or lymph corpuscle ; *p e.*, peritoneal epithelium.

Protoplasm is, as we have said, the living part of the body. It is here that metabolism goes on and all the characteristic processes of life take place. The reception of stimuli, conduction, contraction, secretion, reproduction, and so forth take place in the protoplasm alone. The rest of the body exists only to support and protect it.   Life is the life of protoplasm.

It is sometimes attempted to recognise in protoplasm a truly living part which undergoes relatively little change and a part which is not truly alive, but undergoes the changes which provide the bulk of the life energy, under the influence of the living part acting as a kind of ferment (p. 61).   No doubt it is the case that there are many grades of metabolism, but in the broad view it is better to regard protoplasm as a single complex mixture of substances in which there go on the chemical changes which are the basis of the process we know as life.

Organs of the Cytoplasm. The cytoplasm nearly always contains certain other organs as well as the nucleus.   Under the surface film whose functions we have noted there usually lies a viscid *cortical layer* which gives the cell its shape.   Internally there are certain liquid entities, often rod-shaped, known as *mitochondria* and some strands or spherules called *Golgi bodies* both of which perform some unascertained functions in its chemical activity, and usually also there is a protoplasmic sphere known as the centrosome which, as we shall see, plays an important part in cell division.

Nuclei. When it is " resting " (*i.e.* not dividing) the nucleus is enclosed by a delicate *nuclear membrane* and if it be killed appears to consist of a viscid meshwork of *linin* with a thinner *nuclear sap* in its interstices.   In the linin there lie granules of the deeply-staining substance *chromatin* [1] which at division become evident, both in living and in killed nuclei, in the form of the bodies known as " chromosomes " (p. 129).   There are also in the resting nucleus bodies known loosely as *nucleoli* which may consist of chromatin or not, are variously stainable, and have various but unascertained functions.   The nucleus has been experimentally proved, by operations under the microscope in which it was removed from the cytoplasm, to be necessary to the continuance of life : without it many vital processes, such as fission—which is always preceded by division of the nucleus—assimilation, and secretion, are impossible, and life soon comes to an end.   Also, as we shall see, it

---

[1] Chromatin consists of various compounds of the class known as *nucleins*.   Nucleins contain protein united with another highly complex substance known as nucleic acid, very rich in phosphorus.   Its acidity causes it to unite with basic dyes.

plays an extremely important part in heredity. From these and other facts it appears that the nucleus has a regulative action over the life of the protoplasm. But the nucleus is no more capable of life apart from the cytoplasm than the latter can live without nucleoplasm. Thus the unit of living matter is a portion of nucleoplasm with its accompanying cytoplasm. Such a unit is known as an *energid*. A cell is an energid which is in some way delimited from the rest of the energids which with it form the body of an organism. A cœnocyte is a group of energids.

Every tissue belongs to one of four classes : it is either **Kinds of Tissues : Epithelial Tissues.** epithelial, skeletal, muscular, or nervous. The *epithelial tissues* are those which cover surfaces, internal or external. They consist of cells of simple shape arranged to form a layer, with little or no ground-substance between them. When the cells are one layer deep the epithelium is said to be *simple*; when there is more than one layer it is *stratfied*. Perhaps the least specialised example of this class of issue is the kind known as *columnar* epithelium, found, for instance, lining the intestine of the frog (Figs. 58, 59). This is a simple epithelium, consisting of one layer of tall cells standing side by side like columns.

FIG. 60. —Isolated cells of ciliated epithelium from the roof of the mouth of a frog.

Between the cells exist exceedingly fine crevices which communicate below with lymph-spaces, and across the crevices the protoplasm of the cells is continuous as fine threads. A modification of this kind of epithelium, known as *ciliated* epithelium, is found on the roof of the mouth of the frog. Here the outer border of the cell is set with very fine protoplasmic hairs known as *cilia*, which are in constant lashing motion in one direction. As they bend sharply and recover slowly, the effect of their combined action is to drive the fluid which covers the epithelium in the direction of their lashing. (Fig. 95 D). From each cilium a fine thread runs down into the cytoplasm of the cell. A third modification of columnar epithelium is the kind known as *sensory*. In

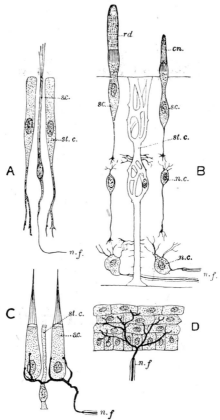

FIG. 61.—Examples of different modes of ending of sensory nerve fibres of the frog.

A, Cells from the olfactory epithelium. *B*, cells from the retina, much simplified. *C*, cells from one of the patches of sensory epithelium in the labyrinth, with which the fibres of the auditory nerve are connected. *D*, a portion of the epidermis, showing the ending of a nerve fibre.

D is ordinary stratified epithelium. *A*, *B*, and *C* are true sensory epithelia—forms of columnar epithelium adapted to the purposes of special senses. In these latter there can be distinguished *sense cells* and *supporting cells*. The sense cells bear processes of various kinds on the surface of the epithelium, and at their other ends come into relation with nerve fibres. In *A* the sense cell is prolonged into a fibre which runs in one of the olfactory nerves as a non-medullated nerve fibre (p. 94). In *B* also the sense cells are prolonged into fibres though these are connected with the nerve by the intermediation of other cells with whose processes their fibres interlock. In *C*, on the other hand, the sense cells are not continued into fibres, but are embraced by branches of nerve fibres belonging to cells in the ganglion of the auditory nerve. Thus they resemble *D*, where the nerve fibres have a similar relation to the cells of the epithelium. In the lower animals, such as the earthworm, the sensory nerve endings in the skin are usually of the type of *A* and *B*, rather than that of *C* and *D*.

cn., Cone; *n.c.*, nerve cells; *n.f.*, nerve fibres; *rd.*, rod; *s.c.*, sense cells; *st.c.*, supporting cells.

this some or all of the cells bear at the outer end one or more stiff processes, the size and shape of which vary greatly in different cases. Each such cell is connected with a sensory nerve, either by being itself prolonged internally into a fibre, which runs in the nerve, or by such a fibre ending against it. Cells of this kind are found, for instance, in the olfactory epithelium, where each bears a tuft of stiff bristles, and in the retina, where each ends in a stout rod-shaped or conical body. These compose the layer of "rods and cones" which lines the retina. *Glandular* epithelium is a kind of simple epithelium in which the cells have become specialised for the secretion of chemical substances. It may occur as single cells scattered among those of ordinary columnar epithelium. This is seen, for instance, in the intestine of the frog, where some of the cells store at their outer ends granules of a substance which, when they discharge it, forms the slimy *mucus* which gives the lining of the alimentary canal and other spaces the name of *mucous membrane*. After the discharge of this substance there is left a cup-shaped hollow in the cell, on which account it is called a *goblet cell*. The hollow is presently filled again by the

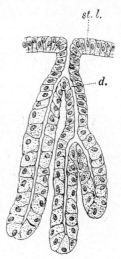

FIG. 62.—One of the glands of the frog's stomach.

d., Duct ; *f.*, the secreting part of the gland, known as the fundus or alveolus ; *st.l.*, epithelium lining the stomach.

activity of the protoplasm of the cell. Isolated gland-cells in an epithelium are sometimes known as *unicellular glands*. Collections of gland-cells form *multicellular glands*. The simplest kind of these is found in the mucous membrane of the stomach. The epithelium here dips down into the underlying connective tissue as hollow tubular processes like the fingers of a glove. The mouths of these tubes are lined with ordinary columnar epithelium which deeper in the tube is succeeded by somewhat lower cells. This region is the duct (p. 6) of the gland. At the end of the tube the cells are large and more nearly cubical and contain in their protoplasm granules of a substance which, when it is discharged, forms the enzyme of the juice secreted by the gland.[1] The granules do not leave a hollow in the cell when they are discharged. Such a gland is known as a *tubular gland*. The pancreas is an example of the more complicated class known as *racemose glands*, in which the tubes are branched and lined with low, *cubical* epithelium up to their ends, which are dilated and lined with glandular epithelium. The dilations are known as *acini* and the tubes leading to them are ducts. The liver is more complicated still, the tubes not

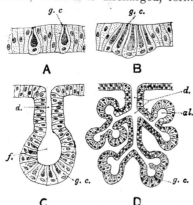

FIG 63.—Diagrams of different kinds of glands.—Partly after Lang.

A, Columnar epithelium containing isolated gland cells or *unicellular glands*. *B*, similar epithelium with the gland cells collected into a group so as to form a *flat multicellular gland*. *C*, a *hollow multicellular gland* of the *simple* kind. The figure represents a type intermediate between the *saccular* glands of the frog's skin (Fig. 60) and the *tubular* glands of the frog's stomach (Fig. 57). The latter, however, may be forked, and thus show a transition to *D*, the *compound or racemose glands*. *al.*, Alveoli or acini of the racemose gland; *d.*, ducts; *f.*, alveolus or fundus of simple gland; *g.c.*, gland cells.

only branching but rejoining to form a meshwork, whose walls consist of gland cells. *Pavement epithelium* also belongs to the simple class, but is very different from any of those we have seen hitherto. In it the cells are flat, and so thin that their surface is raised where the nucleus lies. They are separated by narrow but distinct lines of

---

[1] The granules themselves consist not of the enzyme but of a precursor called the *zymogen.*

intercellular substance which stains strongly with silver nitrate, and the surface has then the appearance of being composed of flat tiles, like a pavement, from which circumstance the name of the tissue is derived. The cœlom, blood vessels, and lymphatic vessels are lined with this epithelium.[1] *Stratified epithelium* consists of several layers of cells. It is found in the *epidermis or scarf skin* which forms the surface of the frog's skin. In it the lowest layer consists of deep cells with unaltered protoplasmic bodies, but successive layers from within outwards become more and more flattened and converted into a horny substance till the outer layer consists of flat, horny scales which are shed, being renewed from within by the division of the lower layer. The inner, softer strata are known as the *Malpighian layer*. *Germinal epithelium* consists of columnar or cubical cells with

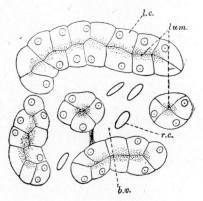

FIG. 64.—A small portion of a section of a frog's liver, highly magnified.

b.v., Blood vessel ; *l.c.*, liver cells ; *lum.*, lumen of liver tubes ; *r.c.*, red corpuscles.

rounded cells derived from them, some of which give rise to ova and spermatozoa. It is found lining the seminiferous tubules of the testes (Fig. 538) and covering the surface of the ovaries. Ova and spermatozoa have each a single nucleus. The *spermatozoa* are minute structures consisting of an elongated *head*, which contains the nucleus in a very thin investment of cytoplasm, a short *neck*, which consists of protoplasm containing a centrosome (see p. 128), and a *tail*, which has the form of a *flagellum* or lash of

[1] See Figs. 8 A (surface view) and 59 (section, showing surface raised by nucleus).

8

protoplasm. The *ova* are large, rounded cells containing numerous granules of food matter or *yolk* and blackened

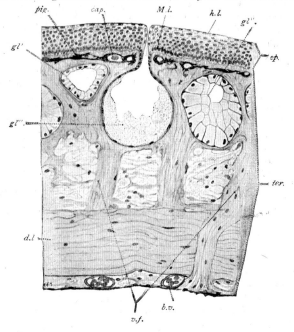

FIG. 65. —A section of the skin of a frog, taken vertically to the surface, highly magnified.

b.v., Small blood vessels; *cap.*, capillaries; *d.l.*, dense layer of connective tissue, consisting of fibres which lie parallel to the surface ; *der.*, dermis or corium ; *ep.*, epidermis; *gl'.*, *gl''.*, *gl'''.*, glands of three kinds ; *gl'.* and *gl''.* secrete a slimy mucus and pass it to the surface of the skin by ducts which are not shown in the section ; *gl'''.* secretes a more watery secretion which probably contains a substance of unpleasant taste ; all three kinds are simple glands of the saccular type ; *h.l.*, horny layer of the epidermis ; *M.l.*, lowest row of the Malpighian layer of the epidermis ; *pig.*, pigment cells ; *v.f.*, strands of vertical fibres in the connective tissue.

on one side by the presence of *pigment* in the surface layer. On this side lies the nucleus. There is no centrosome. Each ovum is enclosed in a *vitelline membrane*, and surrounded in the ovary by a case or *follicle* of cells, derived from the germinal epithelium, which manufacture the yolk and pass it to the ovum.

Nervous tissue consists of cells provided with processes for the purpose of conducting impulses. In

Nervous Tissue.

each such cell or *neurone* (Fig. 67) there may be distinguished (1) a *cell body*, containing the nucleus, (2) a long process known as the *axon*, along which impulses are discharged, (3) other processes, usually short, numerous, and highly branched, known as the *dendrites*, along which impulses reach the cell. The axon ends by breaking up into a tuft of branches, the *terminal arborisation*, from which a stimulus is given either to another nerve cell (Fig. 68) or to the elements of some different tissue, as for instance to one of the fibres which compose muscle (Fig. 69 C). The axon is often of very great length, and is then known as a *nerve fibre*, the term " nerve cell " being applied to its cell body alone. Such a fibre bears at intervals nuclei which, however, do

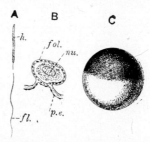

FIG. 66. —Germs of the frog. *A,* spermatozoon; *B,* unripe ovum in the ovary; *C,* ripe ovum. Magnified, but not drawn to scale.

i., Flagellum; *fol.,* follicle of germinal epithelium cells around ovum; *h.,* head; *nu.,* " germinal vesicle," or nucleus of the ovum; *p.e.,* peritoneal epithelium.

not belong to it, but have a small amount of granular cytoplasm of their own. They are called *nuclei of the sheath*, because they underlie and appear to belong to a delicate, membranous *primitive sheath* or *neurilemma* which generally covers the fibre. Nerve fibres are of two kinds, *medullated* and *non-medullated*. In the former a layer of fatty substance, known as the *medullary sheath*, lies between the neurilemma and the axon, which is called the *axis cylinder*. The medullary sheath is broken at intervals at spots known as *nodes of Ranvier*, and the nuclei are arranged one to each internode. In non-medullated fibres the fatty sheath is wanting. Medullated fibres are found principally in the cerebro-spinal system, non-medullated fibres principally in the sympathetic system. Nerve fibres may branch.

The grey matter of the central nervous system consists of cell bodies embedded in an exceedingly fine network composed of dendrites and terminal arborisations, with fibres

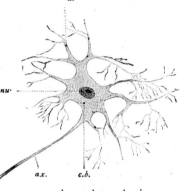

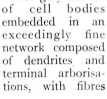

Fig. 67.—Diagram of part of a neurone highly magnified.

ax., Axon ; *c.b.*, cell body ; *d.*, dendrites ; *nu.*, nucleus.

passing through it on their way from the cell bodies. The white matter and the nerves consists of fibres only. Ganglia consist of cell bodies interspersed with fibres, some or all of which make connection with the cells. In the dorsal root ganglia each cell has only one process, and this after running for a short distance divides at right angles, giving off in one direction an axon which enters the central nervous system, and receiving in the other a process (*dendron*) which has the structure of a fibre, but functions as a dendrite, bringing impulses inwards.

Muscular tissue consists of elongated elements, either cells or cœnocytes, the *muscle fibres*, in which the power

of contraction is highly developed. It is of two kinds,
Muscular Tissues. *striped or striated*, and *plain, unstriped or
unstriated.* Involuntary muscle (see p. 49)
is generally unstriped, voluntary muscle striped.
The fibres of plain muscle are cells of an elongated

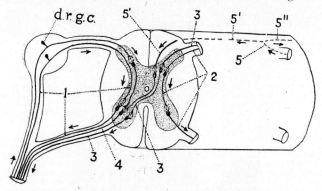

FIG. 68.—A diagram of fibres entering and leaving the spinal
 cord, showing various tracks along which impulses may be
 conducted in the " exchange " system which it constitutes
 (p. 95). The arrows show the direction of impulses.

Note that where the terminal branches of the axon of one
 neurone meet the dendrites of another the two are not
 continuous but interlace, so that the nervous impulse must
 pass an interruption in its track. This arrangement is
 called a *synapse*.

1. The simplest track, one afferent and one efferent neurone ; 2. an
 intermediate neurone is concerned ; 3. the track crosses the cord, so
 that an impulse is discharged along a nerve on the opposite side ; 4. a
 neurone receives impulses from two others ; 5, 5′, 5″. a fibre branches
 to affect neurones in different parts of the cord ; *d.r.g.c.* cells of dorsal
 root ganglion.

spindle shape with a single oval nucleus in the middle.
They show a faint longitudinal striation, have each a
delicate sheath, and when they occur in masses are joined
by a little intercellular cement substance, across which
threads of protoplasm keep them in continuity (Fig. 8 B).
The fibres of striped muscle are larger than those of plain
muscle, and can be seen with the naked eye if a portion

of one of the great voluntary muscles be teased into fragments. Each is a cœnocyte, containing many nuclei. The
fibre is cylindrical, tapering at the ends. It is covered by

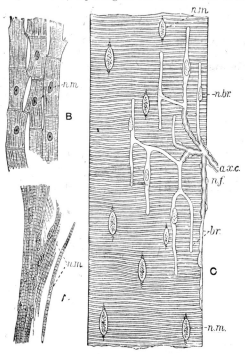

FIG. 69.—Histology of muscle.

A, Cardiac muscle of the frog; *B*, cardiac muscle of man;
  C, part of a skeletal muscle fibre of the frog, showing the
  ending of a motor nerve fibre.

ax.c., Axis cylinder of the nerve fibre; *br.*, branches of the same
  after it has lost its medullary sheath : *n.br.*, nuclei of the
  branches; *n.f.*, nuclei of the nerve fibre; *n.m.*, nuclei of
  muscle fibres.

a transparent elastic membrane, the *sarcolemma*, which
adheres at the end to that of an adjacent fibre or to tendon.
The cytoplasm is characterised by alternate light and dark
stripes which lie across the length of the fibre (Figs. 69, 77).

The nuclei are scattered throughout the substance of the fibre, and often each is surrounded by a little granular undifferentiated protoplasm, unlike the modified protoplasm which composes most of the fibre. A longitudinal fibrillation is present, but its relation to the striation is a matter of dispute. The muscular tissue of the heart is a peculiar kind of striped muscle known as *cardiac muscle*. Its cells, spindle-shaped in the frog, short, square-ended cylinders in Man, have each one nucleus, and often a branch that abuts upon a similar process of a neighbouring cell. It is striped, but less distinctly so than ordinary muscle. It is in this tissue that the automatism of the heart resides.

Skeletal tissues are characterised by a great de-
Skeletal Tissues. velopment of intercellular or ground
substance between the cells whereby it is adapted to support and bind together other tissues. In *cartilage* the ground substance is a homogeneous *matrix* readily stained by silver nitrate. It is firm and elastic, and sometimes toughened by the development in it of fibres, when it is known as *fibrous cartilage*, in contradistinction to plain or *hyaline cartilage*. The cells are simple in shape and often disposed in groups of two or four formed by the division of one original cell. As these secrete additional ground

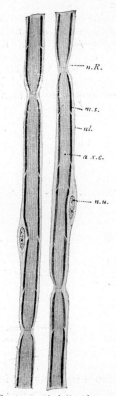

FIG. 70. — Medullated nerve fibres, stained with osmic acid and highly magnified.

a x.c., Axis-cylinder ; *m.s.*, medullary sheath ; *nl.*, neurilemma ; *n R'.*, node of Ranvier ; *nu.*, nucleus.

Note that the axis cylinder contains longitudinal fibrils.

substance they become pushed apart by it. In *calcified cartilage* the structure is the same as in hyaline, but the ground substance is impregnated with salts of lime. *Connective tissue*, like cartilage, has a ground substance which stains readily with silver nitrate, but it is much softer and always contains fibres of two kinds— *white fibres*, which have a wavy course, branch but do not join, and are composed of extremely fine fibrils, and *yellow* or *elastic fibres*, which have a straight course, branch sharply and join to form a meshwork, and are not composed of fibrils. The white fibres swell up and become transparent in acetic acid, the elastic fibres do not. When connective tissue is boiled, the ground substance yields *gelatin*, whereas cartilage treated in the same way gives a substance known as *chondrin*. In the ground substance are a number of irregular spaces occupied by cells or *connective-tissue corpuscles*, of which

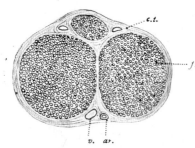

FIG. 71.—A transverse section of a medul-lated nerve of the frog, stained with osmic acid and magnified.

ar., Artery ; *c.t.*, connective-tissue sheath or peri-neurium ; *f.*, funiculus or bundle of nerve fibres ; *v.*, vein.

some are branched and often continuous by their branches, while others are rounded and granular. Connective tissue penetrates every part of the body, holding together the softer tissues and forming in the skin (pp. 34, 35) a continuous envelope known as the dermis, which is covered by the epithelial layer, known as the epidermis, already described (p. 113). Tendon is a modified form of connective tissue in which the white fibres are very plentiful and run paral-lel instead of forming a feltwork. The cells lie in rows between the fibres. *Fatty* or *adipose tissue* (Fig. 80) is a form of connective tissue in which the figures are scanty and most of the cells are swollen into vesicles by the

presence of a droplet of fatty matter to which the protoplasm of the cell forms a fine sheath with the nucleus on one
side. In the early stages of the growth of such a cell small

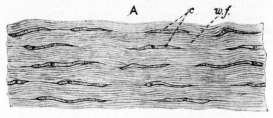

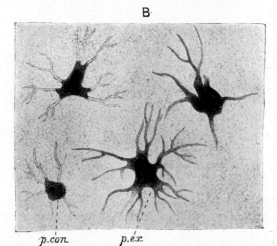

FIG. 72.—Connective tissues of the frog.

A, Tendon : B, pigment cells in the skin, seen through the epidermis.
c. Cells ; p.con., pigment cell with the pigment contracted ; p.ex.,
pigment cell with the pigment extending into the processes;
w.f., white fibres.

droplets of fat are laid up in the protoplasm, and these
grow and run together till they fill nearly the whole cell.

Bone (Fig. 7) has a firm ground substance like cartilage,
but differs from the latter both in composition and in the

arrangement of its cells. The ground substance consists of
an organic basis impregnated with salts of lime—principally
the phosphate. When boiled it yields gelatin. It is
arranged in *lamellæ* separated by rows of minute spaces or
lacunæ which contain the *bone cells* or *bone corpuscles*. The
lacunæ are connected by fine *canaliculi*, through which
the cells are continuous by minute processes. The lamellæ
are arranged in a concentric manner around spaces which
contain blood vessels. Some of these spaces are large and

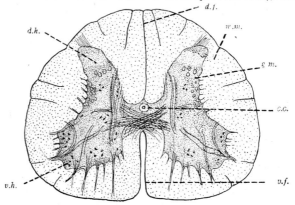

FIG. 73.—A transverse section of the spinal cord of man, taken
through the lumbar region, between nerves, with the pia mater
removed. Lettering as in Fig. 49.

filled with a tissue known as *bone marrow*, rich in fat cells.
When the layer of bone around the marrow cavities is thick,
it is traversed by smaller spaces, known as *Haversian canals*,
in which lie minute blood vessels. The lymph from the
blood vessels permeates the bone through the canaliculi.

Blood is classed among the skeletal tissues on account of
the plentifulness of its fluid ground substance, although it
only acts as a supporting tissue when, under high pressure,
it renders an organ turgid. The fluid part of blood is
known as the *plasma*, the cells as *blood corpuscles*. They
are of two kinds, *red* and *white*. Each red corpuscle is
a thin, biconvex, oval disc, yellow when solitary but
giving with its fellows a red colour. The colour is due to

a compound of a protein with an iron-bearing organic substance. This compound which is called *hæmoglobin*, belongs to a class of substances known as *respiratory pigments*. It has the power of uniting with oxygen to form a loose compound known as *oxyhæmoglobin*, which is formed in the respiratory organs where the pressure of oxygen is high and breaks down, yielding its oxygen, in the capillaries of the tissues, where the oxygen pressure is low (p. 76). Thus it serves as a carrier of oxygen. The carbon dioxide carried by the blood on the return journey is held partly in simple solution but mainly as bicarbonates which dissociate in the chemical conditions of the respiratory organs. Hæmoglobin is found in the red corpuscles of all back-boned animals, but in man and other mammals these corpuscles are round biconcave discs without nuclei. The white corpuscles or *leucocytes* are colourless, smaller and fewer than the red. They have not, like the red, a definite shape, but consist of very soft undifferentiated protoplasm, which

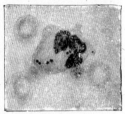

FIG. 74.—A human white-blood corpuscle which has ingested a number of *Micrococcus pyogenes aureus*, the common bacterium of boils, etc. The micro cocci are the small dark spots; the large three-lobed structure is the nucleus.—From Haldane and Huxley.

has kept its power of contraction, and, when the corpuscle lies against a solid surface, is constantly changing its shape, putting forth in all directions irregular processes or " pseudopodia " and as readily withdrawing them again. By continually lengthening a pseudopodium and with-drawing those on the opposite side they can flow along. Movement of this kind is called *amœboid* because it occurs in a minute organism known as *Amœba*, which we shall presently study. In the blood stream the leucocytes take on a rounded shape, so that they are easily bowled along. The white corpuscles are of several kinds. Some of them are of use to the organism by flowing round and thus engulfing into their protoplasm harmful bacteria and other parasitic micro-organisms, which they digest. An-

other kind removes the remains of dead tissues in a similar
manner. Corpuscles which thus devour objects are known
as *phagocytes*. Other leucocytes wage a chemical warfare
against the micro-organisms by secreting substances
(*antibodies*) which act against the latter in various
ways. Some of these substances (*agglutinins*) hamper
the bacteria by causing them to stick together or
" agglutinate " ; others (*opsonins*) facilitate the action

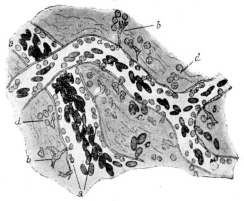

FIG. 75.—Inflamed mesentery of a frog, highly magnified.

a, Leucocytes ranged against the walls of a capillary ; *b*, leucocytes
migrating through the capillary walls ; *c*, escaped red corpuscles ; *d*, accumulation of leucocytes outside the capillaries.
—From Starling, after Adami.

of the phagocytes ; others (*lysins*) kill and break up
the bacteria ; others (*antitoxins*) neutralise the action
of the poisons, secreted by the bacteria, which are the
cause of the harm which the latter do. Most of the
antibodies act only against a particular species of micro-
organisms. If they are successful they confer upon the
animal an *immunity* which may last for years, so that a
second attack of the disease caused by the micro-organism
in question will not occur. *Inflammation* is due to the
flushing with blood of the part attacked, so that it becomes
swollen and red, and, in a warm-blooded animal, hot.
The white corpuscles then line up on the walls of the capil-

laries, pass through them, and engage the enemy. *Pus*
is lymph full of living and dead leucocytes and bacteria.
Leucocytes also carry substances, such as fat globules,
from one place to another.

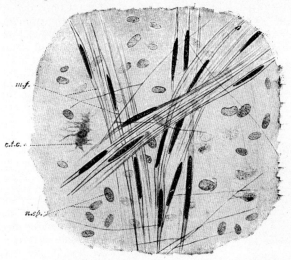

FIG. 76.—A portion of the bladder of a frog, stained and highly
magnified.

c.t.c., Connective-tissue cell; *m.f.*, unstriped muscle fibres; *n.ep.*, nuclei of the
epithelioid cells which cover and line the bladder.

The white corpuscles are semi-independent portions of
the organism living in the blood. Each of
them retains all the powers of a whole
organism. They are irritable, as may be seen
by their increased activity on warming, or by the effect
upon them of various drugs. They appear to be automatic,
for we can often trace their movements to no stimulus.
Their substance must undergo katabolism, for they
expend energy, as we have seen, in contraction and in the
manufacture and secretion of various substances. The
fact that the stimulation of one part of their surface causes
other parts to act, as in changing the direction of move-

The Differentiation of Cells.

ment, shows the existence in them of conductivity. They assimilate from the plasma nourishing matters to repair their waste. They reproduce by fission, first the nucleus and then the cytoplasm parting into two, and each half of the cytoplasm taking a half of the nucleus. Consisting as it thus does of protoplasm which retains all the primary powers of a living being, the white corpuscle shows us that all these powers must be regarded as the birthright of all

protoplasm, and that their possession by every organism is due to this fact, and not to the presence of several kinds of protoplasm. Yet it is important to notice that the independence of the leucocytes is only relative. They are still wholly dependent for their nourishment upon the body by which they were formed, and their activity is directed to the welfare of that body. With the relative independence of the white corpuscles, the condition of the other cells of the body is in contrast. Each of them consists of a portion of the protoplasm of the organism in which certain of its powers are highly developed, while others are degraded or lost. It is probable that all protoplasm retains irritability, either to stimuli through a nerve or at least to changes

Fig. 77.—A portion of a striped muscle fibre, magnified.

in the composition of the fluid surrounds it. It may be, too, that automatism of a kind is widespread ; and disintegration and assimilation are of course universal. But in most tissues the cells have lost in the adult the power of reproduction, and certain of the modes of appearance of the energy liberated by disintegration are developed at the expense of others. Thus in a nerve cell conductivity is highly developed and contractility lost, while in a muscle fibre conductivity is relatively low and contractility highly developed. In both these tissues chemical manufacture and secretion for the benefit of the rest of the body is at a low ebb, while in gland cells, which are neither contractile nor conducting, it is highly developed. In correspondence with these peculiarities of function are the peculiarities of form which we have noted. That is to say, here as everywhere we find differentiation and the division of physiological labour hand in hand.

The blood corpuscles die and are replaced, but not by multiplication in the blood. The white corpuscles arise in *adenoid or lymphoid tissue* which is a connective tissue full of leucocytes and occurs in patches known as *lymphatic " glands "* in various parts of the body, especially under the mucous membrane of the alimentary canal and along the lymph vessels, by which they are conveyed into the blood. The red corpuscles of the frog probably arise in the spleen. Those of mammals are formed in a vascular tissue known as *red marrow* which occurs in the bones of these animals.

When blood is shed it *clots*, owing to the precipitation in the plasma of a protein known as *fibrin*, in the form of a meshwork of fine fibrils which entangles the corpuscles and forms a firm mass.

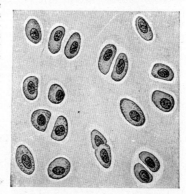

FIG. 78. — Cartilage stained and magnified, showing cells, some of which are in pairs formed by the division of a single cell, matrix, and the newly secreted part of the matrix, which forms capsules around the cells.

Fibrin is formed by the union of the protein *fibrinogen* with a small quantity of another substance *thrombin*, which, under the influence of calcium, arises upon foreign surfaces when the blood is shed. The liquid which remains after the formation of the clot is known as *serum*. The effect of clotting is to close wounds and thus prevent loss of blood.

The innumerable nuclei of the frog's body have all arisen by the division of one original nucleus, that of the zygote formed by the union of the ovum and spermatozoon (see p. 137). The process of *nuclear division* by which the nuclei multiply

Nuclear Division.

is usually followed by a *cell division* in which each half of
the divided nucleus takes its own portion of the cytoplasm
which surrounded the parent nucleus, but in some cases,
as in the division of nuclei for a striped muscle fibre,
cell division does not take place, so that a cœnocyte arises.
Nuclear division is of two kinds. In a few cases, as in

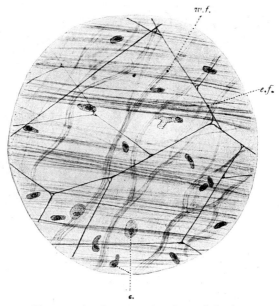

FIG. 79.—Areolar connective tissue **of** the frog.
c., Cells ; *e.f.*, elastic fibres ; *w.f.*, white fibres.

some leucocytes, the process is quite simple. The nucleus
lengthens, then narrows in the middle so that it becomes
dumb-bell shaped, and finally breaks into two at the
narrow part. This is *simple* or *amitotic division*. In most
cases, however, a complicated process known as *karyo-
kinesis* or *mitosis* takes place. Outside the nucleus lies
a minute body known as the *centrosome*. When mitosis
is about to take place, the centrosome divides into two

parts which travel to opposite sides of the nucleus. As they separate, the protoplasm becomes arranged in a radiating manner around each, forming a figure known as the *aster*. Meanwhile the nuclear membrane is breaking up and the nucleus is undergoing certain internal changes (Fig. 83). The linin with its contained chromatin granules appears to form a coiled thread, the *skein* or *spireme*. This, however, is made up of a number of portions, the *chromosomes*, which now shrink apart. The same number of them appears in every nuclear division in the body (but not, as we shall see, in the germ cells). In the frog this number is twenty-four. At this stage there appears, stretching from one centrosome to the other across the site of the nucleus, a gelatinous *spindle*, divided by more fluid " threads " into strands diverging from each centrosome to the equator. The proceedings up to this point constitute the *prophase* of mitosis.

FIG. 80. —Part of one of the fat bodies of a frog, compressed and magnified, showing fat cells with fat globules in various stages.

f.g., Fat globules; *nu.*, nuclei.

Now the chromosomes become attached to the spindle in a ring round its equator. The point of attachment in each chromosome is known as the *chromomere*. At the same time a split, of which there have already been indications, divides each chromosome longitudinally into equal and similar halves, known as *chromatids*. This is the *metaphase*. The next stage (*anaphase*) consists in the passage of the halves as daughter chromosomes along the threads towards the poles of the spindle. There they arrange themselves in a radiating manner. Finally, in the *telophase*,

9

the chromosomes of each group thus formed constitute a daughter nucleus by passing through a series of changes which reverse those by which the mother nucleus broke up. It will be seen that the result of this process is an exact halving of the chromatin of the mother nucleus between the daughter nuclei.

The nuclei of the ova and spermatozoa,

Gametogenesis.

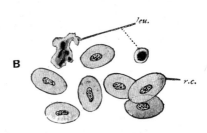

FIG. 81.—Blood of a frog, highly magnified.
A, Fresh ; *B*, stained.
leu., Leucocytes ; *r.c.*, red corpuscles.

destined to form by fusion a single nucleus from which the body nuclei arise, contain each only half the number of chromosomes found in the body nuclei. This is the result of certain peculiarities in the cell divisions by which the gametes arise. The formation of gametes is known as *gametogenesis*. That of spermatozoa is *spermatogenesis*, that of the ovum is *oogenesis*. Gametogenesis ends by *maturation*—two successive divisions of a cell, known as the *gametocyte*, derived from the germinal

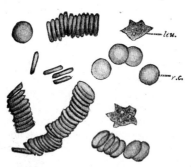

FIG 82.—Human blood, highly magnified.
leu., Leucocytes; *r.c.*, red corpuscles.

epithelium. The gametocytes of spermatogenesis (Fig. 551) are known as *spermatocytes* ; those which give rise to ova are *oocytes*.

The first division of maturation is known as the *meiotic division* and the procedure in it as *meiosis*. It differs from ordinary mitosis in that by it *the number of chromosomes is halved*, and on that account it is said to be a *reducing division*. The reduction is due to the fact that,

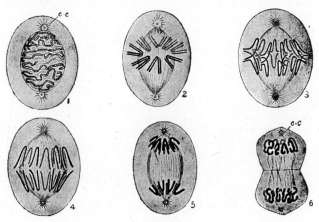

FIG. 83.—Kayokinesis—After Flemming.

1. Spireme stage of nucleus ; *c.c.*, centrosome.
2. Longitudinal splitting of chromosomes, and arrangement of them on the equator of the spindle (*Metaphase*).
3. Separation of halves of chromosomes (*Early anaphase*).
4. Recession of daughter chromosomes from equator of cell.
5. Nuclear spindle, with chromosomes at each pole (*Late anaphase*).
6. Retrogression of nucleus (*Telophase*) and cell division.

instead of dividing to provide one daughter chromosome for each daughter nucleus, each chromosome goes undivided into one of the daughter cells. The process is complicated by the fact that the true chromosomes come together in pairs in the gametocyte before the meiotic division, so that the nucleus appears already to contain half the normal number of chromosomes, but these are really double chromosomes. It is not *any* two chromosomes which become partners in a double chromosome,

but two which (as is known from facts which we shall
note later) are similar—through not identical—in constitution and often have visible common features which
distinguish them from the others. The members of such
a pair are known as *homologous chromosomes*. In fact,
each cell of the body has a double set of chromosomes,
and it is corresponding members of the two sets that

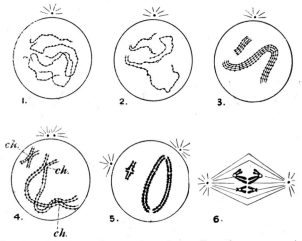

Fig. 84.—Diagrams of stages in meiosis. Two chromosome-pairs
are shown : the members of one are short and form one chiasma,
those of the other are longer and form two chiasmata (*ch*).

1. leptotene ;   2. zygotene ;   3. four-strand pachytene ;
4. diplotene ;   5. diakinesis ;   6. metaphase.

come together at meiosis. The two chromosomes of each
double chromosome part in the meiotic division, so that
the daughter nuclei have each half the normal number of
chromosomes, but these are now of the ordinary single
kind. While they were together, however, the chromatids
which had by then appeared in each of the chromosomes
of a pair exchanged lengths of themselves with the
chromatids of the other chromosome, so that those which
part are not identically these which came together, but
each is a combination of parts of the former pair. The

lengths exchanged are corresponding portions, so that no portion is duplicated in either chromosome. This process is known as *crossing over* (Fig. 85).

Meiosis is a complicated process which varies in detail, and descriptions of it are the harder to follow on account of differences in the application of the terms which have been applied to its phases. In typical instances it proceeds by the following stages :

1. *Leptotene stage.* The chromosomes are slender, not split longitudinally, and tangled much as in the spireme.

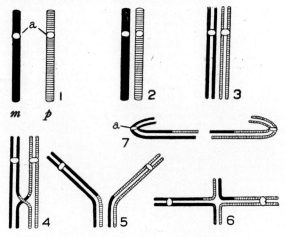

FIG. 85.—A diagram of crossing over.

1. A homologous pair of chromosomes ; *m*, the chromosome of maternal, *p*, that of paternal origin ; 2, pairing ; 3, splitting into chromatids ; 4, chiasma formation ; 5, 6, separation (diakinesis) with adherence at one end ; 7, parting of chromosomes at anaphase ; *a*, point at which chromosome becomes attached to spindle (*chromomere*). The shortening of the chromosomes and the temporary obliteration in the prometaphase of the split between the chromatids are not shown.

2. *Zygotene stage.* The chromosomes, which are shorter, thicker, and less tangled, are coming together in pairs whose members are closely applied (but not fused), the union generally beginning at one or both ends. This union is *pairing* (in earlier accounts *synapsis*, or *syndesis*, or *conjugation*). The chromosomes tend to crowd together towards one side of the nucleus (*synizesis*).

3. *Pachytene stage.* The chromosomes are still shorter and thicker and the pairing has been completed.

   (*a*) *Two-strand pachytene.* The chromosomes remain unsplit.

(b) *Four-strand pachytene.* Each chromosome is split longitudinally into two chromatids. There now happens an
event which is not revealed till the next stage : in places
two adjacent chromatids belonging to different chromosomes of a homologous pair break and unite reciprocally
by their broken ends.

In the late two-strand and the four-strand pachytene stages the
chromosomes of a pair are often twisted round one
another. This is known as the *strepsitene* condition.

4. *Diplotene stage.* The chromosomes continue to shorten and
thicken and the two which joined to form each double chromosome
now separate again, perhaps because the attractive force which held
them together is now used up in holding together the chromatids in
each of them. They do not, however, become completely separated
but remain attached at certain points. These are the points at which
the breaking and reciprocal union of chromatids has taken place.
As the chromosomes separate, the chromatids at each of these points
form an X which is known as a *chiasma.* Presently the chromosomes
draw apart at the chiasmata too, portions of each chromatid being
thus drawn into the chromosome to which it did not at first belong.
Usually the chromosomes of a pair still adhere at both ends, forming
a ring, or at one end where they form a cross. In the *late diplotene
stage or diakinesis* the chromosomes, now very short and thick,
disperse through the nucleus.

5. *Prometaphase (stage of gemini).* Further contraction forms
ring-shaped or cross-shaped double chromosomes. The splits
between chromatids are temporarily obliterated in the chromosomes.

6. *Metaphase.* Each double chromosome has two chromomeres,
one for each of its constituent chromosomes.

7. *Anaphase.* The chromomeres move to opposite poles of the
spindle, each drawing with it two (usually much shortened) chromatids. Chromomeres of the original (paternal and maternal) sets
go indifferently to either pole so that the original sets do *not* segregate.

The *second* or *post-meiotic division* follows the first
without a resting stage. It is an ordinary division, in
which each chromosome splits into two to give rise to
one daughter chromosome in each daughter nucleus, so
that the daughter nuclei still have each half the normal
number. At fertilisation the zygote has therefore the
normal number, which it imparts to the body cells during
the mitoses by which it forms them.

Spermatogenesis takes place in the testis (cf. Fig. 551).
Oogenesis begins in the ovary and finishes after fertilisation.

The actual course of maturation differs greatly in the
two cases. In spermatogenesis the cytoplasm is equally
divided and each of the four products (*spermatids*) becomes a spermatozoon, so that from each spermatocyte four

spermatozoa arise. In oogenesis each division is unequal. At the first division there are formed a large cell and a small one, the latter containing very little cytoplasm

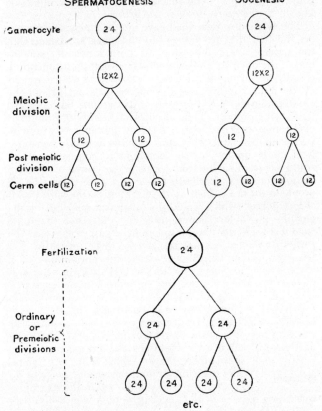

Fig. 86. —A diagram of gametogenesis and fertilisation.-

and being known as the *first polar body*. At the second division, while the first polar body forms two very small cells,[1] the large cell forms again a large and a small

[1] In many animals the first polar body does not divide.

product. The large product is an ovum ; the small is called the *second polar body*. Thus, instead of four ova the oocyte forms one ovum and three vestigial cells which come to nothing. The formation of the polar bodies is known as the *maturation of the ovum*.

The events just described have important consequences : (1) the fact that, so far as chromosomes are concerned, the processes are the same for both kinds of gametes makes the nuclei of the ovum and spermatozoon contribute equally to the zygote nucleus ; (2) owing to what happens at the reduction division, the zygote does not get all the chromosomes of a cell of each of its parents, but only one half their number. Thus at each fertilisation the number of chromosomes does not increase by doubling as otherwise would happen ; (3) while this number remains constant, it is made up by a new combination, consisting of an equal set from each parent ; this is the source of the two homologous sets mentioned above ; (4) since these sets are provided (at the reduction division) not by the splitting of chromosomes (which would give identical sets) but by the parting of whole chromosomes, any difference that may exist between the chromosomes of a pair will cause the germs to which they are transferred to be unlike in that respect ; (5) crossings over cause the chromatids of a chromosome to differ, but the second division separates them, and each gives two like chromatids in a zygote if it enter one. In the upshot, the chromosome material of a zygote has not increased, but is a new entity in two ways— because it has come from two parents, and because the contribution from each parent came (by crossing over) partly from each of two sets of chromosomes.

Only one spermatozoon ever unites with any ovum. **Fertilisation.** While the slime around the eggs is swelling up and setting to a jelly in the water, the spermatozoa which have been shed over it by the male (p. 81) pass through it, swimming by means of their tails. They are far more numerous than the ova and most of them perish, but one succeeds in entering each egg. Thus a zygote known as the *oosperm* or *fertilised ovum* comes into being. After fertilisation the ovum shrinks from its vitelline membrane. The cytoplasm of the spermatozoon disappears in that of the ovum, but the nucleus passes onward and comes to lie side by side with that of the egg. The two nuclei are known as the *male and female pronuclei.* Meanwhile there has arisen from the neck of the spermatozoon a centrosome, around which is formed an aster. As the nuclei approach one another this divides and forms a spindle. The pronuclei break up each into twelve chromosomes, which lie at the equator of the spindle. Thus the normal number of twenty-four chromosomes is restored ; these lie in two groups corresponding to the two pronuclei. Now the chromosomes split in the ordinary way and the halves pass to opposite poles of the spindle, where they form ordinary nuclei. The cytoplasm of the egg meanwhile divides into two cells, known as the first two *blastomeres.* This is the first of the series of divisions known as the *cleavage* or *segmentation of the ovum,* by which the cells of the embryo are formed (see p. 616). At these divisions each cell produced receives, by the mechanism of ordinary mitosis, a complete set of chromosomes from each parent of the original zygote.

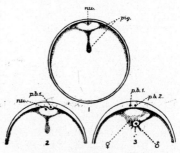

Fig. 87.—Sections of the egg of a frog during maturation and fertilisation.— Semi-diagrammatic.

1, 2, 3, Successive stages.
nu., Nucleus of ovum, still in the pigmented region, but already shrunken and lying in a clear space formed by fluid extruded when the nuclear membrane was dissolved ; *p.b.*1, *p.b.*2, first and second polar bodies ; *pig.*, pigmented protoplasm ; ♀, female pronucleus ; ♂, male pronucleus ; the track along which this has entered is shown by pigment.

The frog which is developed from the fertilised ovum will, like any other animal, inherit the likeness of its parents : large frogs will have large offspring, and so forth. This, of course, because the embryo is physically continuous with each parent through one of the germs. The question suggests itself : is any constituent of the germ specially responsible for heredity ? Since the nucleus is known to exercise a directive influence

Inheritance.

over many of the activities of the cytoplasm, and again since the spermatozoon contributes a full quota of nucleo-plasm but hardly any cytoplasm to the embryo, it is natural to conclude that the principal though perhaps not the only agent of heredity is the nucleus. This probability gives a peculiar interest to the fact, which we have already noted, that, as regards the nucleus, ovum and spermato-zoon make equal contributions to the embryo. Thereby, it would appear, the parents make equal contributions to most, if not to all, of the inheritance of the offspring. Because it is the material in the chromosomes that is meticulously shared out between the offspring, and because in certain cases—most clearly in that of sex (see p. 701)—particular characters of the offspring have been found to follow particular chromosomes, it is held that this contribu-tion is made by means of the chromosomes. As to the way in which such contributions realise themselves when they are of opposite tendency (that is, when two homologous chromosomes differ in some respect)—how they some-times blend and sometimes one dominates over the other so that the offspring " takes after " one parent—we shall have something to say in later chapters (pp. 598 and 697). The shuffling of chromosome material which takes place in the maturation and union of gametes ensures that no two individuals have the same chromosome constitution and thus promotes variety. We shall also see the im-portance of this later on.

It is said that frogs have been known to live twelve years. Sooner or later, however, they, like ourselves, must die. However successful the individual may be in avoiding enemies and accidents, he cannot escape that gradual slowing of the working of the bodily machine which in the long-run brings it to a stand-still. The course of metabolism is in some way limited, so that in the most perfect conditions natural death would eventually result. The nature of this limitation is not understood. The fact that the germs are not subject to it, but produce new individuals with a fresh lease of life, shows that it is not inherent in all protoplasm, but belongs only to that of the cells which constitute the bulk of the body. This it would seem to affect in all the tissues, so that,

Death.

were the body not the complicated machine that it is, death might come as a gradual loss of power in all parts alike. As it is, however, the end is always more or less premature as regards some tissues, being brought about by the breaking down of one of the main parts of the machine, as the brain, or lungs, or heart, though in the long-run any other part than the heart brings about general death through its effect upon that organ, whereby the rest of the body is deprived of fresh blood. It may be that this breakdown is due to the protoplasm of the body cells producing substances which encumber them or act as slow poisons, and that these in course of time accumulate beyond the power of the body to destroy or excrete them. Or it may be that they have not the power of renewing parts in them which wear out. In any case, so far as our present knowledge goes, death in all the higher animals is inevitable.

CHAPTER VI

AMŒBA

AMŒBA PROTEUS is a little, organism found in the mud
and on weeds in freshwater ponds. A large
General Features. specimen is just visible to the naked eye as a
minute, irregular, whitish speck. Under the
microscope (with transmitted light) this is seen to be a mass
of translucent slime, greyish in colour owing to the presence
of numerous small, dark granules. The outer layer is
clear and transparent owing to the absence of the granules.
This layer is called the *ectoplasm*, the granular inner
part being the *endoplasm*. In the endoplasm are usually
to be seen the remains of other little organisms, especially minute plants, which form the food of *Amœba*. At
one spot is a round space filled with a clear fluid, which
grows gradually larger and then suddenly disappears, owing
to a contraction of the protoplasm around it causing it to
burst out and discharge its contents into the surrounding
water. It then gradually re-forms in the same portion of
protoplasm as before. This space is called the *contractile
vacuole*. There are usually other small vacuoles which are not
contractile. With care there may also be seen in the living
specimen a lens-shaped body of moderate size which is
somewhat denser than the rest of the protoplasm. This is
the nucleus. If the animal be killed and stained with
carmine or any of a number of other dyes, the nucleus
takes up the stain more deeply than the cytoplasm. The
irregular shape of the body is constantly changing, owing
to the outgrowth of new processes or *pseudopodia* and the
withdrawal of old ones. 140

The formation of a pseudopodium begins with a slight

Movements. outflowing of the ectoplasm, into which the endoplasm presently flows. The projection continues to grow by the flow of more protoplasm into it for a varying time, and locomotion is brought about by the persistent lengthening of one pseudopodium till the bulk of the body has been transferred into it. During this time it is throwing out subsidiary pseudopodia in various directions. Before very long, however, the main flow is directed into one of these and the animal

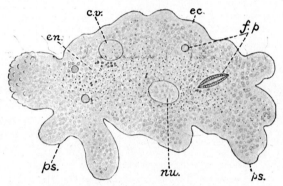

Fig. 88.—*Amœba proteus*, highly magnified.

c.v., Contractile vacuole ; **ec.**, ectoplasm ; **en.**, endoplasm ; **f.p.**, food particles ; **nu.**, nucleus ; **ps.**, pseudopodia.

moves in another direction, the stream in the older pseudopodia setting backward into the body until they disappear. The flow of the endoplasm is always swifter in the middle of a pseudopodium than at the sides. It will be seen that we have here an example of *contraction*, as the word is used in Biology, the shape of the mass of protoplasm being changed by the transference of material, but the size remaining the same. The throwing out of a pseudopodium is not brought about merely by a flowing of the protoplasm, but takes place in the following manner. The ectoplasm and the outer part of the endoplasm together form a firm coat, the *plasmagel*, around the fluid inner endoplasm or *plasmasol.* Where a pseudopodium is to be thrust out the plasmagel softens, and the contraction of the rest of that layer then presses the plasmasol towards this spot, which bulges. As the bulge grows, a covering of plasmagel for its flanks is provided by conversion of plasmasol. Over the ectoplasm is a very thin elastic pellicle, the *plasmalemma,*

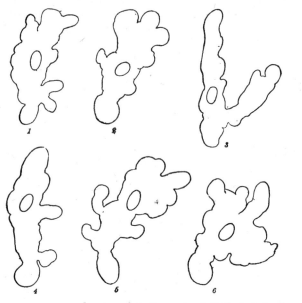

Fig. 89. —Successive changes in shape of an individual of *Amœba proteus,* drawn at intervals of two minutes.

which is sticky and therefore adheres to the ground where it is in contact, so that the effect of the forward thrusting of the protoplasm within is to roll it along, as an india-rubber bag filled with water may be rolled over a surface, and thus the animal travels in the direction of the thrust. Pseudo-podia which do not touch the ground merely protrude without causing locomotion, but the creature may place their tips upon the ground and thus walk upon them.

When it is floating freely it puts out slender, finger-like pseudopodia and appears to be searching with them for foothold. During the movements the contents of the endoplasm—nucleus, food particles, etc.—are carried about freely from place to place in the body, but the contractile vacuole adheres to the inner surface of the ectoplasm and moves with it. The constant changes of position of internal bodies is one of the arguments which support the foam theory of the structure of protoplasm (see p. 104) against theories which demand the existence in it of a meshwork of fine threads, and an examination under high powers of the microscope confirms this by revealing appearances similar to those found in certain artificially made foams.[1] Artificial foams can even be caused to carry out movements which in their general features resemble those of *Amœba*. It should be noted, however, that the special features of the contractions of *Amœba* are not found in them.

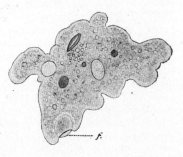

FIG. 90.—*Amœba proteus* in the act of ingesting *f*, a small vegetable organism which is being swallowed.

The pellicle which covers the surface of *Amœba* is believed to be rich in fatty substances.

Nutrition. *Amœba* feeds on small organisms, which it *ingests* by surrounding them with outgrowths of its protoplasm and so engulfing them. The space in the body which the prey comes to fill would thus be lined with ectoplasm, but the ectoplasm here becomes absorbed into the surrounding endoplasm, so that it is clear that there is no essential difference between the materials which compose these layers. There is then secreted around the food particle a layer of water containing substances which kill it and digest its nourishing

[1] Such a foam may be made by mixing together rancid oil and salt and placing little droplets of the mixture in water.

part. The reaction of this fluid is acid at first, but later becomes neutral or slightly alkaline. The space containing the digestive juice is known as a *food vacuole*. The chief food of *Amœba* is protein. It is said also to digest carbohydrates, but not fat. The dissolved substances are incorporated, and the undigested parts are *egested* by the simple process of being left behind as the animal flows along.

The protoplasm of *Amœba* is irritable, automatic, and conductive. Its *irritability* is not, as in higher animals, specially developed in sense organs, but that this property exists in it is shown in various ways. If *Amœba* be stimulated by slight contact or by meeting very dilute solutions of various chemical substances it will form a pseudopodium on the side towards the stimulus. If it be pricked with the end of a fine thread of glass, or come into contact with stronger solutions of chemical substances, it will draw back and flow away. In this case the formation of a pseudopodium in a region of the body other than that which has been stimulated shows the presence of *conductivity*. Again, it does not swallow every particle it comes across, but chooses those that either contain nourishing substances or are in motion (in which case they are probably alive and therefore fit for food). By an unkind deception of this " sporting instinct," it may be induced to capture and swallow moving particles of glass. Its mode of seizing food is not fixed, but adjusted with an uncanny appearance of intelligence to the nature and behaviour of the prey of the moment, which it dogs with perseverance and resourceful changes of method. It will move away from strong light, but does not appear to perceive a particle of food better in the light than in the dark. All this shows that it receives from foreign bodies various stimuli, and discriminates between them. In contrast to these instances, many of its actions cannot be traced to any stimulus, and must therefore be classed as *automatic* in the sense in which we have used that word. In much of its activity it appears to be exploring its surroundings and to continue on a course until it receives some stimulus which repels it, but sometimes, as

Irritability Automatism, and Conductivity.

in capturing food, it appears to be attracted in the direction from which a stimulus comes.

Excretion and Respiration. The contractile vacuole is probably an organ for the regulation of the water content of the protoplasm. Water must enter all over the surface of the organism and more is produced during metabolism. The excess which results is collected into the vacuole. The water expelled must take with it dissolved carbon dioxide, and thus the contractile vacuole aids respiration. Possibly it also removes excreta. At the same time it seems likely that the whole surface of the body serves to some extent both for respiration and for excretion.

Depression. Unfavourable conditions of life may bring about a disease known as *depression*, in which the nucleus of the *Amœba* is enlarged and the various functions become deranged. This disease, however, is more familiar and has been more closely investigated in some other minute organisms, as, for instance, in *Paramecium* (p. 171).

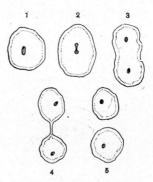

FIG. 91.—A diagram of the fission of *Amœba*. The dark spots represent nuclei.

Encystment. In certain circumstances *Amœba* withdraws its pseudopodia and becomes a rounded mass which secretes about itself a tough case or *cyst*.[1] In this it lies dormant and can survive the drying or freezing of the pond in which it lives or be transferred in mud to other ponds. We have here an instance of a widespread phenomenon known as *suspended vitality*, which is found, for instance, in seeds and in frozen tissues (see p. 107). The exact condition of the protoplasm in such cases is a mystery, but no vital processes can be detected, and it has been

---

[1] It is doubtful whether the resting cyst of *A. proteus* has been seen. Both resting cysts and cysts for spore formation (see p. 147) are known in other kinds of *Amœba*.

10

shown by experiments on seeds that, if they be kept
perfectly dry, not even respiration takes place. We must
conclude that life, regarded
as a process, has slowed
down and, at least in some
cases, ceased, but that the
protoplasm retains the power
of resuming it in certain
circumstances. At death, on
the other hand, the protoplasm passes into a condition
in which it will indeed remain
intact in suitable circumstances (as when it is frozen)
but has lost the power of
resuming life.

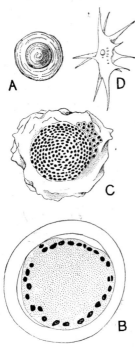

FIG. 92.—Multiple fission of
an *Amœba.*—After Scheel.

A, Amœba encysted ; *B,* section of a
cyst in which numerous nuclei have
been formed, more highly magnified ;
C, surface view of a ripe cyst in
which the spores are beginning to
separate and the cyst wall to break
up; *D,* a single spore highly magnified.

Amœba reproduces by the
process known
Reproduction. as *binary fission*,
in which first the nucleus
and then the cytoplasm parts
asunder into two halves,
each of which appears, at
all events, to differ from the
parent in nothing but size.
In some fissions of *Amœba*
the division of the nucleus
is amitotic, but at other
times there is a peculiar
kind of mitosis in which the
place of centrosomes is taken
by a mass of clear protoplasm
at each end of the nucleus.
These masses are known as
pole plates and arise within
the nuclear membrane,
which does not break up
during division as in ordinary mitosis.[1] After the division
of the nucleus the cytoplasm flows apart into two bodies,

[1] Not all the chromatin takes part in the mitosis. The inner portion
alone does so : the outer portion is halved independently of the spindle.

each of which contains one of the daughter nuclei. The new bodies are at first connected by a bridge of protoplasm, but this becomes narrower until it breaks through and two new individuals come into being.[1] Another kind of fission, known as *multiple fission or spore formation*, takes place at times. Its details differ with the kind of *Amœba*. In one kind it has been described as follows. The animal encysted and its nucleus divided amitotically till a very large number (some 600) of small nuclei had been formed. These passed to the surface of the cytoplasm, which gathered into a little mass around each of them. The cyst wall was now dissolved and the little individuals or *spores* escaped as small *Amœbæ* with fine, pointed pseudopodia unlike the blunt processes of the adult, a residual mass of unused cytoplasm being left behind. The young forms grew and became transformed into adults. In *Amœba proteus* spores are formed without encystment.

Syngamy has not yet been proved to occur in *Amœba proteus*. The animal does, however, occa-

Multinucleate Amœbæ. sionally undergo a process known as *plastogamy*, in which the cytoplasm of several individuals fuses, forming a single mass which contains several nuclei. Such a mass is known as a *plasmodium*. Quite another kind of multinucleate body is found in certain species of *Amœbæ* and in the *Amœba*-like animals known as *Pelomyxa*, where two or more nuclei are formed by the division of a single nucleus. These may be compared with cœnocytes.[2]

We have studied *Amœba* as an example of extreme

Amœba and its Surroundings. simplicity in organisation. That is not to say that it is primitive in the sense in which that term is used by zoologists ; it is quite unlikely that this creature is a survivor from among the earliest living beings. Indeed it is more probable that if we could trace back the descent of the *Amœbæ* we should come to ancestors not unlike the organisms

---

[1] Binary fission takes about an hour.
[2] Groups of similar, unseparated energids are known as *syncytia*. They may be *plasmodia*, formed by the union of free energids, or *symplasts*, formed by the division of the nucleus of a single energid. A symplast may be a *cœnocyte*, or the whole body of an organism.

which will be described in the next chapter. But *Amœba* does contrive to carry on its life with less apparatus than almost any other creature, possessing as it does no obvious permanent organs except the cytoplasm, nucleus, and contractile vacuole and besides these only the temporary organs known as plasmalemma, plasmasol, plasmagel, and pseudopodia. Certain reflections arise from this fact. To begin with, if *Amœba* can live successfully with such a simple organisation, why should there be organisms such as the frog—or man—which use an outfit so much more complicated ? The answer is, of course, that *Amœba* occupies but a narrow niche in its environment. The world offers many possibilities of which it fails to take advantage. The life of the frog is a much greater achievement. Life, as we have seen, consists in the making of adjustments in the living being which enable it to survive and prosper amid the vicissitudes of its environment. The smaller the range of adjustments it can make the smaller will be the range of variation in its surroundings which it can survive—the more limited will be its existence. The capacity of the frog for adjustment to its surroundings is enormously greater than that of *Amœba*. It can live out of water, can feed on relatively large and active organisms, can readily perceive enemies and swiftly and skilfully evade them, can find a mate and carry out a form of reproduction which ensures variety in its offspring. There is no need to show how much more command over the forces of nature man has than the frog. The degree of complexity of organisation in any organism is the degree of variety in circumstances to which it can adjust itself— the degree of mastery that it has over the environment. Higher and lower organisms exist side by side. This is because they are not in competition. The higher organisms avail themselves of circumstances (such as food and facilities for respiration) which are beyond the powers of the lower. When two organisms are indeed in competition the better equipped will oust the other. This, as we shall see when we come to study evolution, has very important consequences in moulding the organic population of the globe.

Nevertheless our survey of the life and structure of *Amœba* has shown us that it must be regarded as an organism in no way inferior to the frog in its fundamental powers. It is irritable and automatic, undergoes katabolism, contracts, conducts, does chemical work, secretes and excretes, respires, incorporates food, and reproduces.

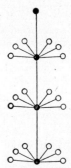

In many points of structure and behaviour *Amœba* resembles closely the white corpuscles of the frog and more distantly the other cells of the frog's body. It is, in short, like them a self-contained mass of protoplasm with a nucleus—an isolated energid. For this reason it has been usual to regard it as a cell, and to call it a *unicellular organism*, and a view is widely held, on which the body of such an animal as the frog is said to be a colony of units, each comparable to a single *Amœba*, specialised for co-operation with the other cells of the body. A nerve cell, for instance, has the function of conduction highly developed but has lost those of secretion and contraction. But the facts may be interpreted in another manner. *Amœba* is a complete and independent organism comparable with the whole body of the frog. Its small size enables all the functions which the nucleoplasm performs to be carried out by a single nucleus. In the frog the size of the body makes necessary a large number of sep-

FIG. 93. — A diagram of the relation of germ and body substance in the frog. The dark circles represent germs, the light circles body cells. The germ gives rise in each generation to numerous body cells which remain together and eventually die, and also to germs (of which only one is shown in each generation). The germs leave the body and give rise each to a new group of body cells and new germs Thus the germ substance is immortal, the body substance mortal.

arate nuclei, and around each of these a part of the cytoplasm is more or less clearly segregated so that an energid (p. 109) is isolated. Such an energid isolated within the body is called a cell. Now the energids which

Is Amœba a Cell?

are thus isolated as cells have not all the properties possessed by the body as a whole, but they have special qualities according to the functions of the part of the body in which they lie. On this interpretation a cell is a portion of the body of a whole organism which is specialised for the performance of particular functions rather than a whole organism which co-operates with other such organisms to form a body of a higher grade. *Amœba* is not a cell, but an organism which is not divided into cells (non-cellular). It is this view of *Amœba* that we shall adopt.

The difference between *Amœba* and the frog may be stated in another way. Viewed broadly, the formation of a germ by the frog is a separation of the body into two portions, one small—the germ—and another large, in which the individuality of the parent is continued. The parent consists mainly of energids which are specialised or differentiated, as nerve cells, gland cells, muscle cells, and so forth, for the performance of certain functions in the body, and are correspondingly unable to produce energids of other kinds. The germ is an energid which is not thus specialised, though of course it has an organisation of its own. Now the energids of the parent body are mortal : that is to say, sooner or later they undergo natural death. But the germ is in a sense immortal : that is to say, unless it be devoured, or starved, or poisoned, or fail to find a mate, or meet with some other fatality, it will not die a natural death, but in giving rise to a new adult organism gives rise also to another generation of germs, in which it continues its existence within the adult organism until the latter in turn sets free germs. The difference between *Amœba* and animals like it on the one hand, and higher animals like the frog on the other, lies in the fact that in the former there are no body-cells, but the whole body has the immortality of a germ. The fission of *Amœba* is a separation of the body into two similar products, neither of which can be said, in virtue either of size or of mortality, to represent the parent. There are two offspring, but the parent has disappeared.

Immortality of Amœba.

In a later chapter (p. 179) there will be found descriptions of organisms known as *Entamœbœ*, closely related to *Amœba*, which are parasitic within the body of man.

CHAPTER VII

FLAGELLATA

Water in which organic matter is decaying always contains numerous small organisms of various kinds. **Polytoma.** Among these, when decomposition is well advanced, there can be found with the aid of the microscope minute, colourless organisms of a species known as *Polytoma uvella*, which feed by absorbing from the water through the surface of their bodies substances in solution derived from the decaying matter. The body of a *Polytoma* is an egg-shaped mass of protoplasm without any internal skeleton. A pair of long protoplasmic lashes or *flagella* project from one end; by a backward lashing of these it swims with a somewhat jerky course, the end at which the flagella are placed being forward (Fig. 95, A, B). The permanent shape of the body is due to a thin *cuticle*; that is, not to a surface layer of the protoplasm, but to a protective covering formed by secretion. It is pierced by two pores for the flagella. Two contractile vacuoles lie close behind the flagella and contract alternately. There is one nucleus, placed somewhat behind the middle, and there is sometimes a spot of red pigment situated in the front part of the body. The hinder region contains numerous *starch granules*. These must be formed by the protoplasm from substances absorbed in the food : they serve as a reserve of nutriment, and are used up during starvation. Their presence is interesting, for starch, though it is common in plants, is rare in the protoplasm of animals, which, if they store carbohydrates, usually do so in the form of glycogen. Together with the spot of red pigment—which is an organ that enables small, motile, green plants to find the sunlight which is necessary to their mode of nutrition (p. 25)—the starch granules betray the fact that *Polytoma*, though it has lost its chlorophyll, is at least as much a plant as an animal. It is, in fact, a colourless *Chlamydomonas* (p. 28). *Polytoma* can encyst, and in the encysted state is carried about in dust, etc., to germinate in favourable circumstances elsewhere.

Reproduction is usually brought about by a process known **Reproduction.** as *repeated fission*, in which binary fission is repeated so as to form four daughters before the young separate, but sometimes there are only two offspring. Fission takes place within the cuticle, this being carried about during the process by the action of the flagella, which remain attached to one of the daughters. The nucleus divides by a kind of mitosis. The first division is nearly transverse, the second at right angles to it. The flagella are then withdrawn, each daughter forms two small flagella, and the cuticle of the parent is dissolved.

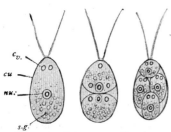

FIG. 94. —*Polytoma uvella:* three stages in ordinary fission.

c.v., Contractile vacuole ; *cu.*, cuticle ; *nu.*, nucleus ; *s.g.*, starch grains.

At intervals of a few days syngamy takes place. Two ordinary individuals come together and fuse, their nuclei joining and their cytoplasm melting into one mass, which then encysts. After a resting period the zygote divides by repeated fission into eight, each of the daughters grows two flagella, and the cyst is dissolved. In regard to this process we must notice (1) that syngamy can occur at any time in the life of the individual, and does not take place between special germs which cannot develop without it : in the frog, on the other hand, syngamy is obviously impossible in the adult and can only take place between the little germs, before they develop the rest of the body ; (2) that the gametes are alike, and not, as in the frog, of two kinds, a passive kind, which bears the bulk of the cytoplasm, and an active kind, by which is carried out the locomotion which the process involves. Both gametes in *Polytoma* are fairly well supplied with cytoplasm and both are motile. Only when one is

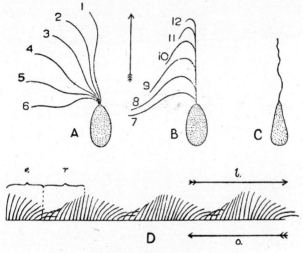

Fig. 95.—Movements of Flagella and Cilia.

A. The effective stroke in a flagellate which is swimming by lashing the water.

B. The recovery stroke by which the flagellum returns to its former posture. Note that the flagellum is stiff during the effective stroke and limp during the recovery, so that in the latter it is bent and does less work. The arrow shows the direction in which the creature moves. For simplicity the beat is represented as taking place in one plane : actually it is usually spiral ; by such a beat a single flagellum can draw the organism forwards with a spin.

C. A flagellate drawing itself forward by undulation of its flagellum. Waves pass from tip to base of the flagellum, and their backward pressure on the water moves the organism forwards, as in the swimming of a fish (see p. 423).

D. A row of cilia contracting successively (in *metachronal rhythm*). *e.*, Effective stroke ; *r.*, recovery ; *l.*, direction in which liquid overlying an epithelium is moved ; *o.*, direction in which an organism is moved, by a covering of cilia. Like the flagellum in A and B, the cilia are more flexible in the recovery than in the effective stroke. The effective stroke is also usually the more rapid of the two.

older than the other is there sometimes a difference in size.

In *Chlamydomonas* (Fig. 10) syngamy takes place, not, as might seem possible, between ordinary individuals, but between special small forms which arise by repeated fission of the ordinary forms. These special gametes,

Varieties of Syngamy. however, are like the ordinary individuals in all but size. In some species of *Chlamydomonas* they are themselves of two sizes, which conjugate large with small, so that,

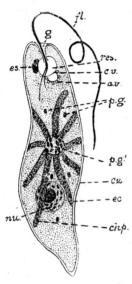

as sometimes in *Polytoma*, there is a difference in size, though not in any other respect, between the gametes. The syngamy of two like gametes, whether they be ordinary or special individuals, is known as *isogamy* ; syngamy of unlike gametes is *anisogamy* ; if, as in the frog, they differ not only in size but also in that the larger is passive and the smaller active, the process is known as *oogamy*.

Euglena viridis, often so common in puddles as to give them a green colour, is a flagellate organism of a rather higher grade than *Chlamydomonas* or *Polytoma*. It is a minute, spindle-shaped creature, which may reach a length of $\frac{1}{6}$ mm. The front end is blunt and bears one flagellum rooted at the base of a funnel-shaped pit, which is known as the "gullet" but probably never used as such. There is a strong pellicle, a distinct ectosarc, and a central, spherical nucleus. Band-shaped, green *chloro-*

Euglena.

Fig. 96.—*Euglena viridis*, highly magnified.

av., Accessory contractile vacuoles ; *cv.*, main contractile vacuole ; *chp.*, one of the chloroplasts ; *cu.*, pellicle ; *e.s.*, eye-spot ; *ec.*, ectoplasm ; *fl.*, flagellum ; *g.*, gullet ; *nu.*, nucleus ; *p.g.*, paramylum granules ; *p.g.'*, protoplasmic mass, with paramylum granules, from which chloroplasts radiate ; *res.*, reservoir.

plasts (p. 24) radiate from a point in front of the nucleus, where granules of the starch-like substance *paramylum* accumulate. Waves of contraction pass along the body (Fig. 97), but contractile strands (myonemes, p. 157)

are lacking. The vacuole system is complicated, consisting of a reservoir opening into the gullet, a contractile
vacuole which discharges at intervals into the reservoir,
and a number of accessory vacuoles which surround
the main vacuole and re-form it. A red pigment spot
or *stigma* lies against the front side of the reservoir and
enables the working of the flagellum to be regulated
by the amount of light in the surroundings. Reproduction is by binary fission, beginning at the front end,
the nucleus undergoing a peculiar mitosis. It may take
place in free individuals after the loss of the flagellum,
or in a gelatinous cyst, within which it may be repeated
several times. The occurrence of syngamy is extremely
doubtful. The nutrition of *Euglena* is normally that of

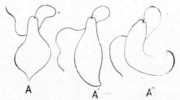

FIG. 97. —*Euglena viridis*,
A, A′, A″, Three positions of the body.

a plant, though it is better if the water contain a little
nitrogenous organic matter. If the solution be rich in
such matter, certain species (but not *E. viridis*) can, and
if light fails them do, nourish themselves entirely from it.
In darkness the chloroplasts of these species grow pale
and shrink.

Copromonas (or *Scytomonas*, Fig. 4) is a flagellate which

Copromonas. lives in the moisture of dung. It is related to
Euglena but colourless, as *Polytoma* is a
colourless *Chlamydomonas*. It nourishes itself, however,
not as *Polytoma* does by absorbing through its surface
the products of decomposition amid which it lives, but
by swallowing through its gullet the bacteria which live
in the same solution. Its syngamy is performed solely by
fully-grown ordinary individuals. Usually the syngamy
takes place when the dung is becoming uninhabitable for

the *Copromonas*, and the zygote becomes encysted. From this condition it only emerges in fresh dung, to reach which it must be swallowed in contaminated food by a frog, and passed intact with the fæces.

Peranema, common in stagnant water, is another colour-less relation of *Euglena*. It is larger than *Copromonas*, pear-shaped at rest but very active in changing its shape, has one flagellum, rooted in a reservoir which opens in front of the gullet, and feeds by swallowing smaller organisms into the gullet, the wall of which is strengthened by stiff rods. Probably *Peranema* is also saprophytic (see below).

Peranema.

The organisms which we have been discussing in this chapter exhibit all the three types of nutrition practised by animals and plants. In *Chlamy-domonas* simple inorganic substances are absorbed through the surface, and from them complex substances are manufactured by means of the energy of the sun's rays. Such organisms are said to be *holophytic*. In *Copromonas* and *Peranema* complex organic substances are taken in through a mouth, after the manner of animals. Such organisms are said to be *holozoic*. In *Polytoma*, organic substances are absorbed in solution through the surface of the body. Such organisms are said to be *sapro-phytic*. The substances which form the food of various saprophytic organisms differs a great deal. In *Polytoma* they are relatively simple (amino-acids, acetates, etc.). *Euglena*, which is both holophytic and saprophytic, prefers for its saprophytism more complex compounds. Many parasites in the alimentary canals of animals nourish themselves saprophytically on the digested food of their holozoic hosts.

Modes of Nutrition.

In later chapters (pp. 183, 200), there will be found descriptions of the organisms known as *Trypanosoma* and the *Choanoflagellata*, which resemble those described in this chapter in the possession of flagella and in certain other respects, and with them are classed by zoologists as *Flagellata* or *Mastigophora*. The green flagellates are, as we have seen, closely related to plants, and it is natural that botanists claim the Flagellata as members of the Plant Kingdom.

Flagellata.

CHAPTER VIII

MONOCYSTIS

AMONG the organs of reproduction of an earthworm are
certain sacs, known as the vesiculæ seminales,
General Features. in which the sperm ripens. Here are generally
to be found specimens of the parasites known
as *Monocystis*, which live by absorbing, through the surface
of their body, the fluid in the vesiculæ which is provided
for the nourishment of the spermatozoa. Two kinds of
these creatures may be present, differing in size and in
certain other particulars. The larger kind, *M. magna*, is
easily visible to the naked eye as white threads, hanging by
one end from the funnels of the vasa deferentia (see p. 252).
The smaller, known as *M. lumbrici*, is more often found free
in the fluid among the developing spermatozoa. The body
of a full-grown *Monocystis* is long and narrow, and consists
of a soft, granular endoplasm and a firm, clear ectoplasm.
The endoplasm contains numerous granules, many of which
consist of the carbohydrate substance *paraglycogen*, and the
ectoplasm is covered with a stout cuticle and has in its
deeper layer a network of contractile threads, the *myonemes*.
While the cuticle makes it impossible for the protoplasm to
flow out into pseudopodia, the myonemes enable it to
change its shape by squeezing the fluid endoplasm from one
part of the body to another. Slow waves of contraction of
this kind are constantly passing along the body. In the
endoplasm there is a large nucleus, but there is no contractile vacuole. At one end of the body an indefinite
knob enables it to adhere to one of the cells of the
funnel.

In the stage which we have just described, the animals

are known as *trophozoites*. When they are full grown,

Reproduction. two of them come together and form themselves into a rounded mass without fusing. Around this mass a double cyst is secreted. Each individual now divides by multiple fission, in which the mitosis resembles that of the frog in that the centrosome appears outside the nucleus and the nuclear membrane disappears. There arise thus, as in the spore formation of *Amœba*, a number of small germs, a certain amount of residual protoplasm being left, which is absorbed by the germs during their development. The germs unite in pairs, in which one member is derived from each parent. Thus, although the parents are to all appearance exactly alike, there happens here what happens also in the frog, where the parents are unlike, namely, that the gametes are derived from distinct parents. This is known as *cross-fertilisation*, and is found in the vast majority of cases throughout the animal kingdom, though instances do occur of what is known as *self-fertilisation*, in which gametes derived from the same parent unite.

It is said that in *M. magna* the germs from the two parents are alike, but in *M. lumbrici* those of one parent—the " female "—are rounded, and those of the other—the " male "—pear-shaped. Each zygote is known as a *sporont*; it now secretes a boat-shaped, horny case, and is known as a *pseudonavicella*. Within the case it divides by

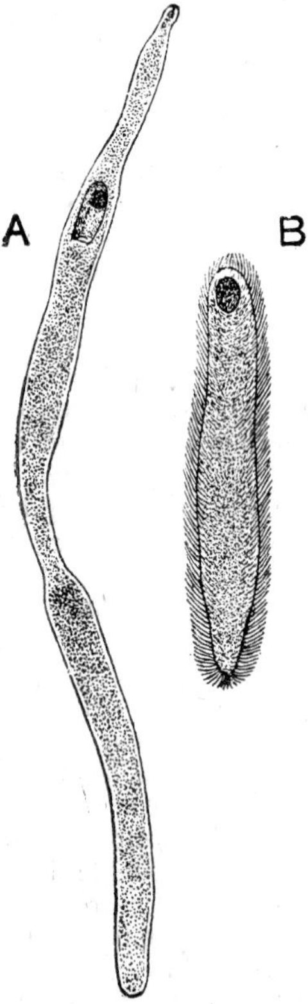

Fig. 98. — *Monocystis.*

A, *M. magna*; B, *M. lumbrici*. The latter is covered with the tails of spermatozoa, the offspring of the sperm mother cell in which it was embedded.

repeated fission into eight sickle-shaped *sporozoites*. There
are thus two generations of spores[1] in the life-history

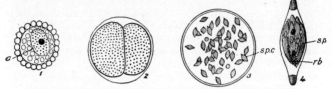

FIG 99. — The life-history of *Monocystis*. — After Bütschli.

1. Young individual (*c*) lying within a sperm mother cell of an earthworm.
2. Association of two individuals within a cyst, ready to form gametes.
3. Numerous spore-cases (*sp.c.*, pseudonavicellæ) within a cyst.
4. A spore-case with eight spores (*sp.*) and a residual core (*rb.*).

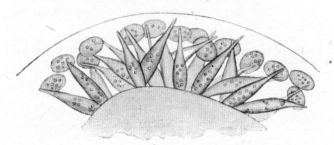

FIG. 100.—Part of a cyst of *Monocystis lumbrici* showing the two kinds
of gametes and the residual protoplasm of one of the parents.—
After Hoffmann.

of *Monocystis*. No further development takes place
until the pseudonavicellæ get free from the worm, which
they generally do by the destruction of the latter.[2]
Probably this takes place by its being eaten by a bird.

[1] A spore is a small reproductive body formed by multiple or repeated fission. It may or may not be a gamete. If it be enclosed
in a case it is known as a *chlamydospore* (*e.g.* pseudonavicellæ),
if it be naked, as a *gymnospore* (*e.g.* spores of the *Amœba* shown in
Fig. 92). Amœboid spores are known as *amœbulæ* or *pseudopodio-
spores*, flagellate spores as *flagellulæ* or *flagellispores*.

[2] The details of the transference of the spores of *Monocystis* are very
imperfectly known. It is said that occasionally they pass from one
worm to another during coition, but this is believed not to be the
usual method, if indeed it be effective at all.

Protected by their horny cases, the sporozoites pass through the gut of the bird and are distributed in its droppings over the soil, where they are washed down by the rain and presently swallowed by another worm with the earth from which it obtains its food. The spore-cyst is dissolved in the intestine of the worm, and the sporozoites come out and bore their way through the wall of the gut and other tissues till they reach the vesiculæ seminales. Here each enters a sperm-mother-cell, where it grows by absorbing the protoplasm which is meant to serve for the nourishment of the spermatozoa (see p. 273). The latter are formed, but wither, their tails only remaining attached to the young *Monocystis*, which looks as though it had a coat of cilia. Finally they disappear, while the *Monocystis* continues to grow. Thus the sporozoites become trophozoites by development.

In a later chapter (p. 188) there will be found descriptions of animals related to *Monocystis* which are parasitic in the body of man, where they are the cause of malarial fevers.

CHAPTER IX

PARAMECIUM AND VORTICELLA. PROTOZOA

PARAMECIUM CAUDATUM, the Slipper Animalcule, is a minute animal found in water in which dead leaves or other remains of organisms are decaying. The decay is brought about by bacteria, and upon these the slipper animalcules feed. A rich culture of *Paramecium* may be obtained by steeping hay in water, allowing it to decay, and adding to the *infusion* thus made mud or weeds from a freshwater pond which contains *Paramecium*. The animals may easily be seen with the naked eye as minute, greyish white, oblong creatures, shooting swiftly about in the water. The body of *Paramecium* is spindle-shaped, somewhat flattened on one side, and with one end blunter than the other. The flat side is called "ventral" and the blunt end is anterior. This end appears as though it had been twisted, so that a groove which it bears is spiral, starting in front on the left and curving round to the ventral side, where it is continued back in the middle line to within about a third of the length of the body from its hinder end. The groove is known as the *peristome* : from its hinder end there passes backwards into the body a funnel-shaped *gullet* or *vestibule*, the opening from vestibule to endoplasm being known as the mouth The whole body is covered with fine protoplasmic threads of the kind known as cilia (see p. 109) by whose lashing the animal swims and gathers its food. The cilia are set at equal distances in rows, which run lengthwise in the hinder part of the body, but follow the spiral twist in front : they also line the gullet, where two or three rows of them are fused to form an *undulating membrane* which hangs from the roof. The cilia work regularly in waves, lashing backwards (Fig. 95, D) and driving the blunt end of the animal forwards, with a rotating movement like that of a rifle bullet owing to its spiral shape. The animal can encyst.

Paramecium, like *Amœba*, *Polytoma*, and *Monocystis*, is not divided into cells. It has a soft, gran-
Ectoplasm and Endoplasm. ular endoplasm and an ectoplasm which is firm and gives the body its shape, but elastic, so that the animal can bend and squeeze through narrow gaps. The outermost layer of the ectoplasm is

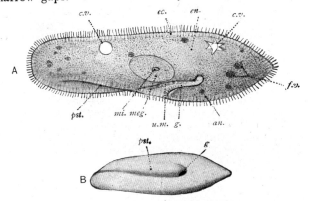

FIG. 101.—*Paramecium caudatum.*

A, An individual seen from the left side, highly magnified ; *B,* a diagrammatic view of an individual from the ventral side, less highly magnified.

an., Position of temporary anus ; *c.v.,* contractile vacuole ; *ec.,* ectoplasm with trichocysts ; *f.v.,* food vacuoles ; *g.,* gullet ; *meg.,* meganucleus ; *mi.,* micronucleus ; *pst.,* peristome ; *u.m.,* undulating membrane.

a tough *pellicle*. Below the pellicle comes the *cortex*, a thicker, clear layer of ectoplasm in which are embeddied peculiar structures known as *trichocysts*. These are spindle-shaped bodies with a fine point, and consist of some semi-liquid substance. They are placed at right angles to the surface, with the point in the outer part of the layer. If the animal be stimulated by impact or by a solution of some irritating substance, they suddenly elongate and project from the body as threads, of which the points are sticky while the rest has hardened. The trichocysts are organs of adhesion by which the animal anchors. When it breaks free the threads are lost and the trichocysts replenished. The pellicle is marked by rows of rectangular or hexagonal pits, in each of which a pair of cilia arise, while the trichocysts lie under the transverse ridges between the pits. Each cilium consists of an axial thread and a covering layer continuous with the pellicle. The axial thread stops short of the tip of the cilium, which is pointed. Below the cilium the thread is continued inwards into the cortex, within which it bears a swelling known as the *basal granule*. The basal granules are united by a system of threads known as *neuronemes* which are possibly conductile. The endoplasm contains numerous granules, some of which appear to consist of waste matters ready for excretion, while others may be stored nutriment. Glycogen is diffused through the endoplasm.

Paramecium caudatum has two

Nuclei. nuclei. These, however, are not both of the same kind, like the nuclei of a *Pelomyxa* (p. 147), but consist of portions of the nucleoplasm specialised for different purposes. One is large and is concerned with the ordinary life of the body. This is known as the *meganucleus*. The other is small and is specialised for the purpose of conjugation. This is the *micronucleus*.[1] We may roughly compare the meganucleus with the nuclei of the body-cells of the frog and the micronucleus with the nuclei of the germs. The nuclei lie in the endoplasm

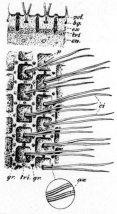

FIG. 102.—A portion of the surface of *Paramecium*, very highly magnified.

Above, a portion of the surface in vertical section. Below, portions of two cilia enlarged, to show axial filaments.

ax, Axial filament ; *b.g.*, basal granule of a cilium ; *ci.*, cilium ; *cx*, cortex ; *en.*, endoplasm ; *gr.*, granules at angles of meshes ; *p.*, pit in the sculpture of the pellicle ; *pel.*, pellicle ; *tri.*, trichocysts.

[1] The species known as *Paramecium aurelia* has two micronuclei.

above the gullet, the micronucleus in a cleft in the side of the meganucleus.

There are two *contractile vacuoles*, which lie in the cortex of the dorsal side, one towards each end. At **Excretion.** its full size each is a large spherical space surrounded by from six to ten pear-shaped radiating canals, whose wide ends lie under it. These are the *formative vacuoles*. Contraction or " systole " affects only the central vacuole. After it has taken place, the formative vacuoles flow together at their inner ends and thus form the

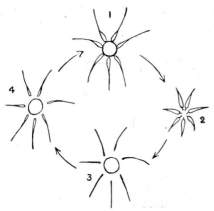

FIG. 103.—Successive stages of the contractile vacuole of *Paramecium*.

beginning of a new contractile vacuole, round which new canals appear, starting as mere slits and swelling to a pear shape by the enlargement of their inner ends. Over each contractile vacuole there is a minute gap in the pellicle, through which the contents of the vacuole are discharged. It is stated that the supposed excretory granules of the endoplasm collect near the formative vacuoles and are gradually dissolved. If so, it may be that they are removed by the vacuoles. In any case these have the same water-regulatory function as those of *Amœba*. Urea is said to accumulate in cultures of *Paramecium*. Possibly it has been excreted by the general surface of the body.

The food consists of bacteria and other minute organisms. These are drawn towards the mouth **Nutrition.** by the current set up by the cilia of the peristome and driven down the gullet by the working of the undulating membrane, which has a waving motion. The pressure of the water driven into the gullet with the food particles causes the naked endoplasm at the bottom of the gullet to bulge inwards, and into the space thus formed the food is forced. A drop of water containing the food particles is now pinched off by a contraction of the endoplasm and becomes a food vacuole, which is carried by a streaming of the endoplasm around the body, passing first backward along the ventral side, then forward nearly to the middle of the body, then through several turns of a short circuit in this region of the body, and finally forward to the front end and back so as to complete the circuit of the body. During these wanderings the food is digested. The undigested remains are then expelled at a spot just behind the end of the gullet, where a passage through the ectoplasm, known as the *temporary anus*, is formed when it is required. Two periods may be recognised in the digestion. In the first period the water taken in with the food is being absorbed.

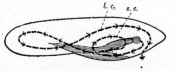

Fig. 104.—A diagram of the course of the circulation of the food vacuoles in *Paramecium*.

l.c., Long circuit; *s.c.*, short circuit.

Substances are secreted into the vacuole during this period which give it an acid reaction and kill the prey. In the second period an alkaline digestive juice is secreted into the vacuole, which increases in size. It appears that *Paramecium* cannot digest fat.

Like all other organisms, *Paramecium* has automatism (p. 8). Its incessant activity is spontaneous so far as immediate external stimuli are concerned, but is continually modified by such stimuli. The movements of *Paramecium* are much more active and definite than those of *Amœba*, and it is correspondingly easier to observe the effect of various stimuli upon the animal. These effects are of two kinds, upon the *rate* of movement and upon its *direction*. (1) Many acids, alkalies, salts, and other substances in dilute solutions cause an increase in the rate of motion owing to a more

Effect of Stimuli.

rapid working of the cilia. Moderate increase of temperature has the same effect. On the other hand, dilute
solutions of narcotics, such as alcohol, ether, or chloroform,
cause the cilia to work more slowly. All these reactions
are probably merely the direct effects which such stimuli
are known to have upon protoplasm. (2) In order that the
effect of stimuli upon the direction of movement may be
observed, it is of course necessary that the stimulus should
fall unequally upon different sides of the animal. It will
then move to or from the direction in which the stimulus
is strongest. This can be arranged by placing with a fine
pipette a small drop of some solution in the vessel in
which the animals are confined, or by heating or lighting
one side only of the vessel. *Paramecium* will move
towards weak acids or moderate warmth and away from
alkalies, strong acids, warmth above 25° C., etc. Such
movement is known as *taxis*. It was believed that it
could be explained in a simple way by the supposition
that the effect of the stimulus in each case was either
to slow or to quicken the working of the cilia on the side
nearest to it, so that the animal was driven mechanically
either towards or away from the stimulus by the unequal
working of its cilia. What really happens, however, is by
no means so simple. The effect of all stimuli to which
Paramecium reacts naturally is to repel it. The animal on
receiving a stimulus first withdraws, by a definite backward
movement due to a reversal of the working of its cilia, from
the stimulus. It then turns towards the dorsal side and
swings the front end of its body round in a circle with that
side outwards so that it comes to point in a new direction,
and in that direction it swims forwards unless it again
meets the stimulus. Thus its approach to conditions which
appear to attract it is in reality due to an avoidance of the
relatively less agreeable conditions which it meets in other
directions during automatic wanderings. It behaves as if
it were " trying " different directions of movement till one
is found from which it is not repelled. It is claimed that
this procedure, known as the *method of trial and error*,
can be discerned in the behaviour of all animals, from
Amœba (see p. 144) upwards.

Paramecium reproduces by binary transverse fission.

The meganucleus divides amitotically, the micronucleus
Reproduction. by a mitosis in which, as in that of *Amœba*, the
nuclear membrane does not break up, and
the place of centrosomes is taken by pole plates. Meanwhile a groove appears round the middle of the body and
deepens till the cytoplasm is sundered into two, each half
containing a daughter nucleus of each kind and one of

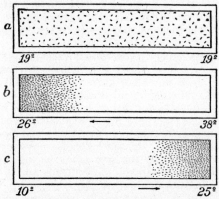

FIG. 105.—The reaction of *Paramecium* to heat
and cold.—From Jennings, after Mendelssohn.

At *a.*, the *Paramecia* are placed in a trough both ends of which
have a temperature of 19° C. They are equally scattered.
At *b.*, the temperature of one end of the trough is raised
to 38° C., while the other is only 26° C. The *Paramecia*
collect at the end which has the lower temperature. At
c., one end has a temperature of 25° C., while the other is
lowered to 10° C. The animalcules now collect at the end
which has the higher temperature.

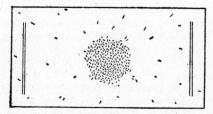

FIG. 106.—*Paramecia* collecting in a drop of $\frac{1}{50}$ per cent
acetic acid.—From Jennings.

the contractile vacuoles. The two bodies formed by this fission are like those of *Amœba*, asexually produced young, analogous to the buds of certain higher animals of which we shall speak in a later chapter (p. 221). Their development involves not only growth but also the re-modelling of the body, since each of them lacks half the outward organs of the parent, while those which it has are too large for it. In a well-fed culture, division takes place two or three times a day, but if the animals be ill-nourished it is much less frequent, and if they be starved they cease to divide.

The conjugation of *Paramecium* is a remarkable process, **Conjugation.** of a kind found only in this creature and in those which nearly resemble it. In it gametes are formed and become rid of the body nuclei of their parents, without being set free as they are from the cellular body of the frog. The individuals which form the gametes are exactly alike and resemble normal individuals, except that they are somewhat smaller. As a rule, the process begins during the late hours of the night and lasts till the next afternoon. The details are as follows : Two individuals, which we will call *conjugants*,[1] come to-gether as those of *Monocystis* do, but without encysting, and lie with their ventral sides touching, the endoplasms becoming continuous in the region of the gullets, which de-generate. We may compare this with coition. The micro-nucleus of each conjugant leaves its normal position, lies free in the cytoplasm, and grows larger. It then divides twice, and three of its four products degenerate. During these divisions the number of chromosomes is halved, as it is in the gametogenesis of the frog (p. 131), though the details of the process differ in the two cases. The remain-ing micronucleus divides again, this time somewhat unequally, the smaller product being the *male pronucleus*, the larger the *female pronucleus*. At this stage we may regard each conjugant as containing two gametes, repre-sented by the two pronuclei. These are analogous to an ovum and a spermatozoon, so that the animal may be said to be hermaphrodite. The true syngamy now takes

[1] They are often alluded to as gametes. This is incorrect. They are not gametes, but parents which form gametes.

place. The male pronucleus of each conjugant passes over into the other and fuses with the female pronucleus of the latter. The body which belonged to each conjugant comes thus to contain a micronucleus of mixed origin. It is, in fact, a zygote. The zygotes separate and are known as *exconjugants*. During conjugation the meganucleus degenerates, splitting up into shreds,

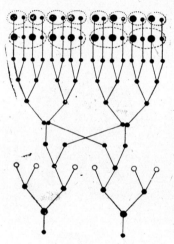

which disappear. Thus the meganucleus resembles in the fact of its mortality the body-cells of the frog, though the body as a whole has the immortality of a germ-cell or an *Amœba*. After separation the joint micronucleus of the exconjugant undergoes a development whereby nuclei of both kinds are provided. It divides three times successively, so that the body contains eight nuclei. After an interval the body divides into two, each half containing four nuclei, and after a further interval these halves divide, so that there are four individuals, each with two nuclei, one

FIG. 107.—A diagram of the behaviour of the micronuclei during the conjugation of *Paramecium caudatum*. The white circles represent the portions which degenerate.

See also Fig. 108, *A*.

of which becomes a meganucleus and the other a micronucleus.

The conditions under which conjugation takes place in *Paramecium* have been, and are still, the subject of much investigation. Many points still remain to be cleared up, but certain results have now been reached. Conjugation generally occurs at the beginning of a falling off in the supply of food after a period of exceptional plenty that has brought about rapid multiplication. Thus it will often take

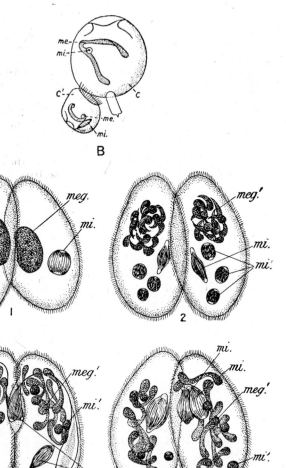

Fig. 108.—Conjugation in Ciliata.

A, Paramecium; B, Vorticella.

c., Pseudo-female conjugant; *c′.,* pseudo-male; *me., me₂.,* meganuclei; *meg′.,* disintegrating fragments of meganucleus; *mi.,* micronuclei; *mi′.,* abortive micronuclei.

place in an infusion in which the bacteria, having used up the nourishment provided by the plant-remains, are falling off in numbers, and thus the *Paramecia*, after a plentiful supply of food, are beginning to experience dearth. But there are some races in which it is difficult to bring about conjugation, others in which it has never been seen, and yet others in which it takes place at short intervals without apparent cause.[1]

In a stock or "culture" of *Paramecium* kept in the **Depression.** laboratory, it often happens that after a time all the members pass into a state of "depression," in which they have an overgrown meganucleus and a

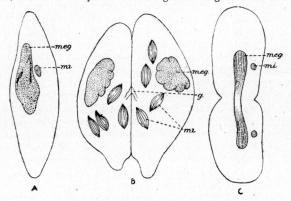

Fig. 109.—Semidiagrammatic views of individuals of *Paramecium caudatum*.

A, In depression; *B*, in conjugation; *C*, in fission.
g., Gullet; *meg*., meganucleus; *mi*., micronucleus.

stunted body, divide more slowly, and show an increasing degeneration in various organs and functions of the body. At last they are unable to digest food and die. Depression is an abnormal event, produced by unnatural conditions of culture. In its earlier stages the animals can be stimulated in such a way as to endow them with a new

---

[1] It has been said that descendants of the same exconjugant will not conjugate, and that individuals from another stock must be introduced, but this has been disproved.

lease of life. This is said to happen if conjugation occur. It can be effected by shaking the culture, or better by a change of diet, as by feeding with beef-tea. After a time the stock can be put back to a diet of hay bacteria and kept till there sets in a deeper depression, which is capable of being averted in the same way. By one means and another (after a while beef-tea failed, and brain and pancreas extracts had to be used) the life of such a culture has been kept up for two years, but the effect of unnatural conditions was in the long run too strong, the recurring periods of depression became more and more severe, and at last the whole brood died. Depression has been re-garded as the old age of the stock, and the alleged averting of it by conjugation has been compared with the renewal of the lease of life in the young of multi-cellular animals produced from a fertilised ovum. Actu-ally depression is a disorder brought on by unnatural conditions of culture, but it is true that even in the best conditions the vitality of a stock of a ciliate protozoon, as estimated from its rate of division, periodically wanes and is restored, and that its restoration coincides either with conjugation or with the occurrence in solitary individuals of an internal process known as *endomixis* which resembles conjugation but does not involve syn-gamy. Both these processes renew the meganucleus, and it is probable that their effect is due to this, just as, in multicellular animals, the renewed vitality of the young is due to the nuclei and cytoplasm in their bodies being newly formed.

Among the most beautiful forms of pond life are the bell-animalcules, of which the scientific name **Vorticella :** is *Vorticella*. Various species of these creatures **General** **Features.** may be found as minute, colourless bodies fastened to weeds by stalks which contract at the slightest disturbance of the water. Some of them also appear in infusions. The body of a *Vorticella* is outwardly shaped like a bell, but has no hollow within, the bell being filled with a mass of protoplasm. In the place of the handle is a long stalk, by which the animal is fastened to some solid object. Animals which are thus fixed are said to be *sessile*. The bell can be bent upon the stalk. The wide end of the bell has a thickened *rim*, within which is a groove, the *peristome*. On one side there passes from the peristome, down into the mass that fills the bell, a tube which is the *gullet*. The first part of this is wider than the rest, and the name vestibule is sometimes restricted to it. The part of the upper surface which is encircled by the peristome is known as the *disc*. It

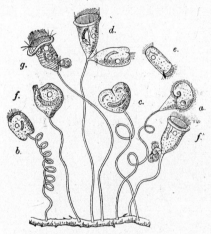

FIG. 110.—A group of individuals of *Vorticella* in various phases of the life-history.

a., Ordinary individual; *b.*, the same contracted; *c.*, ordinary fission; *d.*, a later stage of the same; *e.*, free-swimming individual produced by ordinary fission; *f.*, *f'.*, two modes of fission to form a conjugant; *g.*, conjugation.

is not level, but slopes, being raised on the side where the gullet lies. The disc can be retracted, and the rim of the peristome drawn inward over it. Around the edge of the disc and down into the vestibule two rows of cilia wind spirally counter clockwise, the inner long and upright, the outer short and slanting outwards. In the vestibule the members of the outer row are fused to form an undulating membrane. There are no cilia elsewhere upon the body.

The general character of the ectoplasm and endoplasm is the same in *Vorticella* as in *Paramecium*, but **Ectoplasm and Endoplasm.** the pellicle of the bell-animalcule is sculptured in various ways according to the species, and below it is a distinct alveolar layer. Just under the alveolar layer, in the walls of its bubbles, is a layer of very fine contractile fibres or *myonemes*. Near the stalk the

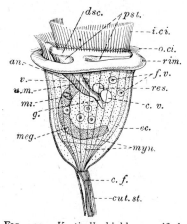

FIG. 11.—*Vorticella,* highly magnified.

an., Position of temporary anus ; *c.f.*, contractile filament ; *c.v.*, contractile vacuole ; *cut.st.*, cuticle of the stalk ; *dsc.*, disc ; *ec.*, ectoplasm ; *f.v.*, food vacuoles ; *g.*, narrower part of gullet ; *i.ci.*, inner row of cilia ; *meg.*, meganucleus ; *mi.*, micronucleus ; *myn.*, myonemes ; *o.ci.*, outer row of cilia ; *pst.*, peristome ; *res.*, reservoir of contractile vacuole ; *rim* ; *u.m.*, undulating membrane ; *v.*, vestibule.

ectoplasm is much thickened and the myonemes pass inwards through it to join in the middle, where they form a central *contractile fibre* which, with a covering of ectoplasm, makes up the stalk. This is enclosed in a cuticular tube formed by secretion. The contractile fibre is not quite straight, but lies in a very open spiral, so that when it contracts it draws the stalk into a close coil. There are no trichocysts. The endoplasm is granular.

A meganucleus and a micronucleus are present, the former a long, curved band, the latter small and placed **Internal Organs.** beside the meganucleus, usually in the upper part of the body. There is a contractile vacuole. which has no canals. It lies in the upper region of the body and communicates with the vestibule through a *reservoir*, which has a narrow permanent opening. The contractile vacuole contracts sharply at intervals, discharging into the reservoir. The latter then contracts slowly, driving its contents into the vestibule, but not itself disappearing. Feeding and digestion take place much as in *Paramecium*. The little organisms which serve as food are collected and driven into the gullet by the action of the cilia. The food vacuoles follow a definite, winding course in the body, passing through stages similar to those in *Paramecium*. The fæces are discharged into the vestibule by an anus, which in some species is a permanent opening through the ectoplasm.

The reproduction of *Vorticella* takes place by binary fission, which is of two kinds—ordinary fission, **Reproduction.** and that which forms conjugants. In ordinary fission, the rim closes in over the disc, the body becomes shorter and wider, and the meganucleus contracts and lies across the body, which then divides into two, the plane of fission being in line with the stalk. The nuclei behave as in *Paramecium*. One of the daughters remains upon the stalk; the other grows a circlet of cilia in the hinder region, at the level at which the ectoplasm thickens, breaks off, and swims away by means of its cilia, to settle down elsewhere by the end which was attached to the stalk of the parent. It grows a new stalk for itself. In this form of reproduction the offspring are equal in bulk. In the fission which forms conjugants the parent gives rise to one large individual and one or more of a smaller size. The small individuals may arise by unequal binary fission, sometimes called budding, or by equal fission, followed by division of one product into four by repeated fission.[1] In

---

[1] The various kinds of fission of *Amœba*, *Vorticella*, and animals related to them (Protozoa, p. 177) may be classed as : (1) equal binary fission (p. 146), (2) budding, (3) repeated fission (p. 152), (4) multiple fission (p. 147).

either case the small individuals resemble the free product of ordinary fission in all but size.

The small individuals thus formed swim away, and each **Conjugation.** attaches itself by its hinder end to the lower part of the body of one of the stalked individuals. Most of the organs of the small individual now disappear, and the ectoplasm between the two conjugants is absorbed into their endoplasm, which becomes continuous. The meganucleus in each begins to break up and disappear. Meanwhile the micronucleus of the small conjugant has divided into two. Now the micronuclei of both conjugants divide twice, so that the larger contains four and the smaller eight micronuclei. In each case all but one of these perish and the survivor divides into two, which correspond to the male and female pronuclei of *Paramecium*. This division takes place while the two micronuclei are lying in the region where the endoplasm of the conjugants became continuous. One half of each micronucleus passes into the larger conjugant, where the two fuse as male and female pronuclei. The other half of each passes into the smaller conjugant, but these halves, instead of fusing, degenerate and disappear. The endoplasm of the small exconjugant is now drawn into the larger, the ectoplasm shrivelling up and falling off. It will be seen that the conjugation of *Vorticella* takes place in the same way as that of *Paramecium*, but that one of the two exconjugants perishes and is partly absorbed by the other.[1]

Carchesium is a small freshwater animal whose body **Carchesium.** consists of a number of members, each of which has the structure of a whole *Vorticella*. It arises from a *Vorticella*-like body, by divisions like those which take place in the ordinary reproduction of *Vorticella*, save that the division passes some way down the stem and then stops, leaving the bells joined by their stalks. Thus the body is increased by the addition of new members which repeat the structure of the old. In that it increases

[1] The student should beware of comparing the smaller conjugant of *Vorticella* with a spermatozoon and the larger with an ovum. Ova and spermatozoa are gametes of unlike kinds. The conjugants of *Vorticella* are unlike, hermaphrodite parents, each of which forms two unlike gametes.

the number of energids in the body, this process resembles cell formation, but the two cases differ in that the new energids of *Carchesium* all repeat the whole structure of the first and inherit all its powers, whereas a cell is a portion of the body with peculiar characters and restricted powers. The whole body of a *Carchesium* is said to be a *colony*, and its members are *zooids*. Reproduction is brought about by the complete fission from the body of certain zooids, which thus become asexually produced young (buds). Each of these swims off, settles down, and forms by growth and nuclear division a new colonial individual. Conjugation like that of *Vorticella* also takes place.

Protozoa. The detailed study which we have made of *Paramecium* and *Vorticella* has shown to what an extent organisation can be carried without the division of the body into cells. Ranging in grade of organisation between the simplicity of *Amœba* and the complexity of *Carchesium* there is an immense number of animals whose structure is non-cellular.[1]

FIG. 112.—A colony of *Carchesium* under low magnification.

These animals are known as *Protozoa*. Cellular animals are known as *Metazoa*. Those Protozoa which move by means of pseudopodia are called *Sarcodina* or *Rhizopoda*, those which move by flagella are *Mastigophora* or *Flagellata*, those which move by cilia are *Ciliata*. Protozoa which, like *Monocystis*, have no external organs of locomotion, are parasites, and form numerous spores, are known as *Sporozoa*. In comparing *Amœba* with the frog we noticed that the absence in the former of cells—that is, of energids in the body which are specialised and therefore liable to natural death—led

---

[1] They are often said to be unicellular, but this, as we have decided (p. 149), is a misleading use of the term " cell."

to its being, in a certain sense, immortal. The same is true of all Protozoa, although, as we have seen, most Ciliata, in which there is a partial separation of body-substance in the form of a special nucleus, do at times purchase their immortality at the price of the loss of the meganucleus, forming a new one from the micronucleus.

In the next chapter there will be found (p. 195) descriptions of several Ciliata which are parasitic in the frog and in man.

CHAPTER X

THE PROTOZOA AS PARASITES OF MAN

The interest which the study of the Protozoa has for mankind is not merely theoretical, in virtue of the remarkable peculiarities of their organisation, but is very near and practical, by reason of the fact that a number of them live in the bodies of men, and that there they sometimes cause very serious diseases. In this chapter we shall study briefly examples, drawn from all the four classes of the group, of which man is a *host*—that is, which he harbours as parasites. In so doing, our attention must be given both to facts which, directly or indirectly, are of medical importance, and to others which have wider biological significance.

The several kinds of *Entamœba* differ from *Amœba* only in that they have no contractile vacuole.[1]

Entamœba.

They have one or two large blunt pseudopodia, chiefly composed of ectoplasm, and they are all parasites, usually in the alimentary canal of one of the backboned or, as they are called, " vertebrate " animals. *E. coli* lives in the upper part of the large intestine of man, feeding upon the bacteria which infest that region, and also upon the remains of the food of its host, which are probably of little value. It is harmless, and possibly sometimes even beneficial by keeping down the bacteria. Its life-history differs considerably from that of *Amœba proteus*. In the intestine it reproduces by binary fission, and, as some of the individuals are being passed down the gut and cast out with the fæces, certain of them undergo another process.

[1] A contractile vacuole has been found in one organism which has been classed with the *Entamœbæ*.

In this the nucleus—after proceedings in which some of its chromatin is lost, while a large vacuole temporarily appears in the cytoplasm—forms eventually two nuclei while a cyst is being secreted around the body. The two nuclei in the cyst divide into eight. The ordinary *Entamœbæ* die in the fæces. So, it is said, do the cysts if the fæces dry, but if they remain moist until they reach water or human food and are swallowed by a man the cysts germinate in the intestine of the new host, the protoplasm dividing and emerging as little individuals each with a nucleus. By these the cycle is re-started.

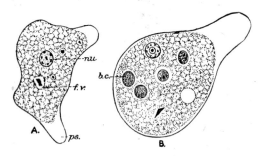

FIG. 113.—*Entamœba.*—After Fantham.

A, *E. coli*; B, *E. histolytica*.

b.c., Ingested red blood corpuscle; *f.v.*, food vacuole; *nu.*, nucleus; *ps.*, pseudopodium.

Entamœba histolytica, sometimes known as *E. dysenteriæ*, also inhabits the human intestine. It varies much in size but reaches greater dimensions than *E. coli*, from which it also differs in being more active, in having a distinct ectoplasm over the whole surface of the body, in taking up strongly, while still alive, the stain known as "neutral red," and in that the principal chromatic body or "karyosome" of the nucleus is centrally placed. Unlike *E. coli* it attacks the mucous membrane of the intestine, probably by the secretion of an enzyme. It then penetrates the blood vessels in the same way, and is carried by the circulation to the liver, where it may set up abscesses. **Its** action on the intestinal wall causes dysentery. It feeds on tissues and also on red blood corpuscles, which *E. coli* does not. *E. histolytica* is widespread in tropical and sub-

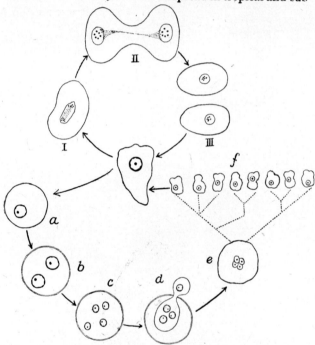

FIG. 114. —The life-cycle of *Entamœba histolytica*.

I–III, Binary fission; *a–f*, encystment and multiple fission.

a, Rounding off; *b*, cyst in which the nucleus has divided; *c*, cyst in which the second division has taken place; *d*, emergence from the cyst; *e*, free amœboid individual with four nuclei, which lie close together; *f*, eight amœbulæ formed from *e* by a complicated process of division.

tropical countries, and is the cause of much sickness and loss of life. An *Entamœba* of small size (*E. minuta*), and another known as *E. tetragena*, with a large karyosome in the nucleus, are now known to be forms of *E. histolytica* which arise in certain circumstances. Its life-cycle appears to differ from that of *E. coli* chiefly in the number of the cyst nuclei, of which there are only four, though after

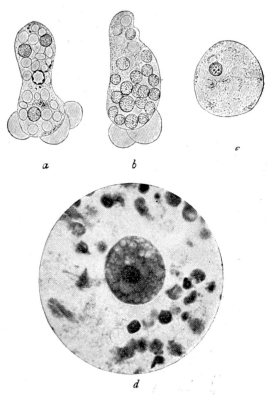

FIG. 115.—*Entamœba histolytica.*

a and *b*, Amœbæ as seen in fresh stools, showing blunt ectoplasmic pseudopodia, non-contractile vacuoles, ingested red corpuscles, and, in *a*, nucleus ; *c*, an amœba as seen in a fixed preparation ; *d*, section of wall of liver abscess, showing an amœba of spherical form. The rounded amœbæ on this plate must not be confused with the encysted form.

emergence these divide with the cytoplasm to form eight little amœbæ.

A flagellate protozoon known as *Trypanosoma* is re-
Trypanosoma. sponsible for various very dangerous diseases
of man and animals in warm countries.
Trypanosoma is parasitic in the blood and other fluids
of backboned animals, but also capable of living in an
invertebrate which sucks the blood of its vertebrate host,
and by this it is transferred from one vertebrate to
another. It has a worm-like body, about one-thousandth
of an inch in length, tapering towards the ends, but
more pointed in front than behind. The shape of the body
is maintained by a strong pellicle. A single flagellum
stands at the front end, and from its base an undulating

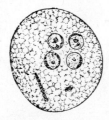

FIG. 116.—*Entamœba histolytica* in the encysted
condition.—After Fantham.

membrane runs along one side nearly to the hind end.
The flagellum is continued as a strongly-staining thread
along the free edge of the membrane, and terminates
behind in a minute " basal granule " or *blepharoplast*,
embedded in the cytoplasm. By the working of the
undulating membrane and flagellum the animal swims
rapidly with a graceful wavy movement, either forwards
or backwards. There is no contractile vacuole. Near
the middle of the body is an egg-shaped nucleus, but
a smaller mass, which stains like the nucleus, stands
close to the blepharoplast. This smaller body has been
called the " kinetonucleus," and supposed to have some
function in connection with movement, while the nucleus
proper, known as the " tropnonucleus " regulates the
other functions of the body. It is now known that the

so-called kinetonucleus is not of the nature of a nucleus, and has no influence upon the movements of the animal, which take place equally well in races in which it has been artificially caused to disappear. It is best called the *parabasal body*. Its function is at present unknown.

Trypanosoma has no mouth, but nourishes itself, like

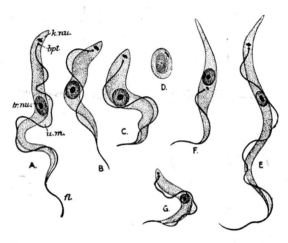

Fig. 117. —*Trypanosoma gambiense.*—After various authors.

A, B, C, Slender, intermediate, and stumpy forms from man ; *D*, latent body ; *E*, slender form from gut of fly ; *F*, crithidial form from salivary gland of fly ; *G*, ripe form from proboscis of fly.

bpt., blepharoplast ; *fl.*, flagellum ; *k.nu.*, parabasal body (kinetonucleus) ; *tr.nu.*, trophonucleus ; *u.m.*, undulating membranes.

Monocystis, by absorbing through the surface of its body substances obtained from the juices of its host.

In spite of the immense amount of investigation of which its medical importance has caused it to be the subject, the life-history of *Trypanosoma* is not yet thoroughly understood. In the case of *T. gambiense*, the cause of the terrible " sleeping sickness " of West and Central Africa, the following facts have been established. In the body of an infected man the parasites live at first in the blood, but presently make their way into the lymphatic glands, and thence into the fluid of the spinal canal and cavities of the brain. While they are in the blood alone the man suffers from " Gambia fever," but when they reach the central nervous system the drowsiness which is characteristic of

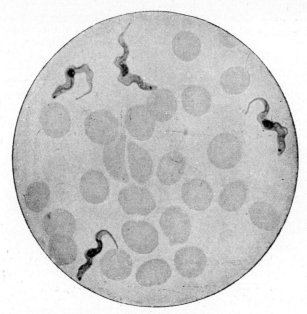

FIG. 118. —*Trypanosoma gambiense.*

A stained preparation of the blood of an infected guinea-pig, showing blood corpuscles and parasites.

sleeping-sickness comes on, and increases, with, presently, a wasting of the body, till death almost inevitably results. The individuals found in the human host are not all alike, some being long and slender, some short and stumpy, and some intermediate in shape. The thin forms are the youngest, the animals growing stouter as they mature, and becoming stumpy in succeeding generations. There are

also differences in size, due to age and to the fact that the
binary longitudinal fission by which reproduction takes
place is sometimes unequal.   In fission first the blepharoplast, then the parabasal body, and finally the nucleus
divide, while the flagellum and membrane are doubled,
but probably not by division.

During the progress of the infection some of the trypanosomes pass into certain of the internal organs of their host,
especially into the spleen and lungs.   There they lose their
flagella and become of an oval shape.   In this condition
they show resemblances to the predominant phase of the
organism known as *Leishmania*, which is the cause of the
kala-azar disease and of Delhi boil.   True *Leishmania*
stages, which presently revert to the flagellate condition, do
occur in the life-cycles of other trypanosomes.   It has been
supposed that these phases of *T. gambieuse* are of a similar
nature and that they revert and thus make good the loss of
flagellates in the blood when, as happens between the fits
of the fever, the flagellates are reduced in number by the
secretion of " antibodies " (p. 124) by the host.   On this
theory they have been called " latent bodies."   It is more
probable, however, that they are individuals in a state of
degeneration.

The invertebrate responsible for the spreading of *Trypanosoma gambiense* is a fly, *Glossina palpalis*, related to the
tsetse fly, *G. morsitans*, which spreads another trypanosome, *T. brucei*, the cause of the South African cattle
disease.   *Glossina* sucks the blood of various backboned
animals—cattle, antelopes, birds, and so forth, as well as
man—and thus takes into its stomach such parasites as may
infest the blood vessels of its victims.   When the object of
the attack of *G. palpalis* is infected with the trypanosome
of sleeping-sickness, the insect becomes capable of inocu-
lating a new host in the course of its feeding.   The power
of inoculation is soon lost, but is regained after about
twenty days.   It seems probable that the first inoculations
are made with trypanosomes which are still fresh in the
proboscis of the insect, but the later ones with individuals
which arise from the stumpy forms after passing through
a course of development in the insect's alimentary canal
and salivary glands.   During this development the stumpy

forms become first long and slender, then, attached to the wall of the salivary gland, pass through a " crithidial phase " in which the membrane starts in front of the nucleus, and finally as stout-bodied, mature individuals are injected with the saliva when a new victim is bitten.

Besides those that we have mentioned, there are known a number of other trypanosomes—*T. rhodesiense* which causes a sleeping-sickness in South Central Africa, *T. equinum* which causes a horse disease in South America, *T. cruzi*, the cause of a disease in children in the same con-

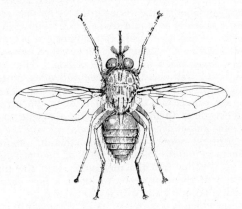

FIG. 119.—The tsetse fly *Glossina palpalis*.—From Thomson.

tinent, and so forth. Many, perhaps all, of these have a wild host in which they are harmless, though in the unaccustomed bodies of men or domestic animals they are highly dangerous. Formerly no treatment was of any avail against them; recent research has produced several synthetic drugs (Germanin, Tryparsamide, etc.) which can cope with at least the African species, but the best way to combat them is to avoid the attacks of the insects which transmit them. Thus the clearing around places frequented by human beings of the bush which is the haunt of *Glossina* has led to a decrease in the number of cases of sleeping-sickness.

A much more widespread though less dangerous type of

disease than sleeping-sickness is malarial fever. This is

Malaria Parasites. brought about by a minute protozoan parasite known as *Hæmamœba* or *Plasmodium*,[1] belonging, like *Monocystis*, to the Sporozoa. The dangerous stage of the parasite corresponds to the trophozoite of *Monocystis*. It lives in the red blood corpuscles, and is at first a round body with the appearance of a ring, owing to the presence of a large (non-contractile) vacuole in its middle. It has a single nucleus and no mouth, and must absorb food from its surroundings through the surface of its body. As it grows, it loses the ring-like appearance, puts out pseudopodia, and forms in its cytoplasm granules of pigment which is no doubt derived from the hæmoglobin of its host. When it is ready to reproduce, it is known as a *meront* or *schizont*. Its reproduction, called *merogony* or *schizogony*, takes place by multiple fission. The pseudopodia are withdrawn and the nucleus divides repeatedly till there are present some sixteen smaller nuclei. These lie in the outer part of the body, and most of the cytoplasm now gathers round them so as to form a rosette of little, uninucleate individuals—the *merozoites* or *schizozoites* — which surround some "residual protoplasm" containing the pigment granules. Next the shell of the red corpuscle breaks up, setting free the merozoites into the plasma, where each of them proceeds to infect a new corpuscle, into which it bores its way with a pointed end.

The time which is required to repeat this cycle of asexual reproduction varies with the species of parasite. Thus of the three kinds (at least) of *Plasmodium* which infest man, *P. vivax* sets free a generation of merozoites in forty-eight hours, *P. malariæ* in seventy-two hours, and *P. falciparum* at irregular intervals. The attacks of fever occur when the corpuscles break up, probably because there are then set free substances formed during the metabolism of the parasite which prove poisonous to the host. So it comes about that the fever caused by *P. vivax* returns every third day, and is known as " tertian ague," and that

---

[1] It is unfortunate that this name is also in use to denote a type of relation of nuclei to cytoplasm—namely, that in which a syncytium is formed by the fusion of free energids (p. 147)—which, as it happens, is not found in the malaria parasite

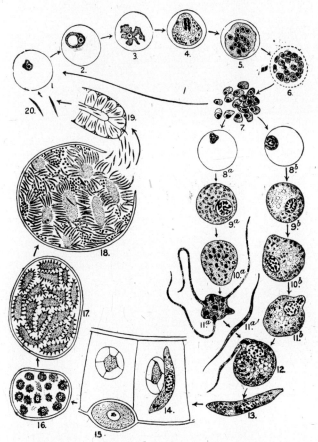

FIG. 120.--The life-cycle of *Plasmodium vivax.*

1-7, Merogony, asexual reproduction which takes place in man; 8-13, gamogony, or sexual reproduction, which takes place in the stomach of a mosquito; 14-20 sporogony, asexual reproduction in the body cavity of the mosquito.

1, Infection of a red corpuscle; 2, signet-ring stage; 3, amœboid stage; 4, full-grown meront preparing to divide; 5, multinucleate stage; 6, rosette stage, corpuscle breaking up; 7, free merozoites; 8, infection of red corpuscles by young gamonts; 9, full-grown gamonts free in the mosquito's stomach; 10, 11, formation of gametes; 12, syngamy; 13, zygote; 14, invasion by zygote (sporont) of endoderm cell of mosquito; 15, encystment; 16, sporoblasts formed by division of sporont; 17, 18, formation of sporozoites; 19, invasion by latter of salivary gland; 20, sporozoites injected into blood of a man.

caused by *P. malariæ* (quartan ague) returns every fourth
day, while *P. falciparum* causes irregular (quotidian) fevers
which are more or less continuous. These latter are the
" pernicious malaria " of the tropics. For about ten days
after infection the parasites are not numerous enough to
cause serious trouble. This period is known as the " period
of incubation." Many generations of merozoites may
succeed one another during the course of the illness, but
eventually the resisting powers of the host begin to get the
better of the infesting organisms, or, on the other hand,
the patient may be about to die.
In either case it behoves the parasite
to arrange for the continuance of
its race elsewhere. This is done by
the provision of a fresh kind of individual, adapted to transmission
by mosquitoes to new human hosts.
These, because they give rise in the
mosquito to gametes, are known as
gamonts, or gametocytes, though
the latter name more properly belongs to cells of similar function in
the bodies of Metazoa (p. 131).

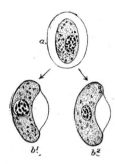

FIG 121.—Gamonts of
Plasmodium falciparum.

a, Before taking on the sausage
shape ; *b*[1], male gamont in
sausage stage; *b*[2], female
gamont in the same stage.
The outline is that of the
red corpuscle.

The gamonts begin to arise when
the period of incubation is past.
In the parasites of tertian and
quartan fevers they are rounded,
in that of pernicious malaria
crescent-shaped. They are larger
than the schizonts and have more
of the dark pigment.

It is said that they have no ring-stage in their development. They remain in the corpuscle where they arose from
a merozoite, and undergo no change unless they be sucked
in by a mosquito ; but in that case, whereas all other forms
of the parasite die and are digested by the mosquito,
the gamonts, becoming free by the breaking up of their
corpuscles, proceed to develop gametes. They are of
two kinds, male and female, the former with a larger
nucleus and more lightly staining cytoplasm than the
latter. In the male gamont the nucleus breaks rapidly into

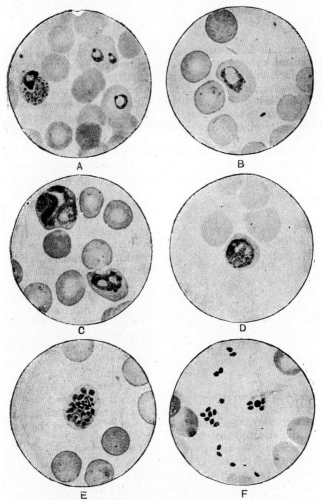

FIG. 122.—*Plasmodium vivax*, the tertian ague parasite.—
From Muir and Ritchie.

A, Several young ring-shaped amœbulæ within the red corpuscles, one of the latter
enlarged and showing a dotted appearance ; *B*, a larger amœbula, containing
pigment granules ; *C*, two large amœbulæ, exemplifying the great variation in
form ; *D*, large amœbula assuming the spherical form and showing isolated
fragments of chromatin, preparatory to schizogony ; *E*, schizont which has produced eighteen schizozoites (merozoites), each of which contains a small collection of chromatin ; *F*, merozoites set free. (× 1000.)

some half-dozen fragments, leaving a residual mass in the central cytoplasm. The daughter nuclei come to the surface, and grow out, with a suddenness which is almost explosive, into fine threads of nucleoplasm, projecting from the body in scarcely perceptible sheaths of cytoplasm. These are the *microgametes*. They lash violently, dragging about residue of the gamont body, till they break free. The remains of the gamont perish. The female gamont, by a process in which the nucleus loses a part of its contents, becomes a single *macrogamete*. It is now ripe for fertilisa-

FIG. 123.—A mosquito (*Anopheles*). —From Lankester's *Zoology*.

tion by a microgamete which penetrates the body, and the nuclei (male and female pronuclei) fuse. The zygote changes from a rounded to a worm-like creature, which glides about by contractions of its body, pierces the epithelium of the insect's stomach with one end, which is pointed for the purpose, and comes to rest in the sub-epithelial tissue, where it rounds itself off and forms a cyst. It is known as the *sporont* on account of its further history, which is as follows.

Through its thin cyst-wall the parasite continues to absorb nutriment, and grows in size, bulging out the wall of the stomach into the body cavity so as to form a kind of blister. As it grows, its nucleus multiplies by binary fission and cytoplasm becomes concentrated round each nucleus to form a body known as a *sporoblast*. Now the nucleus of each sporoblast divides repeatedly and the surface of the body grows out into slender processes, into each of which one of the daughter nuclei passes. Finally the processes break off, and so the cyst contains hundreds of needle-like *sporozoites* together with some residual protoplasm. The ripe cysts burst and scatter their contents into the body cavity of the insect host, from which

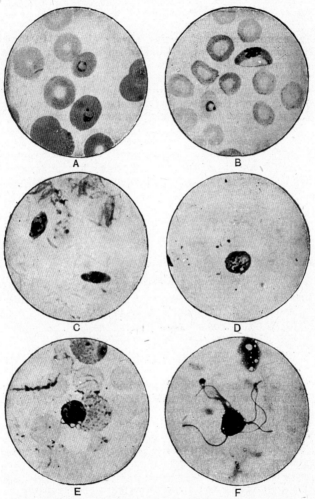

FIG. 124.—*Plasmodium falciparum,* the pernicious malaria parasite.
—From Muir and Ritchie.

A, Two small ring-shaped amœbulæ within the corpuscles; *B,* a "crescent" or gamont, showing the envelope of the red corpuscle. Figs. *C–F* illustrate the changes in form undergone by the gamonts outside the body; Fig. *F* shows a male gamont that has undergone "exflagellation," or the formation of microgametes, which are seen attached to it. (× 1000.)

the sporozoites pass into the salivary glands. In these the mosquito secretes a liquid which is injected into its prey when it bites, and has the effect of stimulating the blood-flow. When next it feeds, the little parasites pass with the saliva along the proboscis into the blood of the man on whom the mosquito is feeding, there to bore their way into red corpuscles and start a new infection.

Long after apparent recovery from an attack of malaria, a patient may suffer a recurrence of the disease. This is probably due to persistence of a few of the trophozoites, though it has been held to be caused by female gamonts acting somewhat as the " latent bodies " of trypanosomes.

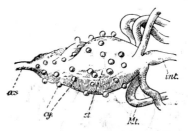

Fig. 125.—Part of the alimentary canal of a mosquito infested with *Plasmodium.*—From Lankester's *Zoology*, after Ross.

cy., Cysts of the parasite ; *int.*, intestine ; *M.t.*, Malpighian tubes ; *œs.*, œsophagus, *st.*, stomach.

In comparing this life-history with that of *Monocystis* some important differences appear. (*a*) In *Monocystis* the trophozoite is not amœboid, eventually outgrows its cell-host, and does not reproduce asexually (*i.e.*, does not become a meront) ; (*b*) in the malaria parasite the gametes are much more unlike than in *Monocystis* and the female gamont gives rise only to one gamete ; (*c*) in *Monocystis* there is no sporoblast generation between the zygote and the sporozoites ; (*d*) in *Monocystis* there is probably no necessity for a second kind of host, sexual reproduction and the division of the zygote both take place in the host in which the parent trophozoites live, and the zygote-cyst (the pseudonavicella) does not burst and set free the sporozoites until it reaches the host in which the new generation of trophozoites are to live. The whole process is more highly developed in the malaria parasite.

Malaria is very widely distributed. It is found in tropical and subtropical lands of every quarter of the globe and even in such temperate countries as England, where it still lingers in marshy districts in the form of ague, once much more prevalent than now. The parasites which cause it are always transmitted by the Anopheline Flies or true " Mosquitoes," being incapable of harbouring in the related Culicine Flies, or " Gnats " in the strict sense, which digest the gametocytes.

Gnats and mosquitoes, though they are much alike to the untrained eye, may be distinguished by sundry small differences, notably by the carriage of the body in the resting position (Fig. 126). Both these kinds of flies lay their eggs in water, and there, on hatching, the young pass through larval and pupal stages (p. 345). It is practically hopeless to attempt to destroy the adults on a large scale, but they may often be prevented from breeding by doing away with all suitable pieces of water, or attacking the young stages by pouring paraffin over the breeding-places, introducing fish which feed upon them, and so forth.

The loss of time, energy, and life itself from this disease is very serious in many warm countries, notably, for instance, on the West Coast of Africa. Formerly quinine was almost the only resource against it, but the discovery of the parasite and its life-history—a romance of Science, in which the English observer Ross played a great part—has made us less helpless to avert its ravages. The measures which are taken to that end are threefold : (1) the destruction of the mosquito, by such measures as have been mentioned ; (2) the use of quinine to overcome the parasite in the blood and thus destroy the supply of it as well as benefiting the individual patient ; (3) the separation of European dwellings from those of the natives.

The Ciliata are not commonly parasites of man, but one at least may cause in him serious disease.

Balantidium coli. *Balantidium coli* is related to *Paramecium*. It has an egg-like body, about one-tenth of a millimetre in length, with a funnel-like depression—the peristome—at the narrow end, and a mouth and gullet at the bottom of the peristome. A coat of cilia arranged in parallel rows covers the body, and some larger cilia stand beside the peristome. There is a good-sized, kidney-shaped meganucleus, with a small, round micronucleus

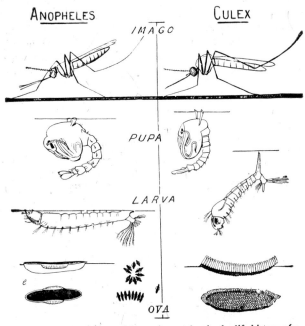

FIG. 126.—A comparison of the various stages in the life-history of a mosquito (left) with those of a gnat (right).—From Shipley.

Note how the larvæ and pupæ hang from the surface film of the water (represented by a thin line). The organs by which they are suspended contain air tubes, and if these be prevented by a film of paraffin from functioning the insect is drowned. Note also that the eggs of the gnat cling together as a raft.

e., two views of an egg, magnified.

against its hollow side, and two contractile vacuoles. Red blood corpuscles are sometimes found in the food vacuoles. *Balantidium* multiplies by transverse, binary fission, and from time to time conjugates. In certain circumstances it encysts. It lives in the large intestine of the pig, to which it appears not to do much harm, and is spread by its cysts passing out with the fæces, getting into water or on to food, and being swallowed by a new host. When this is a human being whose intestine is deranged, it increases the irritation, penetrates the epithelium and lies in the layers below it, and may even be carried by the blood or lymph to other parts of the body and there cause abscesses. More often it brings about dysentery, which may be fatal. It occurs in all parts of the world. A *Balantidium* is found, with other ciliates, in the rectum of the frog.

Ciliata of the Frog. The rectum of the frog contains an interesting population of ciliates, which live chiefly in the lighter-coloured contents of its foremost region. *Balantidium entozoon* differs from *B. coli* in having four contractile vacuoles and a longer peristome. *Nyctotherus cordiformis* resembles the *Balantidia* in its general features, but is bean-shaped, with a long gullet placed in the middle of the hollow side, an undulating membrane, one contractile vacuole in the hinder part of the body, and a remarkable permanent anus, lined with ectoplasm, at the hind end. The related *N. faba* has been found in the intestine of a man suffering from dysentery, but it is doubtful whether it was the cause of the disease.

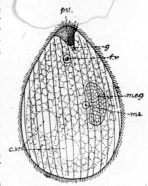

FIG. 127.—*Balantidium coli.*

c.v., Contractile vacuoles; *f.v.*, food vacuole; *g.*, gullet; *meg.*, meganucleus; *mi.*, micronucleus; *pst.*, peristome.

More numerous and conspicuous than either of these is *Opalina ranarum*, a flat, oval, pale-straw-coloured ciliate of very large size (1 mm. long), uniformly covered with equal cilia, and without mouth, peristome, contractile vacuole, or trichocysts. It has many nuclei, unlike those of other Ciliata in being all of one kind. The life-history is also very unlike that of other Ciliata. Nuclei and cytoplasm divide independently (the latter alternately in a longitudinal and a transverse direction), and during the greater part of the year keep pace with one another and with growth, so that the appearance of the mature animals remains the same; but in the spring the division of the cytoplasm gains, so that small individuals with 3–6 nuclei result. It is said that at this time a portion of the chromatin of the nuclei passes in granular or " chromidial " form into the cytoplasm, where it perishes. The little individuals now encyst. The cysts are passed by the frog into the water and there swallowed by tadpoles, in which they hatch and their cytoplasm divides to form uninuclear gametes,

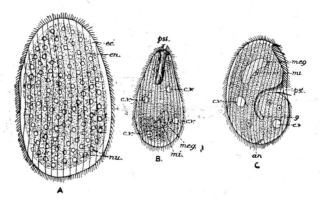

FIG. 128.—Ciliata from the rectum of the frog.

A, *Opalina ranarum* ; B, *Balantidium entozoon* ; C, *Nyctotherus cordiformis*.
an., Anus ; *c.v.*, contractile vacuoles ; *ec.*, ectoplasm ; *en.*, endoplasm ; *g.*, gullet ;
meg., meganucleus ; *mi.*, micronucleus ; *nu.*, nuclei ; *pst.*, peristome.

the nuclei meanwhile undergoing a reducing division. The gametes conjugate, and the zygote encysts. Probably it always at this stage

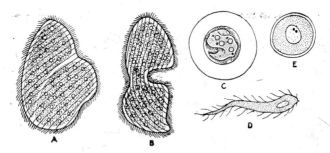

FIG. 129.—*Opalina ranarum.*

A, Ordinary individual in longitudinal fission ; *B*, the same in transverse fission ;
C, small encysted individual (distributive phase); *D*, gamete; *E*, encysted zygote.

passes out of the host and enters another, where it hatches. From the cyst emerges a uninuclear ciliate which grows into the adult. During the whole process cilia are lost only in the zygote cyst. A comparison of this life-history with that of *Paramecium* suggests (1) that the destruction of some of the chromatin corresponds to that of the meganucleus of *Paramecium*, (2) that the divisions of the micro-nuclei of the latter before conjugation may perhaps be the remains of a lost habit of forming a number of gametes like these of *Opalina*. It does not appear that any of these animals is harmful to the frog.

Attention may now be called to certain processes in protozoan nuclei which, doubtful of interpretation though they **Ripening of** be, are none the less suggestive. Protozoa often (perhaps **Protozoan** **Gametes.** always) lose a portion of their nucleoplasm before syngamy. This may take place by mitosis, and in such cases a definite halving by the loss of chromosomes has sometimes been discovered, as in the micronucleus of *Paramecium* (p. 168), in the nuclei of *Opalina* and in those of the Sporozoa and of *Chlamydomonas*. In the latter two cases it happens in the first division of the zygote so that the organism for the rest of its life has only a single set of chromosomes. No doubt the function of such a process is the same as that of the ripening of the gametes of higher animals (p. 136). In other cases (Sporozoa, the chromidial process in *Opalina*) part of the chromatic matter of the nucleus is lost by a non-mitotic process, and this is perhaps comparable, not to the " reduction division " of *Paramecium* and the higher animals, but to the destruction of the body nucleus (meganucleus) of *Paramecium* at conjugation, and thus, more distantly, to the parting of body and germ in the Metazoa. It seems that in *Opalina* and the Sporozoa both " reduction " and the loss of body chromatin take place. Once more in these facts is probably to be seen the analogy of the protozoon with the whole body of a meta-zoon, rather than with one of its cells.

CHAPTER XI

SPONGES

THAT the objects of everyday use known as sponges are the
skeletons of marine animals is tolerably common
knowledge; but what may be the nature of the
soft parts of such animals is less well known.
A living sponge, however, is not only a very remarkable,
but even a fairly highly organised creature. Its nearest
relations, outside its own subkingdom, are to be found
among the Flagellate Protozoa.
Certain of these, known as the
Choanoflagellata, with a shape of
body not unlike that of *Polytoma*,
but having like *Trypanosoma* a
single flagellum, are fastened by

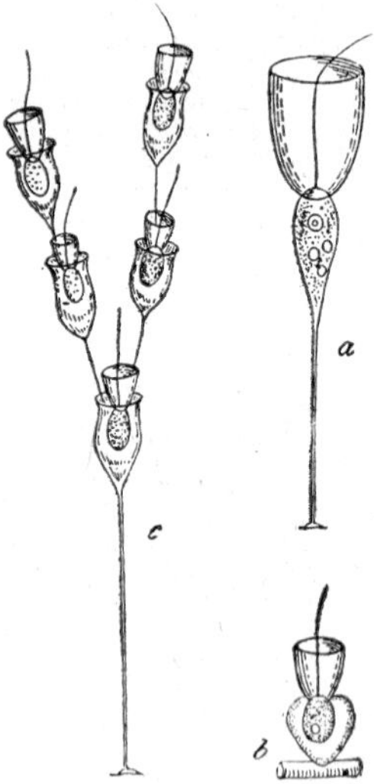

**Choano-
flagellata.**

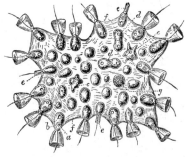

FIG. 130.—Choanoflagellata.

*a, Monosiga; b, Salpingœca;
c, Polyœca.*

FIG. 131.—*Proterospongia.*

a, Nucleus of a collared member of the colony;
b, contractile vacuole; c, amœboid member;
d, division of amœboid member; e, flagellate
member with collar contracted; f, jelly; g,
member forming spores.

a stalk at one end, and have at the other end the flagellum, and around it a delicate *collar* of protoplasm. Fig. 130 *a* shows one of these organisms. The Choano-flagellata often secrete a cup or case which houses and protects the body (Fig. 130, *b*) and sometimes the cups form a kind of colony, being joined into a plant-like growth (Fig. 130, *c*); but in one of them, known as *Proterospongia* (Fig. 131), the substance secreted takes the form of a mass of jelly, in which a number of separate individuals are lodged. Some stand on the outside, half-imbedded, with the collared end projecting; others pass into the jelly and there become amœboid, and some of these divide into minute spores, which may be gametes. The simplest sponge is a multi-cellular organism, the elements of whose body suggest a re-arrangement of those of the colony of *Proterospongia.*

This simple sponge is a little creature, known as **A simple** the *Olynthus,* which **Sponge.** is found only as a fleeting stage in the develop-ment of a few members of the group; but the bodies of all may be regarded as ideally derived from it, even though it may not appear as a stage in their life-history.

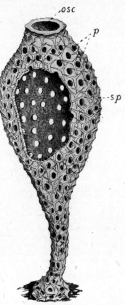

FIG. 132. — The Olynthus stage of a calcareous sponge, from which a portion of the wall has been removed to expose the paragaster.

o., Osculum; *p.,* pores; *sp.,* spicule in wall.

It is a hollow vase, perforated by many *pores*, and having at the summit a single large opening, the *osculum*. Through the pores water con-stantly enters it, to pass out through the osculum Herein it and its kind differ from all other animals, using the principal opening not for intaking—as a mouth

—but for casting out. The wall of the vase consists of two layers, a *gastral layer*, composed of collared flagellate cells, or *choanocytes*, standing side by side but not touching, which lines the internal cavity or *paragaster* except for a short distance within the rim ; and a *dermal layer*, which makes up the greater part of the thickness of the wall and is turned in a little way at the rim. This layer again consists of two parts, a *covering layer* of flattened cells, known as *pinacocytes*, rather like those of a pavement epithelium, but with the power of changing their shape, and the *skeletogenous layer*, between the covering layer and the gastral layer. The skeletogenous layer consists of scattered cells, with a jelly in which they are imbedded.

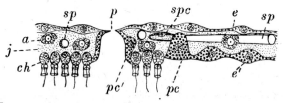

FIG. 133.—Part of a longitudinal section of the wall of an Olynthus, including a portion of the rim of the osculum.

a., Amœboid cell ; *ch.*, choanocyte ; *e.*, flat covering cells (pinacocytes) of dermal layer ; *e'.*, similar cells lining the rim of the osculum ; *j.*, jelly ; *p.*, pore ; *pc.*, young 'porocyte ; *pc'.*, fully developed porocyte ; *sp.*, spicule ; *sp.c.*, spicule cell.

The most numerous of these cells are engaged in secreting spicules of calcium carbonate by which the wall is supported. They wander from the covering layer into the jelly, and then each divides into two, and the resulting pair secrete in their protoplasm, which is continuous, a needle-like spicule which presently outgrows them. Most often the original spicule cells come together in threes before this process, so that the three spicules which they secrete become the rays of a three-rayed compound spicule. This lies in the wall with two rays towards the osculum and one away from it. Sometimes a fourth cell joins the others later, and forms a fourth ray which projects inwards towards the paragaster. Often there are simple spicules which project from the surface of the sponge. Other cells, known as *porocytes*, of a conical shape, extend through the jelly, having their base in the covering layer while their apex reaches the paragaster between the choanocytes. Each is pierced from base to apex by a tube, which is one of the pores.   Besides these cells of the dermal layer there are in the jelly wandering amœboid cells which appear, in some cases at least, to belong neither to the gastral nor to the dermal layer, but to be descended independently from blastomeres of the embryo.   Some of them become ova ; others, it is believed, give rise to male gametes ; the rest are occupied in transporting nutriment and excreta about the sponge.   The current which flows through the body is set up by the working of the flagella of the choanocytes.   It carries with it various minute organisms which serve the sponge for food, being swallowed, in some way which is still in dispute, by the collar cells. These digest the food, rejecting the indigestible parts into the space within the collar ; and passing

FIG. 134.— A branched calcareous sponge of the first grade.—From Sedgwick.

on the digested food to amœbocytes, which visit them to obtain it.

No sponge remains at this simple stage throughout its life.   At the least the body branches and thus complicates its shape, and then often new oscula appear at the ends of the branches.

Complex Sponge Bodies.

A higher grade is reached when, as in the calcareous sponge *Sycon*, the greater part of the vase is covered with blind, thimble-shaped outgrowths, regularly arranged, and touching in places, but leaving between them channels, known as *inhalant canals*, whose openings on the surface of the sponge are often narrowed and are known as *ostia*. The thimble-shaped chambers are known as *flagellated chambers*, and are lined by choanocytes, but these are now lacking from the paragaster, where they are replaced by pinacocytes. Water enters by the ostia,

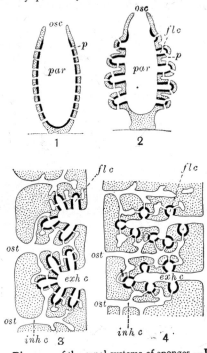

FIG. 135.—Diagrams of the canal systems of sponges.—Partly after Minchin.

exh.c., Exhalant canal ; *inh.c.*, inhalant canal ; *fl.c.*, flagellated chamber ; *osc.*, osculum ; *ost.*, ostium ; *p.*, pore ; *par.*, paragaster.

passes along the inhalant canals and through the pores, now known as *prosopyles*, into the excurrent canals, leaves these through the openings, known as *apopyles*, by which they communicate with the paragaster, and flows outwards through the osculum. A third grade is found in sponges such as the calcareous sponge *Leucilla*, where the wall of the paragaster is folded a second time, so that the flagellated chambers, instead of opening direct into the paragaster, communicate with it by *exhalant canals* lined with pinacocytes.

The three grades of sponge structure, in which successively the choanocytes line the whole paragaster, are restricted to flagellated chambers, or are still further removed by the presence of exhalant canals, are known as the "Ascon," "Sycon," and "Leucon" grades. In many of the sponges whose canal systems are of the third grade, the flagellated chambers are no longer thimble-shaped, but small and round. As the canal system has grown more intricate, complication has taken place also in the skeletogenous layer. It has grown thicker, forming outside the flagellated chambers a layer known as the *cortex*, in which the inhalant canals ramify; and there appear in it branched connective tissue cells which can change their shape.

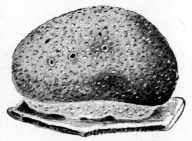

FIG. 136.—The Bath Sponge (*Euspongia*). —From Parker and Haswell.

The effect of these advances in complexity is (*a*) to increase the rate and precision of the currents of water through the sponge, (*b*) by strengthening the wall, to make it possible for sponges to grow to a greater size.

The sponges of which we have so far spoken have calcareous skeletons. A vast number of others **Siliceous and Horny Sponges.** have a skeleton of siliceous (flinty) spicules. In all these the canal systems are of one of the more complicated types, and usually they are made still more intricate by ramifyings of the paragaster, and the appearance of numerous oscula, which put it into communication with the water at many points. The sponges of domestic use belong to a comparatively small group in which the skeleton is not spicular but a network of horny fibres, usually strengthened by sand grains

imbedded in the fibres. Their canal system is of the type
which has small, round chambers, and in most of them these
communicate with the exhalant canals by narrow *aphodal
canals*, as in the majority of the siliceous sponges. In
preparing the sponge for human use, the soft parts are
allowed to die and rot, leaving the horny skeleton, which is

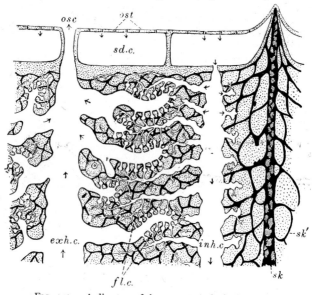

FIG. 137.—A diagram of the structure of a bath sponge.

exh.c., Exhalant canal ; *inh.c.*, inhalant canal ; *fl.c.*, flagellated chamber ; *osc.*, osculum ; *ost.*, ostium ; *sd.c.*, subdermal cavity ; *sk.*, one of the principal pillars of the skeleton, containing imbedded sand grains ; *sk'.*, minor fibres of the skeleton.

then cleaned. The large holes on the upper part of the
dried skeleton mark the position of the oscula ; in its interstices formerly lay the ramifications of the canal system.
The softness and wearing qualities of the sponge depend
upon the fineness of the meshwork of its skeleton, and upon
the amount of the sand particles which are embedded in it.
The true Bath Sponge (*Euspongia officinalis*) has very few
foreign particles. It is gathered in 10 to 15 fathoms of

water, the finest varieties from the Adriatic, coarser ones from elsewhere in the Mediterranean, the West Indies, and Australian seas. Various species of *Hippospongia* yield coarse kinds of sponge.

Sponges have free larvæ, of several different kinds, but all covered with flagellate cells, by which they swim. The remarkable feature of the metamorphoses by which these larvæ become the fixed adults is that the flagellated cells pass into the interior, develop collars, and become the choanocytes.

The sponges are known in Zoology as *Porifera*. In **Porifera.** that their bodies consist of many " cells," they might seem to be Metazoa. But they differ from all members of that group in several important respects. In no metazoan are choanocytes found. In none is the principal opening exhalant. In none is there during development an inversion whereby a flagellated outer covering becomes internal. Lastly, and perhaps most significantly, in a sponge the " cells " are far less specialised and dependent upon one another than the cells of a metazoan. Many of them can assume various forms, becoming amœboid, collared, etc. Many are isolated in the jelly, and when they touch they are not continuous. There is no nervous system. Even the choanocytes, though their efforts together produce a current, do not keep time in their working. In short, the Porifera are practically colonies of Protozoa. For these reasons it is best that, in a classification of animals, they should be given, under the name of Parazoa, the same rank as the Protozoa and Metazoa.

CHAPTER XII

HYDRA. POLYPS AND MEDUSÆ.
CŒLENTERATA.

If a handful of weeds gathered from a freshwater pond
be placed in a beaker of water and allowed
Hydra: General Features. to stand for a while, there will often be found
hanging from the sides of the beaker or from
the weeds some short threads of a green,
brown. or whitish colour. By one end each thread cleaves
to the glass. At the other it bears about half a dozen
finer threads, which hang down in the water if they be left
undisturbed. A touch will cause these to be withdrawn
and take on a shorter and thicker shape, interference with
the thread from which they hang is followed by a similar
change, and in this way the whole can be made to contract
into a vase-shaped mass surmounted by a circlet of little
knobs. From time to time water-fleas and other small
animals swim against the fine threads and may be seen
either to drop through the water as though they were
stunned, but afterwards to recover and swim away, or else
to remain sticking to the fine threads, which shorten and
draw the animal towards the end of the main thread, into
which they are swallowed. It is clear that these objects are
living beings: in point of fact each of them is a specimen
of the animal known as *Hydra*. According to their colour
they have been named *H. viridis*, *H. fusca*, and *H. grisea*.
The three kinds differ slightly in other respects besides
colour, but the following account applies to all of them.

The body of *Hydra* is a hollow cylinder, with a ring of
hollow outgrowths or *tentacles* surrounding an
Shape. opening or mouth at one end, and the other
end closed by a flat *basal disc or foot*. The mouth is raised

upon an *oral cone or hypostome*; it leads into the hollow of the cylinder, with which the hollows of the tentacles are continuous. This space is the *enteron*. The cylinder is rather wider in the middle than near the ends. The wall of the body is composed of two protoplasmic layers, the outer known as the *ectoderm* and the inner as the *endoderm*, with

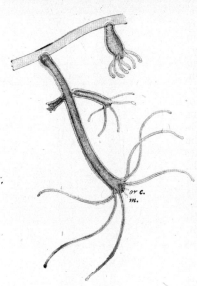

a *structureless lamella or mesoglea* between them, consisting of a gelatinous substance which they secrete. Such a body as this is known as a *polyp*.

The ectoderm **Ectoderm.** consists of several kinds of cells, of which the most conspicuous are those known as *musculo-* or *myo-epithelial cells*. These have broad outer ends, which meet and form the surface of the body, standing on several pillars which reach and expand upon the mesoglea, where each cell is drawn out into one or more *contractile processes*. The

Fig. 138.—Two specimens of *Hydra* magnified, one contracted, the other in a state of moderate expansion, the latter bearing two buds in different stages.

m., Mouth; *or.c.*, oral cone.

processes, each containing a fibre, run along the cylinder and tentacles, at right angles to the cell, forming a distinct layer on the outer side of the structureless lamella. Over the greater part of the body the surface layer of the protoplasm is a firm pellicle, but in the disc this is absent. The cells in this region are also peculiar in containing granules of a substance secreted by the protoplasm which is used to fix the

14

animal to the surface it hangs from. Each musculo-epithelial cell has a large oval nucleus in one of its pillars. In the tentacles these cells are less tall than elsewhere. Between the pillars are spaces which contain small, rounded *interstitial cells.* These form a reserve from which, in various circumstances, any of the other cells of the body can arise. Thus they retain the undifferentiated nature of the germs and are sometimes called indifferent cells. Between the pillars stand also peculiar cells known as *cnidoblasts,* which project through the surface protoplasm. These are very numerous in the tentacles, where they lie in groups or *batteries* (Figs. 139, 140), but absent from the basal disc. Each of them has a pear-shaped body with the narrow end at the surface of the animal, where there projects from it a short process known as the *cnidocil.* On this side the cell contains a pear-shaped sac, called the *nematocyst.* The narrow outer end of the sac is tucked in and

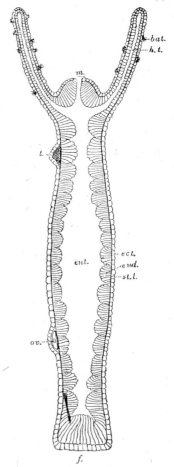

FIG. 139.—A diagrammatic, longitudinal section of *Hydra*, magnified.—From Shipley and MacBride.

bat., Battery of nematocysts. Only a few of these are shown; they cover the tentacles; *ect.,* ectoderm; *end.,* endoderm; *ent.,* enteron; *f.,* foot; *h t.,* hollow of a tentacle; *ov.,* ovary; *st.l.,* structureless lamella; *t.* testis.

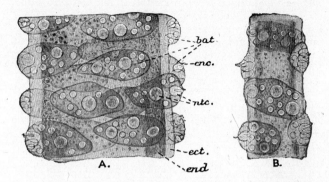

FIG. 140.—Portions of tentacles of *Hydra* magnified.

A, Moderately contracted ; *B*, moderately extended.

bat., Batteries; *cnc.*, cnidocil; *ect.*, ectoderm; *end.*, endoderm; *ntc.*, nemato-
cyst·.
Some of the batteries, and parts of others, are seen through the thickness of the
tentacle.

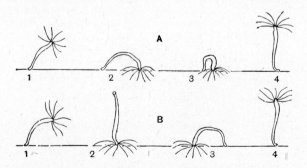

FIG. 141. — Hydra in the attitudes which it assumes successively in
two of its modes of locomotion.

A, "Looping "; *B*, "somersaulting."

produced into a long, hollow thread, which lies coiled up in the sac. The space between the thread and the wall of the sac contains a fluid. The cnidocil is a sense organ. When it is stimulated the thread is expelled, being turned inside out in the process. It is said that this is brought about by pressure which the shortening of contractile fibres in the protoplasm around the sac exerts the fluid in the latter.[1] The nematocysts are of three kinds—a large kind with a straight thread provided with barbs at the base, a small kind with a spiral thread, and a second small kind with a

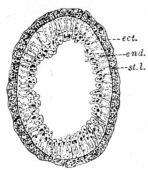

straight thread and a narrower sac than the others. Neither of the small kinds has barbs. The broad end of each cnidoblast is anchored into the body by a process which runs inward to the structureless lamella. The tentacles are covered with a number of warts, each consisting of a large musculo epithelial cell, in which is sunk a battery of cnidoblasts consisting of one or two of the large kind with several of the smaller kinds around them. Each of the kinds of nematocysts has a function of its own. Those of the large, barbed variety are weapons of offence and perhaps also of defence. The sensitiveness of their cnidocils to tactile stimuli is increased by chemical substances, given off from the bodies of other animals. When the nematocysts are discharged, their barbs emerge first and make a wound in the tissues of the prey, into which the thread is driven. In piercing the horny skin of the waterfleas, upon which the *Hydra* principally feeds, they are assisted by the corrosive action of a fluid which they contain, either in the hollow of the tucked-in thread or in that

Fig. 142.—A transverse section of *Hydra*, stained and seen under the low power of the microscope.

ect., Ectoderm; *end.*, endoderm; *st.l.*, structureless lamella.

---

[1] Probably the extension of the thread is continued by the action of a mechanism in the thread itself.

of the sac. This fluid also temporarily numbs the prey, but
the main function of the nematocysts is not to kill but to

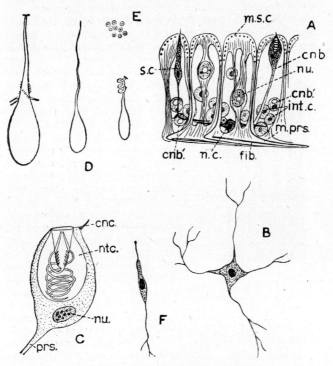

FIG. 143.—The histology of *Hydra*.

The figures are diagrammatic and not drawn to scale.

A, Musculo-epithelial cells ; *B*, a nerve cell ; *C*, a cnidoblast ;
D, nematocysts of three kinds ; *E*, Zoochlorellæ ; *F*, a sense cell.

cnb Cnidoblast ; *cnb'*, interstitial cell which will become a cnidoblast, with vacuole
for nematocyst ; *cnc.*, cnidocil ; *fib.*, fibre ; *int.c.*, interstitial cell ; *m.prs.*, contractile process ; *m.s.c.*, musculo-epithelial cell ; *n.c.*, nerve cell ; *ntc.*, nematocyst ; *nu.*, nucleus ; *prs.*, basal process of the cnidoblast ; *s.c.*, sense cell.

hold the prey until it is swallowed. In this the spiral kind
assist by coiling round bristles upon the body of the prey.

The third kind of nematocysts is of use in attaching the tentacles of the animal, either to its prey or to other objects when necessary, by the stickiness of the threads. The cnidoblasts arise from the interstitial cells by the formation of a vacuole and its gradual modification into a nematocyst. They are formed in the upper region of the cylinder and migrate thence to various parts of the body, where they take up their position in the outer layer. The *germ cells* also arise in the ectoderm from the interstitial cells by a process which we shall describe later. Lastly, among the bases of the ectoderm pillars lies a mesh-work of branching *nerve cells* which is joined by rootlets from tall, narrow *sense cells* that, like the cnidoblasts, pierce the surface protoplasm. How these cells are connected is not certain ; probably it is not by continuity of their processes but, as in the synapses of higher animals (p. 94), by contiguity. Physiologically these connections differ from such synapses in that impulses can pass either way across them. The sense cells are not specialised to serve particular senses. Thus *Hydra* possesses a nervous system, but this is in the most rudimentary condition possible, being a mere net of cells conducting in all directions, without nerves or central nervous exchange such as the frog has, while the cells from whose bodies the afferent fibres arise are among those which form the surface layer, as in the olfactory epithelium of the frog, not removed from it like those of most of the afferent fibres in the latter animal (Fig. 61). The nervous system governs only the muscles. The cnidoblasts are independent of it.

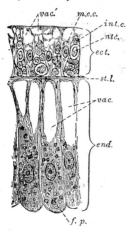

FIG. 144.—A small portion of a transverse section of *Hydra*.

ect., Ectoderm ; *end.,* endoderm ; *f.p.,* food particle. ingested by an endoderm cell ; *int.c.,* interstitial cells ; *m.e.c.,* musculo - epithelial cell ; *ntc.,* nematocyst ; *st.l.,* structureless lamella ; *vac.,* vacuoles in endoderm cells ; *vac'.,* vacuoles in ectoderm cells.

Such a nervous system is known as a *nerve net*. It is at first hard to see how with it any variety of action is possible. It would seem that the only result of any stimulus to it must be a general contraction of the body. Actually, however, the behaviour of *Hydra*, though it is much simpler than that of higher animals such as the frog, is, as we shall see, fairly complicated, and shows a good deal of adaptation to circumstances. This, of course, means contractions which are local and vary with conditions. It is due to several factors, some of which we have already met in considering the nervous system of the frog (p. 94). (1) The stimuli which the system receives vary in strength, and the stronger the stimulus the more effective are the impulses it starts. (2) Owing to the numerous synapses between the many cells of the net, the impulses become less effective as they go, so that those set up by strong stimuli travel farther and set in action a larger part of the body than those of weaker stimuli. (3) Stimuli which are too weak to be effective singly may be summated, so that a small stimulus repeated will have effect where at first it has none. (4) The activity of one part of the body may set up impulses which affect others. Thus the activity of one tentacle brings others to its aid, and the tentacles set the mouth in action. (5) The reaction both of the receptors (sense cells) and of the effectors (muscle fibres) varies from time to time, as with hunger or fatigue. (6) Possibly, as in many other animals, some of the muscle fibres respond more easily than others to stimuli. Inhibitions (p. 95) probably do not occur in the nerve net. By receiving a stimulus, one part of the body becomes dominant and the messages started in it set other parts in action. That is why the body behaves as a whole. That its action is adjusted to particular stimuli is due to the factors just stated.

It is instructive to contrast this nervous system with that of the frog (or any other animal higher than the cœlenterata —the group to which *Hydra* belongs). There each nerve cell has a long process—a nerve fibre—and such processes are gathered into trunks—nerves—which run to and from a central exchange, and, instead of being broadcast as in

Physiology of the Nerve Net.

Hydra, the impulses are directed to particular organs. The advantages which such a system has over the nerve net are great. It requires for a given effect fewer nerve cells and so avoids the weakening of impulses at numerous synapses, is more precise, and gives better facilities for the co-ordination of action in distant parts of the body. We

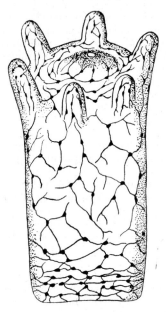

FIG. 145.—A Diagram of the Nervous System of *Hydra*.—After Hadzi.

shall see the beginning of such a system in the Flatworms (p. 240).

In the endoderm the cells are tall and columnar. Some of them, especially numerous in the oral cone and absent from the tentacles, are *glandular*. They have a narrow stem and a wide end, turned towards the enteron and containing granules of a

Endoderm.

substance which they secrete. The most numerous and conspicuous cells are *nutritive*. They are stout, and have their bases produced into contractile fibres, which are shorter than those of the musculo-epithelial cells and run around the body, not along it. Their protoplasm contains large vacuoles, and also, in the green *Hydra*, a number of round bodies of a green colour, each of which consists of a central mass of protoplasm with a covering of a different kind of protoplasm containing the green substance known as *chlorophyll*, to which the colour of plants is due. These bodies multiply by division. In the brown *Hydra* the green bodies are absent, but there are present some yellowish bodies of similar shape, in which, however, no structure can be made out. The ends of the cells which abut on the enteron bear flagella, which can be replaced by pseudopodia. There are some sense cells and a few nerve cells.

The green bodies of *Hydra viridis* are degenerate, non-flagellate individuals of a minute plant, related to *Chlamydomonas*, and are known as *Zoochlorellæ*. Like other green plants they nourish themselves by building up complex organic compounds from simple inorganic ones (carbon dioxide, water, salts, etc., see p. 26). They obtain these simple substances as waste products of the metabolism of the *Hydra*. It may be that the *Hydra* absorbs from them in return the excess of carbohydrates which they form; and this would account for the absence from them of starch, which is so constantly found in plants. Thus there is between the two organisms a partnership, in which the animal benefits by the removal of waste products and the supply of oxygen and possibly of carbohydrates, and the plant benefits by the rich supply of nitrogenous material and carbon dioxide. Such a partnership is known as *symbiosis* and is in contrast with parasitism, in which one of the partners benefits at the expense of the other.

The movements of *Hydra* are carried out mainly by the muscular processes of the cells, though the **Movements and Reactions.** surface of the basal disc can put forth pseudopodia, and it is possible that by means of these the animal can slowly change its position. The muscular processes of the ectoderm cells, when they contract, make the body shorter and wider; those of the endoderm make it narrower and longer. The position of rest is one of moderate extension. *Hydra* does not remain passive in the absence of stimuli, but, after standing for some time extended in readiness for prey, it automatically contracts either the whole body or the tentacles only, and then extends in a new direction. Thus it explores the whole of its surroundings. From time to time it changes its position. This is done by extending the body and bending it, so that the tentacles touch some neighbouring object and adhere to it by means of the nematocysts with sticky threads. The basal disc is then either withdrawn altogether from the spot to which it was fixed and put down in a new spot close to the tentacles, or caused to glide up to the tentacles. In either case the animal moves in somewhat the same way as a looper caterpillar (Fig. 141). A *Hydra* responds to every stimulus, except that of food, by contracting. If the stimulus be weak it affects only the part of the body to which it is applied, as a single tentacle will withdraw from a slight touch; if it be strong its effect spreads to the whole body. A stimulus applied to one side of the body a number of times causes it presently to move away in some other direction. *Hydra* avoids both too feeble and too strong a light.

The food of *Hydra* consists of water-fleas and other small animals. These are caught by the
Nutrition and Excretion. tentacles, and carried by them to the mouth, which then opens and swallows the prey. The animal will not feed unless it be hungry. If it be well fed, creatures which swim against the tentacles are allowed to escape, but, if food has been scarce, as soon as the prey has become temporarily attached by the nematocysts to one tentacle the others bend over towards it and help to secure it and push it towards the mouth. If the animal be starving the mere smell of food in the neighbourhood is enough to set the tentacles working, but usually they are not put into action till the food has been both smelt and touched. It is not possible to deceive the *Hydra* into swallowing substances, such as pieces of blotting-paper, which do not smell like food, but blotting-paper soaked in beef-tea is swallowed when it touches the tentacles. Once swallowed, the food is passed deep into the enteron

and there softened by a juice which the gland cells secrete, broken up by the churning which it gets as the body expands and contracts, and swept about by the flagella. Part of the food is dissolved in the enteron and absorbed in solution, part of it is taken up by pseudopodia of the endoderm cells and digested within their protoplasm. Presumably the ectoderm is nourished by substances passed on from the endoderm, either by diffusion through the structureless lamella or along the fine threads of protoplasm which put the two layers into connection across it. The undigested remains of the food are driven out of the mouth by a sudden contraction of the wall of the body. In unnatural conditions of culture the animals become liable to depression much like that of *Paramecium*, in which the powers of movement, feeding, and fission are affected and death ensues. *Respiration* and *excretion* probably take place from the surface of the ectoderm and endoderm; there is no special organ for either process.

Reproduction. The species of *Hydra* reproduce themselves both sexually and asexually. The sexual reproduction of *H. viridis* and *H. grisea* takes place normally in the spring and summer, that of *H. fusca* in the autumn. The animals are usually hermaphrodite, but strains are met with in which the sexes are separate. The generative organs are ectodermal structures developed when sexual reproduction is about to take place. The ovaries, of which there is generally only one in each individual, are found in the lower part of the body; the testes, of which there are several, are in the upper part. In the early stages of both organs the interstitial cells multiply and push out the musculo-epithelial cells so as to form a swelling. In the case of the ovary one of the interstitial cells becomes an oocyte (p. 131). This increases in size and begins to throw out pseudopodia, by which it swallows the rest of the interstitial cells contained in the swelling. At the same time it lays up in its protoplasm numerous dark, spherical granules of yolk. As the swelling increases, the musculo-epithelial cells are stretched, their conical bodies forming long stalks, which are pushed apart by the oocyte, and their outer layer forming a thin covering for the latter. When the oocyte has swallowed all the surrounding cells it withdraws its pseudo-

podia and becomes a large rounded body, about which a
gelatinous coat is secreted. Polar bodies are now formed,
the covering of musculo-epithelial cells parts and shrinks
back so that the ovum is exposed save for the gelatinous
coat, and fertilisation is effected by one of the spermatozoa
which are present in the surrounding
water. In the formation of a testis
the multiplication of the interstitial
cells stretches the musculo-epithelial
cells as in the ovary. The interstitial
cells become spermatocytes, which
lie among the stalks of the musculo-
epithelial cells and undergo two
divisions as in the frog, the resulting
cells developing into spermatozoa
with a conical head, a neck, and a
tail. By the breaking of the covering layer the spermatozoa are set
free and swim in the water, where
they perish unless they find a ripe
ovum. Since either the ovary or the
testis generally ripens first, cross-
fertilisation will usually take place, but it does not appear that self-fertilisation is always impossible.

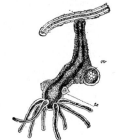

FIG. 146.—*Hydra* hang-
ing from water-weed.

ov., Ovary, with nearly ripe
ovum ; *te.*, testes.

See also Fig. **147.**

Development. After fertilisation the oosperm undergoes cleavage into blastomeres
(p. 137), which as they increase in numbers form at first
a hollow sphere known as the *blastula*, whose wall consists of a single layer of cells. Some of these migrate into the hollow
which they fill. The outer layer now represents ectoderm and the
inner mass endoderm. The cells of the ectoderm become smaller than
those of the endoderm and lose their yolk granules. A thick, spiny
covering of a horny substance is now secreted by the ectoderm, and
the round, prickly body thus formed falls away from the parent and
rests for several weeks, during which it may be carried about by
currents, in mud on the feet of water animals, etc. After a time the
ectoderm differentiates into musculo-epithelial and interstitial cells,
the jelly is secreted, the shell cracks, and the embryo projects. A
split in the endoderm forms the enteron, tentacles grow out, a mouth
is formed, and finally the young *Hydra* frees itself from the remains
of the shell, moves away, and begins to feed and grow.

Asexual reproduction also begins with the formation of a
swelling of ectoderm by the multiplication of the interstitial
cells, which afterwards become converted into musculo-

epithelial and endoderm cells, passing through the structureless lamella in the latter case. The result of this is an

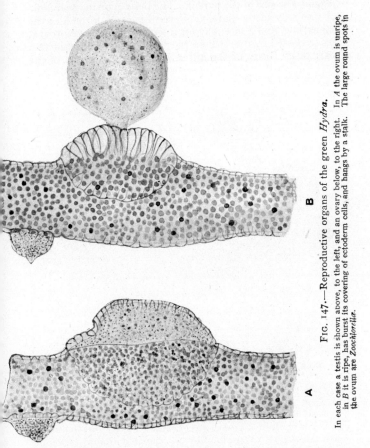

FIG. 147.—Reproductive organs of the green *Hydra.* In each case a testis is shown above, to the left, and an ovary below, to the right. In *A* the ovum is unripe, in *B* it is ripe, has burst its covering of ectoderm cells, and hangs by a stalk. The large round spots in the ovum are *Zoochlorellæ.*

increase in the extent of the ectoderm and endoderm which leads to a bulging of the body wall. The knob or *bud* thus formed becomes longer, tentacles grow out around its free end, a mouth is formed, and finally the base narrows till the bud breaks free as a new individual, which grows till it reaches the size of the parent. The buds arise in the middle of the body of the parent. Several may be formed at the same time, and a bud may form secondary buds before it is set free. While it is still on the parent, the bud is wholly a part of the body of the latter. Each of the layers of the

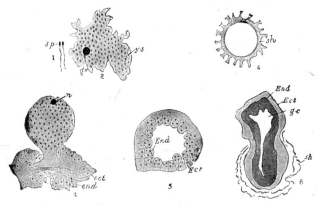

FIG. 148. — The development of *Hydra.*—After Brauer.

1. *sp.,* Spermatozoa.
2. Amœboid ovum ; *g.v.,* germinal vesicle or nucleus ; *y.s.,* yolk spherules.
3. Ovum protruding ; *n.,* its nucleus ; *ect.,* the ruptured ectoderm of the parent ; *end.,* the endoderm.
4. Prickly envelope (*sh.*) of embryo liberated from parent.
5. Section of blastula—*Ect.,* ectoderm ; *End.,* endoderm arising ; it will fill the blastula cavity (blastocoele).
6. Section of young *Hydra* leaving shell. *Ect.,* ectoderm ; *End.,* endoderm : *g.c.,* enteron ; *sh.,* ruptured envelopes.

parent is continuous with the corresponding layer of the bud, a suitable stimulus is transmitted by the nervous system from one to the other, and the entera are in free communication, so that food obtained by either is available for the other. Occasionally a *Hydra* will reproduce by fission into two, either lengthwise or transversely, of the whole body. In this case, as in the fission of a *Paramecium,* structural development as well as the growth of each product of fission must take place after separation, whereas in the bud, as we have seen, the structural development takes place before fission.

A property akin to asexual reproduction is that of **Regeneration.** *regeneration* or the replacement of lost parts, which is possessed by *Hydra* in a very high degree. To some extent all organisms have this power, but as a rule the higher the animal the less is its faculty for regeneration. In man it is little more than the power of healing wounds. Not only will *Hydra* grow anew any part, such as a tentacle, which is cut off, but any fragment of the body, provided it be not too small and contain portions of both layers, will grow into an entire animal.

We must now look at the budding of *Hydra* from a somewhat different point of view. By the out-**Hydroid Colonies.** growth of buds, the animal increases the size of its body in precisely the same way as *Carchesium*; that is to say by the addition of new members, each of which repeats the whole structure of the body as it existed at first. In the case of *Hydra* the process is carried further by the fission of the repeated part from the parent body, so that an act of reproduction takes place, but it is easy to imagine a case in which this would not happen. The result would be the permanent conversion of the body of the *Hydra* into a colony, of which the buds would be the zooids. Now there are a number of animals related to *Hydra* in which this actually takes place. Such animals are known as *hydroids*, and nearly all of them are marine. A common example is *Obelia geniculata*, which is found growing upon seaweeds near low watermark on the British coast.

Certain comparatively unimportant differences distinguish the polyps of *Obelia* from those of *Hydra*. **Obelia : Anatomy of the Polyp.** The tentacles are more numerous and, instead of being hollow, have a solid core of large endoderm cells, with very stout walls of intercellular substance and highly vacuolated contents. In the ectoderm the muscular fibres are independent cells with nuclei of their own, lying below the epithelium. The oral cone is very large and forms a chamber above the rest of the enteron. From the middle of the basal disc of each polyp the body-wall is continued as a narrow tube, which joins the tubes from other polyps so as to form a branching structure like the body of a flowering plant. This is continuous at its base with a root-like arrangement of tubes on the surface of the seaweed, known as the *hydrorhiza*. The tubes of the whole structure are known as the *cœnosarc*, and the polyp heads as *hydranths*. The whole colony is enclosed in a horny case or *perisarc*, which is secreted by the ectoderm and follows closely the outline of the body, but is separated from it by a small space, bridged by processes from some of the ectoderm cells. At the base of each hydranth the perisarc expands into a cup or *hydrotheca* into which the hydranth can be withdrawn.

The generative organs are not borne by the polyps, but by special bodies, which originate as members of the colony, are set free by breaking away as the buds of *Hydra* are, and carry out sexual reproduction as independent individuals. These individuals differ widely from the polyps, being, indeed, so unlike them that their origin from the colony would never have been

The Medusa.

FIG. 149.—Part of a colony of *Obelia* seen under a hand lens.

guessed unless it had been seen to take place. They are small *jelly-fish* or *medusæ*. Each has the shape of an umbrella with a short, thick handle and a fringe of tentacles around the edge. The convex upper side is called the *exumbrella*, the concave lower side the *subumbrella*, the handle the *manubrium*. Around the edge of the umbrella a low ridge projects inwards. This is the *velum* and represents a much larger structure in the same region of many other medusæ. At the end of the manubrium is the mouth,

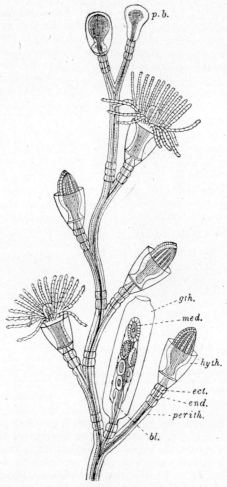

FIG. 150.—Part of a colony of *Obelia*, magnified.

bl., Blastostyle; *ect.*, ectoderm; *end.*, endoderm; *gth.*, gonotheca; *hyth.*, hydrotheca; *med.*, medusa bud; *p.b.*, polyp bud; *perith.*, peritheca.

which leads by a tubular gullet along the manubrium to a stomach in the middle of the body. From this four *radial canals* run outwards to a *ring canal* at the edge of the umbrella. The lining of all these internal spaces consists of endoderm, and the radial canals lie in a sheet of endoderm, known as the *endoderm lamella.* In fact we may regard the internal cavities of a medusa as corresponding to the enteron of a polyp in which the walls have come together over a large area, leaving certain spaces which form the gullet, stomach, and canals. The whole outside of the body and tentacles is covered with ectoderm. Between the ectoderm and the endoderm is a layer of jelly, which is very thick, especially on the exumbrella side. The medusa may be compared

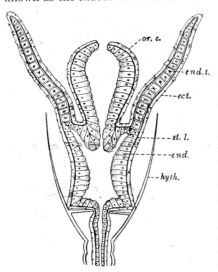

FIG. 151.—A longitudinal section of a hydranth of *Obelia*, highly magnified.

ect., Ectoderm ; *end.*, endoderm ; *end.t.*, endoderm of the tentacles ; *hyth.*, hydrotheca ; *or.c.*, oral cone ; *st.l.*, structureless lamella.

to a polyp which is greatly widened and shortened, the walls of the wide, flat enteron coming together in places, as we have seen, and the structureless lamella increasing in thickness to form the jelly. The manubrium represents the oral cone and the tentacles stand around it at a greater distance owing to the widening of the body. The arrangement of the organs of a medusa is an excellent example of what is known as *radial symmetry*. In bilateral symmetry (p. 33) the parts of the body are arranged on each side

(right and left) of a plane, in such a way that no other plane
will divide the body into two halves which are alike.   In

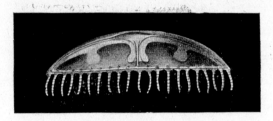

FIG. 152.—A medusa of *Obelia*, magnified.

radial symmetry the parts of the body are arranged about a
point in such a way that innumerable planes divide the
body into like halves.   Polyps are also radially symmetrical.

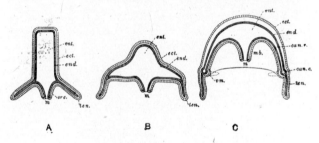

FIG. 153.—A diagram to illustrate the relation between polyp
and medusa.

A, The polyp; *B*, an imaginary intermediate form; *C*, the medusa.

can.c., Circular canal; *can.r.*, radial canal; *ect.*, ectoderm; *end.*, endoderm; *ent.*,
enteron; *m.*, mouth; *mb.*, manubrium; *or.c.*, oral cone; *ten.*, tentacle; *vm.*,
velum. The dotted line represents the velum as it is found in many medusæ
but not in *Obelia*.

The medusa floats in the sea with the manubrium downwards and the tentacles hanging like the
snaky locks of its classical namesake.   It swims
by contractions of the plentiful musculature of
the subumbrella side, which drive water out of the umbrella
and send the animal forwards in the opposite direction.

Movements of the Medusa.

The contractions are started by impulses which originate in the nerve net at the umbrella margin. There nervous transmission is facilitated by the *nerve-rings*—two specially well-developed circular tracts of the net—and there is provision for keeping balance by means of eight sense organs, known as *statocysts*, situated each at the base of one of the tentacles. These are small hollow vesicles each containing a calcareous body which hangs in a single cell that secreted it. The swaying of the calcareous bodies against fine processes on sense-cells which line the outer side of the vesicle gives rise to impulses by which the movements of the animal are regulated through the nervous system, stronger contractions being caused on the side which dips.

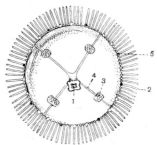

Fig. 154.—The medusa of *Obelia*, seen from the subumbrella side. —From Shipley and MacBride.

1, Mouth, at end of manubrium; *2*, tentacle; *3*, gonad; *4*, radial canal; *5*, statocyst.

The medusæ are of opposite sexes. The

Reproduction

generative organs are not developed till after the animal is set free. They are four in number and lie on the subumbrella below the radial canals. Each consists of a knob of ectoderm, into which passes a short branch from the radial canal. The germ mother-cells originate in the ectoderm of the manubrium, migrate into the endoderm, and pass along the radial canals to the generative organs, where they migrate into the ectoderm again. When the ova or sperm are ripe, they are shed by the rupture of the ectoderm into the water, where fertilisation takes place. As in *Hydra*, segmentation leads to the formation of a hollow blastula. From this, by immigration of cells at one spot, there is reached a stage with a solid mass of endoderm such as that found in *Hydra*. The animal at this stage is of a lengthened egg-shape and has a ciliated ectoderm, by which it swims freely for a while. It is known as a *planula*. The planula then settles down by its broader end, an enteron is formed by a split in the endoderm, tentacles and a mouth form at the other end, and thus there develops a polyp, from which by budding a colony arises. When the colony has reached a certain size there appear, in the angles between the stem and the branches which bear the hydranths, tubular outgrowths known as *blastostyles*, each enclosed in a vase of perisarc known as a *gonotheca*. A blastostyle and its gonotheca are together known as a *gonangium*. The blastostyle is probably an incomplete

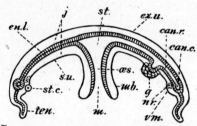

FIG. 155.—A diagram of a vertical section of the medusa of *Obelia*. The section is supposed to pass on one side along a radial canal, and on the other across the endoderm lamella. In reality this would not be possible, since the canals are opposite one another.

can.c., Circular canal ; *can.r.*, radial canal ; *en.l.*, endoderm lamella ; *ex.u.*, exumbrella surface ; *g.*, gonad ; *j.*, jelly ; *m.*, mouth ; *mb.*, manubrium ; *n.r.*, nerve ring ; *œs.*, œsophagus ; *s.u.*, subumbrella surface ; *st.*, stomach ; *stc.*, statocyst ; *ten.*, tentacle ; *vm.*, velum.

zooid. On its sides are formed a number of buds which develop into little medusæ and escape through the opening at the top of the gonotheca.

It will be seen that *Obelia*, like *Hydra*, re-**Alternation of Generations.** produces itself both sexually and asexually. Sexual reproduction is carried out by the medusa and leads to the formation of polyps. The asexual reproduction consists in the budding off of medusæ from the polyp stock. Whereas, however,

FIG. 156.—A diagram to show the development of medusæ as buds on a blastostyle.

bl., blastostyle ; *s.u.c.*, subumbrellar cavity ; 1-6, successive stages in the development of a medusa.

in *Hydra*, the two processes go on side by side, sometimes in the same individual, and succeed one another quite irregularly, in *Obelia* there are two different types of individual—the polyp stock and the medusa—which follow one another regularly and are each confined to one method of reproduction. Thus we have a definite *alternation of generations*, a sexual and an asexual form succeeding one another. It will be remembered that such generations also alternate in *Monocystis* and that the malaria parasite has a more complicated life-history of the same kind. The asexual generation of *Obelia* is relatively inactive, gathering much nourishment and spending little: the sexual generation is active, spending its substance freely in locomotion, which ensures the distribution of the species and thus opens up fresh food supplies and increases the chances of escape from local dangers. The gist of the story is the distribution of labour among individuals of different kinds.

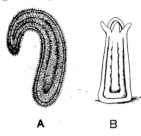

A   B

FIG. 157.—*A*, Planula larva; *B*, the young polyp into which the planula grows after settling.

Metagenesis. The designation " alternation of generations " has been applied to a number of different types of life-history which have in common only the fact that reproduction is accomplished differently in successive phases of the reproducing organism. It is a useful " omnibus " term but should not be taken to imply more than superficial resemblance between the processes it earns. The type met with in hydroids is known as *Metagenesis*. We shall observe a quite different process, which does not involve asexual reproduction, in the Liver Fluke and again in a nematode worm. Yet another is seen in plants, very clearly, for instance, in ferns. That in the Sporozoa has (in respect of chromosome sets) some resemblance to that of plants. In view of this diversity, many biologists prefer not to speak of the life-history of *Obelia* as an alternation of generations, but to use for it the term metagenesis.

The above account of the reproduction of hydroids differs in one respect from that which is generally given. On the analogy of the budding of *Hydra*, it is usual to regard the formation of a hydroid colony by budding as a kind of asexual reproduction in which there are formed numerous "individuals" which do not separate.

Reproduction and Colony-building. In that case the alternation of generations contains an indefinite number of acts of asexual reproduction between each two sexual acts. We have preferred to treat the polyp stock as one individual containing a number of semi-independent parts—the hydranths—each of which repeats the structure of the whole body as it was at first, and having certain other parts—the blastostyles and most of the cœnosarc —which are differently constructed, serve the entire body, and are wholly dependent upon it. This view involves the following considerations. The development of the individual and its reproduction are essentially the same process—*morphogenesis*, which is also at work in regeneration. Any part of an organism, from the smallest organ to the whole body, is liable to be repeated, with or without differences between the repeated parts. This phenomenon has been called *merism* : we have seen it in cilia, trichocysts, contractile vacuoles, cells, limbs, zooids, etc. Sometimes, as in cilia, cells, or zooids of the same kind, it has not involved differences. Sometimes, as in cells or limbs or zooids of different kinds, it has involved differences between the repeated parts. Sometimes the parts are present in their full number from the first ; sometimes they increase in number as growth goes on. From time to time every organism produces a part which not only repeats its whole structure, but also separates from it by an act of fission. This process is reproduction. In some cases of reproduction, as in the budding of *Hydra*, the repetition of structure takes place *before* separation. In other cases, as in the formation of germs,[1] the part which separates is simple in structure, but has the power of repeating the structure of the parent body *after* fission.

The term *individual*, whose application was in question in the foregoing paragraph, has been used in zoology with very different meanings, which are well illustrated by the life-history of the hydroids.

Individuality.

---

[1] In this case there may be the additional complication that two such separated parts so develop as to produce but one body after fusion.

An individual is a single complete living being. There are in *Obelia* three things that might claim to be this : (1) Since the medusa carries out all the functions of life in itself, it seems natural to assert that it is a complete living being, and since, as we have seen, its structure is essentially that of a polyp, we might assume that each polyp is also an individual. (2) On the other hand, the whole polyp stock is a unit, and we might consider it to be one individual, of which the separate polyps are members, still regarding the medusa as an individual. (3) From this we might go further, and claim that, as the medusa is morphologically equivalent to one polyp head, it is but a member of the individual to which the polyps belong, though for purposes of distribution it separates from them, and thus we might regard as one disjoined individual the whole mass of forms which arise from the fertilised ovum which gave rise to the polyp stock.

Of these alternatives the first is open to the objection that it ignores the fact that the stock equally with each of its polyps may be regarded as a whole since it has common nourishment and reproductive organs (the gonangia), and obliges us to regard as individuals the blastostyles, which are morphologically equivalent only to parts of other individuals. The third alternative does indeed recognise what is a true entity, since the development of every ovum (including those which develop without fertilisation) does make a new start in that it creates organisation anew, and with variation owing to a shuffling of the contents of the chromosomes (p. 138) ; but to regard such entities as individuals would compel us to hold, not only that all the vast host of independent living beings which arise by the asexual reproduction of a protozoon are parts of one individual, but also that the " identical " twins formed by the dividing of a single ovum are not, even in the case of man, separate individuals, and this amounts to a *reductio ad absurdum*. The remaining (second) alternative is that which we have adopted above. It may be stated as follows : " Every continuous mass of living matter which arises normally by fission is an individual." That view has the advantage that it does not force us to create artificial units of any kind.

According to it, the act which makes an individual is the act of fission by which it becomes independent of its parent, and fertilisation is the blending of two undeveloped individuals into one, while the polyp stock is an individual which contains a number of units meristically repeated, and the medusa is an individual consisting of one unit of the same type as those which exist in the polyp stock.

The essence of organic unity—that which causes a mass of living matter, whether zooid or free " individual," so to be organised and to behave that the activity of each part is subordinated to that of the whole—is as yet ill understood. But it would seem to be connected with a dominating influence exercised by certain parts which become the seat of activity, and therefore perhaps of a higher rate of metabolism, over the other parts. Thus in the development of a hydroid colony the apical region is the seat of an activity which brings about the formation of a hydranth there, while the basal part, dominated by the apex, remains less active, and merely grows in length, until by this process some point upon it becomes sufficiently removed from the apex to allow the origination of a new hydranth, which in turn dominates its own branch. So the body of the colony is shaped, each new member coming into existence when and where a previous dominating member permits. After this fashion, it is suggested, though with infinite complications and the intervention of many other factors, the bodies of all individuals are built up. The continuous fall in metabolic activity between two points, which on one theory is the cause of these phenomena, is known as a *metabolic gradient*.

The Unifying Factor.

Other kinds of polyps and medusæ are known than those which are represented by *Hydra* and *Obelia*. Sea-anemones (*Actiniaria* : Fig. 532) are polyps of rather complex structure, the edge of the mouth being tucked in to form a gullet lined with ectoderm, while folds or *mesenteries* of endoderm stretch across the enteron from the body-wall, some of them (*primary* mesenteries) reaching the gullet. The testes and ovaries are developed from the endoderm of the mesenteries, and their products are shed through the mouth. The ectoderm is ciliated, and the

Cœlenterata.

mesoglœa contains cells of various kinds derived from the ectoderm and endoderm.[1] At the ends of the oblong gullet are two grooves, the *siphonoglyphs*, down one of which and up the other currents of water flow, even when the rest of the mouth is closed. As in *Hydra*, the tentacles are hollow and there is no medusa, though a planula larva is found. Corals are related to anemones, but possess a calcareous skeleton which sometimes, as in the Red Coral, lies in the

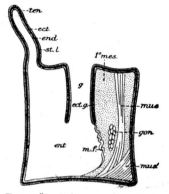

FIG. 158.—A diagram of a vertical section of a sea-anemone.

ect., ectoderm of tentacle ; *ect.g.*, ectoderm lining gullet ; *end.*, endoderm ; *ent.*, enteron ; *g.*, gullet ; *gon.*, gonad ; *m.f.*, mesenterial filament ; *mus.*, longitudinal or "retractor" muscle ; *mus′.*, oblique or "parietal" muscle ; *st.l.*, mesoglœa ; *ten.*, tentacle ; 1°*mes.*, primary mesentery.

jelly, but in the reef corals or madrepores is secreted on the outside of the ectoderm of the lower part of the body. Thus the " coral insect " is a polyp. The large jelly-fish (*Acalephæ*) differ from the little medusæ of the hydroids in having no velum or nerve ring, and developing their

---

[1] Though these cells do not form a third layer or " mesoderm " such as is found in the higher animals (p. 275), yet they foreshadow that dispersed element of the mesoderm which is known during development as " mesenchyme " (p. 625).

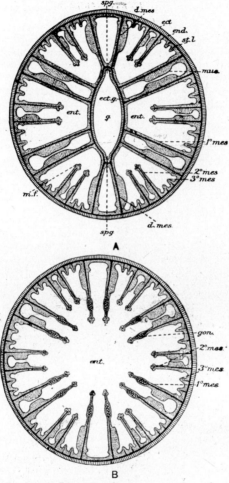

FIG. 159.—Diagrams of transverse sections of a
sea-anemone.

A., Through the gullet ; *B*, below the gullet.

d.mes., " directive " mesentery ; *ect.*, ectoderm ; *end.*, endoderm ; *ent.*, enteron ; *m.f.*, mesenterial filament ; *mus.*,
muscle ; *spg.*, siphonoglyphs ; *st.l.*, mesoglœa ; 1°*mes.*,
2°*mes.*, 3°*mes.*, primary, secondary, and tertiary
mesenteries.

generative cells on the endoderm of the stomach wall ;
their radial canals are often branched. Under the four
generative organs lie *subgenital pits* of the subumbrella
ectoderm. When there is a polyp generation (*hydra-tuba*),
it has solid tentacles and four mesenteries, and gives rise to
the medusa, not by budding, but by dividing transversely

FIG. 160.— A small specimen of the Common Jelly-fish
Aurelia aurita, natural size.

Note the horseshoe-shaped gonads, showing through the transparent tissues ; the
radial canals, alternately branched and unbranched ; the little sense tentacles in
notches each opposite the middle branch of a canal ; the marginal tentacles ;
and the arms of the manubrium, each folded and fringed.
    Water circulates from the stomach by the unbranched (adradial) canals to the
circular canal, and back by the branched (per- and inter-radial) canals.

into slices (*strobilation*), so that it appears for a while like
a pile of saucers. Each saucer then floats off, turns over,
and becomes a little jelly-fish or *ephyra*, which grows and
takes on the adult form. It seems likely that this curious
process arose by a polyp acquiring the habit of breaking
off its free end and sending it floating with the gonads to
distribute the species, and that then this came to be

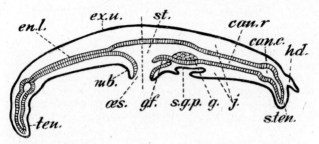

FIG. 161.—A diagram of a vertical section through one of the large jelly-fishes, such as *Aurelia*. The section is divided by a dotted line into two halves, in one of which it is supposed to pass through a radial canal, and in the other through the endoderm lamella.

can.c., Circular canal ; *can.r.*, radial canal ; *en.l.*, endoderm lamella ; *ex.u.*, ex-umbrella ectoderm ; *g.*, gonad ; *g.f.*, gastral filament ; *hd.*, hood covering sense tentacle ; *j.*, jelly or mesoglea ; *mb.*, manubrium ; *œs* , œsophagus ; *s.g.p.*, subgenital pit ; *s.ten.*, sense tentacle ; *st.*, stomach ; *ten.* tentacle.

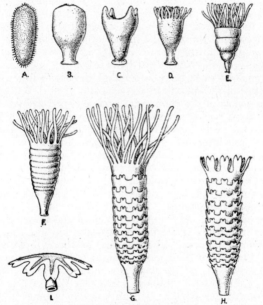

FIG. 162.—The life-history of *Aurelia*.

A, Planula ; *B-H*, stages in the development of the hydra tuba ; *I*, ephyra.

repeated before the first slice was set free. In any case, while the medusa of a hydroid probably represents a whole polyp developed for a floating life, that of the hydra-tuba is only the top of a polyp remodelled, though the structure of polyps is such that the result in the two cases is substantially the same. All these and other animals whose structure is fundamentally that of a polyp or medusa are known as *Cœlenterata*.

We have seen that *Hydra*, like the Protozoa, is liable to the sickness known as " depression," and this **Death in the Cœlenterata.** may prove fatal. But there is no evidence that *Hydra*, any more than the Protozoa, is subject to that natural death which awaits the frog. The same thing may be said of many other cœlenterate polyps, though the Medusa, exhausting itself in producing the reproductive cells, comes to die. This enduring life is probably due to most of the cells which compose the body of a polyp being less highly differentiated for special functions than those of the tissues of a frog, and is a very interesting and important fact, since it shows us that the mortality of the body cells (p. 150) is not an unfailing difference between them and the germ cells, but is a consequence of the specialisation of most of them. What may be the cause of the connection between specialisation and mortality it is not easy to say. Possibly in the devotion of cells to the performance of a special function the faculty of excretion is impaired, so that eventually they are poisoned by their own waste products. More probably the secret is that the course of metabolism brings about in protoplasm some change which hampers its working, and that specialisation abolishes the power of renewing the parts which have undergone this change. It would seem from the wasting of the tissues of old animals that, in a specialised tissue, effete structures can be destroyed but not rebuilt. Whether, again, it is the nucleus, or the cytoplasm, or both, that are in fault does not appear, though the case of *Paramecium*, which has from time to time to destroy its meganucleus (p. 169), suggests that the nucleus is at least partly responsible. In any case it is interesting to notice that the highly differentiated Ciliata show the same weakness which attends differentiation in the Metazoa.

CHAPTER XIII

FLATWORMS

Divers of the lower animals are popularly known as **Platyhelminthes.** "worms." They have little in common save that their bodies are longer than they are broad and have bilateral symmetry, and that their organisation is rather simple. The lowliest of such creatures are known as the *Flatworms* or *Platyhelminthes*. As their name implies the bodies of these worms are flat. They have no anus and no blood vessels or body cavity, being constructed internally of a spongy mass of tissue

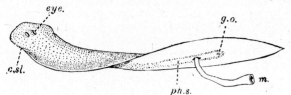

Fig. 163.—A turbellarian (*Planaria polychroa*).—From Shipley and MacBride.

c.sl., Ciliated sensory slit at side of head ; *eye* ; *g.o.*, genital opening ; *m.*, mouth, at end of outstretched pharynx ; *ph.s.*, sheath into which pharynx can be withdrawn.

(parenchyma, p. 243), containing muscle fibres, and, imbedded in this, a gut (except in the tapeworms), a nervous system with a rudimentary brain, an excretory system formed of branched tubes ending internally in ciliated " flame cells " (p. 243), and a complicated, nearly always hermaphrodite generative system.

Some of the flatworms lead a free, if unobtrusive, **Turbellaria.** existence in fresh waters or the sea or in damp places. They are known as *Turbellaria*. The epidermis on the surface of their bodies is a columnar ciliated epithelium which contains gland cells and sense cells of various kinds. The sense cells are most numerous at the front end, which constitutes a rudimentary head, and they may be raised on tentacles or sunk in pits ; there are usually also eyes. The worms crⱥwl on the bottom or under the surface film of the waters by means of their cilia, and the larger kinds swim by muscular undulations of the body. They are carnivorous and predatory, seizing their prey by means of a muscular pharynx, which can be protruded as a funnel. These little creatures are not of great importance either to man or in the economy of nature, but one feature of their organisation calls for our attention. In them better than in the more important parasitic flatworms there can be studied the simplest kind of brain. It consists of a pair of ganglia in the head, united by a commissure and giving off longitudinal nerves to the body. These supply a nerve net under the epidermis and another deeper in the body. The function of this brain is merely to relay and distribute the impulses from the important sense organs on the head. Unlike *Hydra*, where no part of the body *permanently* dominates the rest, these creatures, moving as they do always with the same end forwards, have that end organised for perception and the consequent stimulation of the rest of the body. This permanent organisation of a dominant region of the body unifies the reaction of the body as a whole to changes in its surroundings. It brings into being

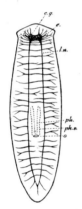

Fig. 164.— A diagram of the Nervous System of a Turbellarian.

c.g. brain ; *e.*, eye ; *l.n.*, longitudinal nerve cord ; *o.*, opening through which the pharynx is protruded ; *ph.*, pharynx ; *ph.s.*, pharynx-sheath.

a brain and nerves, and these have further advantages (see p. 215). But in the Turbellaria the brain does not co-ordinate the activities of different regions of the body. It sets them in action : that each plays its proper part is due to local organisation.

Much more important to man than the Turbellaria are two classes of flatworms that are parasitic—the Flukes or Trematoda and the Tapeworms or Cestoda. We have now to proceed to the study of some examples of these

Trematoda :
the Liver
Fluke.

groups. Sheep which are fed in damp meadows are liable to a serious and usually fatal disease known as " liver rot," in which the wool falls off, dropsical swellings appear, and the animal wastes away. This has been found to be caused by a parasite known as the Liver Fluke, *Distomum hepaticum* or *Fasciola hepatica,* which lives in the bile ducts of the sheep and sometimes of other animals, including occasionally man. It is a flat, brownish worm, about one inch long by half an inch broad, shaped like a leaf with a blunt triangular projection at the broader end. At the tip of this projection lies the mouth, in the midst of an *anterior sucker,* and just behind the projection an imperforate *posterior or ventral sucker* is placed in the middle of the ventral side and serves as a means of attachment. Nearly midway between the suckers is a smaller *genital opening,* at the hind end of the body is a minute *excretory pore,* and on the dorsal surface at about a third of the length of the animal from the front end lies the *opening of the Laurer-Stieda canal* presently to be mentioned.

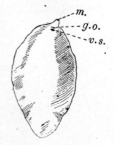

FIG. 165.—The Liver Fluke.

g.o., Genital opening; *m.,* mouth; *v.s.,* ventral sucker.

The body is covered with a cuticle, in which little backward-pointing *spinules* are embedded.

Gut.

The mouth leads into an ovoid, muscular pharynx, from which a short œsophagus passes backwards to divide before the posterior sucker into right and left branches or intestines, which run on either side of the middle line to the hind end of the body, giving off on either side many offsets, which in turn are much branched. There is no anus. The worm feeds on the juices, probably normally on the blood, of its host.

Layers of
the Body.

The ectoderm cells have sunk inward after secreting the cuticle. Below the cuticle lie successively circular, longitudinal, and diagonal layers of muscle fibres, with the epidermal cells among the

16

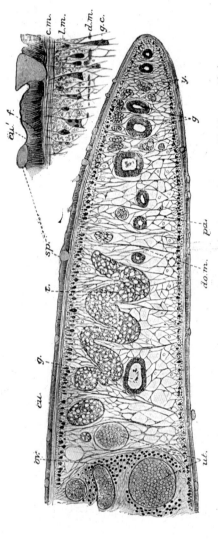

Fig. 166.—A transverse section of a liver fluke, with a portion more highly magnified.

c.m., Circular muscle layer; *cu.*, cuticle; *cu'.*, unfibrillated surface layer of the same; *d.m.*, diagonal muscles; *do.m.*, dorsoventral muscle strands; *g.*, gut; *f.*, vertically fibrillated layer of the cuticle; *g.c.*, gland cells of the skin; *l.m.*, longitudinal muscle layer; *ov.*, ovary; *par.*, parenchyma; *sp.*, spinules cut transversely at various levels   *t.*, testis; *ut.*, uterus, containing eggs; *y.*, yolk gland.

longitudinal fibres. Between these and the endoderm, which is a columnar epithelium lining the gut, lies the parenchyma, a mesh-work of protoplasm with nuclei at the nodes and oval cells in the meshes. Muscle fibres pass across the parenchyma from the dorsal to the ventral side of the body. There are no blood vessels or cœlom. It will be noticed that in the fluke a mass of tissue lies between the ectoderm and endoderm in place of the structureless lamella of *Hydra*. This is known as the mesoderm. We shall allude to it in more detail in describing the earthworm.

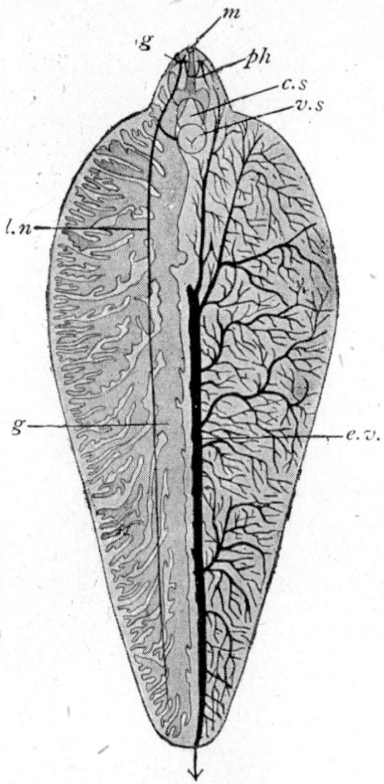

The excretory system lies in the

Excretory System.

parenchyma. It consists of a meshwork of tubules joining into a main duct which lies in the middle line, from a point about a quarter of the length of the body behind its front end to the excretory pore at the hind end. The ultimate branches of the tubules are very fine and end in little structures known as *flame cells*. These

FIG. 167.—The structure of a liver fluke. —After Sommer. From the ventral surface. The branched gut (*g.*) and the lateral nerve (*l.n.*) are shown to the left of the figure, the branches of the excretory vessel (*e.v.*) to the right.

c.s., Position of cirrus sac; *cg.*, lateral head ganglion; *m.*, mouth; *ph.*, pharynx; *v.s.*, ventral sucker. An arrow indicates the excretory aperture.

are minute vesicles containing a few long cilia which keep up a flickering like that of a flame and so perhaps drive towards the main duct the fluid secreted into the vesicle by its walls. Each vesicle has a nucleus and may be regarded as a hollow cell. It is connected with its fellows by fine protoplasmic processes which are said to be hollow.

The nervous system includes a brain which consists of a collar around the pharynx with a mid-ventral **Nervous** swelling and a pair of lateral swellings. From **System.** these swellings or ganglia nerves are given off to the forepart of the body, and from each lateral ganglion

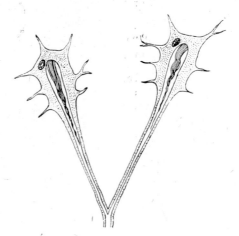

FIG. 168.—Two flame cells, highly magnified.

arises a large lateral nerve cord which runs backwards below the gut to the hinder end of the body, giving off branches on the way. The nerve cords contain nerve cells as well as fibres.

The liver fluke is hermaphrodite, and has very complex generative organs.

Generative
Organs.
    The testes are two much-branched tubes lying one behind the other in the middle part of the body. The branches of each are gathered into a vas deferens, and the two vasa deferentia run forwards side by side to join, above the posterior sucker, a large, pear-shaped vesicula

seminalis. From this a fine, somewhat twisted tube, the ductus ejaculatorius, passes forwards to enter a stout, muscular penis or *cirrus*, which
opens at the generative pore. Normally the penis lies in a *cirrus sac*,
but it can be turned inside out and thus thrust out of the pore. The
ovary is a branched tubular structure on the right side in front of the
testes. Its branches join to form the oviduct, which passes towards
the middle line and there joins the *yolk duct*. This is formed by the
union of two transverse ducts, which lead each from a longitudinal
duct at the side of the body. The *yolk glands* are very numerous, small,
round vesicles lying along the sides of the body, and communicating
by short ducts with the longitudinal ducts. The Laurer-Stieda canal
is a short tube of uncertain function leading from the union of oviduct
and yolk duct to a pore on the back. Possibly it is used for the reception of spermatozoa from another individual. The oviduct and
yolk duct are surrounded where they join by a rounded mass, which is
known as the *shell gland* though its function is probably only to
harden the egg shell, which appears to be secreted by the yolk glands,
composed of numerous, minute, unicellular glands. From this point
the joined ducts proceed forwards as a wide, twisted tube, the uterus,
to the generative opening. The uterus contains eggs, each enclosed
in a shell, within which lie, besides the ovum, a number of yolk cells
derived from the yolk glands, and spermatozoa. The animal is
probably as a rule self-fertilised.

Life-History. The life-history of the liver fluke is a very remarkable
and interesting process. The eggs, which are
very numerous, are laid into the bile ducts of
the sheep. So long as they remain within the body of
the latter they do not develop, but when they have been
carried by the bile to the intestine, and thence passed
to the exterior with the droppings, they will develop in
damp spots if the weather be warm. In a few weeks a larva
known as the *miracidium* emerges. It is conical, covered
with a layer formed by five rings of big, ciliated cells,
provided with two eye-spots, a small gut, and two flame
cells, and filled by a mass of cells. It swims by means of
the cilia, with the broad end forwards. At this end there
is a knob which can be thrust out as a conical spike. If it
can find a member of a particular species of water snail
known as *Limnæus truncatulus* [1] it works its way into the
tissues of the snail, thrusting out its spike and rotating by
means of its cilia so as to bore in. Within the snail the

---

[1] Other species of water snail are sometimes used in foreign
countries.

ciliated cells are lost and the larva increases in size and grows into a hollow sac or *sporocyst*. Sometimes this

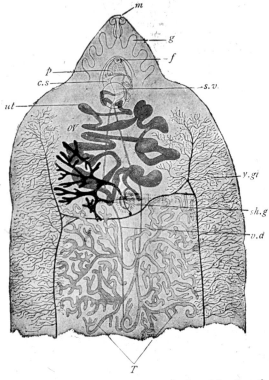

Fig. 169. —The reproductive organs of a liver fluke, from the ventral side.--After Sommer.

c.s. Cirrus sac.	*s.v.* Seminal vesicle.
f. Female aperture.	*sh.g.* Shell gland.
g. Anterior lobes of gut.	*T.* Testes (anterior).
m. Mouth.	*ut.* Uterus.
ov. Ovary (dark).	*v.d.* Vas deferens.
p. Penis.	*y.gl.* Diffuse yolk glands.

multiplies by dividing transversely. Within the sporocyst some of the cells lining the cavity behave like fertilised ova,

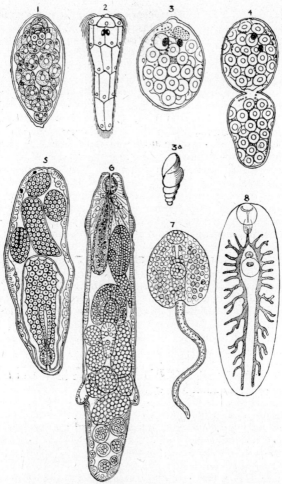

FIG. 170.—The life-history of a liver fluke.—After Thomas.

1. Developing embryo in egg-case; 2. free-swimming ciliated embryo; 3. sporocyst; 3*a*. shell of *Limnæus truncatulus*; 4. division of sporocyst; 5. sporocyst with rediæ forming within it; 6. redia with more rediæ forming within it; 7. tailed cercaria; 8. young fluke.

dividing to form a blastula, which invaginates to give rise
to a two-layered sac or gastrula. These cells, however,
have not undergone fertilisation, and their development is
an example of *parthenogenesis*, the development of unfertilised ova. The gastrula grows into another form
of larva, the *redia*, which bursts out of the sporocyst
and migrates, usually into the liver of the snail. The rediæ
devour the tissues of the snail and finally kill it. Each
redia has an elongated body with an anterior mouth, a
muscular pharynx, and a short, sac-like gut. A little way
behind the pharynx the body-wall is thickened to form a
muscular collar, and not far from the hind end are two
blunt conical processes on one side. Posteriorly there is a
large body cavity lined by an epithelium like that of the
cavity in the sporocyst. Cells derived from the wall of the
body cavity develop in much the same way as in the sporocyst and give rise to daughter rediæ, which escape from the
parent by an opening behind the collar. Several generations
of rediæ usually succeed one another thus, but eventually
they cease to produce daughters of their own kind, and give
birth instead to creatures known as *cercariæ*, with a flat,
heart-shaped body, two suckers, a forked gut, and a tail.
The cercaria emerges from the redia, works its way out of
the snail, and swims by means of the tail. Soon it settles
upon a wet blade of grass, loses its tail, secretes around
itself a cyst by means of special *cystogenous cells* of the
ectoderm, and waits till the grass is eaten by a sheep. In
the gut of the latter the cyst is digested and the cercaria
pierces the intestinal wall, bores into the liver, and there
grows into an adult fluke. When the generative organs are
fully developed, the worms begin to lay their eggs, and
migrate to the duodenum of the host. In the end they are
cast out with the fæces, and if the sheep survives till this
happens it will usually recover, though, owing to permanent
damage to the liver, the recovery is never complete.

It will be seen that in this life-history we have a case of
alternation of generations far more complicated than that
of *Obelia*, and differing from the latter also in that not
sexual and truly asexual, but sexual and parthogenetic
generations succeed one another. The former kind of
alternation of generations is known as *metagenesis*, the

latter as *heterogamy*. It should also be noticed that there are three kinds of individual involved in the cycle. The

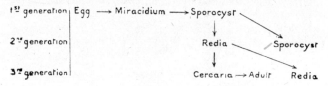

1ˢᵗ generation | Egg ⟶ Miracidium ⟶ Sporocyst
2ⁿᵈ generation | Redia ⟶ Sporocyst
3ʳᵈ generation | Cercaria ⟶ Adult ⟶ Redia

Fig. 171.—A diagram of the life-history of the liver fluke.

life-history of the liver fluke is shown by a diagram in Fig. 171.

Schistosoma. Platyhelminthes which, like the liver fluke, are parasitic and covered with a cuticle, and possess suckers and a gut are known as *Trematoda*. As another example of them, we may notice *Schistosoma* (or *Bilharzia*), which lives in the veins of man and is exceptional in having separate sexes and remarkable in that the female is carried in a groove of the ventral surface of the male. Eggs are laid in the walls of the intestine and bladder, causing inflammation, and thus reach the exterior. The intermediate host is a snail, from which the cercariæ pass into water. Infection takes place by the cercariæ penetrating the skin or the mucous membrane of the mouth of the final host.

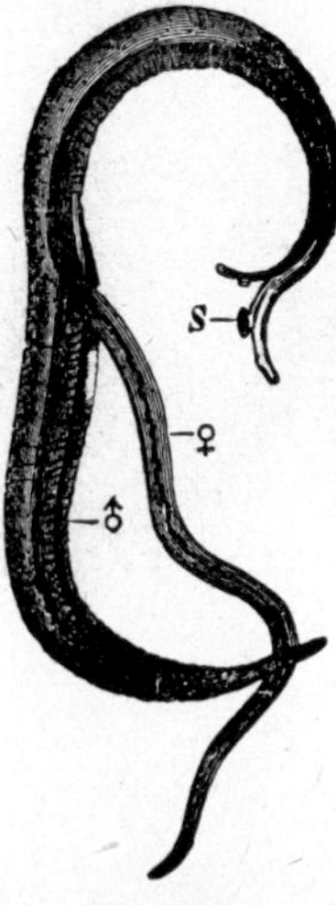

Fig. 172.—*Schistosoma hæmatobium.*—From Sedgwick.

♂, male; ♀, female; S, sucker.

Cestoda. To the Platyhelminthes belong also the *Tapeworms* or *Cestoda*, of which *Tænia solium*, found in man, is an example. In the adult state this worm may reach a length of nine feet. It lives in the intestine, to whose wall it is attached by a head or *scolex*, provided with four suckers and a crown of hooks. Behind the head is a narrow neck, followed by a long chain of joints or *proglot-*

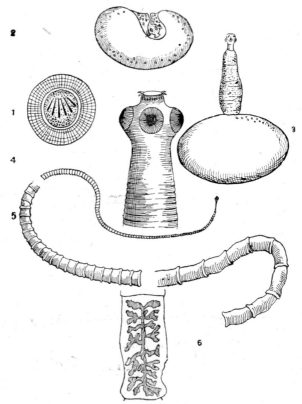

FIG. 173.—The life-history of *Tænia solium.*—After Leuckart.

1. Six-hooked embryo in egg-case ; 2. proscolex or bladder-worm stage, with invaginated head ; 3. bladder-worm with evaginated head ; 4. enlarged head of adult, showing suckers and hooks ; 5. general view of the tapeworm, from small head and thin neck to the ripe joints ; 6. a ripe joint or proglottis with branched uterus : all other organs are now lost.

tides which it buds off. The younger of these, near the head, are small, but they grow larger as they are pushed farther from the head by the formation of new joints. The body is covered with a cuticle, under which lies a layer of circular muscle fibres and then one of very deep epidermal cells with longitudinal muscle fibres between them and a transverse layer of muscle below them. Inside this is a mass of parenchyma like that of the fluke, in which are

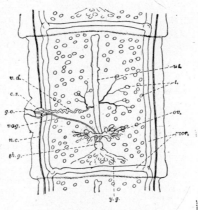

Fig. 174.—A proglottis of *Tænia solium* with the reproductive organs at the stage of complete development.

c.s., Cirrus sac ; *excr.*, excretory canals ; *g.o.*, genital opening ; *n.c.*, nerve cord ; *ov.*, ovary ; *sh.g.*, shell gland ; *t.*, testes ; *v.d.*, vas deferens ; *ut.*, uterus ; *vag.*, vagina ; *y.g.*, yolk gland.

embedded the excretory, generative, and nervous systems. There is no alimentary canal, nutriment being absorbed through the surface of the body. The excretory system is of the same type as that of the fluke, with flame cells and a larger and a smaller main duct on each side, connected by a transverse vessel on the hinder side of each proglottis. In the last proglottis these vessels open by a median pore. The nervous system consists of a ring in the head, small forward nerves, two lateral nerve cords and branches. The

reproductive organs have the same general structure as in
the liver fluke : they are shown in Figs. 174 (and 173, 6).
Each proglottis contains a complete set of them. It is
fertilised either by another proglottis or by itself. From
time to time the last proglottis breaks off, singly or with
others, and passes out of the anus. It has some power of

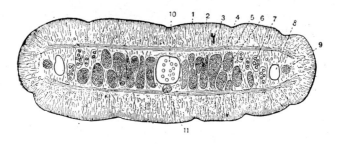

Fig. 175.—A transverse section through a proglottis of *Tænia* in
    which the reproductive organs are well developed.—From
    Shipley and MacBride.

1, Cuticle ; 2, long-necked cells of ectoderm ; 3, longitudinal muscle fibres cut
    across ; 4, layer of transverse muscles ; 5, split in the parenchyma which lodges a
    calcareous corpuscle ; 6, ovary ; 7, testis with masses of male germ-mother-cells
    forming spermatozoa ; 8, longitudinal excretory canal ; 9, longitudinal nerve
    cord ; 10, uterus ; 11, oviduct.

independent movement by contraction of its muscles. The
eggs are set free by its rupture. If, as may happen in various circumstances, they are now swallowed by a pig, or, as
occasionally, by man, their shells are dissolved in the alimentary canal and a little spherical *six-hooked embryo* or
onchosphere is set free from each. This bores its way from
the intestine of the host into his blood vessels and is carried
to the muscles and other organs, where it loses its hooks, increases in size, and becomes a *bladder-worm* or *cysticercus*.
The wall of this becomes tucked in at one spot, forming a
pouch, on the inner wall of which the suckers and hooks of
the future head appear. No further change takes place
unless the flesh of a pig infested with such bladder-worms
(known as " measly " pork) be eaten raw or " underdone "
by man. When this happens, the stimulus of the new surroundings causes the head to be turned inside out. The

bladder is digested, but the head fixes itself and begins to bud off proglottides. The life-history of *Tænia solium* may be summed up as follows :—

Egg→Onchosphere→Cysticercus→Scolex→Adult.

It will be seen that only one generation is involved,

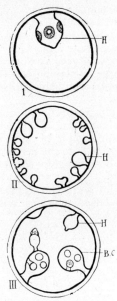

FIG. 176.—Diagrams of bladder-worms.—From Thomson.

    I. The ordinary Cysticercus type, with one head (*H.*).
    II. The Cœnurus type, with many heads.
    III. The Echinococcus type, with many heads, and with
           secondary cysts or brood capsules (*B.C.*) pro-
           ducing many heads.

unless each proglottis be regarded as a complete individual, and not merely as a part of the parent body broken off to carry the eggs.

Other common tapeworms are : *Tænia saginata*, without **Other** hooks, found in man, with the bladder-worm **Tapeworms.** stage in the ox ; *T. serrata* in the dog, with a bladder-worm in rabbits, hares, and mice ; *T. cœnurus* in the dog, with the bladder-worm known as *Cœnurus cerebralis* in the brain of sheep, and other hoofed animals, where it causes " staggers " ; and *T. echinococcus*, which has only three proglottides, in the dog, with the bladder-worm *Echinococcus* in sheep, oxen, pigs, and sometimes in man. The latter two species produce in the bladder-worm stage numerous heads. Since only one of these can be regarded as continuing the individuality of the bladder-worm, the others must be looked upon as buds from it, so that there is here a metagenesis. The bladder produced by *T. echinococcus*, is known as a " hydatid cyst " ; it is very large, containing sometimes as much as a gallon of fluid, and its wall buds off secondary cysts into the cavity.

The harm which tapeworms do by robbing their host of food is generally insignificant. Their action in setting up irritation in the intestine and in secreting substances which prove poisonous, especially to the nervous system, is more serious. They may be avoided by care taken in regard to food, and are treated with vermifuges, such as extract of male fern, and purgatives. The cysticercus stage is beyond the reach of medical remedies, but may sometimes be treated surgically.

CHAPTER XIV

THE EARTHWORM. ANNELIDA. TRIPLO-
BLASTIC ARCHITECTURE

ALMOST everywhere in England earthworms are found.
They live usually in the upper layers of the soil
Habits. in burrows, which they make partly by boring
with the pointed front ends of their bodies, partly by
swallowing the earth in front and passing it out behind, in
which case the earth which is passed out forms the well-
known "worm casts." The sides of the burrow are lined
with a slime secreted by unicellular glands in the skin, and
if the opening be not protected by a worm cast it is usually

FIG. 177.—The Earthworm.—From Thomson.

closed by leaves or small stones. Such leaves may often be
seen sticking up from the ground, and will be found to
have been pulled into the burrow skilfully, with the
narrowest part foremost. At night, if the weather be warm
and not too dry, the worms will stretch themselves out of
their holes, keeping the hinder end of the body fixed in the
opening, so that they can pull themselves back at once if
danger threatens. In dry weather or hard frost they burrow
deep and retire to a small chamber, which they line with
little stones. In wet weather they are sometimes flooded

out, but they rarely leave their burrows in other circumstances, except when they are about to die owing to the attacks of parasitic maggots which are the young of certain flies. The food of earthworms consists of the organic matter in the soil, which they swallow, and of leaves both fresh and decaying. They will also eat animal matter, and are said to be very fond of fat. Charles Darwin has shown the remarkable effects which these insignificant creatures have upon the surface of the earth. By making the soil more porous they expose the underlying rocks to the disintegrating action of water, by solution owing to the presence of carbon dioxide and other acids of the soil, and by frost; and the small stones which eventually result from this action are made still smaller by friction and solution within their bodies. Thus they help in the formation of the soil. At the same time they are aiding in its removal. Their castings dry and crumble, and are blown about by the wind or else are washed down by the rain. On sloping ground this fine material tends to be carried away downwards, and thus the denudation of hills is largely due to the action of earthworms. On the other hand, their work is highly beneficial to the farmer. The soil is by them thoroughly mixed, submitted to the action of the air, and constantly supplied with a fine "top dressing." It has been calculated that earthworms bring up annually a layer of soil one-fifth of an inch in thickness, which is spread by the weather in the way we have described. Organic matter is converted into a useful form and amalgamated with the earth, and the latter is made easier of penetration by the roots of plants.

The commonest English earthworm is *Lumbricus herculeus.*

External Features. The body of this animal is roughly cylindrical, but pointed in front and broadened behind. It reaches a length of seven inches. There is no distinct head, but a lobe known as the *prostomium* overhangs the mouth, which is a crescentic opening on the lower side of the front end. The body is divided into a series of rings, the *segments* or *somites,* and at the hinder end is the terminal *anus.* The first somite is the *peristomium* and the mouth lies between it and the prostomium. On the dorsal side, the latter projects across the peristomium.[1] There are about 150 somites. At about one-third of the length of the body from its front end, in somites 32-37 inclusive, a glandular thickening of the epidermis lies athwart the back like a saddle and is often mistaken for the scar of a wound. This is known as the *clitellum*. The skin of the worm is brownish above and paler below; it is covered with a fine, tough, iridescent cuticle secreted by the underlying cells. In every somite except the first and the last there are eight bristles, the *chætæ*, in two pairs on each side, a *lateral pair*, slightly above the middle of the side, and a *ventral pair* between the lateral and the mid-ventral line. The chætæ can be felt with the fingers; they consist of a horny nitrogenous organic substance known as *chitin* and are embedded in sacs of the epidermis, by which they are secreted, and to these sacs are attached muscles, by which they can be moved. The chætæ, as we shall see later, are organs of locomotion. The ventral chætæ of the clitellum,

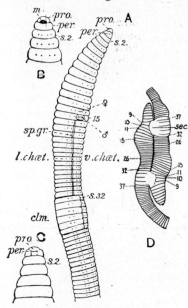

FIG. 178.—*A*, The forepart of the body of an earthworm (*Lumbricus herculeus*), from the right side; *B*, the first four segments from below; *C*, the same from above; *D* (after Grove), worms in coition.

clm., Clitellum; *l.chæt.*, lateral chætæ; *m.* mouth; *per.*, peristomium; *pro.*, prostomium; *s.2 s.32, 9 37* numbers of segments; *sec.*, clitellar secretion uniting worms; *sp.gr.*, spermatic groove. *v. h t.* ventral chætæ; ♂, opening of vas deferens; ♀, opening of oviduct.

[1] In the related *Allolobophora* the prostomium reaches only half-way across the peristomium.

17

of the twenty-sixth, and of the tenth to the fifteenth somites are straighter and more slender than those of other somites, which are stout and somewhat hooked. This modification is in connection with the use of the chætæ of the twenty-sixth somite during coition, and of the other straight chætæ during the formation of the cocoon in which the eggs are laid.

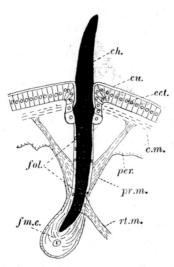

FIG. 179.—A diagram of a chæta of the earthworm and the structures connected with it.—From Potts, after Stephenson.

c.m., Circular muscle of body-wall ; ch., chæta ; cu., cuticle ; ect., ectoderm ; fol., follicle, and fm.c., formative cell of chæta ; per., peritoneum ; pr.m., protractor, and rt.m., retractor muscles of chæta.

External Openings. A number of internal organs open separately upon the surface of the body. We have already mentioned the mouth and anus. The *openings of the vasa deferentia* are a pair of slits with swollen lips found on the under side of the body in somite 15. In front of them, in somite 14, are the two small *openings of the oviducts.* The *spermathecal pores* are two pairs of small, round openings in the grooves between somites 9–10 and 10–11 at the level of the lateral chætæ. The *nephridiopores* are openings which lead from the excretory tubes or nephridia. They are found, as a pair of minute pores in front of the ventral

FIG. 180.—One of the ordinary chætæ of an earthworm, removed from the chætæ sac and magnified.

chætæ, in each somite except the first three and the last.

The *dorsal pores* are small, round openings on the mid-dorsal line in the grooves between the somites. The first is behind the eighth somite, and there is one in each subsequent groove. They open into the body cavity, the

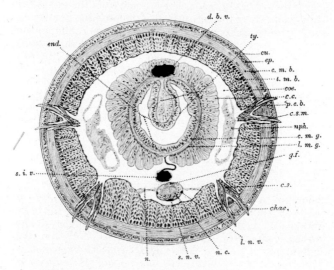

FIG 181.—A tranverse section through an earthworm in the region of the intestine.

cœ., Cœlom ; *c.c.*, chloragogenous cells ; *c.m.b.*, circular muscle of body-wall ; *c.m.g.*, circular muscle of gut ; *c.s.*, chæta sac ; *c.s.m.*, chæta sac muscles ; *cu.*, cuticle ; *d.b.v.*, dorsal blood vessel ; *ep.*, epidermis, *end.*, ednoderm ; *g.f.*, giant fibres ; *l.m.b.*, longitudinal muscle of body-wall ; *l.m.g.*, longitudinal muscle of gut ; *l.n.v.*, lateral neural vessel ; *n.*, nerves ; *n.c.*, nerve cord ; *nph.*, nephridium ; *p.e.b.*, peritoneal epithelium of body-wall ; *chæ.*, chæta ; *s.i.v.*, subintestinal blood vessel ; *s.n.v.*, subneural blood vessel ; *ty.*, typhlosole.

Some of the structures seen in this section are shown more highly magnified in Fig. 186.

fluid in which oozes out through them and moistens the surface of the body, mingling with the slime secreted by the unicellular glands of the skin. As this fluid contains amœboid cells which attack bacteria and other small parasites, it is a valuable defence to the worm against such enemies, which are numerous in the soil.

The body of the worm may be said to consist of two
tubes, one within the other. The inner tube is
the gut, the outer the body-wall. Between the
two lies the cœlom or body cavity, divided into compartments by a series of *septa*, which reach from the gut to the
body-wall, where they are attached opposite the grooves on
the surface of the body. The compartments communicate
by numerous openings in the septa. The cœlom contains
a fluid, and in this float the leucocytes already mentioned,
by which small parasites are surrounded and destroyed,
both within and without the body. The *body-wall* is
covered by a *cuticle*. Under this lies the *epidermis*, an
epithelium consisting of columnar cells, many of which
are glandular or sensory, with small cells between their
bases. The cuticle is composed of hardened protein and
is perforated by a pore over each gland cell. The epidermis of the clitellum consists of several layers of gland
cells. Below the epidermis is a *circular layer of muscle*,
consisting of unstriped fibres running around the body, and
below this again lies a much thicker *longitudinal layer of
muscle*, composed of similar fibres running along the body
and placed in rows which stand at right angles to the
surface, supported by connective tissue. Within the
longitudinal muscle is the cœlomic epithelium, which is
here a layer of pavement cells lining the body cavity.

The earthworm has a well-developed central nervous
system which consists of (1) a pair of *suprapharyngeal ganglia*, rounded bodies lying
above the mouth, and sometimes known together as the *brain*, (2) two slender *circumpharyngeal
commissures* running from these round the pharynx, and
(3) a *ventral nerve cord* which starts from the commissures
between the third and fourth somites and runs the whole
length of the body in the cœlom below the gut, swelling
into a ganglion in each somite. The first of these ganglia
is bilobed and is known as the *subpharyngeal ganglion*.
Nerves are given off to the prostomium from the suprapharyngeal ganglia, and to the first two somites from the
commissures, and the ventral cord gives off in each somite
three pairs of nerves which run upwards as girdles in the
body-wall, giving off branches as they go. The alimentary

Body-wall.

**Nervous
System.**

canal receives nerves from the circumpharyngeal commissures and fibres from plexuses in the septa. Though the ventral cord appears to be single, it is really double, and can be seen in transverse sections to be rather imperfectly divided into right and left halves by connective tissue. Transverse sections also show that the middle and upper part of the cord consists of fine, chiefly longitudinal, nerve fibres, and the lower and outer parts contain nerve cells. Above the mass of fine fibres are three longitudinal bundles of such fibres, each bundle being enclosed in a sheath and known as a *giant fibre*. Nerve cells are more numerous in, but not confined to, the ganglia. The nerves consist of afferent fibres, which start from sense cells in the epidermis

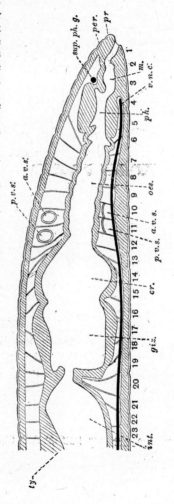

FIG. 182.—A diagram of a longitudinal section of an earthworm.

a.v.s. Anterior vesicula seminalis.
a.v.s'. Posterior lateral horn of the same overhanging the œsophagus.
cr. Crop.
giz. Gizzard.
int. Intestine.
m. Mouth.
œs. Œsophagus.
p.v.s. Posterior vesicula seminalis.
p.v.s'. Horn of the same overhanging the œsophagus.
per. Peristomium.
ph. Pharynx.
pr. Prostomium.
sup.ph.g. Suprapharyngeal ganglion
ty. Typhlosole.
v.n.c. Ventral nerve cord.
1-23. Segments.

The blood vessels are omitted.

and muscles (Fig. 185) and end as bunches in the central
nervous system, efferent fibres, which start from nerve cells
in the ganglia and end against muscle and other cells, and
also fibres which join nerve nets in the skin, muscles, and
septa.

The muscular and nervous apparatus is used in the
following manner to bring about the movements of the
worm. In ordinary locomotion it works somite by somite.
Simultaneous contraction of the circular musculature of

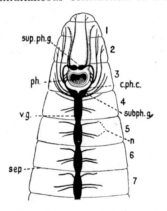

a somite and relaxation
of its longi-

Mechanism of Locomotion. tudinal musculature causes the somite
to extend. Its chætæ
are then thrust out and
the action of the mus-
culature is reversed,
so as to shorten the
somite. Since the
chætæ, which point
somewhat backwards,
hold firm in the earth
and prevent any draw-
ing back, the result is
to pull forwards the
somite behind. In this
the process is being
repeated, and so a wave
of forward movement
passes back along the

FIG. 183.—A diagram of the forepart of
the nervous system of the earthworm.

c.ph.c., Circumpharyngeal commissure; *n.*,
nerves; *ph.*, pharynx cut through; *s.p.*,
septa; *subph.g.*, subpharyngeal ganglia;
sup.ph.g., suprapharyngeal ganglia; *v.g.*,
ganglia of ventral cord; 1 7, somites.

body. The passage of the wave is due partly to a
mechanical stimulation of nerves of the muscles of a
somite by the pull from in front. This is shown by an
experiment in which a worm was cut into two and the
anterior and posterior halves joined together by threads
hooked into the tissues. When the forward movement of
the anterior half pulled upon the hinder somites these
performed the usual contractions. But if the body-wall
and gut be severed and the nerve cord left as the only
connection between the halves of the worm the wave of

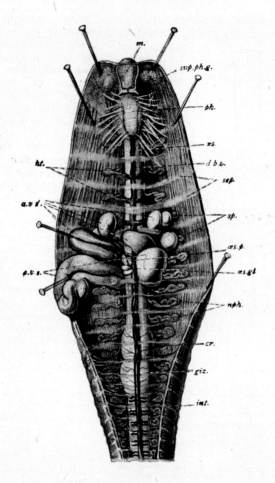

FIG. 184.—An earthworm (*L. herculeus*), dissected from above.

a.v.s'., Horns of the anterior vesicula seminalis ; *cr.*, crop ; *d.b.v.*, dorsal blood
vessel ; *giz.*, gizzard ; *ht.*, hearts ; *int.*, intestine ; *m.*, mouth ; *nph.*, nephridia ;
œs., œsophagus ; *œs.gl.*, œsophageal glands ; *œs.p.*, œsophageal pouch ; *p.v.s'.*,
horns of the posterior vesicula seminalis ; *ph.*, pharynx ; *sep.*, septa ; *sp.*,
spermathecæ ; *sup.ph.g.*, suprapharyngeal ganglia.

contraction still passes normally, and in fact, as might be expected, the principal agent in co-ordinating the action

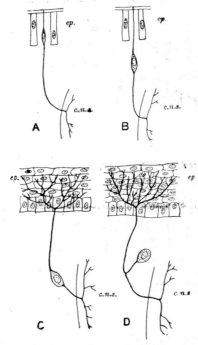

of the musculature is the nervous system. The contraction of circular or longitudinal muscles in a somite causes, through a "reflex arc" (p. 96) along the ventral cord, the contraction of the corresponding muscles in the somite behind. Further, in each somite the contraction of the circular musculature sends, by afferent and efferent fibres, through the ganglion, impulses which relax the longitudinal musculature; and similarly the longitudinal muscles in contracting relax the circular. Sudden movements of the whole body, such as those by which the worm withdraws from the region in which it receives a powerful stimulus — which probably indicates danger—are brought about by a different nervous mechanism.

Fig. 185.—A diagram showing the mode of ending of the sensory nerve fibres in the epidermis of the earthworm and the relation of this type to that which is found in most of the sensory fibres of the frog. See also Fig. **61.**

A, The arrangement found in the earthworm; *B*, that of the worm-*Nereis*; *C*, that of a fish; *D*, that of a frog or man.
c.n.s., Ending of the neuron in the central nervous system; *cp.*, ending in the epidermis.

The giant fibres, which give off branches to the muscles of each somite, are a means of direct communication between distant ganglia. They conduct more rapidly than the other fibres of the nervous system, and it is by their agency, conveying impulses to a number of somites at the same time, that large, sudden movements are carried out when one point on the body is strongly stimulated.

An earthworm has no well-developed organs of sense,
Sense Organs. but certain of the columnar cells of the epidermis are rod-shaped and prolonged at their inner ends into fibres, which run in the nervous system (Fig. 185). These are sense cells, and in the forepart of the body some of them are collected into groups, which are rudimentary sense organs. There are also sense cells which contain a refractive body and are probably affected by light. Experiment shows that the worms are sensitive to light and to vibrations of the ground and can smell, but gives no evidence of a sense of hearing.

The alimentary canal is straight. It begins with a short,
Gut. wide, thin-walled mouth or buccal cavity in the first three somites, which leads to a muscular region known as the pharynx. This lies in front of the septum between the fifth and sixth somites, but pushes that septum backwards as far as the seventh. Its dorsal wall is thickened by the presence of a number of glands, whose secretion, containing mucin and a ferment which digests proteins, is poured over vegetable tissues while the animal is feeding upon them. Numerous strands of muscle run from it to the body-wall. Behind it lies the œsophagus, a straight, narrow, thin-walled tube, which extends to the fourteenth somite. In the eleventh somite it bears at the sides a pair of *œsophageal pouches*, and in the twelfth two pairs of *œsophageal glands*. These contain large cells which secrete calcium carbonate and pass it through the pouches into the œsophagus. In the fifteenth and sixteenth somites the œsophagus expands into a large, thin-walled *crop*, which in turn communicates behind with the *gizzard*, another swelling, with thick muscular walls and a horny lining, in somites 17 and 18. From the gizzard to the anus runs a wide, thin-walled tube known as the intestine. The intestine is narrowed where it passes through the septa, and its dorsal wall is infolded to form a longitudinal ridge known as the *typhlosole*. The gut is lined with a layer of

columnar epithelium, outside which are thin longitudinal
and circular muscular layers, covered by the cœlomic epi-

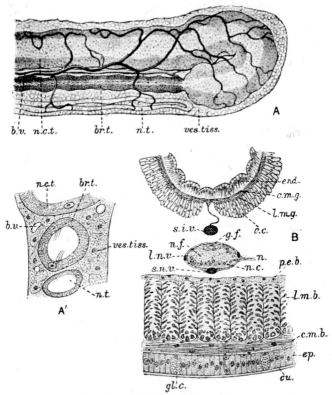

FIG. 186.—Histology of the earthworm.

A, The end of the first hank of the nephridium (Fig. 188) ; *A′*, part of a section of
the same ; *B*, part of a transverse section of the body.

b.v., Blood vessel ; *gl.c.*, gland cell in the epidermis. Other letters as in Fig. 188
(*A* and *A′*) and Fig. 181.

thelium, which here consists of the *chloragogenous cells*.
These cells, which also fill the typhlosole, are large and
contain yellow granules of an excretory product. They
fall off into the cœlomic fluid, and there break up and set

free their granules, which are taken up by leucocytes. It is said that they are by these conveyed to the exterior, probably through the skin or dorsal pores, and also that they are deposited as pigment in the tissues. There are also amœboid yellow cells which take up excreta in the blood, pass into the gut, and are voided with the fæces.

Food is drawn into the mouth by a sucking action of the muscular pharynx, passed along the œsophagus, stored in the crop, ground up in the gizzard with the aid of small stones which have been swallowed, and in the intestine first digested by juices secreted from the epithelium, and then absorbed, for which processes the surface is increased by the presence of the typhlosole. The contractions which cause the passage of the food are alternately caused through the nerves to the pharynx and inhibited through the plexuses in the septa. The function of the œsophageal glands is probably the excreting of the calcareous matter which is very plentiful in the dead leaves of which the food is largely composed. Possibly their secretion is also of importance in removing carbon dioxide in the form of calcium carbonate.

Besides the chloragogenous and yellow cells, the earth-worm has excretory organs which, like those of the frog, consist of tubes with walls that are glandular and excretory and richly supplied with blood vessels ; but the tubes, instead of being collected into compact kidneys, are distributed along the body, one pair to each somite, except the first three and the last. Each tube or *nephridium* is thrown into loops, bound together by connective tissue containing blood vessels. The nephridium begins as a flattened, kidney-shaped funnel or *nephrostome* hanging from the front side of a septum near the nerve cord. The nephrostome has an overhanging lip which consists of a large crescentic *central cell* with a row of marginal cells around it. This lip is ciliated. The lower lip is not ciliated. From the funnel there leads a narrow tube, ciliated on its sides. This passes through the septum to the main part of the nephridium, which lies behind the septum, in the cœlom of the next somite, opening to the exterior by the nephridiopore in that somite. The narrow part of the tube is long and winding

Excretions.

and loses its cilia in places. It is followed by a wider, short, brown region, ciliated throughout, this by a still wider tube which is not ciliated, and finally a short, very wide, muscular tube leads to the nephridiopore. The whole tube, except the muscular region, is formed of hollow cells shaped like drain pipes and lying end to end.

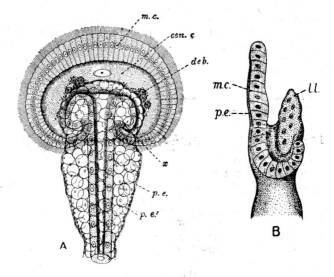

FIG. 187.—The nephrostome or funnel of a nephridium of the earthworm. *A*, seen from in front as a transparent object ; *B*, in side view, opaque, semidiagrammatic, and without its cilia.

cen.c., Central cell ; *deb.*, debris of cœlomic corpuscles and excretory granules which is probably not able to enter the funnel ; *l.l.*, lower lip of opening ; *m.c.*, marginal cells ; *p.e.*, superficial layer of the peritoneal epithelium ; *p.e.'*, thickened deeper layer of the same ; *x.*, point at which the marginal cells join the lining of the tube, which turns over round the opening.

The cilia set up a stream of cœlomic fluid which carries off the substances excreted by the walls of the tubes and probably also fine granules of excreta which it brings from the cœlom. It is not known whether water is conserved by reabsorption in the nephridium of the earthworm as it is in the excretory tubules of many other land animals (p. 79). The principal nitrogenous substance excreted is urea. Earthworms have no special *respiratory organs*, but an interchange of gases with the air takes place in the skin, which is richly supplied with blood vessels.

Blood Vessels. The blood of an earthworm is red owing to the presence in it of hæmoglobin, which is in solution, not in corpuscles. Colourless corpuscles are also present. The blood-vascular system is very complicated.

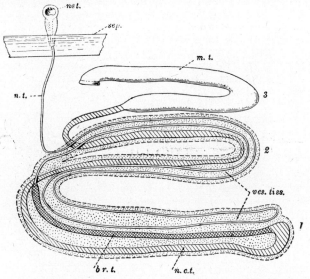

Fig. 188 —A diagram of a nephridium of the earthworm.

br.t., Brown, ciliated tube ; *m.t.*, muscular tube ; *n.c.t.*, glandular, non-ciliated tube ; *n.t.*, narrow tube, ciliated in parts ; *nst.*, nephrostome ; *sep.*, septum ; *ves.tiss.*, connective tissue with vesicular cells and blood-vessels ; 1, 2, 3, the three hanks of the tube.

For details of structure see Fig. 185.

Its main outlines are as follows. A large *dorsal vessel* runs the whole length of the body from the hinder end to the pharynx. It is contractile, and in it the blood is driven forwards. It receives blood by many small vessels from the intestine and by two larger vessels in the tenth somite from the œsophagus, and ends in front by breaking up into branches which supply the pharynx. In each of the somites 7–11 it gives off a pair of large contractile vessels or *pseudo-hearts*. These encircle the œsophagus and join a *ventral or subintestinal vessel* which hangs by a mesentery below the gut. In the pseudo-hearts the blood flows downwards from the dorsal to the ventral vessel, and in the latter it flows backwards and forwards from the region of the hearts. From the ventral vessel the blood passes by a series of small vessels to the intestine, and by *parietal vessels* to the nephridia and to the body-wall. From these organs, it is returned along various paths to the dorsal vessel. Among the subsidiary vessels are a *subneural* and

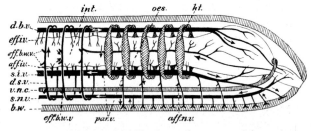

FIG. 189.—A diagram of the blood-vascular system of the earthworm.

aff.i.v., Afferent vessels of the intestine ; *aff.n.v.*, afferent vessels of the nephridia ; *b.w.*, body-wall ; *d.b.v.*, dorsal blood vessel ; *d.s.v.* dorso-subneural vessel ; *eff.b.w.v.*, efferent vessel from body-wall ; *eff.i.v.*, efferent vessel from intestinal wall ; *ht.*, pseudo-hearts ; *int.*, intestine ; *œs.*, œsophagus ; *par.v.*, parietal vessel ; *s.i.v.*, subintestinal vessel ; *s.n.v.*, subneural vessel ; *v.n.c.*, ventral nerve cord.

A simpler form of this diagram will be found on p. 742.

two *lateral neural vessels*, in which the blood flows backwards, and *dorso-subneural vessels*, a pair in each somite of the intestinal region of the body, which carry blood to the dorsal vessel from the subneural vessel, the nephridia, and the body-wall. The main blood vessels of the earthworm cannot be distinguished into arteries and veins, but their ends are joined by capillaries. The dorsal vessel and the pseudo-hearts are provided with valves which keep the blood flowing in the proper direction.

Earthworms are hermaphrodite, every individual having **Reproduction.** a complete set of organs of each sex. The *female organs* include the ovaries, oviducts, and spermathecæ. The ovaries are two small, pear-shaped bodies

hanging into the cœlom of the thirteenth somite from the
septum in front of it. Each ovary is a local thickening of
the cœlomic epithelium. The broad end of the pear is
attached to the septum and contains a fused mass of unripe
ova. Ova fall from the stalk into the cœlom and are taken
up by the oviducts, which lead by wide funnels from the
cœlom in the thirteenth somite, pass through the septum
behind, and open to the exterior in the fourteenth. In
the latter somite, each bears a swelling, the *receptaculum
ovorum* or *egg
sac*, in which
the eggs are
stored and
maturation divi-
sions take place.
The *spermathecæ*
are two pairs of
small, round sacs
which lie in the
ninth and tenth
somites and open
in the grooves
behind them.
Their function is
to receive sperm
from another
worm. The *male
organs* consist of
testes, vesiculæ
seminales, and
vasa deferentia.

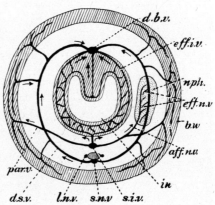

FIG. 190.—A diagram of a transverse section
of the earthworm in the intestinal region to
show the arrangement of the blood vessels.

eff.n.v., efferent vessel from nephridium; *l.n.v.*, lateral
neural vessel; *nph.*, nephridium; other lettering as
in Fig. 189.

These testes are two pairs of small, flat, finger-lobed
bodies attached to the hinder side of the septa in front
of somites 10 and 11. Like the ovaries, to which they
correspond in position, they are local thickenings of
the cœlomic epithelium. The testes bud off cells known as
sperm-mother-cells, which give rise to spermatozoa in the
vesiculæ seminales. The latter are large sacs, formed by
the walling-off of parts of the cœlom, which enclose the
testes. Each consists of a median part and lateral horns.
The anterior vesicula seminalis, in somite 10, has four

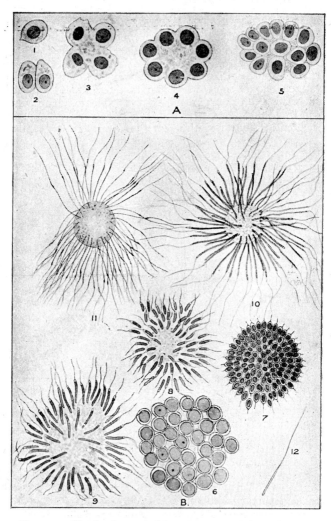

FIG. 191. — The development of the spermatozoa of the earthworm.

A, Stages from the vesicula seminalis of a young worm ; *B*, from that of an older worm.

1, Sperm mother-cell ; 2–7, stages in the division to form spermatozoa ; 7–11, shaping of the spermatozoa, which are still adherent to the mass of residual protoplasm (cytophore) ; 12, a ripe spermatozoon, unstained. The head in 12 is represented rather too broad.

The dark bodies are the nuclei, stained.

lateral horns, two in front and two behind, which push out the septa and bulge into the ninth and eleventh somites. The posterior vesicula seminalis, in somite 11, has only two such horns, which project into the twelfth somite. Each sperm-mother-cell forms by multiple fission, in the course of which the usual reduction division takes place, a mulberry-like mass (Fig. 191), consisting of little cells attached to a central mass of residual protoplasm known as the *cytophore*, by which they are nourished. The little cells become pear-shaped, with the broad ends on the cytophore, gradually increase in length, and change their shape till the mulberry has become a tuft of threads, each thread being a spermatozoon with a very slender head. Finally the spermatozoa break loose. In the median part of each vesicula seminalis, directly behind the testes, is a pair of large ciliated funnels with folded walls, known as *sperm rosettes*. These funnels lead into the vasa efferentia, of which the two on each side join and pass back as a vas deferens to open on somite 15. The cilia of the rosettes draw the ripe sperm into the ducts.

FIG. 192.—One of the ovaries of an earthworm.

Pairing takes place at any time from spring to autumn in warm, damp weather. Two worms stretch themselves out of their burrows and place their ventral sides together with the heads pointing in opposite directions, their bodies being held together by a substance secreted from the clitella. Sperm is passed from the vas deferens of each worm, along a temporary groove, into the spermathecæ of the other, after which the worms separate. The eggs are laid in a cocoon, which, secreted by the clitellum as a broad band round the body, is passed for-

wards over the head.   The cocoon contains a nutrient fluid.
While it is still on the clitellum eggs are passed back to it
along a temporary groove from the oviducal opening, and

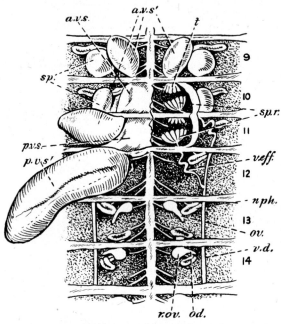

Fig. 193.—A dissection of the reproductive organs of an earthworm.   The dissection is made from above, and the median
parts of the vesiculæ seminales have been opened on the
right-hand side.

a.v.s., Anterior vesicula seminalis ; *a.v.s'.*, horns of the same ; *nph.*,
nephridium ; *od.*, oviduct ; *ov.*, ovary ; *p.v.s.*, posterior vesicula
seminalis ; *p.v.s'.*, horns of the same ; *r.ov.*, receptaculum ovorum (the
funnel of the oviduct lies immediately in front) ; *sp.*, spermathecæ ;
sp.r., sperm rosettes (funnels of the vasa efferentia) ; *t.*, testes ; *v.d.*,
vas deferens ; *v.eff.*, vasa efferentia.

as it passes the spermathecal openings, sperm received
from another worm is squeezed into it.   In passing over
the head the ends of the elastic cocoon close, and it becomes
a small, lemon-shaped body, which is left in the earth.

Each cocoon contains eight to sixteen ova, which are fertilised in it, but usually only one completes development.

Earthworms have an extensive power of regeneration,

Regeneration. though it is not so great as that of *Hydra*. If the body be cut in half, the head end will grow a new tail, and the tail end, though more slowly, a new head.

In comparing the body of an earthworm with those of the other examples of the Metazoa that we

Mesoderm, Cœlom, and Hæmocœle. have studied, it will be seen that in one respect of importance it resembles the frog rather than *Hydra*. The body of *Hydra* consists of two epithelia—the ectoderm and endoderm—with only a structureless lamella between them. In a frog, a flat-worm, or an earthworm these epithelia reappear as the epidermis and the lining epithelium of the gut, but be-tween them is a great mass of tissue which comprises the skeletal tissues, muscles, excretory and generative organs, and so forth. These tissues are together known as the *mesoderm*, and animals which possess this third layer are known as *Triploblastica*, whilst those, like *Hydra*, which possess only two are *Diploblastica*. Both in the earth-worm and in the frog the mesoderm contains cavities of two kinds, the *primary body cavity* or *hæmocœle* or *blood vessels*, and the " *true* " *or secondary body cavity* or *cœlom*. The functions of the cœlom are threefold. (1) It forms a *perivisceral cavity*, which surrounds the principal viscera and so gives room for their movements. (2) From its walls are derived the generative cells. This is clearly seen in the case of the ova, which are shed into the perivisceral cavity, but it is less clear in the case of the spermatozoa, because these are developed in special vessels, derived from the cœlom but closed off. (3) It is concerned in excretion. In an earthworm, where the yellow cells of its walls form excreta which are expelled from the body, this is more obvious than in the frog, but the kidney tubules of the latter—which are not nephridia but cœlomoducts (see below)—in the tadpole (p. 635) are, like the nephridia of the earthworm, open to the cœlom, and draw thence a fluid which contains substances that are excreted. The hæmocœle is a system of spaces of more complex form than the cœlom, and rarely (p. 298) perivisceral. Its function is to contain the blood and lymph. A blood-vascular system is a means of transport made necessary in most triploblastic animals by the presence of the great mass of internal tissues which constitute the mesoderm.

The mesoderm necessitates not only means of transport within it but also means whereby materials **Nephridia and Cœlomoducts.** may be conveyed from it out of the body. There are two principal types of organ which have this function—the *nephridium* and the *cœlomoduct*. The nephridial system arises by ingrowth from the ectoderm and consists of tubules, usually fine and branched, the branches ending in cells where a tuft of flagella hang into it. In this condition it constitutes the flame-cell system of Platyhelminthes. Here it is imbedded in parenchyma but when it occurs in animals with a cœlom—in the annelid worms of which the earthworm is one, and the lancelet (*Amphioxus*)—it lies in that cavity. It then consists of a series of separate nephridia. These may—as in some of the worms and in *Amphioxus*—end blindly in cells called *solenocytes* which differ from the flame-cells of the Platyhelminthes in having a longer neck and fewer flagella. In other cases, as in the earthworm, each nephridium opens to the cœlom by a multicellular funnel—the nephrostome. The nephridial system is primarily an apparatus for the removal of excess water (if necessary) and of excreta. Cœlomoducts are mesodermal tubes, often of considerable diameter, which in typical instances open by a funnel from the cœlom and lead thence to the exterior, one pair in each somite if the animal be segmented. Their primary function is perhaps the removal of gametes which, as we have seen, are developed on the wall of the cœlom, but they often usurp the excretory function of the nephridia. In the earthworm most somites possess nephridia only but those in which the gonads lie have also cœlomoducts in the form of oviducts and vasa deferentia. In certain annelid worms each nephridium has united with the adjacent cœlomoduct to form a *nephromixium*, in which the funnel of the cœlomoduct opens through the duct of a nephridium. In others (as in *Nereis* described below) the cœlomoduct does not open and is reduced to a patch of cilia on the cœlomic wall.

Another feature of the morphology of an earthworm to

Segmentation. which attention must be called here is its *segmentation.* We have seen that merism or the repetition of parts is universal among animals. In an earthworm the whole body consists of similar divisions (the somites) arranged one after the other in a line or series. Each division contains a ring of the body-wall, with chætæ and openings, a separate portion of the cœlom, a section of the gut, a ganglion, nephridia, and

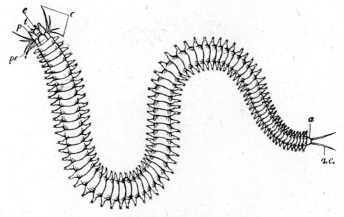

FIG. 194 —*Nereis cultrifer.*—From Thomson.

a., Anus ; *a.c.,* anal cirri ; *c.,* tentacular cirri ; *e.,* eyes ; *p.,* palp ;
pe., peristomium ; *t.,* tentacles.

blood vessels. A body so constructed is said to be *metamerically segmented.* Most of the somites resemble one another closely, but in the forepart of the body they show considerable differences in the reproductive, alimentary, and other organs. A modification of the foremost somites to form a head (cephalisation) is, as we shall see, a conspicuous feature of some animals, but it can hardly be said to exist in the earthworm. The body of an earthworm is actually composed of similar divisions, because all the organs are repeated together at regular intervals. There are other animals in which only some of the organs are thus repeated, as in the frog where the vertebræ, nerves, and to some extent the muscles exhibit segmentation, so that the regions of which the body might be regarded as composed are much less distinct than they are in the earthworm. In such cases segmentation is said to be incomplete. The tapeworm presents an example of a kind of segmentation, known as *strobilation*, which is very complete, but is of quite a different nature from that

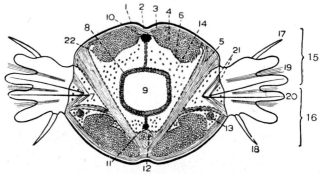

FIG. 195.—A transverse section through *Nereis cultrifer*, slightly simplified. The parapodia are shown in perspective. Magnified. —After Shipley and MacBride, with modifications.

1, Cuticle ; 2, epidermis ; 3, circular muscles ; 4, longitudinal muscles ; 5, oblique muscles forming a partition ; 6, somatic layer of peritoneal epithelium ; 7, cœlom ; 8, splanchnic layer of epithelium ; 9, cavity of intestine ; 10, dorsal blood vessel ; 11, ventral blood vessel ; 12, ventral nerve cord ; 13, nephridium in section ; 14, ova ; 15, notopodium ; 16, neuropodium ; 17, dorsal cirrus ; 18, ventral cirrus ; 19, chætæ ; 20, acicula ; 21, muscles which protrude the acicula, and thus the noto- and neuropodium ; 22, ciliated organ (vestige of cœlomoduct).

of the earthworm, the youngest segments being at the front end and the old ones becoming independent and dropping off, whereas in the earthworm the youngest segments are those at the hind end and the segments are not shed but are integral and necessary parts of the body.

The term *segmentation* is used in zoology to denote very various phenomena. Its primary meaning is the division of an object into parts. Such parts are *segments,* and when they are arranged in linear series the segmentation is said to be *metameric.* The term is applied to the division of the whole body, of parts of it, such as limbs, or of the ovum. When it is used to indicate that the whole body of an organism is composed of integral parts, metamerically arranged the segments are known as *somites* ; when a limb is similarly composed its segments are *podomeres*. When an organism reproduces asexually by breaking off successive portions of itself in a linear series such segments are known until they separate as *strobilæ*. The segments into which an ovum divides are *blastomeres*.

Nereis.
The earthworm is adapted to a burrowing habit and a vegetarian diet. Many marine worms, however, while they resemble the earthworm in most respects, lead a free and predaceous existence. Of

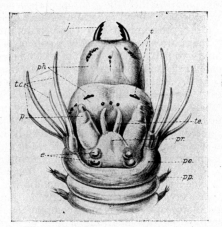

Fig. 196 —The head of *Nereis*, with the pharynx protruded.

e., Eyes ; *j.,* jaw ; *p.,* palp ; *pe.,* peristomium (first two segments, fused) ; *ph.,* pharynx ; *pp.,* first ordinary parapodium ; *pr.,* prostomium ; *t.,* accessory teeth ; *tc.,* tentacular cirri ; *te.,* tentacle.

these, *Nereis cultrifer*, common under stones on the south coast of England, where it is known as the Red Cat and is used as bait, is a good example. The body of this worm is about six inches in length, of a greenish colour, with red on the limbs and where the dorsal blood vessel shows through, roughly cylindrical, tapering towards the hinder end, and divided into about eighty somites. Like the earthworm, it is covered with a thin cuticle and provided with chætæ, but the chætæ are longer and much more numerous than in the earthworm, and are borne on movable limbs or *parapodia*, of which a pair is placed on each somite. A parapodium is a flat, hollow vertical process of the body-wall, standing out at the side of its segment and serving to pull the animal along in creeping, or to row it in swimming. It is cleft into two principal lobes, a dorsal *notopodium* and a ventral *neuropodium*. Each of these is again divided into smaller lobes and bears at its base a slender process known as a *cirrus*. A stout, deeply embedded chæta or *aciculum* supports the notopodium and another the neuropodium. The front end of the body is modified to form a definite head. This consists of the prostomium and the peristomium. On the prostomium are situated dorsally a pair of *prostomial tentacles* and two pairs of eyes, each of which is a pit lined by pigmented cells and enclosing a gelatinous mass which serves as a lens. Ventrally the prostomium bears a pair of stout *palps*. The peristomium carries on each side two pairs of long, slender *tentacular cirri*, and probably corresponds to two fused somites. A bilaterally symmetrical animal which leads an active life always has a head, and if the animal be segmented there is a tendency for the foremost somites to enter into the composition of the head. This is known as *cephalisation*. Behind the last segment is a conical region without parapodia which bears a pair of slender *anal cirri* and the terminal anus.

The musculature of *Nereis* is more complicated than that of the earthworm, the longitudinal muscle fibres being grouped into four powerful longitudinal bundles, two dorsal and two ventral, while there are oblique muscles to move the parapodia. As might be expected from the better provision of sense organs on the head, the brain also is more complex. The alimentary canal is simpler than that of the earthworm, but the pharynx can be caused to protrude by being turned inside out, and is lined with cuticle, thickened in places to form numerous small teeth and a pair of strong jaws with which the prey is seized. The sexes are separate. The reproductive organs are very simple, consisting of temporary masses of cells, which arise from the cœlomic epithelium. The ova and sperm probably escape by temporary openings formed in the body-wall, and fertilisation takes place in the water. The free young are at first very unlike the parents, being minute, globular creatures, known as *trochospheres*, which swim by means of a girdle of cilia in front of the mouth and have an apical tuft at the front end. They undergo a gradual change into the adult, becoming oval and then lengthening and segmenting. Their mesoderm is formed as two ventro-lateral bands, each thrown off by the continual division of a *pole cell* at the hinder end, and spreads round the gut, between ectoderm and endoderm, the cœlom appearing in it. The larva of *Nereis* is not in all respects a typical trochosphere. In Fig. 197, B a more typical example is shown, in a later stage of development than that represented in Fig. 197, A. It has between ectoderm and endoderm a large space (blastocœle) which is lacking in the trochosphere of *Nereis*.

The leeches are another group of segmented worms related to

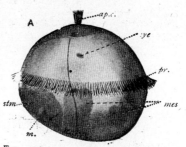

FIG. 197.—A. The trochosphere of *Nereis*. Modified, after Wilson.

ap.c., Apical tuft of cilia; *eye*; *m.*, opening of mouth; *mes.*, mesoderm; *pr.*, preoral ring of cilia; *stm.*, stomodæum (the pouch of ectoderm which forms the mouth and gullet).

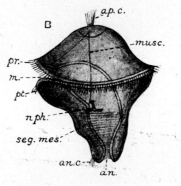

B. A typical trochosphere in an early stage of the transformation into the adult.

an., Anus; *an.c.*, anal tuft of cilia; *ap.c.*, apical tuft of cilia; *m.*, mouth; *musc.*; larval muscles; *nph.*, larval nephridium; *pr.*, preoral ring of cilia; *pt.*, postoral ring; *seg.mes.*, segments beginning to form in the mesoderm.

the earthworms. *Hirudo medicinalis*, the Medicinal Leech,
a dweller in freshwater pools, marshes, and
The Leech.   sluggish streams, is found sometimes in this
country but more commonly on the Continent, where,
when it was more used in medicine than at present, it
was bred in large numbers in special ponds. It lives
normally by sucking the blood of frogs and fishes, but also,
when it is full grown, on that of warm-blooded animals
which enter its haunts, and it will feed on man, though to
induce it to do so his skin may have to be moistened with
blood or milk or pierced by a small cut. An active specimen
will draw one or two drams of blood. The body of the
leech is 3–5 inches in length, somewhat flattened, and provided at each end with a downward-facing sucker. It is
encircled by 95 minute rings or *annuli*, and brightly marked
in various shades of green, yellow, and black, paler below
than above. The annuli do not indicate the true segmentation. In the greater part of the body five of these lesser
rings go to a somite, but towards the ends there are fewer,
and in the head or region of the anterior sucker (prostomium
and first five somites) there are eleven annuli, while the
posterior sucker represents seven somites fused without
annulation. Unlike that of the earthworm or *Nereis*, the
number of somites is a definite one, amounting in all to
33, including those of the head and hinder sucker. The
mouth lies in the midst of the anterior sucker, and the anus
is a minute opening above the base of the hinder sucker.
The male and female genital openings are median on the
second annuli of the 10th and 11th somites respectively.
On the last annulus of each somite from the sixth to the
twenty-second, are the openings of a pair of nephridia.
On the first annulus of each somite is a transverse row
of minute sense-papillæ. On the head a pair of these
in each somite are transformed into minute eyes, recognisable by their pigment as dark spots. There are no
chætæ. The worm can walk by looping like a " looper "
caterpillar, and swim by undulation of its body.
    The body is covered by a thin cuticle, which is shed
from time to time. Under this lies an epidermis, between
the bases of whose cells run blood capillaries, so that the
skin is a respiratory organ, in which the blood is exposed

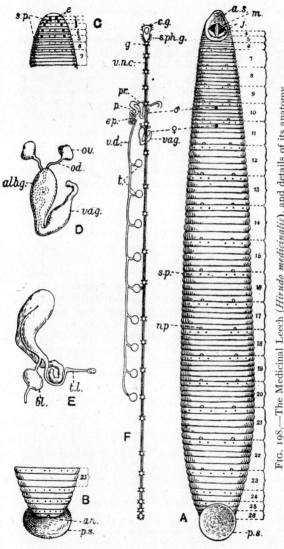

FIG. 198.—The Medicinal Leech (*Hirudo medicinalis*), and details of its anatomy.

A, Ventral view; B, dorsal view of hinder end; C, dorsal view of head and succeeding region; D, female genital organs; E, anterior view of nephridium; F, nervous and genital organs (male organs of right side removed).

a.s., Anterior sucker; *alb.g.*, albumen gland; *an.*, anus; *bl.*, bladder; *c.g.*, cerebral ganglion; *e.*, eyes; *ep.*, epididymis; *g.*, second ganglion of ventral cord; *j.*, jaws; *m.*, mouth; *np.*, nephridiopore, by which a nephridium opens; *od.*, oviduct; *ov.*, ovary; *p.*, penis; *p.s.*, posterior sucker; *pr.*, prostate; *s.p.*, sense papillæ; *s.ph.g.*, subpharyngeal ganglion; *t.*, testes; *t.l.*, lobe of nephridium which ends in testis sinus; *v.d.*, vas deferens; *v.n.c.*, ventral nerve cord; *vag.*, vagina; ♂ male opening; ♀ female opening; 1–26, somites.

283

to the surrounding water. Below stand circular and longitudinal muscle-layers, and within these a layer of *botryoidal tissue*, composed of branched canals, whose walls are laden with black pigment, while their cavity is full of blood. This tissue takes the place of a peri-visceral cavity and imbeds the gut.

The mouth is provided with three jaws, which are compressed cushions of muscle covered with a finely toothed layer of cuticle : by these the skin of the prey is pierced with a characteristic tri-radiate wound. A muscular pharynx succeeds the mouth ; it pumps the juices of the prey, and into it open numerous unicellular glands whose secretion prevents blood from clotting so that the leech's food remains fluid while it is being taken and passed backward to be digested. It is owing to this secretion that bleeding continues for some time after the leech is removed from its wound, and an extract of the heads of these worms is sometimes used in physiological experiments to prevent clotting. After the pharynx stands the very large crop (segs. 8–18) with eleven pairs of lateral cæca, of which the last is much larger than the rest and extends backwards on each side of the remainder of the alimentary canal. This consists of the stomach—a narrow tube, with an enlargement at its start and a spiral fold of its inner wall—the intestine, narrower than the stomach, and the rectum, somewhat wider. The blood sucked for food is stored in the crop, whose cæca are more or less dilated according to the amount of their contents, and passed drop by drop into the stomach, where it at once turns green and then is digested. A

FIG. 199.—A diagram-matic view of the alimentary canal of the medicinal leech, as seen when it is not gorged with blood.

*cr.*i., *cr.*ii., Cæca of the crop ; *int.*, intestine ; *ph.*, pharynx ; *rm.*, rectum ; *st.*, stomach.

full meal will last the animal for several months or a
year. Seventeen pairs of nephridia lie in somites 6–22.
Each is a mass of glandular tissue traversed by a system of
intracellular ductules. There is no internal opening, but
those which lie in the testis somites have a swollen end
lying in the capsule of the testis, and bearing a number
of ciliated funnels which do not communicate with the
ductules. There are two systems of tubes which contain

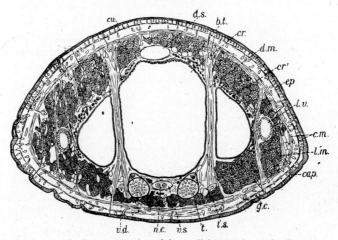

FIG. 200. — A transverse section of the medicinal leech. —After Bourne.
b.t., Botryoidal tissue; *c.m.*, circular muscles; *cap.*, capillary; *cr.*, crop; *cr'.*, a
cæcum of the same; *cu.*, cuticle; *d.m.*, dorsoventral muscle; *d.s.*, dorsal
sinus; *ep.*, epidermis; *g.c.*, gland cells; *l.m.*, longitudinal muscles; *l.v.*, lateral
vessel; *n.c.*, nerve cord; *t.*, testis; *t.s.*, testis sinus, with end of nephridium;
v.d., vas deferens.

a fluid like blood—a red plasma with a few colourless
corpuscles. One of these systems is the true blood-vascular
system : its principal vessels are two lateral trunks, which
unite before and behind, and are connected also by a network of capillaries. There are no hearts, but the lateral
vessels are contractile. The other vascular system consists
of a dorsal and a ventral longitudinal sinus, which are also
connected before and behind and by means of a capillary
system. The walls of this system are thinner than those

of the true blood vessels. They represent the cœlom, as may be seen from the fact that the ventral sinus encloses the nerve cord and communicates with capsules around the ovaries and testes. The botryoidal tubes are also in communication with the sinus system. It is said that the capillaries of the true blood system are connected with it. The nervous system is of the same type as those of the earthworm and *Nereis*. A small brain, above and before the pharynx, is connected by a pair of very short circumpharyngeal commissures with a ventral cord which carries at wide intervals twenty-three ganglia. Of these the first or subpharyngeal and the last each represent several fused. Nerves are given off from the brain and the ganglia. The commissures which unite the ganglia of the ventral cord are seen in section to be double, with a slender median strand.

The animal is hermaphrodite. There are nine pairs of testes, enclosed in spherical capsules in the 12th–20th somites, with on each side a common vas deferens, which is coiled as an " epididymis " in the 10th somite, where the vas deferentia join to open on a muscular, protrusible penis, surrounded at its base by a " prostate " gland. The single pair of ovaries lies in the 11th somite, in which its short oviducts open by a common vagina. The eggs are laid in cocoons secreted by " clitellar " glands in the skin of the 10th-12th segments and placed in holes made in the banks, above water. The young resemble the parents and feed at first on the juices of water insects, and the like.

Segmented, cœlomate animals, with a thin cuticle, a
Annelida.   closed blood-vascular system, nephridia, and
a nervous system on the same plan as that of the earthworm, are known as *Annelida*. The earthworm, *Nereis*, the lug-worm (*Arenicola*), which is often used for bait, and leeches belong to this group.

CHAPTER XV

THE CRAYFISH. ARTHROPODA

CRAYFISHES are found in many English rivers, especially in those which rise in chalk or limestone hills.

Habits. They are little, lobster-like creatures, which make burrows in the river banks. They dislike strong light and during the daytime generally remain in their holes with only their pincers and long feelers projecting. When they come out they crawl stealthily about, searching constantly for their food, which consists of organic matter of any kind, plant or animal, dead or alive, that they are able to seize and break up with their pincers. If danger threatens, they dart backward suddenly and swiftly They are used for food, especially for garnishing salads, and were formerly caught in large numbers in this country by means of wicker crayfish-pots, but in 1887 their numbers were greatly reduced by a disease, and at present crayfishes for the table are imported from the Continent.

The English crayfish, *Astacus torrentium*, is about three inches long, and of a dull, greenish colour,

External Features. which harmonises well with the surroundings in which it lives. The species imported from the Continent is *A. fluviatilis*, which is larger and has red colouring on the pincers and legs. The body of a crayfish is armoured with a thick chitinous cuticle, strengthened by salts of lime, which in places is thinned to form joints : it is segmented, each segment (somite) bearing a pair of jointed limbs, but in the front part the segments are fused to form a *fore-body* or *cephalothorax*, where the only conspicuous sign of their existence is the presence of several pairs of limbs, though parts of the armour and certain internal organs are also segmentally arranged. The rest of the body, known as the *hind body* or *abdomen*, is more completely segmented. At the end of the abdomen is a flat piece known as the *telson*, on the under side of which the anus opens. The telson bears no limbs, and is divided by an imperfect transverse joint. The armour of each segment of the abdomen consists of a broad back-piece or *tergum* and a narrow belly-plate or *sternum*, with a pair of V-shaped prolongations, known as the *pleura*, joining them at the sides. There are no pleura on the first abdominal somite. The tergum, sternum, and pleura of each somite form a continuous ring. The limbs are jointed to the hinder side of the sternum near its outer ends, and the part of the sternum between each limb and the adjoining pleuron is sometimes called an *epimeron*. The terga overlap one another from before backwards and slide over one another as the abdomen is straightened and bent, the armour of each somite being joined to that of the next by thin cuticle, which allows of movement. In the cephalothorax the terga are fused to form a *shield* or *carapace*. This is prolonged in front into a beak-like *rostrum* and is crossed by a furrow, which is called the *cervical groove* because it is supposed to mark the separation of two regions known as the head and thorax. At each side of the body a fold of the carapace overhangs as a lean-to roof, the *gill cover* or *branchiostegite*, which encloses between itself and the side of the body a chamber in which the gills lie. Behind the cervical groove a *branchiocardiac groove* on each side marks off the branchiostegite from a median *cardiac region* which roofs the thorax. The cuticle of the inside of the branch-

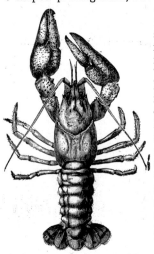

FIG. 201.—View of a crayfish from above.—After Huxley.

Note cervical groove, cardiac region of carapace, rostrum, and tail fan.

iostegite and part of the side of the body underneath it are thin. On the ventral side of the cephalothorax the limbs of each pair are close together, but small sterna lie between them. The head is, of course, the region which contains the mouth and the principal sense organs. The mouth is placed on the ventral surface at some distance from the front end, and in front of it the sternal surface slopes upwards to the rostrum. At the sides of the latter, upon a pair of short, movable stalks, are placed the eyes, and below these stand two pairs of feelers or antennæ.

The *limbs* or *appendages* number nineteen pairs, without counting the eyes, which are by some authorities reckoned as limbs. We shall not take this view, but as there is evidence in the development of the crayfish and of related animals that the foremost region of the head corresponds to a somite, we shall regard the body as containing twenty somites, of which the foremost bears no limbs. The telson is not a somite. Of the twenty segments, the first six form the head, the next eight the thorax, and the last six, with the telson, the abdomen. The parts of which a complete limb consists are best seen in the limbs known as the third pair of maxillipeds (Fig. 205, A), which lie immediately in front of the great pincers. In each of these we may distinguish a two-jointed basal region or *protopodite*, the segment nearest the body being known as the *coxopodite*, the next as the *basipodite*. On its outer side the coxopodite carries a large, flat, thin-walled structure, known as the *epipodite*, bearing many small finger-processes, which constitute a *gill*. At the base of the epipodite is a knob bearing a tuft of threads known as the *coxopoditic setæ* or *setobranch*. The basipodite bears two structures. From its outer side arises a slender, jointed appendage known as the *exopodite*. At its end, continuing the axis of the limb, is the stout, five-jointed *endopodite*, whose segments (podomeres), starting from the basipodite, are known as the *ischiopodite, meropodite, carpopodite, propodite* and *dactylopodite*. The other limbs are built upon the same general plan as the third maxilliped, but in detail the structure of every one of them is adapted to the particular work it has to perform, each part being of a different shape in each pair of limbs, or sometimes

Limbs.

19

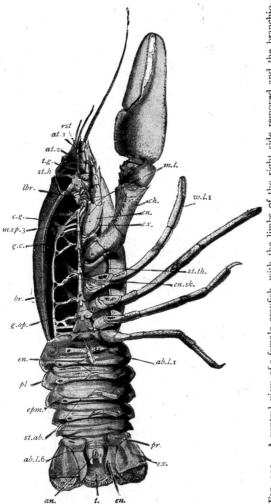

FIG. 202.—A ventral view of a female crayfish, with the limbs of the right side removed and the branchiostegite of that side partly cut away.—Partly after Howes.

*ab.l.*1,6, First and sixth abdominal limbs; *at.*1, antennule; *at.*2, antenna; *an.*, anus; *br.*, branchiostegite; *c.g.*, cervical groove; *ch.*, cheliped; *en.*, endopodite; *en.sk.*, endophragmal skeleton; *epm.*, epimeron; *ex.*, exopodite; *g.c.*, gill chamber; *g.op.*, openings of oviduct; *lbr.*, labrum; *m.l.*, limbs adjoining the mouth; *mxp.*3, third maxilliped; *pl.*, pleuron; *pr.*, protopodite; *rst.*, rostrum; *st.ab.*, abdominal sterna; *st.h.*, sternal region of body in part of mouth; *st.th.*, thoracic sterna; *t.*, telson; *t.g.*, tubercle on which green gland opens; *w.l.*1, first walking leg.

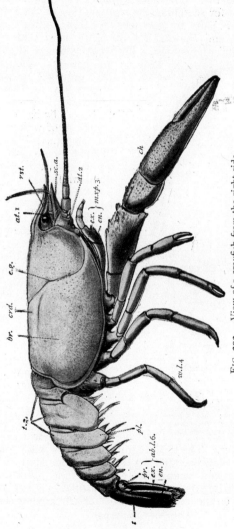

FIG. 203.—View of a crayfish from the right side.

ab.l.6, Sixth abdominal limb; *at.1*, antennule; *at.2*, antenna; *b.*, branchiostegite; *c.g.*, cervical groove; *ch.*, cheliped; *crd.*, cardiac region of carapace; *en.*, endopodite; *ex.*, exopodite; *mxp.3*, third maxilliped; *pl.*, pleuron; *pr.*, protopodite; *rst.*, rostrum; *sc.a.*, scale of antenna; *t.*, telson; *tg.*, terga; *w.l.4*, last walking leg.

absent altogether. The first two pairs are sensory, and have long lashes for searching the surroundings of the animal. The next six pairs are jaws, used for bringing the food to the mouth and chewing it : these are short and stand close behind the mouth. Then come two great shears

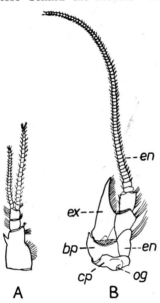

or pincers which are the principal grasping organs, next four pairs of legs, and then the six pairs of limbs of the abdomen, of which some are concerned in reproduction, some help the animal forward by paddling while it is walking, and the last pair are used in rapid swimming. Exopodites are wanting from the legs, great pincers, and first two pairs of jaws, and epipodites are found only upon the limbs of the thorax.

The first limb of each side is known as the *antennule* or *first antenna*. It is peculiar in having three, instead of two, segments in its protopodite. The first segment [1] is large and three-sided : upon its upper side there opens, by a slit edged with bristles, the statocyst, which will be de-

Fig. 204.—The antennule and antenna of a crayfish.

A, External view of the antennule of the left side ; *B,* ventral view of the antenna of the right side.
bp., Basipodite ; *cp.,* coxopodite ; *en.,* endopodite ; *ex.,* exopodite ; *o.g.,* opening of the green gland.

scribed later. The third segment bears two many-jointed lashes or flagella. These are often compared to the exopodites and endopodites of the other limbs, but the comparison is probably not justifiable. The outer lash bears on the under side of most of its segments certain

[1] See the note opposite.

peculiar bristles which are supposed to serve the sense of smell. The second limb is the *antenna* (or *second antenna*). Its coxopodite is short and wide and bears below a knob, upon which opens the green gland or kidney. The basipodite bears the endopodite on the median side. The exopodite is a flat, triangular, pointed *scale*, and the

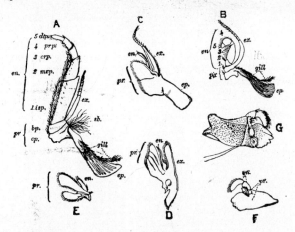

FIG. 205.—The mouth appendages of the left side of a crayfish.

A, Third maxilliped ; *B*, second maxilliped ; *C*, first maxilliped ; *D*, maxilla (second maxilla) ; *E*, maxillule (first maxilla) ; *F*, mandible in ventral view ; *G*, the same in dorsal view, somewhat enlarged, showing molar process.

bp., Basipodite ; *cp.*, coxopodite ; *crp.*, carpopodite ; *dtp.*, dactylopodite ; *en.*, endopodite ; *ep.*, epipodite ; *ex.*, exopodite ; *gill* ; *isp.*, ischiopodite ; *mrp.*, meropodite ; *pr.*, protopodite ; *prp.*, propodite ; *sb.*, setobranch or tuft of coxopodite setæ ; 1–5, joints of endopodite.

endopodite is a very long flagellum. The third limb or *mandible* has a large, broad, and very strong coxopodite [1] with a toothed *incisor edge* which bites against that of its

---

[1] Perhaps really a joint known as the *precoxa*, which corresponds to the first joint of the antennule and is in the other limbs obscured or absent. There is reason to believe that the true coxopodite of the mandible is absent. In the maxillule the precoxa and coxopodite appear to be fused. In the second maxilla the precoxa may be represented by the first lobe of the protopodite, and in the thorax the precoxa of each limb is absorbed into the side of the body. There is no evidence as to its identity in the abdominal limbs.

fellow on the other side of the body. Above the incisor
edge, and therefore hidden in ventral view, is a broad,
irregular ridge known as the *molar process*. The basipodite and an endopodite of two segments form a small
three-jointed appendage or *palp* in front of the coxopodite.
The mandibles lie at the sides of the mouth. Behind it
come the limbs of the fourth pair, known as the *maxillules*
or *first maxillæ*. Each of these consists of three thin
plates joined to a small basal piece. One plate is an
expansion of the coxopodite,[1] the second represents the
basipodite, and the third the endopodite. The fifth limb is
the *maxilla* (or *second maxilla*). It is a flat structure,
deeply cleft into several parts. The protopodite bears two

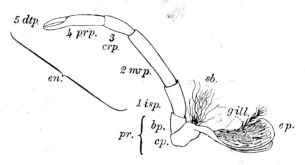

FIG. 206.—The first walking leg of a crayfish. Letters as in Fig. 205.

thin lobes directed towards the middle line of the body and
each in turn divided into two.[2] The endopodite is a narrow
structure directed forwards. The exopodite is a wide plate
projecting backwards and forwards from the outer side of
the limb and known as the *scaphognathite*. The second
maxilla lies under the front end of the branchiostegite, and
the function of the scaphognathite is to set up a current of
water over the gills by bailing it forwards out of the gill
chamber. The sixth limb, or *first maxilliped*, is the first

[1] See note to p. 293.
[2] The first double lobe probably represents the precoxa and
coxopodite ; the two parts of the second lobe probably belong to the
basipodite and the segment which succeeds it.

of those which belong to the thorax. Two broad lobes represent its coxopodite and basipodite, the endopodite is small and two-jointed, and the exopodite, shaped like that of the third maxilliped, is large. The epipodite is present as a very large plate, which does not bear a gill. The *second maxilliped* is much like the third, but has a smaller endopodite and a relatively larger exopodite. The *third maxilliped* has already been described. Behind the maxillipeds come five pairs of *legs* or *pereiopoda*, of which the first, the ninth of the whole series of limbs, bear great pincers and are called the *chelipeds*, the rest being the *walking legs*. In each of these limbs the exopodite is wanting and the endopodite is long and strong and consists of five podomeres, named as in the third maxilliped. In the chelipeds and the walking legs of the first two pairs the propodite has a projection, against which the dactylopodite bites so as to form a pair of pincers. An epipodite bearing a gill is present upon each of the legs except the last pair. On the coxopodite of the second walking leg of the female is a round opening, through which the eggs are laid, and the sperm of the male is passed through a similar opening upon his last leg. Of the *abdominal limbs* the first and second pairs are best studied after the third, fourth, and fifth. The latter are alike and consist each of a short coxopodite, a long basipodite, and an endopodite and exopodite each composed of a number of imperfectly separated podomeres, of which the first is longer than the rest. The endopodite is rather longer than the exopodite, and both bear numerous, plumed bristles. The *second abdominal limb* of the female is like those behind it. In the male the first podomere of the endopodite is much elongated and bears at the end on the outside a thin plate rolled into a scroll. The *first abdominal limb* has no exopodite in either sex. In the female it is minute. In the male the basipodite and endopodite are fused, flattened, and rolled scrollwise into a tube for conveying sperm to the female. The limbs of the *last* (*sixth*) *abdominal pair* have short, undivided protopodites, and very broad endopodites and exopodites, the former of one, the latter of two podomeres. They are directed backwards, and form with the telson the *tail fan* used in backward swimming.

Table of the Segments of the Crayfish

Head	1. Preantennal limbless segment		
	2. Antennules . . .	} Sensory limbs.	
	3. Antennæ (II) . .		
	4. Mandibles . . .		
	5. Maxillules . . .	} Jaws.	
	6. Maxillæ (II) . .		
Thorax	7. Maxillipeds (I) . .		
	8. ,, (II) . .		
	9. ,, (III) . .		
	10. Chelipeds . . .		
	11. Walking legs (I) . .		
	12. ,, ,, (II) ♀ .	} Legs.	
	13. ,, ,, (III) .		
	14. ,, ,, (IV) ♂ .		
Abdomen	15. Abdominal limbs (I) .	Uniramous limbs.	
	16. ,, ,, (II) .		
	17. ,, ,, (III) .		
	18. ,, ,, (IV) .	} Paddles.	
	19. ,, ,, (V) .		
	20. ,, ,, (VI) .		
	Telson . . .	} Tail fan.	

♀ Female opening.   ♂ Male opening.

The ectoderm or epidermis of the crayfish consists of a
layer of protoplasm with nuclei, which in many
Cuticle and Epidermis. parts is not divided into cells and is therefore
a syncytium (p. 147), though in places it
forms a columnar epithelium. Outside it, lies a cuticle
which it secretes, and, as we have already seen, this
cuticle contains chitin (p. 257), and is for the most part
thick and hardened with salts of lime, but remains thin and
flexible in certain places so as to form joints which allow the
parts of the body to move upon one another, and also in the
gill chambers. In places it bears bristles (*setæ*) of various
shapes. These are hollow, and the epidermis is continued
into them and is here often connected with nerve fibres, so
that the bristles serve as sense organs of various kinds.
From time to time the cuticle is shed and a new one
secreted; this allows of growth. Moulting takes place
frequently while the animal is young, but the old male
sheds its cuticle only twice a year, and the female only once.
As the time for moulting draws near, a new cuticle begins

to form under the old one, which is loosened from the epidermis, and the crayfish goes into hiding, because the new cuticle is soft and the animal will be helpless for some days while it is hardening. The shell then splits across the back and along the limbs, and the crayfish, lying on its side, draws itself out of the old cuticle.

There is in the crayfish no continuous muscular body-wall, but numerous muscles, composed of striped

Skeleton, Muscles, and Locomotion. fibres, move the various parts of its body, being attached to the inside of the pieces of the armour. Thus the skeleton is external, not, like that of a frog, internal. Its pieces, known as *sclerites*, usually abut upon one another across the soft jointing membranes by hard knobs which serve as hinges. In the thorax ingrowths of the cuticle provide a kind of false internal skeleton. This has the form of a complicated scaffold-

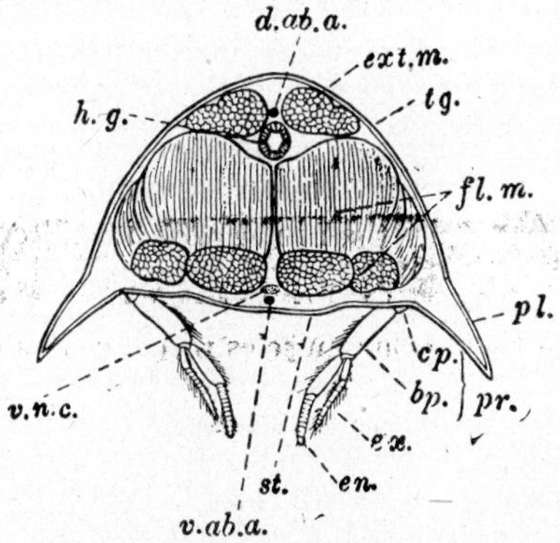

FIG. 207.—A semi-diagrammatic drawing of a transverse section of the abdomen of the crayfish.

bp., Basipodite; *cp.*, coxopodite; *d.ab.a.*, dorsal abdominal artery; *en.*, endopodite; *ex.*, exopodite; *ext.m.*, extensor muscles; *fl.m.*, flexor muscles; *h.g.*, hind-gut; *pl.*, pleuron; *pr.*, protopodite; *tg.*, tergum; *st.*, sternum; *v.ab.a.*, ventral abdominal artery; *v.n.c.* ventral nerve cord.

ing along the ventral side of the animal, and is known as the *endophragmal skeleton*. In the limbs, as in those of the frog, opposing muscles (flexors and extensors) bend and straighten each joint. Ingrowths of the cuticle serve as tendons for them. The abdomen also is moved by two sets of muscles. A dorsal set of extensors starts from the inside of the carapace and is inserted into the terga of the abdominal somites. When they contract, these muscles draw forward the terga and thus straighten the abdomen. Ventrally, powerful and complicated flexors connect the

sterna with one another and with the endophragmal skeleton
(Fig. 210). The flexors, when they contract, draw closer
the sterna and thus bend the abdomen. By this movement,
spreading at the same time its tail fan, the crayfish makes
the sudden backward jumps by which it escapes from
its enemies. Its gentle forward movements are carried
out by the walking legs, aided by a padding of the
abdominal limbs. The legs of the first three pairs pull
and those of the last pair push, and their movements are
carried out in such a way that the animal is always standing
upon six legs while two—which are on opposite sides and
of different pairs—are in motion.

The power of regeneration, though it is less in the
crayfish than in earthworms and much less
Regeneration and Autotomy. than in *Hydra*, is still considerable. A whole
limb which is injured can be grown again.
The injured leg is first cast off by a spasmodic contraction
of some of its muscles which causes it to break through at
the basipodite, the internal cavity—which, as we shall see,
is a blood space—being here crossed by a partition which
leaves only a small opening, through which the nerves
and blood vessels pass. When the limb is cast off this
opening is quickly closed by a blood clot, after which the
cuticle grows across the wound. Beneath the scar the
new limb is formed as a sort of bud and gradually takes
shape. At the next moult it becomes free, though it is
still small, and it increases in size at each moult, until a
normal limb has been provided. This power of casting
off limbs is known as *autotomy*. It is sometimes used
as a means of escape from enemies which have seized one
of the limbs, but this is not so common in the crayfish as
in some animals that are related to it.

The body of the crayfish contains a spacious perivisceral
cavity, in which the internal organs lie. This
Perivisceral Cavity and Alimentary System. is not a cœlom, but an enlarged portion of the
hæmocœle (p. 275), and communicates with
the blood vessels. The alimentary canal fills
the greater part of this cavity. The mouth is an elongated
opening below the head between the mandibles. It has
in front a wide *upper lip* or *labrum*, and behind it is a pair
of lobes (*paragnatha*) known together as the *lower lip* or

metastoma. A short, wide *gullet* leads upwards into the large *proventriculus,* often called the " stomach." This

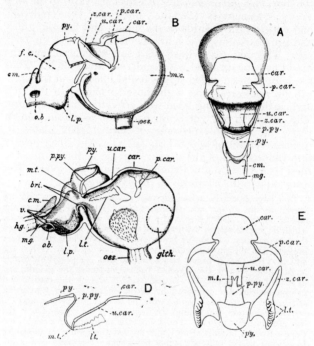

FIG. 208.—The proventriculus of the crayfish.

A, The whole organ from above ; *B,* the same from the right side ; *C,* the left half from within, the muscles being relaxed ; *D,* the ossicles of the mill in median section, the anterior and posterior gastric muscles being contracted ; *E,* the mill in plan. All the figures are semi-diagrammatic, much detail being omitted.

bri., Bristles for filtering ; *car.,* cardiac ossicle ; *cm.,* cæcum ; *f.c.,* pyloric or filter-chamber ; *glth.,* position of gastrolith ; *h.g.,* hind-gut ; *l.p.,* lateral pouch ; *l.t.,* lateral tooth ; *m.c.,* mill-chamber ; *m.g.,* mid-gut ; *m.t.,* median tooth ; *o.b.,* opening of bile duct ; *œs.,* œsophagus ; *p.car.,* pterocardiac ossicle ; *p.py.,* pre-pyloric ossicle ; *py.,* pyloric ossicle ; *u.car.,* uorocardiac ossicle ; *v.,* the several pieces of an arrangement of valves which directs the solid residue of the food into the hind-gut, there to become the fæces ; *z.car.,* zygocardiac ossicle.

consists of two chambers, a large *forepart* or *mill-chamber,* often known as the " cardiac division of the stomach," and a smaller *hind part* or *filter-chamber,* often known as the

" pyloric division of the stomach," separated from the mill-chamber by a pit in the roof. From the filter-chamber the short *mid-gut* or *mesenteron* leads backwards to the long *hind-gut*, sometimes called the " intestine." The epidermis and cuticle turn inwards at the mouth and line the gullet and proventriculus, which are together known as the *fore-gut*. The mid-gut is lined with soft endoderm, and the hind-gut is again lined with epidermis and cuticle. Thus the regions often called stomach and intestine in the cray-fish do not correspond with those so named in the frog and earthworm, being lined with ectoderm, not endoderm. The cuticle in the gut is for the most part thin, but in places in the proventriculus it forms stout plates or ossicles, certain of which bear strong teeth which project into the forepart of the organ. By the action of muscles these can be brought together to crush the food. The whole apparatus is known as the *gastric mill.*

Two large plates lie across the roof in the two divisions, and are known as the *cardiac* and *pyloric ossicles.* They are joined in the middle by two smaller pieces, the *urocardiac* and *prepyloric ossicles*, which lie respectively in the front and hinder walls of the pit between the two divisions. From the lower end of the prepyloric ossicle there projects into the proventriculus the forked *middle tooth.* When the mill is at rest the pit passes backwards, so that the prepyloric ossicle in its hinder wall is also directed backwards under the pyloric, and its tooth points backwards. At each side of the pit the cardiac and pyloric ossicles are connected by two more pieces, the *zygocardiac ossicle*, which articulates behind with the side of the pyloric, and the *pterocardiac ossicle*, which joins the front end of the zygocardiac to the side of the cardiac ossicle. These side ossicles do not run straight, but slope outwards to meet at an angle, so that the outline of the whole framework of the mill is roughly hexagonal. Internally each zygo-cardiac ossicle bears a large, ribbed, *lateral tooth. Anterior* and *posterior gastric muscles* run from the cardiac and pyloric ossicles respectively to the carapace. When they contract they pull these ossicles apart. The result is that (1) the upper end of the prepyloric ossicle, being pulled backward by the pyloric, stands upright, thus turning the middle tooth forwards ; (2) the zygocardiac and pterocardiac ossicles are straightened out, so that the lateral teeth are brought together in the middle line. Thus all three teeth meet inside the proventriculus. The ossicles are brought back to their former position partly by the elasticity of the walls of the proventriculus and partly by the contraction of *cardiopyloric muscles* (Fig. 208).

The filter-chamber is also complicated, having internal ridges covered with bristles which serve to strain out the

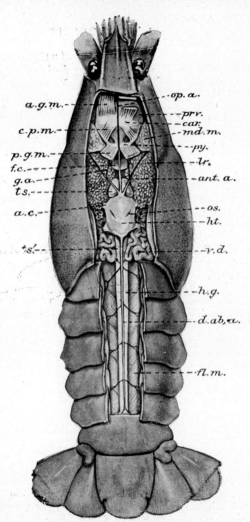

FIG. 209.—A male crayfish dissected from the dorsal side, after injection of the arteries.

a.c., ala cordis; *a.g.m.*, anterior gastric muscle; *ant.a.*, antennary artery; *c.p.m.*, cardiopyloric muscle; *car.*, cardiac ossicle; *d.ab.a.*, dorsal abdominal artery; *f.c.*, part of filter chamber, blue coloured in fresh specimens; *fl.m.*, flexor muscles of abdomen; *g.a.*, gastric artery; *h.g.*, hind-gut; *ht.*, heart; *lr.*, liver; *md.m.*, muscle of mandible; *op.a.*, ophthalmic artery; *os.*, ostium; *p.g.m.*, posterior gastric muscle; *prv.* proventriculus ("cardiac" division); *py.*, pyloric ossicle; *ts.* anterior lobe of testis; *ts'.*, posterior lobe of the same; *v.d.*, vas deferens.

301

particles of the food, so that only the finely crushed matter passes into the mid-gut, while the coarser particles are passed on into the hind-gut by an apparatus of valves. Into the mid-gut opens on each side the *liver* or *hepato-pancreas*, a large, lobed, yellow gland, consisting of numerous short tubes joined by ducts which finally communicate with the mid-gut by an opening on each side. The roof of the mid-gut is prolonged into a short *blind gut* or *cæcum*. Food is either raked up by the third maxillipeds or seized by the chelipeds and torn up by them and the smaller pincers. It is passed forwards by the jaws to the mouth, where pieces are cut from it by the mandibles and thrust by the mandibular palps and the maxillules into the mouth. It is chewed in the proventriculus, strained, and in a finely divided state passed into the mid-gut. The juice secreted by the liver digests all classes of food-stuffs, and digestion and absorption take place within the liver as well as in the mid-gut. The cuticle of the gut is shed with that of the body. Shortly before a moult two flat calcareous bodies, known as " *crabs' eyes* " or *gastroliths*, are laid down in the forepart of the proventriculus. They are ground up before the moult takes place. It is uncertain whether they consist of matter removed from the armour of the body to weaken it in preparation for the moult or are a store of material for the strengthening of the new cuticle. Possibly they serve both purposes.

The heart is a hollow organ with thick, muscular walls.

Blood Vessels. It is roughly hexagonal in outline, as seen from above, and lies in the thorax, above the hind-gut and immediately below the cardiac region of the carapace, in a space, known as the *pericardial sinus*, with membranous walls, to which the heart is connected by six fibrous bands called the *alæ cordis*. Three pairs of valved openings or *ostia* admit blood from the pericardial sinus to the heart : one pair is dorsal, another lateral, and the third ventral. From the front end of the heart arise three vessels—a median *ophthalmic artery*, which runs straight forwards over the proventriculus to supply the eyes and other organs of the head, and a pair of *antennary arteries*, which start one on each side of the ophthalmic, run forwards and

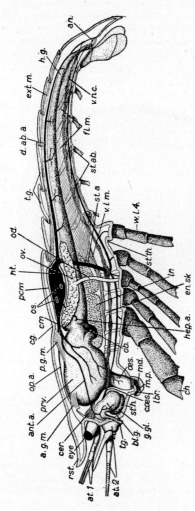

FIG. 210.—The internal organs of a female crayfish *in situ*. Slightly diagrammatic.

a.g.m., Anterior gastric muscle; *an.*, anus; *ant.a.*, antennary artery; *at.1*, antennule; *at.2*, antenna; *bl.g.*, bladder of the green gland; *c.g.*, cervical groove; *c.œs.*, circumœsophageal commissure; *cer.*, cerebral ganglion; *ch.*, cheliped; *cm.*, cæcum; *d.ab.a*, dorsal abdominal artery; *en.sk.*, endophragmal skeleton; *eye*; *ext.m.*, extensor muscles; *fl.m.*, flexor muscles, looping from one sternum to another over *v.l.m.*; *g.gl.*, green gland; *h.g.*, hind-gut; *hep.a.*, hepatic artery; *ht.*, heart; *lr.*, liver; *lbr.*, labrum; *md.*, mandible; *m.p.*, mandibular palp; *o.b.*, opening of bile duct; *od.*, oviduct; *œs.*, œsophagus; *op.a.*, ophthalmic artery; *os.*, ostia; *ov.*, ovary; *p.g.m.*, posterior gastric muscle; *pcm.*, pericardium; *prv.*, proventriculus; *rst.*, rostrum; *st.a.*, sternal artery; *st.ab.*, abdominal sterna; *st.h.*, sternal region of the body in front of the mouth; *st.th.*, thoracic sterna; *t.*, telson; *t.g.*, tubercle for green gland; *lg.*, terga; *v.l.m.* ventral longitudinal muscles; *v.n.c.*, ventral nerve cord; *w.l.4*, last walking leg.

outwards, and divide each into two branches, one *gastric* and the other to the antennæ and green gland. Behind and below the antennaries arise a pair of *hepatic arteries*, which supply the liver, and from the hinder angle of the heart there is given off a vessel that at once divides into

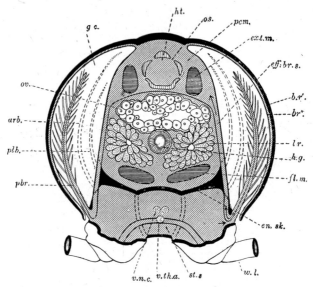

FIG. 211.—A diagram of a transverse section through the thorax of a crayfish.

arb., Arthrobranch ; *br'*., outer layer of branchiostegite ; *br''*., inner layer of the same ; *eff.br.s.*, efferent branchial sinus ; *en.sk.*, endophragmal skeleton ; *ext.m.*, extensor muscle of abdomen ; *fl.m.*, flexor muscles of abdomen ; *g.c.*, gill-chamber ; *h.g.*, hind-gut ; *ht.*, heart ; *lr.*, liver ; *os.*, ostia ; *ov.*, ovary ; *pcm.*, pericardium ; *pbr.*, podobranch ; *plb.*, pleurobranch ; *st.s.*, sternal sinus ; *v.n.c.*, ventral nerve cord ; *v.th.a.*, ventral thoracic artery ; *w.l.*, walking leg.
Small arrows in the sinuses on the right-hand side show the course of the circulation of the blood.

a *dorsal abdominal artery*, which runs backwards above the intestine and supplies it and the muscles of the abdomen, and a *sternal artery*. This passes downwards, through an opening in the ventral nerve cord, and divides into a *ventral abdominal* and a *ventral thoracic artery*,

by which the limbs are supplied. Each of the arteries
branches many times, till it finally gives rise to minute
vessels in the organs it supplies, but there are no capillaries.

It will be seen that in the crayfish, as in the earthworm,
there is a dorsal contractile blood vessel, but that in the
crayfish the contractile organ—the heart—is very short and
wide, and is prolonged in front and behind by non-contractile vessels—the ophthalmic and dorsal abdominal arteries.
We shall find in the cockroach a similar but longer heart.

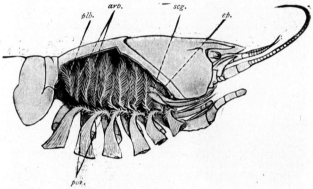

FIG. 212.—The forepart of the body of a crayfish, viewed from the right-
   hand side, with the legs and the branchiostegite cut away and the
   gills displayed.

arb., Arthrobranchiæ ; *ep.*, epipodite of the first maxilliped ; *pbr.*, podobranchiæ ;
   plb., pleurobranchia ; *scg.*, scaphognathite.

From the organs the blood passes into great *sinuses* which
surround them. The largest of these is the perivisceral
cavity, but there are also blood spaces in the limbs and
elsewhere. The blood from the limbs and a great part of
that from the perivisceral cavity is gathered up into a
sternal sinus, which lies in a tunnel formed by the endophragmal skeleton and contains the ventral nerve cord
and ventral thoracic artery. From this a series of *afferent
branchial sinuses* carries the blood to the gills, where it is
oxygenated. From the gills it passes by *efferent branchial
sinuses* to the pericardial sinus. Part of the blood from

20

around the stomach, however, passes on each side into the space between the two sides of the fold of carapace which forms the branchiostegite, and thence to the pericardial sinus by a vessel which follows the hinder edge of the branchiostegite. It will be noted that the pericardial cavity of the crayfish is a part of the hæmocœle and contains blood, unlike that of the frog, which is a separate part of the cœlom. A blood-vascular system in which, as in the crayfish, the

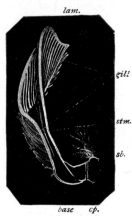

FIG. '213.—A podobranch of the crayfish, seen from behind.

Base; *cp.*, coxopodite; *gill*; *lam.*, lamina; *sb.*, setobranch or tuft of coxopoditic setæ; *stm.*, stem.

blood on leaving the arteries bathes the organs of the body is said to be *open*. One in which, as in the worm and the frog, it is carried through the organs in capillaries which lead direct to veins is said to be *closed*. The blood of the crayfish is a clear fluid, which contains white corpuscles and clots readily—an obvious advantage to an animal whose open vascular system causes it to bleed freely from any wound. A respiratory pigment known as *hæmocyanin*, which is an organic compound of copper, is dissolved in it, and plays the same part as hæmoglobin, taking up oxygen in the respiratory organs and parting with it to the tissues. In the oxidised condition it is of a blue colour and tinges the blood.

The respiratory apparatus of the crayfish is contained in the gill-chambers. The *gills* are branched, thin-walled structures, standing upon the coxopodites of the thoracic limbs and the inner wall of the gill-chamber. In them the blood circulates and exchanges its carbon dioxide for the oxygen which is dissolved in the water that is kept flowing through the chamber by the action of the second maxilla. This limb is held firm by the curved end of its endopodite,

Respiratory Organs.

which fits into a groove upon the mandible at the base of the palp, while the exopodite or scaphognathite, flapping at the rate of sixty strokes a minute, bales water forwards, out of the gill-chamber and under the opening upon the antenna of the green gland, whose excreta it thus sweeps away with the foul water from the gills. By this action fresh water is drawn into the chamber between the bases of the legs. No doubt the blood in the branchiostegite is oxygenated through the thin inner wall of that organ.

The gills receive different names according to their position. Those which are attached to the epipodites of the limbs are known as *podobranchiæ*. Others stand upon the membranes which join the limbs to the body, and are known as *arthrobranchiæ*, and a few stand upon the inner wall of the gill-chamber (the side wall of the thorax) above the legs, and are known as *pleurobranchiæ*. A podobranchia is found on every thoracic limb, except the first pair of maxillipeds, which have no gills,[1] and the last pair of legs, which have only a pleurobranchia. Two arthrobranchiæ, an anterior and a posterior, are found upon each limb that has a podobranchia, except the second maxilliped, which has only the anterior arthrobranchia. Well-developed pleurobranchiæ are only found above the legs of the last pair, but in the same position above each leg of the three preceding pairs there is a minute process which represents a gill. The following table shows the position of the gills :—

	Maxillipeds.			Legs.					Total.
	I.	II.	III.	I.	II.	III.	IV.	V.	
Podobranchiæ . .	Ep	I	I	I	I	I	I	0	6+Ep
Anterior arthrobranchiæ .	0	I	I	I	I	I	I	0	6 ⎫
Posterior arthrobranchiæ .	0	0	I	I	I	I	I	0	5 ⎭ 11
Pleurobranchiæ .	0	0	0	0	R	R	R	I	I+3R
Total . .	Ep	2	3	3	3+R	3+R	3+R	I	18+3R+Ep

Ep=epipodite without a gill.   R=abortive rudiment.

Each arthrobranchia has a tree-like structure, consisting of a trunk or *axis* arising from the body by one end, with numerous short branches or *filaments*. The two pleurobranchiæ have the same structure. In the podobranchiæ the axis is fused to the epipodite along the greater part of its length, so that the filaments appear to arise from the

---

[1] In *A. fluviatilis* they have each a vestigial arthrobranchia.

epipodite. The tip of the gill, however, stands free. The epipodite itself is a long plate with a wide *base*, a narrower *stem*, and at the end a second expansion, the *lamina*. The stem and lamina are folded along the length of the epipodite, so that a groove is formed, into which fits the gill of the limb next behind.

The excretory organs of the crayfish are a pair of organs, known as the *green glands*, which lie in the head, immediately

Excretory Organs. behind the antennæ, upon whose basal joints they open. Each consists of a glandular mass and above it a thin-walled bladder from which a short duct leads to the opening. In the centre of the mass is a small, brownish sac, known as the *end-sac*. This is a vestige of the cœlom, which otherwise is in the crayfish represented only by the hollow of the gonad. Partitions project into it from its wall, and it communicates by a small opening with the rest of the mass, known as the *labyrinth*, which

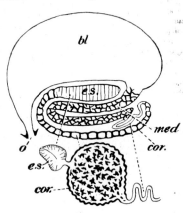

FIG. 214.—A diagram of the structure of the green gland of a crayfish. Above, the whole gland is seen in longitudinal section; below, the end sac and cortex are seen as dissected out and viewed from the surface.

bl., Bladder; *cor.*, cortex; *e.s.*, end-sac; *med.*, medulla; *o.*, opening on antenna.

is essentially a winding and much complicated tube leading from the end-sac to the bladder. This tube is a cœlomoduct. Its first section, which forms the outer part of the gland, known as the *cortex*, is greenish in colour and broken into a meshwork of channels. The rest, the *medulla* of the gland, is a whitish, coiled tube, simple for a short distance and then made spongy by ridges of its wall. The process of excretion by the green glands appears to be as follows : in the end-sac, as in the glomeruli of the frog, there is formed a filtrate from the blood, containing some of its solids but not its proteins. In the cortex other solids are probably added. In the medulla salts which were in the end-sac lost by the blood are taken back. The resulting fluid is of lower concentration than the blood, so that the body gets rid of water. We have seen (p. 79) that a similar process occurs in other freshwater animals. Certain gland cells found on the gills are possibly also excretory. The principal nitrogenous excreta are ammonia and amino compounds

Nervous System. In its general plan the nervous system of the crayfish resembles that of the earthworm. In the front part of the head, between the green glands, lies a *supra-œsophageal* or *cerebral ganglion,* or *brain,* which corresponds in position to the supra-pharyngeal ganglia of the worm. It gives nerves to the eyes, antennules, and antennæ, and from it two long *circumœsophageal commissures* pass backwards to join behind the œsophagus in the *subœsophageal ganglion.* This gives nerves to the limbs as far as the second maxillipeds, inclusive, and immediately behind it lies the *first thoracic ganglion,* which supplies the third maxillipeds. In each of the remaining somites of the thorax lies an indistinctly double ganglion which supplies by several nerves the limbs and other organs of its somite. These ganglia are set at some distance apart and are connected by double commissures, forming thus a *ventral cord.* Between the fourth and fifth ganglia the commissures part widely to allow the sternal artery to pass between them. In the abdomen the cord is continued and consists of a ganglion in each somite united to its fellows by longitudinal commissures, which are really double, but appear at first sight to be single. The last ganglion supplies the telson as well as its own somite. The commissures contain no nerve cells. The brain is more complex than those of annelids and exercises more control over the rest of the nervous system. Giant fibres run from cells in it along the whole length of the cord and enable it to bring about sudden movements which involve distant parts of the body, such as the backward escape movement.

A *transverse commissure* immediately behind the œsophagus joins the two circumœsophageal commissures. It contains fibres which take this roundabout course between the portions of the brain which supply the antennæ, thus indicating that these limbs belong to the same series as those behind the mouth. That is probably also true of the antennules, and the fact that the antennules and antennæ are innervated from the supracœsophageal ganglia must be connected with the position of the mouth, which, as a result of cephalisation (p. 280) to a high degree is farther back than in the earthworm, where it lies in front of the first somite. The alimentary canal is supplied by two *visceral nerves*. The first has a three-fold origin, being formed by the junction of a nerve from the cerebral ganglion with two nerves which arise

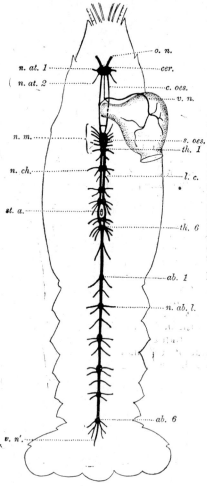

FIG. 215.—A semi-diagrammatic view of central nervous system of a crayfish.

*ab.*1, *ab.*6, The first and sixth abdominal ganglia; *cer.*, cerebral ganglion; *c.œs.*, circumœsophageal commissure; *l.c.*, longitudinal commissures of ventral cord; *n.ab.l.*, nerves to abdominal limbs; *n.at.*1, nerve to antennule; *n.at.*2, nerve to antenna: *n.ch.*, nerve to cheliped; *n.m.*, nerves to limbs adjoining the mouth; *o.n.*, optic nerve; *s.œs.*, subœsophageal ganglion; *st.a.*, sternal artery; *th.*1, *th.*6, first and sixth thoracic ganglia; *v.n.*, nerve to proventriculus; *v.n'.*, nerve to hind-gut.

each from a small ganglion on the course of the circumœsophageal commissure. The second arises from the last abdominal ganglion.

The *eyes* of the crayfish are *compound*, containing a number of elements, known as *ommatidia*, **Sense Organs.** each of which is a small complete eye. The whole eye is black, owing to the presence of pigment in some of its cells, and is covered with a colourless portion of the cuticle known as the *cornea*, divided into a number of square facets, each of which corresponds to an ommatidium.

The structure of the ommatidia is complex : each is an elongated body consisting of a number of cells derived from the epidermis with refractive bodies secreted by them. Over each ommatidium is a cuticular lens corresponding to one of the facets. Under the lens are two *lenticular cells* by which it is secreted. Below this again is a group of four cells called *vitrellæ* whose inner borders secrete a refractive *crystalline cone*. Innermost is a group of *visual cells* known as the *retinula*. The central borders of these cells secrete an axial refractive body known as the rhabdome. The inner ends of the visual cells are continued into fibres which pass into an *optic ganglion* in the eyestalk, and from this arises the optic nerve.

The ommatidia are separated by pigment cells and the retinular cells also contain pigment. The way in which such eyes give rise to vision has been the subject of various theories. It appears that the pigment flows about within the cells, being in weak light retracted inwards and outwards so as to expose the sides of the ommatidia, and in strong light expanded so as to isolate each of them. When it is retracted the eye gives a single image ; when it is expanded each retinula gives a separate image of a small part of the thing seen, sharper than that given when the eye acts as a whole, though formed with a greater loss of light, and thus a *mosaic image* is made up.

The *statocysts* are a pair of sacs, situated in the basal joints of the antennules and provided with nerves. Each has a cuticular lining beset with hairs, with which the nerve fibres are in communication. Within it are grains of sand, which are scattered over the opening of the sac by the pincers and fall into it. It is probable that the principal function of the organ is informing the animal of its position by the movements of the sand grains against the hairs, and thus enabling it to keep its equilibrium. If the statocysts

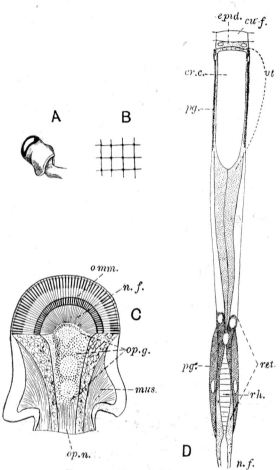

FIG. 216.—The eye of the crayfish.

A. The left eye removed ; *B*, a portion of the cornea magnified to show the facets ;
C, a longitudinal section of the eye under low magnification ; *D*, a single
ommatidium highly magnified.—*D* after Parker.

cr.c., Outer refractive body or crystalline cone ; *cu.f.*, cuticular facet ; *epia.*, epidermis
(hypodermis) ; *mus.*, muscles which move the eye ; *n.f.*, nerve fibres ; *omm.*,
ommatidia ; *op.g.*, optic ganglion ; *op.n.*, optic nerve ; *p.g.*, outer pigment cells ;
p g'., inner pigment cells ; *ret.*, retinula cells (the sense cells)—these cells
contain pigment ; *rh.*, inner refractive body or rhabdome ; *vt.*, vitrellæ or cells
which secrete the crystalline cone.

be removed, the crayfish loses its sense of position and will often swim upside down. Experiments upon the prawn, an animal related to the crayfish, illustrate the function of the statocysts. A prawn that by moulting had lost the

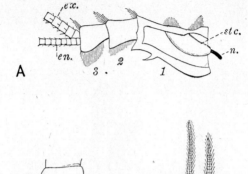

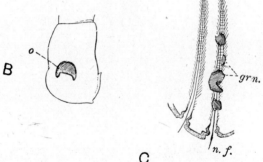

Fig. 217.—The statocyst of the crayfish.

A, The right antennule, seen from the median side with the basal joint opened **and** the flagella cut short ; *B,* basal joint of the left antennule from above ; *C,* two hairs from the statocyst.—*C* partly after Howes.

en., Inner flagellum ; *ex.,* outer flagellum ; *grn.,* sand grains ; *n.,* nerve of the statocyst ; *n.f.,* nerve fibres ; *o.,* opening of the statocyst ; *stc.,* statocyst.

lining of its statocysts with the sand grains was kept in filtered water and supplied with finely powdered iron in place of sand. When it had placed some of these in its statocysts, a magnet was brought near it, and by moving the magnet the particles of iron were caused to move as they would be by a change in the position of the animal. By this means the prawn was made to alter its position in correspondence with the movements of the magnet. It was formerly supposed that the statocysts subserved the sense of *hearing*, but though the animals appear to perceive vibrations, and this may be due to the statocysts, it is doubtful whether the latter are true organs of hearing. We have seen that the antennules bear on their outer flagella bristles which subserve the sense of *smell*. Various of the setæ, especially those of the antennæ, are organs of *touch*.

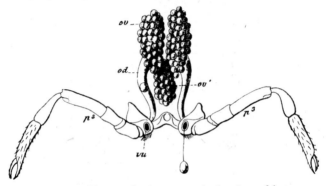

Fig. 218.—The reproductive organs of a female crayfish.— After Suckow.

od., Oviduct ; *ov.*, ovaries ; *ov'.*, fused posterior part (median lobe); *vu.*, female aperture on the second walking leg (*p³*).

The sexes of the crayfish are separate. The generative organs lie in the thorax, above the gut and below the pericardium. They have the same general shape in the two sexes, consisting of three lobes, two anterior and one posterior, with a pair of ducts, which start from the junction of the anterior and posterior lobes and run to openings on walking legs. The ovary is larger and broader than the testis, and has an internal cavity into which the eggs are shed. The oviducts are short, straight, and wide ; they open upon the coxopodites of the second pair of walking legs. The testes consist of a number of branching ducts which end in small alveoli,

Reproduction.

in which the spermatozoa are formed. The vasa deferentia are narrow and much coiled ; their first part is very slender and translucent, the second part, which forms most of the duct, is wider and glandular, and a short terminal region has muscular walls which force out the sperm. The *spermatozoa* are discs with stiff, pointed processes round the edge. The nucleus is a round capsule and to one side of this is a small, oval body. Pairing takes place in September and October.

The male seizes the female, throws her upon her back, and passes sperm through the tubular limbs of his first abdominal segment on to the parts in the neighbourhood of her oviducts, the limbs of his second abdominal pair aiding the process by working to and fro on the hollows of the first. The sperm consists of a sticky substance, secreted by the vasa deferentia, carrying the spermatozoa, and forms white masses on the sterna of the female. The eggs, which are large and yolky, are laid in November. The processes of the spermatozoa adhere to them, and by a sudden expansion of the contents of the capsule the rest of the body is forced into the

FIG. 219.—The reproductive organs of a male crayfish — After Huxley.

t, Testes ; *vd*., vas deferens ; *vd'*., opening of vas deferens on last walking leg.

ovum. Each egg is attached to one of the hairs on the abdominal limbs by a stalked shell formed of a substance secreted by certain glands on the sterna, and is thus under the protection of the mother during its development. By the division of the nucleus of the fertilised ovum a syncytium is formed which does not divide into cells until a number of nuclei have arisen. The young are hatched at the beginning of the next summer. They do not differ greatly from the adult, but have curved tips to the pincers, by which they cling for a time to the empty shell or the abdominal limbs of the mother, and are thus protected from enemies and kept from being swept away by currents and so eventually reaching the sea, where they would perish.

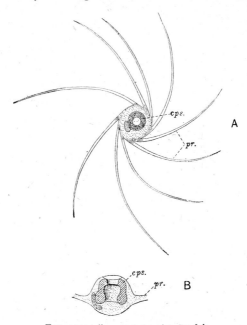

FIG. 220.— Spermatozoa of a crayfish.

A, Whole spermatozoon from above ; *B*, part, enlarged, in section.
cps., Capsule ; *pr.*, stiff processes.

Segmented animals with jointed limbs, a thick cuticle, an open blood-vascular system, and a nervous
Arthropoda. system like that of the crayfish are known as *Arthropoda.* To this group belong Crustaceans—water-fleas, *Cyclops* (Fig. 269), crayfish, crabs, etc.—Arachnids (scorpions, spiders, mites, ticks, etc.), Myriapods (Centipedes and Millipedes), and Insects. Crustaceans (*Crustacea*) have two pairs of antennæ and are almost all

water animals, breathing by gills. Arachnids (*Arachnida*) are without antennæ, have four pairs of legs, and nearly all, by various devices, breathe air. Insects (*Hexapoda*) have one pair of antennæ and are usually land animals, breathing

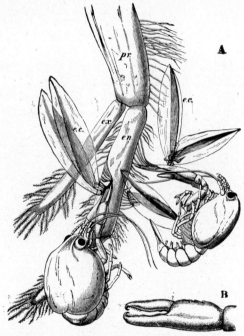

FIG. 221.—*A*, Two recently hatched crayfish holding on to one of the swimmerets of the mother ; *B*, pincers of the young more highly magnified.—From Huxley.

e.c., Ruptured egg cases ; *en.*, endopodite ; *ex.*, exopodite ; *pr.*, protopodite.

air by tubes which take it direct to the tissues (p. 330) and winged. They have three pairs of legs. The Arthropoda are far more numerous than any other group of animals, and are of very great importance to man, partly because some of them serve him as food, but more because they damage his crops, annoy him as parasites, and in sucking his blood convey to him the germs of very serious diseases.

In spiders (*Araneida*) the first pair of limbs (*cheliceræ*) are sharp poison-claws, and the second (*pedi-palpi*) are tactile organs. These and the four pairs of legs are borne upon a so-called " cephalothorax " or *prosoma*. The animals breathe by means of *lung-books*, which are pits of the wall of the under side of the abdomen, containing a number of leaflets in which the

Arachnida : Araneida.

FIG. 222.—The Garden Spider (*Epeira diademata*).—From Parker and Haswell.

Note, from behind forwards: abdomen and prosoma ; on latter, four pairs of legs, one pair of pedipalpi, one pair of cheliceræ (barely shown).

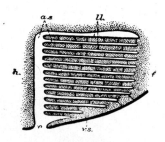

FIG. 223.—A diagram of a vertical, longitudinal section through a lung-book.

a.s., Air space ; *f.*, anterior end ; *h.*, hinder end ; *ll.*, "leaves" of book in which the blood flows; *o.*, opening, on *v.s.*, ventral surface of body.

blood circulates and is thus exposed to the air over a wide surface. There are one or two pairs of these near the front end of the abdomen, and at the hind end lie two or three pairs of *spinnerets*, from which are secreted the silken threads that spiders have the power of forming. Both lung-books and spinnerets are regarded as representing abdominal appendages.

Mites and ticks (*Acarina*) have neither lung-books nor spinnerets. Many of them live as parasites upon animals or plants, or on decaying organic matter. The cheliceræ are often transformed into piercing

Acarina.

organs to enable the animal to suck the juices of its host. A system of air-tubes (*trachéæ*) for purposes of respiration is often present. There is a larva with three pairs of legs, followed by a stage known as the "nymph," which has four pairs of legs but has not yet reached the adult form. During part of this stage the animal is quiescent. *Demodex*

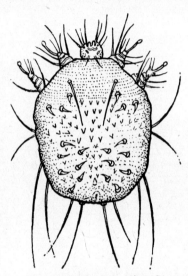

FIG. 224.—The Follicle Mite (*Demodex folliculorum*), in ventral view. —From Thomson.

FIG. 225.—The Itch Mite (*Sarcoptes scabiei*), in dorsal view. The two hinder pairs of legs are hidden under the body.—From Thomson.

folliculorum is a minute, long-bodied mite which lives in the grease-secreting or "sebaceous" glands of the human face. It is generally harmless, but appears sometimes to set up skin disease and is accused of spreading the bacillus of leprosy. In dogs it is the cause of a kind of mange. Larvæ and adults live in the glands and are transmitted by contagion. *Sarcoptes scabiei* causes the "itch" in man, and a related species gives rise to mange in dogs. The adult itch-parasite lives in burrows in the skin and there lays its eggs. The larvæ pass to the surface of the skin, where they live for the most part under the scabs which the burrowing has caused to form, till the last stage, when the female makes the burrow. The treatment consists in baths and rubbing with various ointments, which generally contain flowers of sulphur. Neither *Demodex* nor *Sarcoptes* possesses tracheæ or eyes. The ticks, of which *Ixodes* may

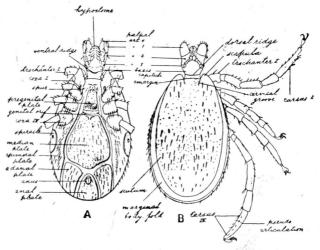

Fig. 226.—The Sheep Tick (*Ixodes ricinus*).—After Nuttall.

A, Ventral view of male ; *B*, dorsal view of the same.

be named as an example, are larger animals with tracheæ and often with eyes. Their larvæ generally live on and among plants, but presently seize hold of passing animals, generally warm-blooded vertebrates, and proceed to suck their blood. Sometimes they pass their stages on this host, sometimes they fall off and seek another for adult life. The host's skin is pierced by a rostrum formed by the pedipalps, which contains the cheliceræ and a mid-ventral piece, the *hypostome*, which is barbed, so that the parasite cannot be pulled off. The female swells greatly by gorging blood. The male, which is smaller, swells less. Fertilisation takes place on the host, and the female then falls off and lays her eggs. Ticks spread the minute parasites which cause various serious diseases, such as red-water fever in cattle, heart-water in sheep, and tick fever in man.

CHAPTER XVI

THE COCKROACH. INSECTS

COMMON as they now are, cockroaches have only been introduced into England comparatively recently.

Cockroaches. The first specimens were brought from the East by trading vessels at the beginning of the seventeenth century, and one hundred and fifty years later Gilbert White could still speak of the cockroach as "an unusual insect" at Selborne. This species was the Common Cockroach, *Periplaneta orientalis*. More recently another species, *P. americana*, a native of tropical America, has been introduced and is spreading rapidly. Both are nocturnal insects which haunt human dwellings, hiding in corners and crevices by day. They seek warmth, as is natural in view of their origin, and devour any kind of food they can find.

In its main lines the anatomy of a cockroach resembles that of a crayfish. The animal is segmented, the segments (somites) being unlike and grouped into three regions known as head, thorax, and abdomen, but these do not correspond with the parts similarly named in the crayfish. There is a thick chitinous cuticle, not moulted by the adult, and some somites bear jointed limbs. The thorax bears also two pairs of wings. At the sides of the head lie a pair of large, unstalked, compound eyes. The cœlom, of which traces are found in development, disappears in the adult, but there is a hæmocœlic perivisceral cavity containing blood.

Anatomy of a Cockroach.

The head is short and deep. Seen from in front it has a pear-shaped outline, with the narrow end downwards. Its armour consists of several pieces— two *epicranial plates* side by side above, two *genæ* at the sides below the eyes, a *frons* and *clypeus* in front. A labrum

Head.

is hinged on to the clypeus below ; its lining is known as the *epipharynx*. The appendages of the head are as follows : There is one pair of long, slender, unbranched,

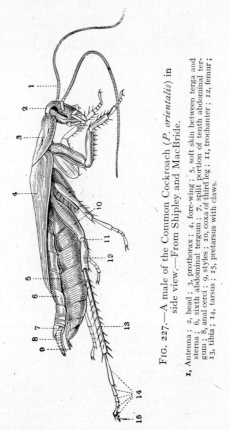

FIG. 227.—A male of the Common Cockroach (*P. orientalis*) in side view.—From Shipley and MacBride.

1, Antenna ; 2, head ; 3, prothorax ; 4, fore-wing ; 5, soft skin between terga and sterna ; 6, sixth abdominal tergum ; 7, split portion of tenth abdominal tergum ; 8, anal cerci ; 9, styles ; 10, coxa of third leg ; 11, trochanter ; 12, femur ; 13, tibia ; 14, tarsus ; 15, pretarsus with claws.

many-jointed antennæ, corresponding to the antennules of the crayfish. The second antennæ of the latter are not represented in the cockroach. The mandibles are stout, toothed structures without palps, not unlike the basal

parts of those of the crayfish. They are followed by a pair
of maxillæ, often called first maxillæ. These consist of
(*a*) a protopodite of two joints known as the *cardo* and
stipes, (*b*) a five-jointed endopodite known as the *maxillary
palp*, (*c*) two lobes—an inner *lacinia*, and a softer outer
galea—borne on the stipes to the
median side of the palp. Behind
the maxillæ lie a pair of appendages which are known sometimes
as the second maxillæ, though
better as the *labium*. Their
protopodites are fused so that
they form a single lower lip.
This has three joints, the *submentum*, the *mentum*, and the
prementum, which bears on each
side an endopodite or *labial
palp* of three joints, set upon a
projection known as the *palpiger*.
At the end of the prementum
stand four lobes, known collectively as the *ligula*. On each
side the inner lobe is known as
the *glossa*, the outer as the
paraglossa.

The head is joined by a soft
neck to the thorax.
This consists of three
segments—the prothorax, mesothorax, and metathorax. Each
has a tergum or *notum* above
and a sternum below, joined to
one another at the sides by
membrane in which lie small

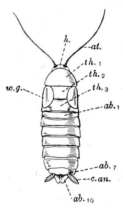

Fig. 228.—A female of
the common cockroach.
The body is somewhat
compressed so as to
show the membranes
between the abdominal
terga. The legs have
been removed.

ab.1-*ab*.10, Abdominal terga;
at., antenna; *c.an.*, anal
cerci; *h.*, head; *th.*1, pro-
thoracic tergum; *th.*2,
mesothoracic tergum; *th.*3,
metathoracic tergum; *v.g.*,
vestige of fore wing.

Thorax.

sclerites—the *pleura*—which are really basal podomeres
of the legs. The pronotum is the largest and projects in
front so as to hide the neck. Each sternum bears a pair
of legs. The shape of these legs and the names of their
podomeres are shown in Fig. 227. The third and fourth
joints bear bristles which are used in cleaning the body,
the fifth (*tarsus*) is subdivided and bears under each of its

subsegments a pad or *plantula*, and the last joint bears two hooked claws used in climbing, and also has between the claws a pad known as the *arolium*. The plantulæ and arolium prevent slipping. The mesothorax and metathorax bear each a pair of wings jointed to the anterior corners of the notum. The wings are membranous folds of the skin, in which the epidermis has practically disappeared and the two layers of cuticle have come together. Branched ridges known as " veins " or *nervures* strengthen the wings. The veins are hollow and each contains a trachea (p. 330) and a nerve. The first pair of wings are dark-coloured and horny and form a cover for the second, which, when they are at rest, are folded lengthwise and laid along the back. In the female of *P. orientalis* the wings are very small. Wings are not appendages of the same kind as the limbs, but movable expansions of the terga.

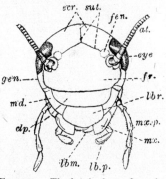

FIG. 229.—The head of a cockroach, seen from in front.

at., Antenna ; *clp.*, clypeus ; *ecr.*, epicranium ; *eye* ; *fen.*, fenestra ; *fr.*, frons ; *gen.*, gena ; *lbm.*, part of the labium ; *lb.p.*, labial palp ; *lbr.*, labrum ; *md.*, mandible ; *mx.*, part of the maxilla ; *mx.p.*, maxillary palp ; *sut.*, sutures.

Abdomen. The abdomen consists of ten somites, each with a tergum and a sternum, joined at the sides by soft cuticle. The hinder somites are telescoped, so that the eighth and ninth are hidden.[1] The first sternum is rudimentary, and the tenth tergum projects backwards as a plate with a deep notch in its hinder edge. A pair of many-jointed, spindle-shaped *cerci anales*, which may represent limbs, are attached under this plate, and below it is the anus, between two *podical plates* or *paraprocts*, which may represent the sternum of an eleventh somite. In the

[1] In the male *P. orientalis* portions of the eighth and ninth terga remain uncovered.

female the seventh sternum is produced backwards into a large boat-shaped process, which forms the floor of a *genital pouch*, and in the male the ninth sternum bears a pair of limbs in the form of slender, unjointed *styles*.

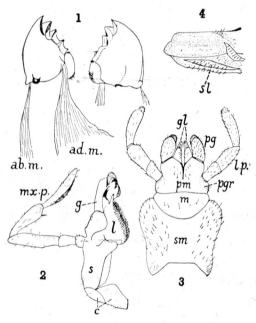

FIG. 230.—The mouth-parts of a cockroach.— From Imms.

1, Mandibles ; *ab.m.*, *ad.m.*, abductor and adductor muscles ; 2, maxilla ; *c.*, cardo ; *g.*, galea ; *l.*, lacina ; *mx.p.*, palp ; *s.*, stipes ; 3, labium ; *gl.*, glossa ; *l.p.*, palp ; *m.*, mentum ; *pg.*, paraglossa ; *pgr.*, palpiger ; *pm.*, prementum ; *sm.*, submentum ; 4, hypopharynx ; *sl.*, left vestigial superlingua.

The genital opening is placed below the anus and is surrounded by a complicated set of processes known as *gonapophyses*. A pair of stink glands, deterrent to most enemies, open on the membrane between the fifth and sixth terga. Somites one to eight are limbless.

In walking, the legs are used in two tripods. On one side the first leg pulls and the third pushes while on the opposite side the second leg acts as a prop. Meanwhile the other three legs are being moved forwards to repeat the process. In flight, the hinder wings do the work. They are beaten in such a way as both to support the body and to drive it forwards. The

Locomotion.

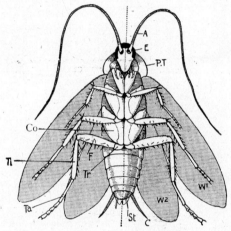

FIG. 231.—The ventral aspect of a male cockroach with the wings extended. An imaginary median line has been inserted.—From Thomson.

A., Antennæ ; *C.*, cercus ; *Co.*, coxa, the breadth of which makes it look, in its present position, like a ventral plate on the body ; *E.*, eye ; *F.*, femur ; *P.T.*, prothorax ; *St.*, style ; *Ta.*, tarsus ; *Ti.*, tibia ; *Tr.*, trochanter ; *W*¹., first pair of wings ; *W*²., second pair of wings.

fore wings are held at right angles to the body and serve as those of an aeroplane.

They are moved by two sets of muscles—an *indirect* set, consisting of vertical and longitudinal muscles of the thorax which by alternately lowering and raising the tergum, to which the wings are attached, lever the wings up and down upon the side plates (pleura) upon which they rest, and a *direct* set attached to the base of each wing, which they can both rotate upon its axis and also extend from the body or retract. The hind-wings are beaten down and up, and at each downstroke the strong front edge (*costa*) is by muscular action rotated downwards and forwards so that the somewhat concave lower surface faces obliquely downwards and backwards. This process is assisted by the resistance of the air below bending the thin hinder part of the wing upward. As a result, during the beat the wing exerts pressure both downwards and backwards while a region of decreased pressure is created above and in front of it. Thus the insect is pressed and drawn upwards and forwards.

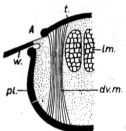

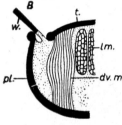

FIG. 232.—A diagram to show how the wings of an insect are lowered and raised in flight.

A, The downstroke : the tergum (*t*) is raised, owing to being arched fore and aft by the contraction of the longitudinal muscles (*l.m.*) ; this forces the wing down, pivoting over a point on the pleuron (*pl.*). *B*, the upstroke : the tergum is lowered by contraction of the dorso-ventral muscles (*do.m.*) ; this levers the wing up.

Alimentary System. The alimentary canal has long, ectodermal fore- and hind-guts, lined with cuticle as in the crayfish. The fore-gut comprises (i) the mouth, with a tongue-like ridge (*hypopharynx*) which bears on its under surface the duct of the salivary glands and at its sides a pair of minute structures, the *superlinguæ*, which may represent the paragnatha of the crayfish (p. 298) ; (ii) the narrow gullet, lying in the neck ; (iii) the swollen crop ; (iv) the proventriculus or gizzard, which has muscular walls and contains six hard, cuticular teeth and some pads covered with bristles which form a strainer. A pair of diffuse salivary glands lie on each side of the crop, and between each pair lies a salivary bladder or receptacle. The ducts of the two glands of each side join ; the ducts of the two sides then unite to form a median duct, and this is joined by another

median duct formed by the union of the ducts of the receptacles. The mid-gut or mesenteron, lined by soft endoderm, is short and narrow and bears at its beginning seven or eight club-shaped *hepatic cæca*. The gizzard projects funnel-wise into the mid-gut. The hind-gut is coiled and divided into a narrow ileum, a wider colon, and a wide rectum, which has six internal ridges. At the beginning of the hind-gut are attached a number of long, fine *Malpighian tubules* whose epithelium is excretory.

The food is cut up by the mandibles and maxillæ, moistened with saliva, and pushed by maxillæ **Digestion and Excretion.** and labium into the mouth ; it is held up for a time in the crop, where it is acted upon by the saliva, which digests only starch, and by the mid-gut secretion which leaks forward. It is then admitted,

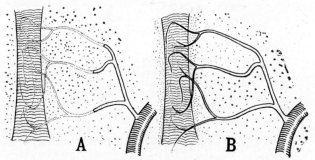

FIG. 233.—Tracheoles running to a muscle fibre.—From Imms, after Wigglesworth.

A, Muscle at rest ; the terminal parts of the tracheoles (shown dotted) contain fluid. *B*, Muscle fatigued ; air extends far into the tracheoles.

little by little, into the gizzard and there broken up fine by the teeth and strained by the bristles and passes into the mid-gut. The juice secreted here digests all classes of foodstuffs : it is secreted by the break up of epithelial cells, which are replaced from reserve cells. The delicate, uncuticulate epithelium is protected from hard particles not, like that of backboned animals, by the secretion of mucus (p. 111) but by a very delicate chitinous envelope, the *peritrophic membrane*, which is secreted by the epithelium but adheres to it only around the entrance from the gizzard. This membrane is permeable both to digestive enzymes and to digested food. It is in the mid-gut that absorption mainly takes place. The pyloric cæca are mere extensions of the mid-gut and do not differ from it in function. In the hind-gut water, which is so precious to land animals, is absorbed both from the fæces and from the urine excreted by the Malpighian tubules. Nitrogen is excreted as uric acid. In most insects some is got rid of by the Malpighian tubules and some laid up in the fatty body (see p. 332), but the cockroach appears not to eliminate nitrogen in the urine.

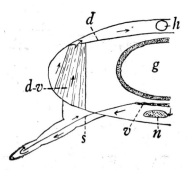

FIG. 234.—A diagram of a cross-section of the thorax of a cockroach, showing by arrows the course of the circulation.—From Imms.

d., Dorsal diaphragm (floor of pericardium) ; *d.v.*, dorso-ventral muscle ; *h.*, heart ; *n.*, nerve cord ; *s.*, septum in leg ; *v.*, ventral diaphragm.

Respiratory Organs. The respiratory system consists of branching tubes or *tracheæ*, of ectodermal origin with a spirally thickened lining of cuticle, which arise from ten pairs of openings or *stigmata* at the sides of the body. There are two large stigmata on each side of the thorax, one between prothorax and mesothorax, one between mesothorax and metathorax, and in each of the first eight abdominal somites a stigma is placed on each side between the tergum and the sternum. Air is pumped in and out of the larger tracheæ by contraction and expansion of the abdomen, and by diffusion renews the gases in the fine branches of the tracheal system (*tracheoles*), which have no cuticular lining, ramify in the tissues, and end upon or actually in the cells (Figs. 233, 238, 239). Though the cockroach obtains all its oxygen in this way, much of the carbon dioxide it discharges is lost through the skin.

When the insect is at rest the ends of the tracheoles are full of fluid. When the muscles are active products of their metabolism raise the osmotic pressure in the tissues and this withdraws the fluid so that air extends more deeply into the tracheoles and reaches their cells.

Blood Vessels. The direct supply of air to the tissues is no doubt the reason for the simple condition of the blood-vascular system, which consists of a long heart (Fig. 541), lying along the mid-dorsal line of the abdomen and thorax, an anterior aorta, and a system of ill-defined

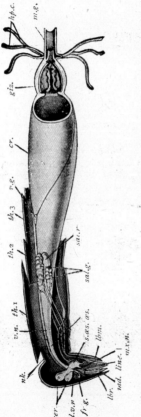

Fig. 235.—A semi-diagrammatic drawing of the head and thorax of a cockroach, dissected from the left side.

cer., Cerebral ganglion; *cr.*, crop; *fr.g.*, frontal ganglion; *giz.*, gizzard; *hp.c.*, hepatic caeca; *l.v.n.*, left visceral nerve leaving the brain; *lbm.*, labium; *ling.*, tongue; *lbr.*, labrum; *m.g.*, mesenteron; *md.*, mandible; *mx.n.*, maxillary nerve; *nk.*, neck; *œs.*, oesophagus; *s.œs.*, suboesophageal ganglion; *sal.g.*, salivary gland; *sal.r.*, salivary receptacle; *th.1*, *th.2*, *th.3*, segments of the thorax; *v.g.*, visceral ganglion; *v.n.*, visceral nerve.

sinuses, of which the principal is the perivisceral cavity.
The heart is enclosed in a pericardial space and is divided
into thirteen chambers corresponding to the somites.
Each chamber communicates by a pair of ostia at its sides
with the pericardial space. Blood from outlying parts of
the body flows to the perivisceral cavity, thence into the
pericardial cavity through openings in the floor of the
latter, and so through the ostia into the heart, which,
contracting from behind forwards, drives it through the
aorta into the sinus system, by way of the sinuses of
the head. Paired triangular *alary muscles,* whose outer

ends are attached to the terga,
move the pericardial floor, and
thus cause the flow of blood
from the perivisceral cavity into
the pericardial. Both these cavities are hæmocœlic (p. 275). They
contain a white tissue known as
the *fatty body,* of whose cells
some hold reserves of fats, carbohydrate, and proteins, others at
least temporarily retain nitrogenous excreta as uric acid, and
others harbour micro-organisms
(bacteroids) which are probably

Fig. 236.—A section through
a lobe of the fatty body of
a cockroach × 650.—
From Imms.

in some sort of symbiotic relationship with the insect. The
blood resembles that of the crayfish but, as might be expected

in view of the mode of respiration, contains no respiratory
pigment.

The nervous system is on the same general plan as that
of the crayfish. It comprises a pair of supra-
œsophageal ganglia, which receive optic and
antennary nerves, a pair of short, wide circumœsophageal commissures, a subœsophageal
ganglion, and a double ventral cord with a ganglion in
each of the first nine segments behind the head. The
alimentary canal is supplied by a visceral nervous system
which receives nerves from the circumœsophageal commissures and the brain. Its principal ganglion lies on

**Nervous
System and
Sense Organs.**

the upper side of the crop. The sense organs include the large compound eyes, which resemble those of the crayfish in structure, the antennæ, which are tactile and olfactory, the maxillæ, which are said to possess the sense of taste, the anal cerci, which are tactile and also sensitive

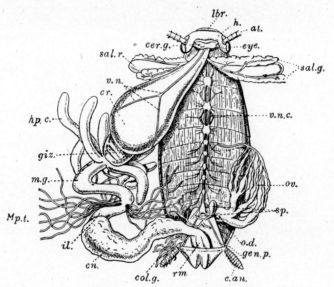

FIG. 237.—A female cockroach, dissected from above.—Adapted from Shipley and MacBride.

at. Antenna; *c.an.*, anal cerci; *cer.g.*, cerebral ganglia; *cn.*, colon; *col.g.*, colleterial gland; *cr.*, crop; *eye*; *gen.p.*, genital pouch; *giz.*, gizzard; *h.*, head; *hp. c.*, hepatic cæca; *il.*, ileum; *lbr.*, labrum; *m.g.*, mesenteron; *Mp.t.*, Malpighian tubes; *o .*, oviduct; *ov.*, ovary; *rm.*, rectum; *sal.g.*, salivary glands; *sal.r.*, salivary receptacle; *sp.*, spermathecæ; *v.n.*, visceral nerves; *v.n.c* ventral nerve cord.

to sound vibrations, various sensory bristles, and possibly a pair of oval white patches which are found above the bases of the antennæ and are known as the *fenestræ*.

The sexes are separate. The testes are small, paired organs, embedded in the fatty body below the fifth and sixth abdominal terga. In the adult the testes are no longer

functional.   Two vasa deferentia lead backwards and
Organs of Reproduction. downwards from them to the seminal vesicles, which are beset with short finger-like processes and lie side by side to form the so-called *mushroom-shaped gland*. The seminal vesicles join behind to form a muscular tube, the *ductus ejaculatorius*, which opens by a median pore between the ninth and tenth abdominal sterna.   A gland of doubtful function, known as the *conglobate gland*, lies below the ductus ejaculatorius and opens with it.   The ovaries are paired organs in the hinder part of the abdomen, each consisting of eight tapering tubes, which show swellings corresponding to ova.

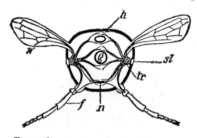

FIG. 238.—**A diagram of a transverse section of an insect.**—After Packard.

f., Femur of leg; *g.*, gut; *h.*, heart; *n.*, nervecord; *st.*, stigma; *tr.*, trachea; *w.* wing.

There is a single, short, wide oviduct which opens on the eighth abdominal sternum. On the ninth sternum a pair of branched *colleterial glands* pour out by two openings a secretion which forms the egg-cases. There is an unequal pair of spermathecæ, which open between the eighth and ninth abdominal sterna and store spermatozoa received from a male.   The eggs are laid in cases, each of which contains sixteen ova and some spermatozoa from the spermathecæ. The young are like the adults, save for the absence of the wings till after several moults (p. 296).   Thus the metamorphosis found in so many insects is practically absent.

The number of different kinds of insects is enormous.
Insects. Probably it is not less than 500,000 and equals that of all other animals together.   All insects resemble the cockroach in the main features of their anatomy, but many of them depart widely from it in detail, the differences affecting principally the mouth-parts, the wings, and the life-history.   The mouth-parts vary in structure with the way in which they are used.   In some

insects, as in beetles, they are not very unlike those of the cockroach, and are used for biting the food. In others, as in bugs and many flies, they are adapted for piercing the bodies of other organisms, animals or plants, and sucking their juices, the labium forming a tube in which lie the

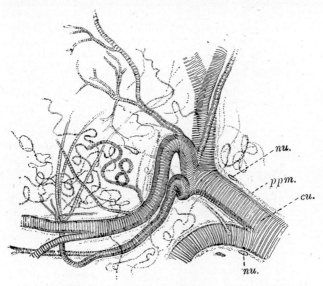

FIG. 239.—A portion of the tracheal tissue of a cockroach, highly magnified. Only parts of the tubes are in focus.

cu., Cuticular lining with spiral thickening ; *nu.*, nuclei of the protoplasmic layer ; *ppm.*, protoplasmic layer continuous with the epidermis (" hypodermis ") of the surface of the body.

other parts in the form of slender knives or needles (Fig. 250). In the house-fly and insects akin to it the piercing organs are lacking (Fig. 252). In fleas the labial palps form a tube in which the mandibles lie as stylets. In butterflies (Figs. 254, 255) the maxillæ are long and grooved, and placed against one another so as to form a tube or proboscis through which nectar can be sucked

from flowers, the other mouth-parts being vestigial with
the exception of the labial palps. In bees (Fig. 242) the
mouth-parts are adapted for biting and sucking, the
mandibles being not unlike those of a cockroach, and
the laciniæ of the maxillæ blade-like, while those of the
labium form a grooved structure, along which liquids can
be drawn up. Wings are occasionally absent. They may
both be gauzy and used in flight, or, as in beetles, the
first pair may be hard and horny and form a case for the
second, or, as in
flies, the first pair
alone may be
used in flight and
the second pair
represented by
two minute sen-
sory organs used
in maintaining
balance and
known as *hal-
teres*. In butter-
flies both pairs
are covered, like
the rest of the
body, with little
scales, which can
be brushed off as
a powder.

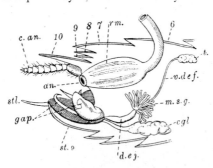

FIG. 240.—A semi-diagrammatic view of the
hinder part of the body of a male *P. americana* dissected from the right side to show
the generative organs.

an., Anus; *c.an.*, anal cerci; *cgl.*, conglobate gland;
d.ej., ductus ejaculatorius; *gap.*, gonapophyses;
m.s.g., mushroom-shaped gland; *rm.*, rectum; *st.9,*
ninth sternum; *stl.*, style; *t.*, testis; *v.def.*, vas
deferens; 6–10, terga.

The life-his-
tories of insects
are of three types. (1) In certain wingless insects such
Life-Histories.   as the silverfish and springtails, known as
Apterygota or *Ametabola*, the young very
closely resemble the adults, and the change from the
one stage to the other consists practically only in the
development of the reproductive system. (2) In many
other insects, known as *Heterometabola*, the young
resemble the adults in form of body, type of mouth-
parts, and the possession of compound eyes, but differ
in not possessing wings. Such young are known
as *nymphs*. They may change into the adult gradually

in a series of moults like the cockroach, or suddenly at a
final moult like the dragonflies, but they never pass through
a quiescent, " pupal " stage. When a free-living young
animal undergoes an obvious change in becoming adult,
the transformation is known as its *metamorphosis*. The
adult form of an insect is known as its *imago*, and the
Heterometabola are said to have an *incomplete metamorphosis*. As we have seen, this metamorphosis may be

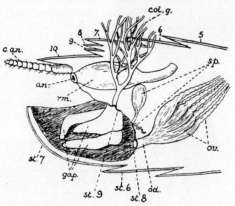

FIG. 241.—A semi-diagrammatic view of the
hinder part of the body of a female *P. americana* dissected from the right side to show
the generative organs.

an., Anus ; *c.an.*, anal circi ; *col.g.*, colleterial gland ; *gap.*, gonapophyses ; *od.*,
    oviduct : *ov.*, ovary ; *rm.*, rectum ; *sp.*, spermathecæ ; *st. 6–st.* 9, sterna :
    5–10, terga.

gradual, but when the nymphs are aquatic it has to be
sudden. (3) In the highest insects, including beetles, ants,
bees and wasps, flies, and butterflies, there is a larva which
differs from the adult in body-form, type of mouth-parts,
and the lack of compound eyes ; and in metamorphosis
the insect passes through an almost motionless stage
known as the *pupa*. These insects are called *Holo-
metabola*, and in them the metamorphosis is said to be
complete. The body of the pupa, undergoes a profound
reorganisation. A few of the most important systems of

22

organs, such as the reproductive, nervous, and circulatory, last on, but the others are devoured by a phagocytic action (p. 124) of the blood corpuscles and re-formed by the growth of certain clumps of cells, known as *imaginal discs*,

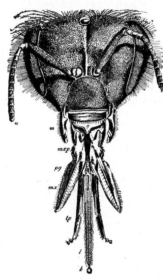

which have retained the embryonic power of growing into new organs. The larvæ of insects differ greatly. They may resemble the imago in the general shape of the body, as in some beetles, or they may be caterpillar-like and have the thorax ill-marked, as in butterflies, sawflies, etc., or they may be mere grubs, as in many flies, bees, etc.

According to these and other characters the principal kinds of insects may be classified as follows :—

1. *Orthoptera.* — Jaws adapted for biting, wings usually unlike. Metamorphosis incomplete. Cockroaches, Grasshoppers, etc.

2. *Odonata.*—Jaws for biting. Wings alike, membranous. Metamorphosis without pupa. Dragonflies.

FIG. 242.—The head and mouthparts of a bee. — After Cheshire.

a., Antenna ; *m.*, mandible ; *g.*, labrum or epipharynx ; *mx.p.*, rudiment of maxillary palp ; *mx.*, lamina of maxilla ; *lp.*, labial palp ; *l.*, ligula ; *b.*, bouton at end. The paraglossæ lie concealed between the basal portions of the labial palps and the ligula, opposite the letters *pg*.

3. *Hemiptera.*—Jaws for piercing and sucking. Wings alike or different ; sometimes absent. Metamorphosis incomplete. Bugs, Lice, Plantlice, etc. The Bed Bug (*Cimex lectularius*) is without wings, save for vestiges of the first pair, which in other bugs are wing-covers. Its body is flattened, so that it can hide in crevices, and it

secretes from glands a stinking substance. Its eggs are laid in batches in its hiding-places and hatch in about ten days. The young resemble the parents, but have no vestige of wings. They moult five times, feeding before each moult, and become adult in about a dozen weeks, the time depending upon the temperature and amount of food. Bugs can live for more than a year without food. They have been accused of transmitting the organisms which cause various diseases, but the evidence of this is not convincing. They may best be exterminated by fumigation with sulphur after sealing the infected building,

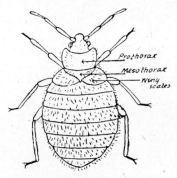

Fig. 243.—**The Bed Bug,** *Acanthia* (= *Cimex*) *lectularia.*— From Murray, after Butler.

or by applying paraffin to walls, etc., in such a way as to work it into all crevices. Lice differ from the bug in lacking any vestige of wings and having the segments of the thorax indistinct. They are smaller, and more dependent on their host, separated from which they soon die. *Pediculus vestimenti*, the Body Louse, and *P. capitis*, the Head Louse, live respectively in the clothing and the hair of the head. They have a life-cycle of about six weeks and need constant feeding. They are acquired by contact of person or clothing, and have been proved to transmit typhus and other fevers. They may be destroyed by applying paraffin or turpentine to the body and clothing, or by scalding the latter. *Phthirius inguinalis*, the Crab

Louse, frequents the hairs about the pubic region of man, and is conveyed by personal contact.

The Plantlice, of which the well-known Greenfly (*Aphis*) is an example, are not only of much practical importance as pests in gardens, farms, and orchards, but also of considerable zoological interest in more ways than one. They are animals parasitic upon plants ; they are generally

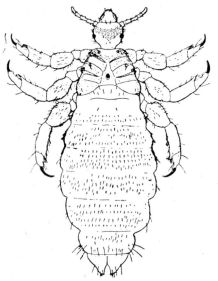

FIG. 244.—The Body Louse (*Pediculus vestimenti*)
In dorsal view.—From Nuttall.

wingless, but spread and often fertilised by means of winged individuals ; they are in many of their generations viviparous (p. 553) : and in most they are parthenogenetic (p. 593). Throughout the summer the females reproduce in a manner which is both viviparous and parthenogenetic, and, as the young are all females and all capable of producing offspring in a few days, the plantlice multiply very rapidly. Sooner or later, generally towards the autumn, there appears a generation which contains males as well as females. These pair, and the female lays a fertilised egg which survives the winter and gives rise in the spring to a parthenogenetic female again. Most of the generations are wingless, but

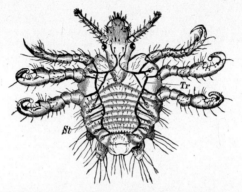

Fig. 245.—The Crab Louse (*Phthirius inguinalis*).—
From Sedgwick, after Landois.

St., Stigma ; *Tr.*, trachea.

from time to time there appears a generation of winged females by which the animal is spread ; usually, at least,

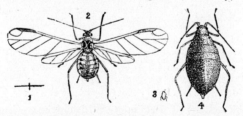

Fig. 246.—The Turnip-leaf Plantlouse (*Aphis rapæ*).—
After Curtis.

2 and 4 winged and wingless parthenogenetic females ;
1 and 3 natural size of the same

this happens when the plant is ceasing to afford a good supply of food. The males are generally winged. Food is taken at such a rate that much of it passes through the

alimentary canal but little altered, and oozes from the
hinder opening as a sugary fluid much relished by other
insects, especially by ants, which in some cases actually
domesticate the aphides in order to obtain it. This fluid,
known as " honey dew," was formerly believed to be
secreted by a pair of remarkable tubes which project from
the fifth abdominal segment. The great plenty of food
supports the rapid reproduction by which plantlice with-

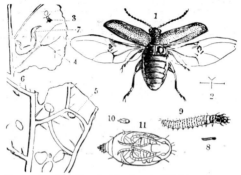

FIG. 247.—The Turnip Flea-beetle (*Haltica nemorum*).
From Theobald.

1, Adult, magnified ; 2, true length and wing expanse ; 3, adult
feeding on leaf ; 4, egg, natural size ; 5, the same magnified ;
6, 7, tunnel made by larva in leaf ; 8, 9, larva, natural size and
magnified ; 10, 11, natural size and magnified view of pupa,
which lies in soil.

This very destructive insect feeds, as larva and adult, on
the leaves of turnips, cabbages, broccoli, and other Cruciferæ.
It has many broods in the year, the last hibernating under
stones, etc. Its worst damage is done to seedlings. Paraffin,
Derris powder, and a mixture of soot and lime are remedies.

stand the attacks of their many bird and insect enemies.
They may be destroyed by spraying with various mixtures,
containing such substances as paraffin, quassia, and
nicotine, which are injurious to them in various stages of
their lives.

4. *Coleoptera.*—Jaws for biting. First pair of wings
form a hard cover for the membranous second pair.
Metamorphosis complete. Beetles.

5. *Hymenoptera.*—Jaws for biting and sucking (Fig.

242). Four membranous wings. Metamorphosis complete. Many live in communities, the majority of the members of which are sterile females or "workers." Bees, Wasps, Ants, Saw-flies (with caterpillars on plants, p. 351), Ichneumon flies, which lay their eggs in the larvæ of other insects, especially caterpillars. The ichneumon larvæ live upon the bodies of their hosts till the latter are killed, when the parasites pupate. In this way thousands of harmful insects are destroyed (Fig. 258).

6. *Diptera*.—Jaws for piercing and sucking. Hind wings represented by minute structures known as halteres, having the form of a rod ending in a knob, and sensory in function. Fore-wings membranous. Metamorphosis

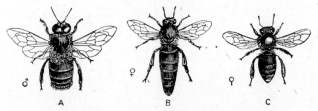

FIG. 248.—**The Honey Bee.**—From Shipley and MacBride.

A, Male or drone ; *B*, female or queen ; *C*, sterile female or worker.

complete. Gnats and Mosquitoes, Crane-flies, House-flies and Blow-flies, Tsetse-flies (p. 186 and Fig. 119), Bot-flies, etc.

Mosquitoes and Gnats. The mosquitoes (Fig. 123), and the related gnats (*Culex*) are delicately-built insects with slight bodies (save when they are distended with food), slender legs, and narrow wings, which, like the body, are powdered with scales. Their eyes are very large. The antennæ are feathery, but less so in the female than in the male. The mouth-parts constitute a piercing and sucking *proboscis*. The labium forms a long gutter which contains the slender mandibles (absent in the male), maxillæ, and tongue (*hypopharynx*), and is closed above by the labrum. The latter is grooved below so as to form almost a closed tube, and along it the fluid food is sucked up. A pair of long, tactile maxillary palps stand at the sides of the proboscis. All the mouth-parts except the labium and the maxillary palps are sharp-pointed and pierce the tissues of the organism whose juices are being sucked. The hypopharynx bears a minute groove down which flows the secretion of the salivary glands. The

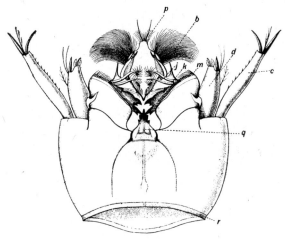

FIG. 249.—A ventral view of the head of a fully grown larva of the mosquito *Anopheles maculipennis.*—From Nuttall and Shipley.

b., Brush with which food is swept from the surface film of the water (*Culex* larvæ, hanging with the head down, collect from a lower stratum); *c.,* antenna; *d.,* palp of maxilla; *j.,* stout hairs which arrange the brush; *k.,* teeth of mandible; *m.,* hooked hairs at edge of maxilla; *p.* a median tuft of hairs; *q.,* a median structure known as the *metastoma*; *r.,* rim of head.

labium ends in a pair of *labellæ*, which guide the piercing organs, and, as the latter penetrate, the flexible labium is bowed back. The insects normally feed on the juices of plants, but take blood when they can get it. The male, however, does not suck blood. There are several generations in the course of the year. The eggs—which in the mosquito are boat-shaped—are laid upon the water, where they remain upon the surface owing to the presence of floats, containing air, on their shells. The larva (Fig. 126)

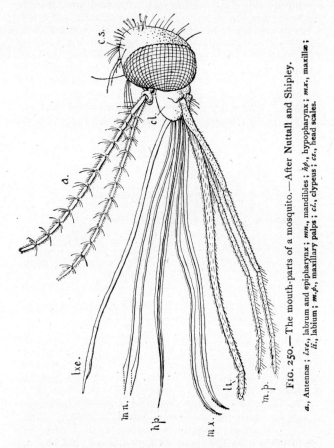

FIG. 250.—The mouth-parts of a mosquito.—After Nuttall and Shipley.

a., Antennæ; *l.e.*, labrum and epipharynx; *mn.*, mandibles; *hp.*, hypopharynx; *mx.*, maxillæ; *li.*, labium; *m.p.*, maxillary palps; *cl.*, clypeus; *c.s.*, head scales.

has the three regions of the body distinct, though the thorax and abdomen bear no appendages. It passes its life hanging, by palmate (palm-leaf-shaped) hairs on its abdominal segments, from the surface-film of the water, with its dorsal surface uppermost, breathing by a pair of dorsal stigmata on the eighth abdominal segment, and feeding by collecting minute organisms and other organic particles from the water. This it does by means of a pair of brushes on the head (Fig. 249), which are combed by the mandibles and maxillæ. The pupa (Fig. 126) has a swollen cephalothorax and clings to the surface-film by two trumpet-shaped stigmata just behind the head, and by a pair of palmate hairs at the beginning of the abdomen, the rest of the abdomen hanging down into the water. It does not feed. After a few days its cuticle splits down the back, and the perfect insect (*imago*) draws itself out, standing

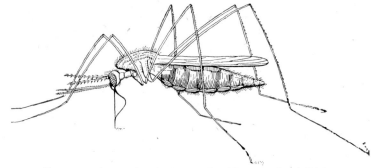

FIG. 251.—A mosquito, sucking blood.—After Nuttall and Shipley.
The curved line under the head is the labium.

upon the pupal cuticle as on a raft until its own soft cuticle has hardened in the air. The mosquito and the gnat are both British insects. The principal points of difference between them are shown in Fig. 126 (see also p. 195).

The House-Fly, *Musca domestica*, a heavily-built insect **The House-fly.** with short, three-jointed antennæ, differs greatly in build and habits, at all stages of its life-history, from the gnats and mosquitoes, but is much less unlike the tsetse-fly. Its proboscis, lacking mandibles and having only the palps of the maxillæ, is unable to pierce, and is adapted only to sucking. As in the mosquito, the labrum is grooved underneath, and the groove is closed by the hypopharynx, so as to form a tube. The labium can be folded up, and has at the end a pair of large labellæ. These bear many fine grooves, the *pseudotracheæ*, which lead to a central spot to which the tip of the labral tube can be applied, so that fluid collected by the pseudo-

tracheæ can be sucked up the tube by the pumping action of the pharynx. The fly feeds largely on fluid matter, but in the presence of solid food passes saliva on to it to dissolve it. It lays its eggs in rotting matter, by pre-ference in stable manure, for which reason heaps of such substances should never be allowed to accu-mulate near houses. The larvæ hatch in one day, feed on their surround-ings, and pupate in a week. They are soft, white, and legless, with twelve somites, tapering forwards, and a head that can be withdrawn under the first somite and carries a pair of sharp hook-like man-dibles and two minute antennæ. The second and last somites bear each

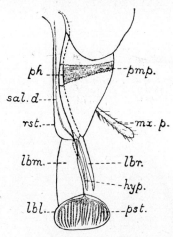

Fig. 252.—A semi-diagrammatic view of the extended proboscis of a house-fly or blow-fly.

hyp., Hypopharynx; *lbl.*, labella; *llm.*, labium; *lbr.*, labrum with epipharynx; *mx.p.*, maxillary palp; *ph.*, part of pharynx exposed by cutting open the rostrum, the course of the pharynx is indicated by dotted lines; *pmp.*, part o pumping muscles of the pharynx, simi-larly exposed; *pst.*, pseudotracheæ; *rst.*, rostrum, morphologically part of the head; *sal.d.*, salivary duct.

a pair of spiracles, and the fifth and following somites have each a spiny pad below. The pupa case is formed from the last larval skin. The imago emerges a fortnight after laying, becomes sexually mature in a week, and lays its first batch of eggs four days after mating. It may deposit half a dozen batches of 150 eggs, and this, with the shortness of its life-history, enables it, in favourable circumstances, to become immensely numerous. House-flies are dangerous pests, because they pick up, from excrement, sputum, etc., the bacilli of typhoid, diarrhœa, tubercle, and other diseases, carry them on their legs and in their alimentary canal, and infect food with them. Blow-flies (*Calliphora*), which lay

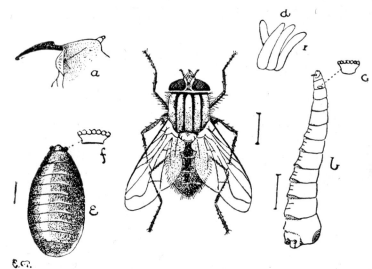

FIG. 253.—The life-history of the House Fly (*Musca domestica*).—From Theobald.

a, Mandible of larva with adjacent structures ; *b*, larva ; *c*, anterior spiracle of the same ; *d*, eggs ; *e*, pupa case ; *f*, remnants of spiracle on the same.

their eggs in fresh or decaying flesh, including that of open wounds, have a similar life-history.

7. *Aphaniptera.*—Jaws for piercing and sucking. No wings. Metamorphosis complete. Fleas. The body of these insects is compressed from side to side (thus in the opposite direction from that of the bed bug), their eyes are small or absent, and their legs very long and strong. They spend part of their time on the body of the host and part on the ground, where they lay their eggs. The larvæ have

long, narrow bodies, without legs but with bristles by which they pull themselves about actively. They have biting

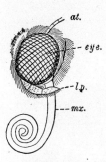

FIG. 254.—A side view of the head of a butterfly.

at., Antenna; *eye*; *l.p.*, labial palp; *mx.*, maxilla.

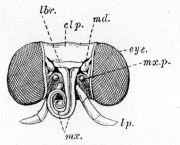

FIG. 255.—The head of a tiger moth (*Arctia caja*), seen from in front and partly from below, after the removal of the scales.

clp., Clypeus; *eye*; *lp.*, labial palp; *lbr.*, labrum; *md.*, structure supposed to represent a mandible; *mx.*, maxillæ; *mx.p.*, maxillary palp.

mouth-parts and feed on any kind of organic matter which they find in dust, etc. After about twelve days (in the case

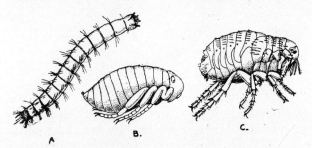

FIG. 256.—The Common Flea (*Pulex irritans*).

A, Larva; *B*, pupa; *C*, adult.

of the Human Flea, *Pulex irritans*) they spin a cocoon and pupate. Various species infest different warm-blooded animals, but many can live for a time on other than their proper hosts. The plague is transmitted by rat fleas.

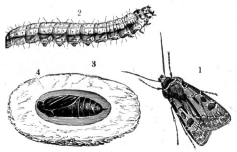

FIG. 257.—The Heart-and-Dart Moth (*Agrotis exclamationis*).— From Theobald, after Curtis.

1, Imago : 2, larva ; 3, earthen case ; containing 4, pupa.

8. *Lepidoptera.*—Jaws for sucking, formed by the maxillæ only. Four wings alike and covered with scales,

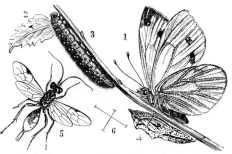

FIG. 258.—The Green-veined White Butterfly (*Pieris napi*), and the ichneumon fly that preys upon it (*Hemiteles melanarius*).— From Theobald.

1, Imago ; 2, egg ; 3, caterpillar ; 4, chrysalis or pupa ; 5, the ichneumon fly ; 6, natural size of the latter.

as is also the body. Metamorphosis complete. Butter-flies and Moths. Butterflies are the members of one of a.

number of groups into which Lepidoptera may be divided. They have knobbed antennæ (rare among moths) no *frenulum* (a bristle on the hind wing of most moths, which links it with the fore wing), a habit of folding the wings upward over the back and not down at the sides, and day-light flight. The caterpillars of Lepidoptera have biting mouth-parts, three pairs of true legs, four, or fewer, pairs of soft " prolegs," and a pair of " claspers " at the hind end of the body. They possess silk glands, which open on a spinneret situated below the mouth. (The caterpillars of saw-flies have usually more prolegs than those of Lepidoptera, have a pair on the second abdominal somite where there are none in Lepidoptera, and lack the ring of hooked bristles which the prolegs of lepidopterous larvæ possess.) The butterfly and moth which are figured as examples in this chapter are both of interest as being harmful to crops. The dull-coloured larvæ of the Heart-and-Dart Moth live under the soil by day and come out at night to feed, doing much damage to a variety of plants in gardens and in fields. The best remedy against them is a dressing of soot and lime. The Green-veined White Butterfly lays its eggs upon cabbages and other Cruciferæ, to which the larvæ do injury, though they are responsible for less damage than the Large and Small Whites (*Pieris brassicæ* and *Pieris rapæ*), whose habits are similar. Hand picking is practically the only remedy.

CHAPTER XVII

THE NEMATODA. PARASITISM

Nematoda. THE size of an animal is no measure of its importance in the economy of nature. All the elephants and whales together have far less effect on the course of events in the world than is achieved by some half-dozen kinds of Protozoa, or again by a few species of parasitic worms. We have dealt already with some of these little organisms. There remains one group of them which now demands our attention. These are the Nematoda. The Arthropoda, to which the last two chapters have been devoted, are the most active and conspicuous of invertebrate animals. Utterly unlike them in most respects, yet strangely resembling them in certain particulars, the Nematodes are a group of worm-like animals, mostly of small size and always of retiring habits. One of the largest of them is *Ascaris lumbricoides*, the Human Roundworm.[1]

Ascaris. *Ascaris lumbricoides* lives normally in the small intestine of man. It is a yellowish-white worm, which reaches a length of 25 centimetres in the female and 17 in the male, cylindrical, but tapering towards the ends, and quite smooth. Along the middle of the back and of the ventral side run dead white lines, and there is a brownish line along the middle of each flank. At the front end is the *mouth*, guarded by three *lips*, one above and one at each side below. The dorsal lip bears at its base two *papillæ* and the ventro-lateral lips one each. The edges of the lips are finely toothed. Median on the under side, about two millimetres from the mouth, is a

---

[1] A still larger species is *A. megalocephala* of the horse, to which the following description will apply almost equally well.

so-called "*excretory*" *pore*. The female bears a median *genital pore* at about one-third of the length of the body from the front end, on the ventral side of a region which is slightly narrowed. The tail is curved downwards, slightly in the female and strongly in the male. The *anus* lies below, about a couple of millimetres from the hind end.

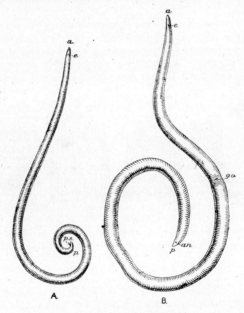

FIG. 259.—*Ascaris lumbricoides.*

A, Male ; *B*, female.

a., Anterior end ; *an.*, anus ; *e.*, " excretory " pore ; *g.o.*, genital opening ; *p.*, posterior end ; *p.s.*, penial setæ.

In the male this opening serves also as a genital pore, and there project from it a pair of *penial setæ.*

Internally, a spacious *perivisceral cavity* separates a straight, simple gut from a simple body-wall. The cavity is traversed by numerous delicate strands of a remarkable connective tissue, which is composed of processes of a

23

few cells, notably of one very large cell placed on the
dorsal side just behind the nerve ring. Over the gut and
the muscle fibres of the body-wall the strands join a thin
covering layer which lines the cavity. Thus the body
cavity may be regarded as intracellular, and on this account
it is held to be neither cœlomic nor hæmocœlic.

The body-wall is made up of three layers : a stout,
smooth, albuminoid cuticle which consists of several
layers and is shed four times, an ectoderm (" hypodermis ")
which is without cell-limits and must therefore be classed
as a syncytium (p. 147), and a single layer of peculiar
muscle fibres. The nuclei of the ectoderm, except at the
hinder end, are collected along the mid-dorsal, mid-ventral,

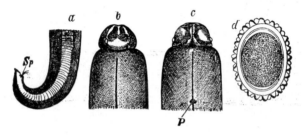

FIG. 260.—*Ascaris lumbricotdes.*—From Sedgwick. after Leuchart.
a, Hind end of male ; *b,* head, from above ; *c,* head, from below ; *d,* egg, in shell ;
p, "excretory" pore ; *Sp,* penial setæ.

and lateral lines. Along these lines the protoplasm bulges
towards the body cavity. A nerve cord is embedded in the
dorsal and ventral lines, and a canal in each lateral line. The
canals have no internal openings ; they unite in front to
open by the " excretory " pore, but there is no proof that they
excrete. The two have but one nucleus, which is very
large, and lies in the wall of the left-hand canal, near its
front end. Thus they may be said to be hollowed in the
body of one immense cell. Two more nuclei lie in the wall
of the median duct to the exterior. Four very large,
branched cells lie upon the lateral lines near the anterior
end of the body and have the power of taking up particles

from the body cavity. They are known from this function as the *phagocytic cells*. The *nerve cords* are connected by transverse commissures in the ectoderm, and in front join

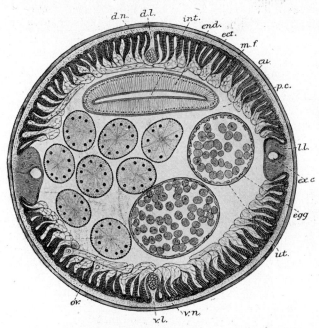

FIG. 261.—**A transverse section through the middle of the body** of a female *Ascaris lumbricoides*.

cu., Cuticle; *d.l.*, dorsal line; *d.n.*, dorsal nerve; *ect.*, ectoderm; *egg*; *end.*, endoderm; *ex.c.*, excretory canal; *int.*, intestine; *l.l.*, lateral line; *m.f.*, muscle fibre; *ov.*, ovary; *p.c.*, perivisceral cavity; *ut.*, uterus; *v.l.*, ventral line; *v.n.*, ventral nerve.

a ring a little way behind the mouth. From this ring four other cords run back at the sides, and six forwards. The nerve ring is slightly thickened above and rather more below, and contains some nerve cells. The only other ganglia are placed at the sides of the nerve ring and at the hinder end of the ventral cord. A few cells are scattered among the fibrils of which the cords are composed, but there is no sign of segmental arrangement in these or any other organ of the body. The number of the cells which compose the nervous system is small and remarkably constant, each cell being recognisable in the same position in

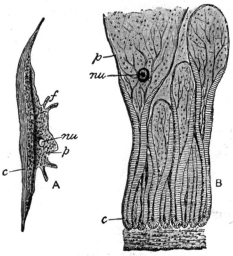

Fig. 262.—Muscle fibres of *Ascaris.*—From Parker and Haswell, after Leuckart.

A, A single fibre; *B,* several fibres in transverse section, with a portion of the ectoderm (below).

c, Contractile part of the fibre; *f,* processes; *nu,* nucleus; *p,* undifferentiated protoplasmic part of the fibre.

every individual. Each *muscle fibre* consists of an outer longitudinally-fibrillated part and an inner part of un-differentiated cytoplasm containing a nucleus. Strands of protoplasm stretch from the inner parts of the muscle fibres to the dorsal and ventral nerves. The *alimentary canal* consists of three parts : a short stomodæum, or fore-gut, known as the pharynx, a long mid-gut, and a short procto-dæum, or hind-gut, known as the rectum. The fore- and hind-guts are lined by inturned ectoderm, with a prolongation of the outer cuticle, which is shed with the latter.

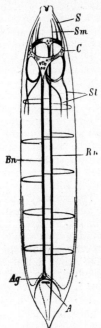

FIG. 263.— A diagram of the nervous system of a nematode.— From Sedgwick, after Bütschli.

A, Anus; *Ag*, anal ganglion; *Bn*, ventral nerve; *C*, lateral ganglion on circumœsophageal ring; *Rn*, dorsal nerve; *S*, lateral nerve; *Sl*, sublateral nerve; *Sm*, submedian nerve.

They have in their walls muscular fibres. The mid-gut is composed solely of a layer of columnar epithelium, with a basement membrane outside it. The food consists of solids and liquids taken up from the contents of the intestine of the host.

There is no vascular or respiratory system. Excretion probably takes place through the cuticle.

The *genital organs* are of a type peculiar to the Nematoda. They are paired in the female and unpaired in the male, and lie free in the body cavity. The *male apparatus* is composed of (*a*) the *testis*, a long, coiled thread consisting in its anterior part of a solid mass of immature sex-cells, and in its hinder part containing a cord or " rachis " in the middle with riper sex-cells attached to it, (*b*) the *vas deferens* of much the same width as the testis, (*c*) the *vesicula seminalis*, a wider tube, (*d*) a short, narrow, muscular *ductus ejaculatorius*. The spermatozoa are simple rounded cells, which become amœboid when they have been transferred to the female. The *female organs* correspond with those of the male. Each *ovary* has the same general structure as the testis, a hollow region which may be called the *oviduct* connects it with the wide *uterus*, and the two uteri unite in a short, muscular *vagina*. The eggs are produced in immense numbers —some 1500 a day—fertilised in the upper part of the uterus, enclosed in a chitinoid shell, passed into the gut of the host, and by it voided with the fæces. Before they can

bring about a new infection, they must pass through a
period of ripening, which needs moisture, a temperature
above 60° F., abundant oxygen, and the absence of putrefaction, and therefore cannot take place except in the outer
world. The most favourable situation for it is the upper
layer of damp soil. The eggs stand drought, and, by being
swallowed with food or water, may reach a new host.
Usually they hatch in his intestine, but in warm, damp
places may do so in soil. In the egg occur the first two of
the four moults which *Ascaris*, like other nematodes, undergoes in the course of its life. The worms hatch as *infective
larvæ* which in the new host do not at once become intestinal parasites but undertake first a remarkable journey.
Freeing themselves from the remains of the second cuticle
and piercing the wall of the intestine, they enter venules
and lymphatics and are carried through the heart to the
lungs, where they cause congestion and hæmorrhage and
are thus discharged into the alveoli. Thence they travel
along the bronchi and trachea into the gullet and descend
the alimentary canal to reach the intestine once more. On
this journey they undergo their remaining two moults,
acquire as swimming-organs lateral membranes, which they
afterwards lose, and grow from .28 mm. to 2 mm. in length.

Ascaris lumbricoides is found throughout the world,
and can only be avoided by care taken in regard to the
cleanness of raw foods and drinking water. It may cause
little trouble to the host, or be the source of diarrhœa,
and of anæmia and other complaints, the latter apparently
through an enzyme formed by it which interferes with
digestion. In severe infections with the eggs, temporary
bronchitis may occur during the passage of the larvæ
through the lungs. Santonin, thymol, and other vermifuges are used against the worm.

Though many nematode worms are known, none of them
has been found to differ anatomically from *Ascaris* in
any important respect : all are either, like it, parasitic, or
live in damp spots where decaying matter is plentiful ;
and the same simple organisation is adapted by slight
differences to the needs of each of them. Their life-histories
however, are as diverse as they are remarkable, probably
because it is only by strange and various shifts that they

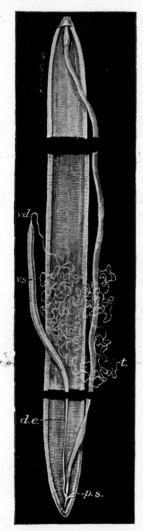

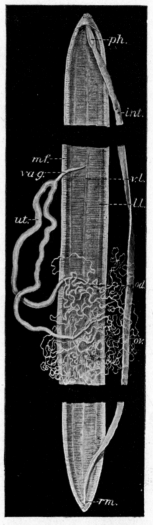

FIG. 264.—A male *Ascaris lumbricoides* dissected from above.

FIG. 265.—A female *Ascaris lumbricoides* dissected from above.

d.e., Ductus ejaculatorius; *p.s.*, sacs of the penial setæ; *t.*, testis; *v.d.*, vas deferens; *v.s.*, vesicula seminalis.

int., Intestine; *l.l.*, lateral lines; *od.*, oviduct; *ov.*, ovary; *ph.*, pharynx; *rm.*, rectum; *ut.*, uterus; *v.l.*, ventral line.

can obtain entry to their several hosts.   The following are brief outlines of examples of the principal types of nematode life-history :—

1. *Free-living throughout life.*—The Vinegar Worm, *Anguillula aceti,* found in vinegar.   *Rhabditis,* in soil.

2. *Free as larvæ, parasitic in plants as adults.*—The Cockle Worm, *Tylenchus scandens,* cause of " ear-cockles " in corn. Small worms from the soil wriggle up the stems of young corn plants, pair in the flowers when these form, cause galls to arise in place of grains, and lay eggs, from which hatch larvæ. These can survive dry for twenty years but in damp earth become active.

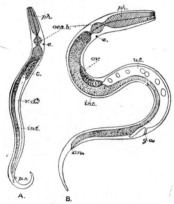

FIG. 266.—The Vinegar Worm (*Anguillula aceti*), somewhat dia-grammatic, to show arrangement of organs.

A, Male ; *B,* female.

an., Anus ; *e.,* excretory pore ; *g.o.,* genital opening ; *int.,* intestine ; *oes.b.,* bulb of œsophagus ; *ov.,* ovary ; *p.s.,* penial setæ ; *ph.,* pharynx ; *t.,* testis ; *ut.,* uterus ; *v.d.,* vas deferens.

3. *Free as larvæ, parasitic in animals as adults.*—The Miners' Worm, *Ancylostoma duodenale,* of a pink colour, the male 8–11 mm. long, the female 10–18mm, lives and pairs in the small intestine of man. Eggs are passed with the fæces of the host and hatch in warm, damp places, but are killed by drought or frost. The little, thread-like larvæ pierce the human skin, usually on the foot, hand, or mouth, enter venules or lymphatics, and are carried in the blood through the heart to the lung wall, which they penetrate. Thence they reach the gut by way of the glottis. Browsing on the villi, they cause intestinal hæmorrhage, and thus anæmia, often fatal. The worm is widespread in warm countries, but elsewhere can exist only where the conditions are favourable, as in mines in Britain. Strict sanitation is necessary for avoiding its ravages. Male fern and thymol are the principal vermifuges used against it.

4. *Larvæ parasitic, adults free.*—The Rain Worm, *Mermis nigres-cens*, whose larvæ bore through the skin of young grasshoppers and live in the body cavity till they are full grown, when they escape into damp earth, become sexually mature, and pair. After rain the adults

FIG. 267.—The Corn-cockle Worm.—From Theobald.

A, Cockle gall ; *C*, larvæ ; in *D*, gall cut open ; *E*, larvæ magnified.

sometimes climb the stems of plants in such numbers as to give rise to the legend of " showers of worms."

5. *Larvæ and adults parasitic in different animals, with a free stage.*—The Guinea Worm, *Dracunculus medinensis*. The female, about

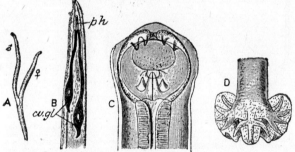

FIG. 268.—The Miner's Worm (*Ancylostoma duodenale*).—From Parker and Halswell, after Leuckart.

A, Male and female *in coitu* ; *B*, anterior end ; *C*, mouth, with spines ; *D*, hinder end of male, with expansion known as *bursa*.
cv.g., Cervical glands ; *ph.*, pharynx.

90 cm. long, encysts beneath the skin of man, usually in the leg, with the head in the host's foot, causing an abscess. She is viviparous. The young escape through the abscess when the host wades in water, and enter the small crustacean *Cyclops*, with which they are swallowed by a new host. The male is small and has rarely been seen. The disease is common in tropical Africa and parts of Asia. The worm is removed by coiling it on a twig. If it be broken during this process,

and larvæ escape into the host's tissues, sepsis, fever, and even death may result.

6. *Larvæ and adult parasitic, without free stage, in animals of unlike kinds.*—The supposed cause of elephantiasis, *Filaria bancrofti*,

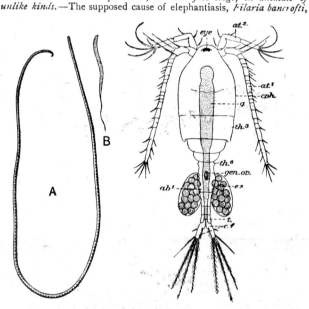

FIG. 269.—The Guinea Worm (*Dracunculus medinensis*).

A, Adult female, reduced ; *B*, larva, much magnified.

FIG. 270.—*Cyclops.*

*ab.*1, First abdominal segment ; *at.*1, antennule ; *at.*2, antenna ; *c.f.*, caudal fork ; *cph.*, cephalothorax (fused head and first two thoracic segments) ; *e.s.*, egg sac ; *eye* (single and median) ; *g.*, alimentary canal ; *gen.op.*, genital opening ; *t.*, telson ; *th.*3, *th.*6, third and sixth thoracic segments.

In comparing this crustacean with the crayfish, note the absence of proventriculus, paired eyes, uropods, and carapace, the presence of median eye and caudal fork, and the difference in the number of segments.

lives and pairs (male 8–9 cm., female 15 cm.) in the human lymphatics. The female is viviparous, setting free embryos into the lymph, whence they reach the blood and are sucked up by mosquitoes or gnats, in which they bore through the wall and develop in the muscles. Later they enter the salivary glands and are injected into man during blood-sucking. They may cause no ill effects, but the adults may block lymphatics, or unripe eggs, freed by injury to the mother, being broader than the larvæ, may choke capillaries. Thus dropsy, and it is believed elephantiasis, are caused. Three kinds of *Filaria* have similar habits : *F. perstans*, whose larvæ remain in the surface vessels of the host day and night ; *F. bancrofti* (or *F. nocturna*), whose larvæ retreat to deeper vessels, out of reach of mosquitoes, by day ; and

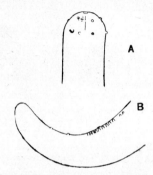

FIG. 272.—*Filaria bancrofti.* — From the *Transactions* of the Society of Tropical Medicine, after Leiper.

A, Head ; *B*, tail of male—showing the arrangement of papillæ characteristic of the species.

FIG. 271.— The female of *Filaria bancrofti.*

F. loa (or *F. diurna*), whose larvæ retreat at night. The carrier of *F. loa* is the blood-sucking fly *Chrysops*. If the patient be made to sleep by day, the larvæ reverse their habit. The parasites cannot be destroyed, but may be avoided by measures against their insect-carriers. They are widespread in warm countries.

7. *Adult and larvæ parasitic, without free stage, in the same host.*— The cause of trichinosis, *Trichinella spiralis*, lives, when it is adult, in the small intestine of rat, pig, or man, and there pairs (male 1 mm. long, female 3–4 mm.). The females penetrate to the intestinal lymphatics, and produce viviparously young which reach blood vessels, and are carried to muscles, where they encyst. The tissues of the host enclose the cyst in a capsule, and the larvæ remain till the host be eaten by another individual of the same or another species, when they become adult in the intestine. The symptoms produced in the host are intestinal catarrh during the piercing of the gut wall, rheumatic pains and fever during migration, and general cachexia during encystment. The disease may or may not prove fatal. It can be avoided by meat inspection and *thorough* cooking. It is found in all parts of the world.

8. *No larval stage. Adult parasitic in the gut of a vertebrate : eggs pass out in fæces and are swallowed by another individual of the same*

host. Trichocephalus or *Trichuris* (male 30–45 mm., female 35–50 mm.) lives in the human cæcum, appendix, and colon, attached

FIG. 273.—*Trichinella spiralis*, young encysted in muscle of host.—From Thomson, after Leuckart.

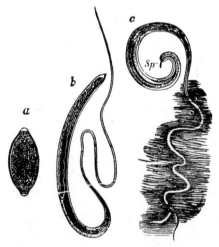

FIG. 274.—*Trichocephalus dispar.*—From Sedgwick, after Leuckart.

a, Egg ; *b*, female ; *c*, male, with forepart of body buried in mucous membrane of host ; *Sp*, penial seta.

by its long whip-like fore-end. It is generally harmless, but may cause inflammation. It is widely distributed. *Oxyuris* (male 2–5 mm., female 9–12 mm.) has the same habitat as *Trichocephalus*. It rarely causes more than irritation. The eggs are ripe when they leave the host's rectum, so that self-infection by him is possible. The animal is cosmopolitan. As a precaution against infection with these parasites and others of similar life-history, the thorough washing of raw vegetables and strawberries is desirable.

9. *A free bisexual generation alternates with a parasitic hermaphrodite.*—*Rhabdonema nigrovenosum.* The hermaphrodite is a blackish worm which lives in the lungs of the frog, where several specimens may often be found in dissecting. It is protandrous. Embryos escape by the glottis, are passed with fæces, and become sexual adults. Their young wander, and are swallowed with food by a frog. An example of heterogamy (pp. 248, 249).

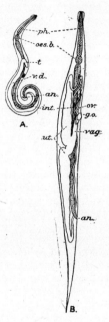

FIG 275.—*Oxyuris*, somewhat diagrammatic, to show arrangement of organs.

A, Male; *B*, female.

an., Anus; *g.o.*, genital opening; *int.*, intestine; *oes.b.*, bulb of œsophagus; *ov.*, ovary; *ph.*, pharynx; *t.*, testis; *ut.*, uterus; *v.d.*, vas deferens; *vag.*, vagina

Parasitism. The foregoing paragraphs give only a small sample of the life-histories of Nematoda. These animals have experimented with almost every kind of host, and almost every kind of internal parasitism, and in every line their organisation betrays their adaptation to this way of life. As they are the last important group of parasitic animals with which we have to deal, we may pause here briefly to survey the phenomena of parasitism. A parasitic organism is one which lives on or in the body of another without conferring any advantage on it. Parasites may be external, as the Greenfly (*Aphis*) or the Flea, or internal, as those with which we have just dealt. An internal parasite may live (i) in the hollows of the body of its host, as *Entamœba*, *Tænia*, and *Ascaris* in the gut, and *Trypanosoma* and *Filaria* in the blood vessels and lymph spaces, (ii) in the tissues, as *Dracunculus* and young *Trichinella*, or (iii) in protoplasm, as the young trophozoite of *Monocystis*, or that of the malaria parasite. Its life is passed in the following conditions : (i) Food is plentiful, needs no hunting, and is usually easy of digestion, (ii) there are no enemies to be escaped, (iii) means of fixation (*e.g* to the gut-wall) are sometimes needed, (iv) provision must be made for distribution from one host to the next, (v) the surroundings are often devoid of free oxygen. We find accordingly in internal parasites (i) an absence or poor development of organs of locomotion, of defence and offence, and of sense, (ii) simplicity in the organs of nutrition, (iii) often the presence of organs of fixation (suckers, hooks, etc.), (iv) many adaptations of the life-history to distribution. Such are : (*a*) the vast numbers in which the young are usually produced, so that some survive the "passage perilous," (*b*) the occurrence of special distributive individuals, either active, as the miracidium of the liver fluke and the larval stages of *Tylenchus*, or adapted to passive transmission, as the gamonts of the malaria parasite, various encysted Protozoa, and hard-shelled eggs of worms—thus the parasite has a *multiplicative phase* in which it takes advantage of the rich supply of food in its host to produce many offspring, and a *distributive phase* in which temporarily non-reproductive individuals find new hosts—(*c*) often the passage through an *intermediate host*. When there are two different hosts, the *principal host* is that in which the parasite passes its sexual phase (not necessarily the larger host, as is seen in the case of the malaria parasite). This host usually preys on the intermediate host.[1] The intermediate host of the malaria parasite is man, that of the pork tapeworm is the pig, that of *Filaria* is the mosquito, that of the guinea worm is the freshwater crustacean *Cyclops*. The advantages of this arrangement are twofold : (1) the parasite finds a means of re-entering its principal host, (2) very often the intermediate host provides a richer supply of nourishment than the principal host, and the parasite there undergoes most of its growth and reproduces asexually. (v) Internal parasites often obtain the energy for their life,

---

[1] *Filaria bancrofti* is an exception to this.

by an anaerobic process, the complex molecules of carbohydrates being decomposed to form simpler ones without the intervention of free oxygen (see p. 4).

To this end such parasites lay up in their tissues large quantities of the starch-like substance glycogen of which carbohydrate stores in animals are usually composed (p. 62). Thirty per cent. of the dry weight of an *Ascaris*, and nearly half that of a tapeworm, consist of this substance. The glycogen is decomposed according to the following equation :

$$(C_6H_{10}O_5)n + nH_2O = 2nC_3H_6O_3$$
$$\text{(Glycogen)} \qquad \text{(Lactic acid)}$$

As we have seen, this process yields considerably less energy than would be obtained by total oxidation. Apparently, at least in many animals, it cannot go on indefinitely unless the lactic acid be removed. This may happen either by the acid being discharged into the surrounding fluid and swept away by movements of the latter (which would occur, for instance, in the host's intestine), or by an access of oxygen with which some of the lactic acid is oxidised so as to give energy for building the rest back into glycogen. In the latter case the process becomes ultimately aerobic. It is probable, indeed, that even in aerobic animals the process by which energy is liberated is at first anaerobic, but that this phase is quickly followed by one in which, by the use of oxygen, a part of the product is destroyed and the rest built back, so that the process as a whole appears aerobic. Thus anaerobic animals differ from those that are aerobic only in the length of time for which the anaerobic process goes on.

It should be noted that parasites are not necessarily harmful. In fact, those which are so have not yet reached that accommodation with their host which the course of generations usually brings about. An organism which suffers injury from a parasite, either by loss of food, or by destruction of tissues, or by poisonous by-products, fights the intruder in various ways—by expelling it, by attacking it with leucocytes, and by the secretion of counter-poisons. It also lessens the effects of the parasite by taking enough food to supply it as well as itself, and, if poisons be in question, by the secretion of " antitoxins " which neutralise them. It is usually to the interest of the parasite not entirely to overcome these measures, for by so doing it deprives itself of a host. Most parasites have reached an equilibrium with their host, which is able to keep them from destroying, and often even from harming it, but cannot destroy them altogether.

Allusion has already been made to certain broad resemblances between the Nematoda and the Arthro-
Nematoda and Arthropoda. poda. These may now be specified. The stout
cuticle, shed at intervals, with its underlying
syncytium, both inturned in the fore and hind guts, the
lack of perivisceral cœlom, the absence of cilia, and the
unflagellated spermatozoa have been held to show an
affinity between the groups. But the excretory system,
much of the histology, and some features of the nervous
system of the Nematoda are entirely peculiar to that
group, and both segmentation and limbs are wanting in
them. The Nematoda, indeed, are one of the most isolated
groups of the animal kingdom.

CHAPTER XVIII

THE SWAN MUSSEL. MOLLUSCA

FRESHWATER mussels may be found in most streams,
canals, and large ponds in Britain, though they
are often overlooked on account of their habit
of burying themselves in the mud with at most a small part
of the body projecting. The commonest of them is the
Swan Mussel, *Anodonta cygnea*. When it is removed from
the mud it is seen to be enclosed in a flat, dark-green
shell, four to six inches long and roughly oval in outline,
with one end (the front) rounded and the other more
pointed. The shell consists of two similar pieces, known
as *valves*, which lie one on each side of the animal
joined by a hinge above the back, where their edges are
almost straight. On being disturbed the mussel holds the
valves tightly together, but when it is at rest in the water
they gape somewhat, and at the hind end, which projects
slightly from the mud, there may be seen between them
two fleshy lobes enclosing an opening shaped like a figure
of 8, through one of whose limbs a current sets into the
shell, while through the other, the upper of the two, the
water is driven out. At times the animal moves about,
thrusting out a yellowish, ploughshare-shaped organ known
as the *foot*, with which it ploughs its way through the mud
at the rate of about a mile a year. Freshwater mussels are
not unfit for food and are sometimes eaten. They are preyed
upon by water-fowl and other animals, and in places are
fished for on account of the pearls which they contain,
which may be of considerable value. They are not killed
by the freezing of the water even if they themselves be
frozen solid, but can only survive a few hours of drought.

The shell consists of an outer horny layer, the *periostracum.*

24

a thick middle *prismatic layer* impregnated with salts of
lime, and an inner *nacreous layer* of mother-
**Shell and
Mantle.**   of-pearl, which consists of thin calcareous
laminæ. *Lines of growth* parallel with its edge
mark the outside of the shell, centering upon a point about
a quarter of its length from the front end. This point is
known as the *umbo* and shows the position of the first shell

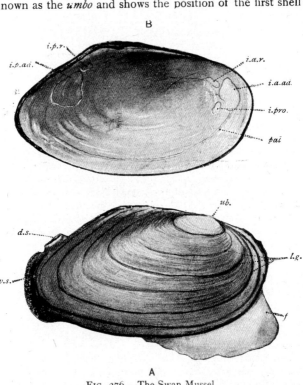

FIG. 276.—The Swan Mussel.

A, The shell with the animal, from the right side ; *B,* the left valve of the shell, from
      within.

d.s., Dorsal siphon ; *f.,* foot ; *i.,* impressions of muscles ; *i.a.ad.,* of anterior
      adductor ; *i.a.r.,* of anterior retractor ; *i.p.ad.,* of posterior adductor ; *i.p.r.,*
      of posterior retractor ; *i.pro.,* of protractor ; *l.g.,* lines of growth ; *pal.,* pallial
      line ; *ub.,* umbo ; *v.s.,* ventral siphon.

of the young mussel. On the inside of the shell may be seen the *marks of attachment* of the adductor, retractor, and protractor muscles presently to be mentioned, and parallel with its edge is a mark known as the *pallial line*, where the fold of the body-wall known as the mantle is attached. Above the hinge the two valves are joined by an elastic ligament, which pulls them together and thus causes them to gape below when the adductor muscles are relaxed. To open the shell of a living mussel the blade of a knife is passed between the valves and they are prised apart till the

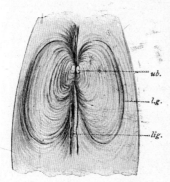

muscles can be cut close to the shell on one side. The body of the animal is then found to be soft, without a cuticle, and provided with a flap of tissue which hangs down on each side and covers the other organs. This is the *mantle*. It has a thick edge which secretes the two outer layers of the shell, while the pearly layer is laid down by the whole outer surface of the mantle and skin of the back. Pearls are formed in the same way in pockets of the mantle surface around foreign bodies which have

FIG. 277.—Part of the shell of a swan mussel, seen from above.

l.g., Lines of growth ; *lig.*, ligament ; *ub.*, umbo.

intruded between mantle and shell. The origin of the mantle from the side of the body is not straight but higher in the middle than near the two ends, though at the extreme ends it turns upwards to the hinge line. At the hind end each mantle edge is fused for some distance with its fellow ; it then separates widely from it twice, so as to form the figure of **8** already mentioned, and lies against its fellow for the rest of its length. The upper opening is known as the *dorsal siphon*, the lower as the *ventral siphon*. The lips of the latter bear a fringe of small tentacles. The space enclosed by the two *mantle lobes* is known as the *mantle cavity*.

It will have been noticed that the shell and mantle of the mussel are bilaterally symmetrical. The same symmetry is found in all the other organs of the body, both internal and external. Above the attachment of the mantle, at its lowest point near each end, may be seen on each side the cut surface of the great *adductor muscles*, anterior and posterior, which

External Features: Locomotion and Feeding.

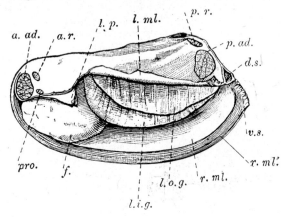

Fig. 278.—A swan mussel removed from its shell and lying on its right side with the greater part of the left lobe of the mantle cut away.

a.ad., Anterior adductor muscle; *a.r.*, anterior retractor; *d.s.*, dorsal siphon; *f.*, foot; *l.i.g.*, left inner gill; *l.ml.*, remains of left mantle lobe turned back; *l.o.g.*, left outer gill; *l.p.*, labial palps; *p.ad.*, posterior adductor muscle; *p.r.*, posterior retractor; *pro.*, protractor; *r.ml.*, right mantle lobe; *r.ml'.*, thickened edge of the same; *v.s.*, ventral siphon with papillæ.

pass through the body from side to side and draw together the valves of the shell. To the upper and inner sides of these lie the anterior and posterior *retractor muscles*, which draw the body forwards upon the foot when the latter has been thrust out. Behind the lower end of each anterior adductor is a *protractor muscle*, which draws the body backward upon the foot. On turning back the mantle the rest of the external organs are laid bare. The most conspicuous of these are the foot and two pairs

of flaps which hang down on each side of the body
One pair is large, extends from the hind end along the
greater part of the length of the animal, and consists of
the gills. The other is smaller, lies in front of the gills, and
is known as the labial palps. The foot is a wedge-like
structure with an angle directed forwards, placed under
the front half of the body. Its lower part is muscular, its

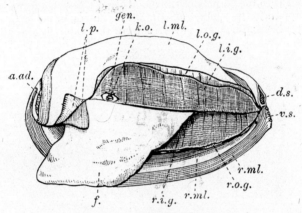

Fig. 279.—A swan mussel removed from its shell and lying on its right
side with the left mantle lobe and left gills turned back. A portion
of the inner lamella of the left inner gill has been cut away to show
the openings of the kidney and gonad.

a.ad., Anterior adductor muscle; *d.s.*, dorsal siphon; *f.*, foot; *gen.*, opening of the
duct of the gonad; *k.o.*, opening of the kidney; *l.i.g.*, left inner gill; *l.ml.*, left
mantle lobe; *l.o.g.*, left outer gill; *l.p.*, labial palps; *r.i.g.*, right inner gill;
r.ml., right mantle lobe; *r.ml.*, thickened edge of the same; *r.o.g.*, right
outer gill; *v.s.*, ventral siphon.

upper part soft, containing the genital organs and intestine.
It is thrust out between the valves by the forcing of blood
into the sinuses which it contains, and withdrawn by the
removal of the blood by the contraction of muscles. In
locomotion it is wedged into the mud or between stones,
and the body is then drawn forwards upon it by the
retractor muscles. Above the foot, between it and the
anterior adductor muscle, lies the mouth, bordered by
upper and lower lips. At the sides of the mouth these lips

are continuous with the *labial palps,* which are a pair of triangular flaps, one outside the other, on each side of the body, the outer palps being joined in front of the mouth by the upper lip and the inner behind the mouth by the lower lip. The palps are ciliated, and their surfaces which are towards one another are crossed by fine furrows, whose cilia work outwards. The groove between the palps leads to the corners of the mouth, and the whole forms an apparatus by which small organisms and other fine organic particles which are gathered from the water by the gills

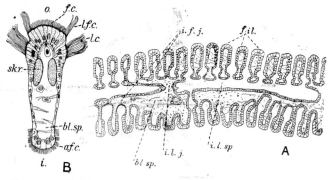

FIG. 280.—*A,* A horizontal section through a gill of the swan mussel, under low magnification ; *B,* a single filament of the same, more highly magnified.

af.c., Abfrontal cilia ; *bl.sp.,* blood spaces ; *f.c.,* frontal cilia ; *fil.,* filaments ; *i.,* side of filament towards interlamellar space ; *i.f.j.,* interfilamentar junction ; *i.l.j.,* interlamellar junction ; *i.l.sp.,* interlamellar space ; *l.c.,* lateral cilia ; *l.f.c.,* laterofrontal cilia ; *o.,* outer side of filament ; *sk.r.,* sections of the chitinous skeletal rods which support each filament.

are sorted and swallowed or rejected. Each of the *gills* consists of two *lamellæ* continuous along their ventral edges. As there are two gills on each side of the body, there are on each side four lamellæ. Each lamella is composed of very numerous vertical *filaments* which inwardly (that is, at the side towards the other lamella) are fused together at irregular intervals, so as to form a ribbed plate pierced by numerous openings between the ribs leading into the *interlamellar space* of the gill. The filaments of the two lamellæ of a gill are continuous, each

filament passing down one lamella and up the other, so
that the whole gill may be said to be composed of a
number of bent filaments fused side by side so as to form
two lamellæ. The two lamellæ of each gill are connected
at intervals by thick vertical folds parallel to the filaments
The lamellæ diverge upwards, so that in transverse section
the two gills of each side have the form of a **W**. The
space into which each interlamellar space widens at the top
is known as an *epibranchial space*. The outer lamella of the
outer gill of each side is attached along the whole length of

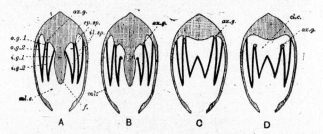

FIG. 281.—Diagrams of transverse sections through the swan mussel.

A passes through the middle of the foot and shows the inner lamella of the inner
   gill attached to the side of the foot ; *B* passes through the hinder part of the
   foot and shows the inner lamella of the inner gill free ; *C* is taken behind the
   foot and shows the inner lamellæ of the inner gills joining in the middle line ;
   D is further back and shows the axes of the gills free.

ax.g., Axes of the gills ; *cl.c.*, cloacal chamber ; *ep.sp.*, epibranchial space ; *f.*, foot ;
   *i.g.*1, inner lamella of inner gill ; *i.g.*2, outer lamella of inner gill ; *il.sp.*, interlamellar space ; *o.g.*1, inner lamellæ of outer gill ; *o.g.*2, outer lamella of outer
   gill ; *ml.*, mantle lobe ; *ml.c.*, mantle cavity.

its upper border to the inner surface of the mantle, close to
the origin of the latter from the body-wall. The inner
lamella of the outer gill is attached along the whole length
of its upper edge to the outer lamella of the inner gill.
The line of their junction is thickened and may be called
the *axis* of the gills. The axis is attached for most of
its length to the ventral side of the body, but behind
becomes free. The inner lamella of the inner gill is
attached in front to the top of the foot, its middle portion
has a free edge, and behind the foot it is attached to its
fellow of the opposite side. The result of this arrangement
of the attachments of the gills is that the epibranchial
spaces, which are separate in front, join behind to form a

cloacal space which communicates with the outside by the dorsal siphon. Into this space opens the anus, which is placed above the posterior adductor muscle. The gill filaments (Fig. 280 B) bear strong lateral cilia (*l.c.*), which set up a current of water through the perforations of the lamellæ into the interlamellar spaces and so by way of the epibranchial and cloacal spaces to the exterior at the dorsal siphon. The current is maintained by the entry of water at the ventral siphon, where it passes over the tentacles, which test its purity, causing if necessary a sudden closure of the valves which drives water out at both siphons and washes any obnoxious substance away. The incoming current has a double function. It brings oxygen to the gills and mantle, which are the respiratory organs, and also carries the food particles, which some of the gill-cilia (*l.f.c.*) retain on the outer surfaces of the gills, where others in certain definite tracts pass them on to the labial palps. Particles rejected by the labial palps (p. 374) are carried by ciliary action over the inner surface of the mantle to its edge, and there, from time to time, driven out by a sharp closing of the shell valves. The outgoing current bears away carbon dioxide, fæces from the anus, and excreta from the kidneys, which, as we shall see, open into the inner epibranchial chambers at their front ends.

The swan mussel is a cœlomate animal, intermediate between the earthworm and the crayfish in respect to its cœlom and hæmocœle. It has a perivisceral cœlom, situated in the back, enclosing the heart and rectum and communicating with the exterior by an excretory tube on each side. This space is the pericardial cavity. In the rest of the body the organs are separated by blood sinuses, the circulation being an open one. The gonads represent a part of the cœlom. Most of the viscera lie in the upper part of the body, known as the *visceral hump*, but the gonads and intestine lie in the soft region of the foot. The mouth leads into a gullet, which passes upwards into a moderate-sized stomach situated behind the anterior adductor muscle. Into the stomach opens by several ducts a large " liver " which surrounds it, whose cells absorb soluble products of digestion and in an

General Anatomy and Alimentary System.

amœboid manner take up minute particles for intracellular digestion. The hinder end of the stomach communicates on the right side with a closed groove of the intestine, the

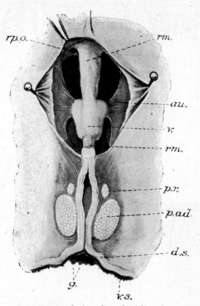

FIG. 282.—Part of the dorsal side of a swan mussel in which the pericardial cavity has been opened.

au., Auricle; *d.s.*, margin of dorsal siphon; *g.*, hinder tips of gills, fused to form floor of cloacal chamber; *p.ad.*, posterior adductor muscle; *pr.*, posterior retractor muscle; *rm.*, rectum; *rp.o.*, renopericardial opening; *v.*, ventricle; *v.s.*, margin of ventral siphon (opened out by spreading the mantle).

Note between the posterior adductor muscles the fusion of the mantle edges for a short distance, roofing in the cloacal chamber just above the dorsal siphon.

cæcum, which contains a transparent, gelatinous rod, known as the *crystalline style*. This is composed of a protein substance and projects into the stomach, where it dissolves. Its function is to digest carbohydrates by

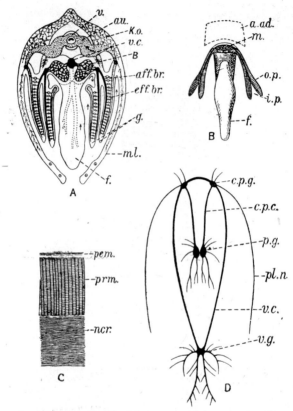

Fig. 283.—Details of the anatomy of the swan mussel.

A, Diagram of a transverse section through the foot, showing the principal
blood vessels and, by means of arrows, the course of the circulation : each
gill is cut at an interlamellar junction.—After Howes. *B*, the mouth and
neighbouring structures from in front ; *C*, a portion of the shell, in section ;
D, a plan of the nervous system from above, with the visceral commissures more
widely parted than they are in the animal.

a a.d., Position of anterior adductor ; *aff.br.*, afferent branchial vessel ; *au.*, auricle ;
B, glandular part of kidney ; *c.p.c.*, cerebropedal commissure ; *c.p.g.*, cerebral
(cerebropleural) ganglion ; *eff.br.*, efferent branchial vessels ; *f.*, foot ; *g.*, gills ;
i.p., inner labial palp ; *K.o.*, Keber's organ ; *m.*, mouth ; *ml.*, mantle ; *ncr.*,
nacreous layer ; *o.p.*, outer labial palp ; *p.g.*, pedal ganglion ; *pem.*, periostracum ; *pl.n*, pallial nerve ; *prm.*, prismatic layer ; *v.*, ventricle ; *v.c.*, vena
cava ; *v.cm.*, visceral commissure ; *v.g.*, visceral (parietosplanchnic) ganglion.

setting free a ferment which it contains. The intestine starts from the lower side of the stomach, takes several coils in the soft upper part of the foot, turns upwards, and runs straight backwards in the middle line of the upper part of the body to the anus. The straight part of the intestine is known as the rectum. It lies in the

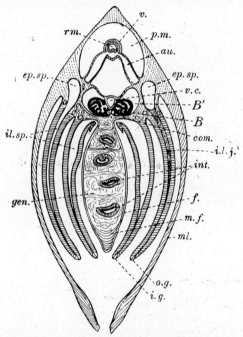

FIG. 284.—A semi-diagrammatic drawing of a transverse section of the swan mussel in the region of the hinder part of the foot.

au., Auricle ; *B*, glandular limb of kidney ; *B′*, non-glandular limb of the same ; *com.*, commissures between cerebral and parietosplanchnic ganglia ; *ep.sp.*, epibranchial spaces ; *f.*, foot ; *gen.*, gonad ; *i.g.*, inner gill ; *i.l.j.*, interlamellar junction ; *il.sp.*, interlamellar spaces ; *int.*, intestine ; *m.f.*, muscular part of the foot ; *ml.*, mantle lobe ; *o.g.*, outer gill ; *pm.*, pericardial cavity ; *rm.*, rectum ; *v.*, ventricle *v.c.*, vena cava.

pericardial cavity surrounded by the ventricle of the heart.
The ventral wall of the rectum is folded to form a longitudinal ridge or typhlosole. Digestion in the intestine is intracellular, in the cells of the epithelium and in white corpuscles which pass through the epithelium to take up food particles.

The kidneys or *organs of Bojanus* are two in number

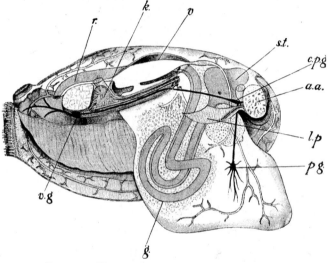

Fig. 285.—The structure of *Anodonta*.—After Rankin.

a.a., Anterior adductor ; *c.p.g.*, cerebral or cerebropleural ganglia ; *st.*, stomach ; *v.*, ventricle, with an auricle opening into it ; *k.*, kidney, above which is the posterior retractor of the foot ; *r.*, rectum ending above posterior adductor ; *v.g.*, visceral ganglia with connectives (in black) from cerebropleurals ; *g.*, gut coiling in foot ; *p.g.*, pedal ganglia in foot, where also are seen branches of the anterior aorta and the reproductive organs ; *l.p.*, labial palps behind mouth. At the posterior end the exhalant (upper) and inhalant (lower) siphons are seen.

and lie side by side below the pericardium. Each is a
wide tube, doubled on itself, with one limb
above the other, and the two ends together
in front. The lower limb has spongy walls
lined with a dark, glandular epithelium. It
opens into the front end of the pericardial cavity by a

**Excretory
Organs and
Gonads**

crescentic *renopericardial opening* in the floor. The upper
limb has thin walls. It opens on the side of the body
into the adjoining inner epibranchial chamber, shortly
before the point at which the inner lamella of the inner gill
becomes free. Thus the two ends of the kidney tube cross,
the lower opening upwards and the upper downwards.
The organ is a cœlomoduct. A pair of glandular bodies
known as *Keber's organs* which lie on each side in front of
the pericardium store excreta in their cells. They are
derived from the cœlomic wall and, like the yellow cells
of the earthworm, represent a portion of its epithelium

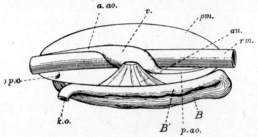

FIG. 286.—A diagram of the pericardium and kidney of the swan
mussel, from the left side.

a.ao., Anterior aorta ; *au.*, auricle ; *B*, glandular limb of kidney ; *B'*, non-glandular
limb of the same ; *k.o.*, opening of the same ; *p.ao.*, posterior aorta ; *pm.*,
pericardial cavity ; *rp.o.*, renopericardial opening ; *rm.*, rectum ; *v.*, ventricle.

specialised for excretion. Cœlomic fluid is drawn by
ciliary action through the renopericardial opening into the
kidney and is discharged as urine by contractions of the
organ. The urine is of lower concentration than the
cœlomic fluid or the blood so that solids must be reabsorbed in the kidney, and the mussel, like other freshwater animals, keeps down its water content by excretion.
The principal nitrogenous excreta discharged through the
kidney are ammonia and amino compounds. The opening
of the kidney has thick, yellowish lips. Immediately below
it is a somewhat larger opening with thin lips. This
belongs to the gonad, which is a branched structure lying
in the upper part of the foot and alike in its general
structure in both sexes.

The blood is colourless and contains white corpuscles.

Vascular System. The heart (Fig. 282) consists of a ventricle, which forms a jacket around the rectum,[1] and two auricles, which are triangular, thin-walled structures, one on each side of the ventricle. From the front end of the ventricle an *anterior aorta* passes forwards above the rectum, and from the hind end a *posterior aorta*

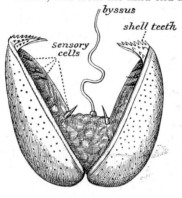

Fig. 287.—A glochidium larva, as cast out from the parent, viewed from behind.—From Latter.

passes backward below it. From branches of these the blood passes into spaces between the organs. From the foot and viscera it is gathered into a *vena cava* which lies below the pericardium between the kidneys. Thence it

[1] The ventricle of the heart of the swan mussel is really a wide, contractile part of a dorsal blood vessel, which is continued forwards as the anterior aorta. In various animals related to the mussel it lies altogether above the gut, but here it extends downwards at the sides and encloses it. A similar vessel is found above the gut in Annelida (*e.g.* the earthworm) and in Arthropoda (*e.g.* the crayfish and cockroach). See p. 305.

passes outwards through the kidneys to the gills, where it circulates in irregular spaces in the inner parts of the filaments. From these it is returned to the auricles. The blood from the mantle returns direct to the auricles.

The nervous system comprises three pairs of ganglia with commissures uniting them. The *cerebral ganglia* are two small, orange-coloured bodies, placed one on each side behind the mouth, above which they are connected by a *cerebral commissure.* They are sometimes known by the name " cerebro-pleural,"

Nervous System.

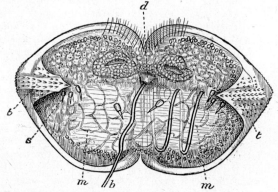

FIG. 288.—A glochidium larva in ventral view.—From Latter.

b., Byssus (cut short); *d.,* future mouth ; *m.,* adductor muscle ; *s.,* sensory cells; *t.,* main teeth and denticles on ventral edge of each valve.

because each contains the elements of two ganglia, the cerebral proper and the *pleural*, which are distinct in certain other bivalves and in whelks. The cerebral ganglia supply the fore-part of the body, and each gives off a *cerebropedal commissure* to one of the two *pedal ganglia* which lie side by side in the foot, just above the muscular region, about one-third of the length of the organ from its front end. The pedal ganglia bear the same relation to the cerebral that the subpharyngeal do to the suprapharyngeal in the earthworm. The pedal ganglia give off several nerves to the foot, and each sends a nerve to a *statocyst* which lies shortly behind it. Each cerebral ganglion also gives off a *visceral commissure*, which runs backwards between the kidneys to join one of the *visceral or parietosplanchnic ganglia* which lie as a fused pair on the under side of the posterior adductor muscle, immediately within the skin. The sense organs are inconspicuous. They include the statocysts, the tentacles of the ventral siphon, a sensory epithelium, believed to be olfactory, which covers the visceral ganglion and is known as the *osphradium*, and tactile nerve endings in various parts of the skin. There are no eyes.

The sexes of the swan mussel are separate. Sperm is passed out through the dorsal siphon and **Life-History.** spermatozoa are drawn into the females with the inward stream. The eggs are fertilised in the cloacal chamber and then passed into the space between the lamellæ of the outer gill, where they develop. This takes place in the summer. In the following spring the young are set free. They are larvæ, very unlike the parent, and are known as *glochidia* (Figs. 287, 288). Each has a shell composed of two triangular valves, hinged along the base and with the apex drawn out into a strong hook. There is no posterior adductor muscle, anus, or foot, but in the place of the latter is a gland which secretes a long sticky thread known as the *byssus*, comparable with the threads by which the adult sea mussel anchors itself. When some small fish, such as a stickleback, passes over the glochidium, the latter flaps its valves so as to drive out the byssus, which if it touches the fish sticks to it. The movements of the fish now bring the glochidium against its body, whereupon the hooks are used to hold on to its skin. The tissues of the fish become inflamed and swell up, enclosing the little parasite, which lives for some months by absorbing the juices of its host, during which time it undergoes a change into the adult form. Eventually the skin enclosing the young mussel withers and it drops off to lead an independent life. By means of this larva, the slow-moving mussel is dispersed into fresh feeding grounds by the fish, without the risk, which would be considerable if so small a larva were free-swimming, of being carried downstream to the sea. We have seen that the young of the crayfish escape the same danger by holding on to the body of their mother. It

is interesting to note that marine relations of both these
animals have free-swimming larvæ, and to recall that
Hydra lacks the free larva of the sea-dwelling *Obelia*.

Mollusca. Soft-bodied, shelled, unsegmented, cœlomate animals
with a mantle, foot, and nervous system like
those of the swan mussel are known as
Mollusca or *true Shellfish*. Snails and whelks (*Gastro-poda*), and cuttlefish (*Cephalopoda*) belong to this group.
These animals have heads, with eyes and a rough tongue
or *radula*, which are wanting in mussels, and their shell
is in one piece (or occasionally is lacking). The body of
a snail or whelk is flattened, not from side to side as in

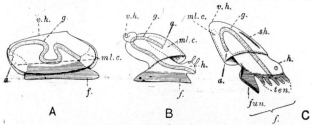

A   B   C

FIG. 289.—Diagrams of a mussel (A), a whelk (B), and a cuttle-fish (C).—Partly after Lankester.

a , Anus ; *f.*, foot ; *fun.*, funnel through which water is squirted by the cuttle-fish in
swimming ; *g.*, gut ; *h.*, head ; *ml.c.*, mantle cavity ; *sh.*, internal shell found
in some cuttlefish (the "cuttle bone") ; *ten.*, tentacles of the cuttlefish ; *v.h.*,
apex of visceral hump.

a mussel, but from above downwards. Its foot has a flat
sole, and the visceral hump, with the shell, is twisted.
The hollow axis of the spiral shell is known as the *columella*
and the animal is attached to it by a *columellar muscle*.
There is only one kidney and one auricle, which correspond
to those of the right side of the mussels. The pericardium
is small and encloses only the heart, and not the rectum.
The mantle cavity is represented by a deep sack, which lies,
not behind, where the main part of the mantle cavity is in a
mussel, but over the back, opening forward (Fig. 289, B).
In rotating to this position it has brought forward the
anus with it. In the snail, but not in the related whelks,
this sack is converted into a lung, with a narrowed opening
and a vascular roof, and the gills are lost. Snails also

25

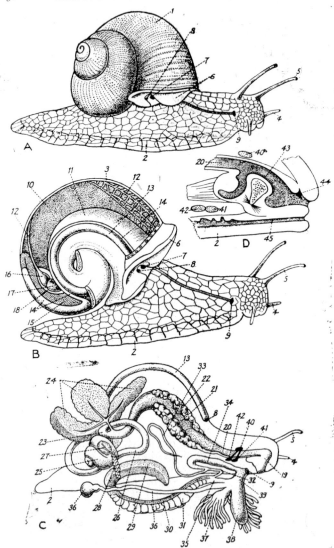

differ from mussels in having the ganglia concentrated into a clump around the gullet (the cerebral above, pedal, pleural, and visceral below), and a complicated, hermaphrodite reproductive system, which opens far forwards on the right. The snail has one gonad, which produces, in the same follicles, sperm during most of the year, but ova for a short period in the summer. The "hermaphrodite duct" which leaves the gonad presently reaches a gland by which a coat of albumen is provided for the ova ; after this the common duct has two channels one for the ova, the other for the sperm. These channels eventually separate, but meet again at the genital opening. There is a penis, with a "flagellum" in which is formed a slender spermatophore or sperm packet ; for the reception of the spermatophore of the partner a long spermatheca is provided. Impregnation is reciprocal (Fig. 458), and just before it each partner drives into the other a sharp calcareous "love dart," which is supposed to impart a sexual stimulus. The eggs, which are laid in the earth, have albumen and chalky shells. The young, at birth, resemble the adult. The snail is a vegetable feeder, rasping off portions of the tissues of plants between a horny upper jaw and the rows of horny teeth which roughen its tongue. The alimentary canal begins as a "buccal mass," which

Fig. 290.—Anatomy of the edible snail, *Helix pomatia.*

A, View from the right side ; *B,* the same after removal of the shell, part of the mantle, and the upper part of the spiral visceral hump ; *C,* dissection ; *D,* section through buccal mass, enlarged.

1, Shell (note lines of growth) ; 2, foot ; 3, mantle ; 4, anterior tentacle ; 5, posterior tentacle, at the end of which lies a retractile eye ; 6, edge of mantle ("collar") ; 7, opening of lung ; 8, anus ; 9, common genital opening ; 10, mantle cavity or lung ; 11, dorsal wall of body (floor of lung) ; 12, pulmonary vein ; 12', plexus of pulmonary vessels from which pulmonary vein collects; 13, rectum ; 14 ureter ; 15, kidney ; 16, auricle ; 17, ventricle ; 18, pericardium; the renopericardial opening (not shown) is near the end of this index-line ; kidney, pericardium, and heart lie in the hinder part of the roof of the mantle cavity ; ureter and rectum run along its right side ; 19, buccal mass, which contains radula ; 20, œsophagus ; 21, crop ; 22, left salivary gland ; 23, stomach ; 24, right liver ; 25, left liver ; 26, intestine ; 27, ovotestis ; 28, hermaphrodite duct ; 29, albumen gland ; 30, male part of compound genital duct ; 31, female part ; 32, vas deferens ; 33, "flagellum" of penis ; 34, penis (protrusible) ; 35, oviduct ; 36, spermatheca ; 37, "mucous" glands of uncertain function ; 38, sac of "love dart" ; 39, vagina ; 40, cerebral ganglia ; 41, pedal ganglia ; 42, viscero-pleural ganglia ; 43, radula (note, behind it, the sac in which it grows, and is pushed forward as it wears away in front) ; 44, jaw ; 45, pedal gland, which secretes the slime of the snail's track.

contains the buccal cavity and the radula with its muscles, and continues as œsophagus, crop, stomach, intestine, and rectum ; digestion of carbohydrates takes place in its cavity by means of fluids secreted by a pair of salivary glands and by the paired liver. The latter, like the liver of the swan mussel, is also the seat of absorption and of the digestion of proteins, which is intracellular. The excreta comprise uric acid as well as urea and ammonia. The blood contains hæmocyanin (see p. 306). In the winter the animal retires to some sheltered spot and closes the mouth of its shell by a disc, the *epiphragm*, which it secretes from the edge of the mantle. The anatomy of the snail is displayed in Fig. 290, and further details concerning it are stated in the explanation of the figure.

In a cuttlefish the body is flattened from before backwards, and the foot forms a funnel, the squirting of water through which from the mantle cavity causes the animal to move in the opposite direction. The sucker-bearing tentacles which surround the mouth are said also to represent part of the foot. There are two feather-like gills; and an ink-gland, which opens with the rectum into the mantle cavity, enables the animal to cloud the water behind it in escaping from its foes. In some cuttlefishes, as in the Squid (*Sepia*), the shell is present as an internal vestige, the " cuttle bone " ; others, as the Octopus, lack it altogether. Only in the Nautilus is it well-developed and external.

CHAPTER XIX

THE STARFISH. ECHINODERMS

ONE of the most familiar animals of the seashore is the
Common Starfish, *Asterias rubens*. It may
often be found dead or dying upon the beach
where it has been thrown up, or living in pools,
but its principal haunts are in somewhat deeper water.
For all its seeming helplessness, it is an exceedingly
voracious animal, and is particularly destructive to shell-
fish, so that it is a pest in oyster beds. Its body, of a
colour varying from orange to purplish and darker above
than below, has the shape of a star, with five tapering
rays, or *arms*, meeting in a central region known as the
disc. The upper side is called *aboral*, the lower *oral*,
because on it, in the middle of the disc, lies the *mouth*.
The direction of each arm is known as a *radius*. The
region between two arms is an *interradius*. Along each
arm runs on the oral side a deep *ambulacral groove*, and
the grooves meet around the mouth, which has a membranous lip or *peristome*. The surface of the body is
soft and ciliated, but below it is a tough body-wall,
strengthened by a meshwork of rod-shaped, calcareous
ossicles, which can be felt and seen through it. Over the
interspaces between the ossicles the skin is raised into
delicate, hollow outgrowths, the *dermal gills*, into which
the body cavity is prolonged. From the junctions of the
ossicles arise blunt *spines*, each of which is surrounded by
a cushion of skin. Crowded upon these cushions, and
scattered between them, are remarkable little organs known
as *pedicellariæ*, each of which is a minute pair of pincers,
supported by little ossicles, one at its base and one in each
jaw. The pedicellariæ are defensive organs. They are

of two kinds, a smaller kind, found upon the cushions of the spines of the back, in which the supporting ossicles cross at the base like the blades of a pair of scissors, and a larger kind, scattered between the spines, whose ossicles do not cross. In an interradius, on the aboral surface,

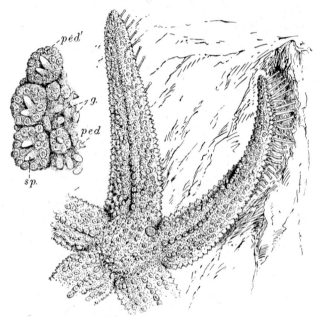

FIG. 291.—Part of an aboral view of a starfish (*Asterias rubens*).

FIG. 291A.—An enlargement of a small part of the surface of the same.

g., Gills ; *ped.*, large pedicellaria ; *ped'.*, small pedicellaria ; *sp.*, spine.

is a conspicuous button-like ossicle, covered with fine grooves, and known, from its coral-like appearance, as the *madreporite*. Its grooves are pierced with fine pores through which, by the action of cilia, water is drawn in. The *anus* is a small opening, almost in the middle of the aboral surface, but slightly displaced towards the inter-

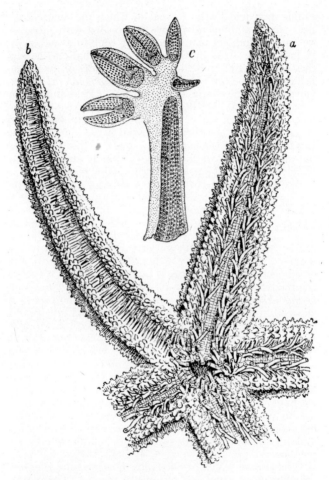

FIG. 292.—Parts of an oral view of a starfish (*Asterias rubens*).

a, An arm with tne ambulacral groove widely open ; *b*, an arm with the ambulacral groove closed by the contraction of its sides and the bending over of the adam-bulacral spines ; *c*, an ambulacral spine, with its tuft of large pedicellariæ, enlarged.

radius next (clockwise) to that in which the madreporite
lies. Each ambulacral groove is crowded with *tube-feet*,
delicate, cylindrical tentacles, ending each in a sucker, set
in four rows. It is by these that the animal crawls, and
they are also used to hold prey. At the sides of the ambulacral grooves stand a number of *adambulacral spines*,
which bear pedicellariæ of the uncrossed kind and can be
brought together over the groove so as to protect the tube-
feet. At the bottom of the groove a longitudinal *nerve
ridge* marks the position of a radial nerve cord. At the
end of the groove is a single *sense-tentacle*, like a tube-foot
but smaller and without sucker, which subserves the
olfactory sense and has at its base a red eye-spot.

    The body-wall is covered by a ciliated, columnar epi-
thelium, which contains gland cells and sense
cells. Among the bases of the cells lies a
dense tangle of fine nerve fibrils, some of
which start as processes of the bases of sense
cells, while others belong to nerve cells imbedded in the
tangle. Above the nerve ridge around the mouth and
down each arm, this plexus is thickened to form a special
conductive system in the form of an *oral nerve ring* with
radial nerve cords, which send branches to the tube feet
and end in the sense tentacles. Many of the fibrils in this
system are arranged to run in the directions of its strands.
Under the peritoneal epithelium is a similar but slighter
system which communicates with the ectodermal system
and consists of motor fibres for the muscles of the large
ossicles and body-wall. Thus the nervous system is in a
more primitive condition than that of any other animal
we have studied, except *Hydra*. Below the epithelium,
the body-wall is composed of connective tissue, in which
the ossicles are imbedded. The deeper part contains some
muscular fibres running in various directions. On opening
the body, there is revealed a spacious cavity, the perivisceral *cœlom*, which extends into the arms, and contains
the alimentary canal and generative organs. The cœlom
is lined by a ciliated peritoneal epithelium, and along the
oral side of each arm, where the body-wall roofs the
ambulacral groove, runs a ridge, the *ambulacral ridge*,
caused by the projection of a double row of large, trans-

**Body-wall,
Nervous
System,
and Cœlom.**

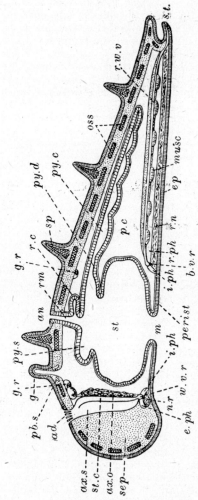

FIG. 293.—Diagram of a section of a starfish passing through the madreporic interradius and along the opposite arm, a little to one side of the septum of the radial perihaemal vessel.

n., Anus; *ax.o.*, axial organ; *ax.s.*, axial sinus; *b.v.r.*, so-called blood vascular ring; *ep.*, epidermis ; *g.*, gill; *g.r.*, genital rachis, in an aboral cœlomic ring sinus ; *i.ph.*, inner perihaemal ring; *m.*, mouth; *mad.*, madreporite; *musc.*, one of the muscles that narrow the ambulacral groove; *n.r.*, nerve ring ; *o.ph.*, outer perihaemal ring; *oss.*, ossicles ; *p.c.*, perivisceral cavity; *pb.s.*, peribranchial sinus ; *perist.*, peristome ; *py.c.*, pyloric cæcum ; *py.d.*, pyloric duct; *py.s.*, pyloric sac ; *r.n.*, radial nerve ; *r.ph.*, radial perihaemal vessel; *r.w.v.*, radial water vessel; *rm.*, rectum ; *sep.*, septum ; *sp.*, spine ; *st.*, stomach; *st.c.*, stone canal; *w.v.r.*, water vascular ring.

versely placed *ambulacral ossicles.* At the outer ends of these, alternating with them, lie smaller *adambulacral ossicles,* and upon the adambulacral ossicles stand the adambulacral spines. In each interradius a stiff *interradial septum* projects into the cœlom between the arms. To the septum which is situated in the interradius of the madreporite there is attached a sack, the *axial sinus,* also a part of the cœlom, and in this are lodged the *stone canal,* which, as will presently be stated, runs downwards from the madreporite, and a spongy, brown organ, the *axial organ,* to which also we shall return.

The mouth opens through a short œsophagus into a great sack, the *stomach,* which has in each interradius a wide pouch, attached to the ambulacral ridge by two *retractor muscles.*

Alimentary Canal, Feeding, and Excretion.

Above, the stomach communicates by a wide opening with a five-sided *pyloric sac,* each angle of which is prolonged into a tube or *pyloric duct,* that runs into an arm, and there forks into two branches, the *pyloric cæca,* each beset with numerous little pouches and slung from the aboral wall of the arm. From the pyloric sac a short, conical rectum leads to the anus. It bears interradially two small brown branches, the *rectal cæca.* The star-fish will eat any animal that it can master. Small prey may be taken into the mouth, but usually digestion is performed in a remarkable manner outside the body, the arms bending round the prey and holding it with their tube feet, while the stomach is forced out, by contraction of the body-wall compressing the cœlomic fluid, enwraps and digests the prey, and is afterwards withdrawn by the retractor muscles. Bivalves, which are a great part of the food, are opened by arching the body over them and parting their valves by the pull of the tube feet, and the stomach is then inserted into the shell. The digestive juice is secreted by the cells which line the pyloric cæca. Shells are left behind by the stomach, or rejected through the mouth, very little matter being cast out through the anus. Excreta, which contain ammonia and amino compounds and some urea, are got rid of through the walls of the gills, partly in solution, partly as granules carried by amœboid cells which pass through to the exterior. The

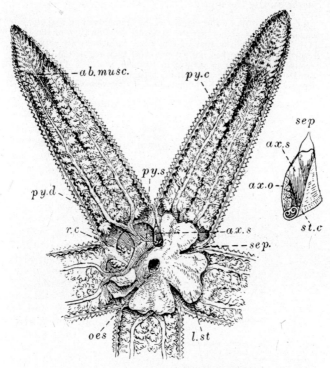

FIG. 294.—Parts of the aboral half of a starfish (*Asterias rubens*), removed, with the alimentary canal, from the rest of the body, and viewed from within. One lobe of the stomach has been cut away, and another partly turned back. The detached figure represents an enlarged view of the axial sinus and adjoining structures.

ab.musc., Aboral muscle; *ax.o.*, axial organ; *ax.s.*, axial sinus; *l.st.*, one of the lobes of the stomach; *py.c.*, pyloric cæcum; *py.d.*, pyloric duct; *py.s.*, pyloric sac; *r.c.*, rectal cæcum; *sep.*, septum; *st.c.*, stone canal.

rectal cæca appear also to excrete waste matter, which passes out by the anus.

Regulation of the water content of the animal is in normal circumstances unnecessary because the optimum concentration of the body fluids is the same as that of sea water, which varies very little. Accordingly the starfish has no power of such regulation. On this account it is unable to survive in fresh or brackish water. Such animals are said to be *stenohaline*. Animals that can endure great changes in salinity, as the salmon does, are *euryhaline*.

The working of the tube feet is brought about by a peculiar system of tubes, derived during development from the cœlom, known as the *water vascular system*. This starts at the madreporite as the *stone canal*, so called because it is strengthened by calcareous matter. The wall of this canal makes a curious projection into it, Y-shaped in section, with the arms of the Y rolled, so that the surface is greatly increased, and it is ciliated. The lower end of the stone canal joins a *ring canal* around the mouth, above the peristome, and from this a *radial canal* runs down each arm, below

Water Vascular Systems.

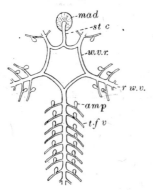

FIG. 295.—A diagram of the water vascular system of a starfish.

amp., Ampulla; *mad.*, madreporite; *r.w.v.*, radial water vessel; *st.c.*, stone canal; *t.f.v*, vessel of tube foot; *w.v.r.*, water vascular ring.

the ambulacral ossicles. From the radial canals small transverse canals run, one to each tube foot. The hollow of the tube foot is prolonged inwards into a bulb called the *ampulla*, which projects into the cœlom of the arm. The transverse canal joins it just below the ampulla, by a valved opening which prevents fluid from flowing into the radial canal, so that, when (by a circular muscle layer) the ampulla contracts, the fluid in it stretches out the tube foot. Divers muscles in the foot direct it against the ground, by cupping the sucker cause it to adhere, and then shorten the foot, so that it tends to draw the body forward. Owing to the shortening of the foot the fluid passes back into the ampulla. The pressure of the fluid in the water vascular system is regulated by gain, and perhaps also by loss, of water through the madreporite.

Like most animals, from the *Amœba* to man, the starfish moves towards the side from which it has received a slight stimulus but away from one strong enough to be caused by some event with which the creature might find it difficult to cope. In crawling one (or sometimes two) of the arms is directed forwards. On this leading arm each tube foot—not moving in step with any other but quite independently—is extended in the direction of the arm, takes hold with its sucker, shortens so as to take part in pulling the arm forwards, swings back, lets go with a slight kick so as to push it on, and then swings forwards to take another such step. On the other arms the tube feet behave in the same manner but swing to and fro in the direction in which the animal is crawling—that is, more or less transversely to their arms. A starfish which falls on its back can right itself. In this process also one or two arms take the lead, turning over so as to touch the ground and holding on with their tube feet, while the other arms, probably stimulated by the first movers, arch over by muscular action till the creature topples over on to its oral side. The arms which take the lead are those which had previously led in crawling. Pedicellariæ bend towards the site of a gentle stimulus on the skin, opening their blades and closing them upon any object that comes against their inner sides. The larger kind are set in motion by a weaker stimulus than is needed to move the smaller ones ; these are brought into position for action by the rising of the cushions upon which they stand. If the ambulacral groove be touched the adambulacral spines come together over it. We have already seen how the animal feeds.

The nature of the nervous processes by which these activities are brought about will appear if we examine the course of events in locomotion. A stimulus which is not too strong affecting an arm sets up an impulse which, spreading through the nerve net and reaching to a distance by means of the radial " nerve," causes the tube feet of the arm to extend towards its tip. Thus they make contact with the ground in front of them, and this sets up in them a reflex which makes them step in the way we have described. The arm being thus pulled forwards drags the rest of the body after it, so that the tube feet on the other arms make contact with the ground on the side towards which the leading arm is moving and thus they step in the same direction. A strong stimulus affecting an arm contracts the tube feet instead of extending them, and reaching the other arms along the nerve ring and radial nerve, has there the same effect. But, as we saw in *Hydra*, excitation through a nerve net weakens as it travels, so that the arms on the opposite side are the least stimulated and are the first to recover. On doing so their tube feet extend and so make contact with the ground and start stepping

Behaviour.

away from the stimulus. All muscular activity in the starfish is
brought about essentially in the same manner as its locomotion.
Tube feet are extended, spines moved, pedicellariæ opened, or large
muscles contracted by impulses reaching them through the nerve
nets. "Nerves" enable these impulses to come from a distant point
which has become dominant by being stimulated. Stepping of the
feet or closing of the pedicellariæ or protrusion of the stomach when

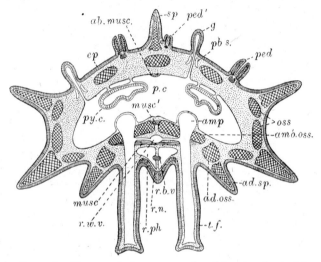

FIG. 296.—Diagram of a transverse section of the arm of a starfish.

ab.musc., Muscle which straightens the arm; *ad oss.*, adambulacral ossicle;
ad.sp., adambulacral spine; *amb.oss.*, ambulacral ossicle; *amp.*, ampulla
of tube foot; *musc'.*, muscle which opens the ambulacral groove; *ped.*,
pedicellaria; *r.b.v.*, radial "blood vessel"; *t.f.*, tube foot. Other lettering
as in Fig. 254.

food stimulates the mouth are reflexes performed by means of stimuli
received in the organ themselves. The whole procedure is much like
that in the nerve net of *Hydra*; only in the starfish the transmission
of impulses from the temporarily dominant region to distant parts is
improved by the system of "nerves," and there are definite and
complicated local nervous mechanisms. Although these features
enable the animal to react as a whole more promptly and completely
to a stimulus there is no permanent dominance of one part organised
for that purpose. The starfish shows what can be achieved by the
nerve net; it also shows the slowness and vagueness of action which

is inevitable in the absence of a brain. Its lack of that organ is due to its radial symmetry, which provides no suitable site for one.

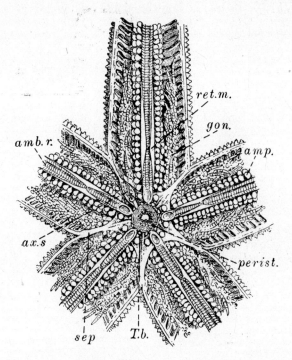

FIG. 297.—Part of a view from above of the oral half of a starfish (*Asterias rubens*), after removal of the alimentary canal.

amb.r., Ambulacral ridge; *amp.*, ampullæ of tube feet; *a.x.s.*, axial sinus, with stone canal and axial organ; *gon.*, generative organ; *perist.*, peristome; *ret.m.*, retractor muscle of the stomach; *sep.*, septum; *T.b.*, Tiedemann's body.

The radial water vessel in each arm lies close under the ambulacral ossicles; below it there is a cœlomic space, roughly diamond-shaped in transverse section, which is known as the *radial perihæmal cavity*. Below the

Perihæmal and Pseudo-hæmal Systems. perihæmal cavity the epidermis is thickened by an increase in the nerve plexus, and folded so as to project into the ambulacral groove as the nerve ridge. Round the mouth, the radial perihæmal vessels are joined by an *oral perihæmal ring*.[1]

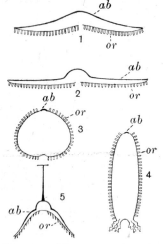

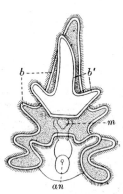

FIG. 298.—The *Bipinnaria* larva of a starfish, in ventral view.

an., Anus; *b.*, postoral ciliated band; *b'.*, preoral band; *m.* mouth.

The depressed region between the ciliated bands is shaded.

FIG. 299.—Diagrams to show the relative extent of the oral and aboral surfaces, and to compare the form of body, in the several classes of Echinodermata. The diagrams are in the same morphological position.

1, Asteroidea; 2, Ophiuroidea; 3, Echinoidea; 4, Holothuroidea; 5, Crinoidea.

ab., aboral surface; *or.*, oral surface.

Each such radial vessel is divided longitudinally by a vertical septum, and in this septum lies a strand of a peculiar tissue which in the starfish takes the place of the blood vessels. This is a part of the connective tissue in

---

[1] Adjoining this is another cœlomic tube, the so-called "inner perihæmal ring," which is connected not with the perihæmal vessels but with the axial sinus.

which the fibres are more sparse and the ground substance more fluid than elsewhere, and it is believed that along the strands which are formed of it substances diffuse, and amoeboid cells wander, more readily than elsewhere. Around the mouth a ring strand joins the radial strands, with this is connected the tissue of the axial organ, and with the aboral end of the axial organ is again connected an aboral ring, from which strands extend to the generative organs.

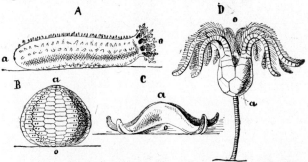

FIG. 300.—Semidiagrammatic views of a starfish (*C*), a sea urchin (*B*), a holothurian (*A*), and a crinoid (*D*), in the natural position.— From Lang.

a. Aboral side; *o*, oral side.

The axial organ, however, is primarily of importance, not as a part of this "pseudohæmal system," but as the original seat of the genital cells, for which reason it is often known as the "genital stolon," while the aboral ring is the "genital rachis." Along the latter the genital cells wander from the stolon to the actual gonads. These are ten in number, shaped like bunches of grapes, and varying in size with the season of the year. They are attached to the body-wall by their ducts, which open one on each side of the base of each arm, towards the oral aspect. The sexes are separate, but do not differ externally. Eggs and sperm are shed into the water, where fertilisation takes place. The cleavage of the ovum is complete ("holoblastic," p. 637) and practically equal. It leads to the formation of a remarkable, bilaterally sym-

Reproduction.

26

metrical larva (the *Bipinnaria*, Fig. 298), which swims by
two bands of cilia. This, after passing through a *fixed stage*
(Fig. 301), gives rise to the radially symmetrical adult,

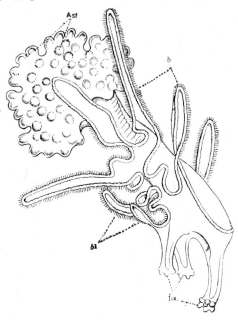

FIG. 301.—The larva of a starfish at the fixation stage, viewed
   from the right-hand side.—From MacBride, after Johannes
   Müller.

The *Bipinnaria* larva has passed into a stage known as the *Brachiolaria*, by the
   development of three fixing processes at the anterior end. *A st.*, rudiment of the
   future body of the starfish ; *b.*, postoral ciliated band ; *b′*, preoral band ;
   fix., fixation processes at the anterior end of the larva.
The larva is seen from the right-hand side, and its position is inverted from that
   of Fig. 298

through a peculiar metamorphosis, in which its left and
right sides become the oral and aboral surfaces.

It is evident that the Starfish is a peculiar animal, which
differs greatly from any of those that we have studied
hitherto.   It is tripoblastic and cœlomate, but with-

out blood vessels. It has an exceedingly complex system
of cœlomic spaces, part of which subserves the
working of the altogether peculiar tube feet.

Echinoder-mata.

It forms in its mesoderm calcareous ossicles, but
these are quite unlike bone in fine structure. Its nervous
system is of a grade not much above that of the Cœlenterata.
It is radially symmetrical, but starts life as a bilaterally
symmetrical larva. Animals which share with it these
peculiarities are known as *Echinodermata* (Figs. 299, 300).
To them belong: the Starfishes (*Asteroidea*); the
Brittle Stars (*Ophiuroidea*), whose arms are slender,
mobile, and muscular, arise abruptly from the disc, and
contain no pyloric cæca, whose madreporite is on the
oral side, and whose nerve cords are covered over; the
Sea Urchins (*Echinoidea*), whose ossicles form a plate-
armour in the wall of the body, which latter is swollen
and without arms, so that the rows of tube feet (*ambulacra*)
run meridionally over the surface, where the nerve cords
are enclosed as in the Brittle Stars; the Sea Cucumbers
(*Holothuroidea*), which are soft-walled sea-urchins, drawn
out, from mouth to anus, into a sausage-shaped body;
and the Sea Lilies (*Crinoidea*), which are starfishes with
branched arms and with suckerless " tube feet," fastened
either temporarily, in a post-larval stage, or permanently,
by a stalk upon the aboral surface, while the anus lies
upon the oral side.

The fixation of the Sea Lilies, and the fact that starfishes are fixed when the bilateral symmetry
of the larva changes to the radial symmetry of
the adult, are interesting facts in view of the fixation
which is general in the other great group of radially
symmetrical animals, the Cœlenterata. Radial symmetry
is essentially the symmetry of a sessile animal, which is
in the same relation with its surroundings on all sides,
whereas bilateral symmetry is that of a travelling animal,
which needs differentiation of the upper side from that
which faces the ground, as well as of the fore from the
hind end. It is likely that at one time all echinoderms
were fixed, and that those which are now free retain the
radial symmetry of their sessile ancestors.

Symmetries.

CHAPTER XX

THE LANCELET. CHORDATA

THE Common Lancelet, *Amphioxus lanceolatus*, is a little,
fish-like creature found on most European
Habits and coasts, including those of Britain, living in shal-
External low water on a sandy bottom. It passes most
Features. of its time buried in the sand, with its length
upright and the fore end projecting, gathering small
organisms for food by a ciliated apparatus around the
mouth. From time to time, usually at night, it leaves the
sand, and then shows that it can swim swiftly by movements
of its muscular body. It is about an inch and a half long,
lustrous but translucent, slender, pointed at each end, and
flattened from side to side. The head is in no way marked
off from the rest of the body, and there are no ears, nostrils,
or limbs. A low *dorsal fin* runs along the middle of the
back from end to end, becoming deeper at the hinder end
as the upper lobe of a *caudal fin*, which passes round the
end of the tail. The under lobe of this is continuous with
a low, median *ventral fin* which extends along the hinder
third of the body. In front of the ventral fin the belly is
flattened and bears at each side a continuous *lateral fin* or
metapleural fold. At the narrow front end (*rostrum*) the
dorsal fin passes round the tip of the body and runs back
below to become continuous with the right side of the oral
hood (see below). The sides of the body are marked by a
series of about sixty v-shaped lines, with their apices
forwards, due to septa of connective tissue known as
myocommata, which divide the muscles of the body-wall
into segments called *myomeres*. Certain of the internal
organs are repeated in correspondence with these, so that
the body is segmented, though not so completely as that of
the earthworm. The segmentation is peculiar in that the

myomeres of opposite sides alternate. About seven
myomeres lie in front of the mouth. The anus lies against
the left side of the ventral fin where that fin passes into the

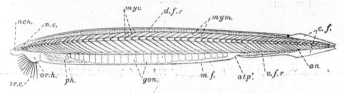

FIG. 302.—*Amphioxus*, from the left side, with the atrial floor
contracted.

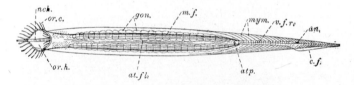

FIG. 303.—The same, from the ventral side.

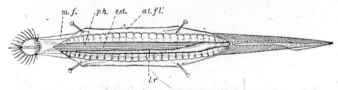

FIG. 304.—The same, from the ventral side, after the floor of the
atrium has been cut open.

an., Anus; *at.fl.*, floor of atrium; *at.fl'.*, the same cut through and turned back;
atp., atriopore; *atp'.*, line indicating position of same in side view; *c.f.*, caudal
nn; *d.f.r.*, rays of dorsal fin; *est.*, endostyle; *gon.*, gonads; *lr.*, liver; *m.f.*,
metapleural fold; *mym.*, myomeres; *myc.*, myocommata or septa of connective
tissue between the myomeres; *n.c.*, nerve cord; *nch.*, notochord; *or.c.*, oral
cirri; *or.h.*, oral hood; *ph.*, pharynx; *v.f.r.*, rays of ventral fin.

caudal fin. Behind it is a region of the body of some length
which does not contain any part of the alimentary canal.
Such a region is known as a *tail*. At the end of the flat
region of the belly is a mid-ventral opening known as
the *atriopore*, through which a current of water escapes.

Below the pointed front end is a cavity, the *buccal cavity*
or *vestibule*, surrounded by an *oral hood*, the edge of
which is beset with slender, ciliated tentacles or *cirri*.
At the hinder side of the vestibule is a muscular partition,
known as the *velum*, whose opening is bordered with
about a dozen *velar tentacles*. On the inside of the hood
a lobed tract of epithelium, which bears long cilia and is
known as the *wheel organ*, encircles the vestibule just in
front of the velum ; between its two main branches is a
median pit, known as *Hatschek's pit*. The opening of the
buccal cavity is the *mouth*. The opening in the velum has

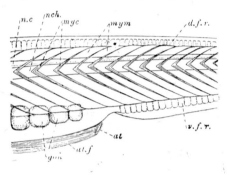

Fig. 305.—A view from the left side of the region around the atriopore
    of a specimen of *Amphioxus* with the atrial floor expanded.
    Lettering as in Figs. 302–304.

also often been called the mouth ; it is better named the
enterostome.

The atriopore leads from a large space which lies below
and at the sides of the middle part of the body
Atrium.   and is known as the *atrium*. This space is not
really within the body, but is enclosed between the body
and two longitudinal folds of the body-wall, like those
which form the branchiostegites of the crayfish, save that
they meet in the middle line below, leaving at their hinder
end an opening which is the atriopore. The atrium
communicates with the pharynx by a number of slits
at each side, known as the *gill slits*, separated by narrow
gill bars, and a current of water which is passed into the

mouth by the cilia around it is caused by cilia on the gill
bars to flow through the slits into the atrium, and so out
at the atriopore. The atrium is prolonged backwards on
the right side behind the atriopore almost as far as the anus.

The skin is covered with a columnar epithelium, ciliated
only within the oral hood and in parts of the
atrium. The connective tissue is scanty, and
consists of fibrillated ground substance with
some cells. There is a thick muscular body-wall, divided,

**General
Anatomy.**

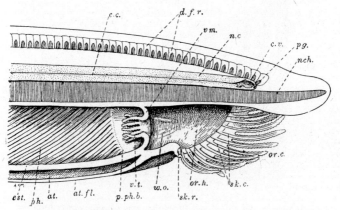

FIG. 306.—*Amphioxus.* The forepart of the body cut in half
longitudinally.

at., Atrium; *at.fl.*, atrial floor; *c.c.*, central canal of nerve cord; *c.v.*, cerebral
vesicle; *d.f.r.*, dorsal fin rays; *est.*, endostyle; *n.c.*, nerve cord; *nch.*, notochord;
or.c., oral cirri; *or.h.*, oral hood; *p.ph.b.*, peripharyngeal band; *pg.*, anterior
pigment spot; *ph.*, pharynx; *sk.c.*, skeleton of cirri; *sk.r.*, skeleton ring in oral
hood; *v.t.*, velar tentacles; *vm.*, velum; *w.o.*, part of wheel organ.

as we have seen, into segments, which are V-shaped and
fit into one another so that several are cut in a transverse
section. Within the body-wall lies a perivisceral cœlom,
not divided by septa, but greatly complicated by the
presence of the gill slits, which reduce it in the region of
the pharynx to a number of canals presently to be described.
There are numerous other cœlomic cavities, of which
the most important are those in the region in front of the
mouth, in the velum, in the metapleural folds of the

larva,[1] and in the gonads.   As in the frog, the dorsal body-
wall is much thicker than the ventral.   In it there lies a longitudinal, hollow central nervous system, comparable to that
of the frog, but at the front end not enlarged into a brain,
though the cavity, which behind is narrow like the central
canal of the frog's spinal cord, is in front wide like that of the
frog's brain.   Below the central nervous system, along the

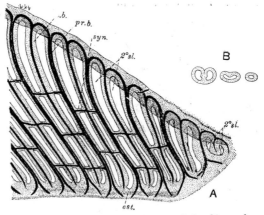

FIG. 307.—*A*, the hinder end of the pharynx of *Amphioxus*, from the
    left side, highly magnified ; *B*, a diagram of the mode of origin of
    the gill clefts.

est., Endostyle ; *pr.b.*, primary bar ; *syn.*, synapticulæ ; *t.b.*, tongue bar ; *2°sl.*, the
    two secondary gill slits which arise from a primary slit.   The skeleton is
    shown in black.

whole length of the body, lies an elastic rod, the *notochord*,
derived from the roof of the gut in the course of development and bound to the nerve cord by a connective tissue
sheath which surrounds them both.   In front it extends
beyond the nerve cord.   There is no skeleton of bone or
cartilage, but stiff rods of organic material support the
gill bars and cirri, and gelatinous " rays " the dorsal and
ventral fins.

[1] The metapleural canals of the adult are perhaps not cœlomic.

The opening in the velum leads into a wide cavity known as the pharynx, which forms about half the

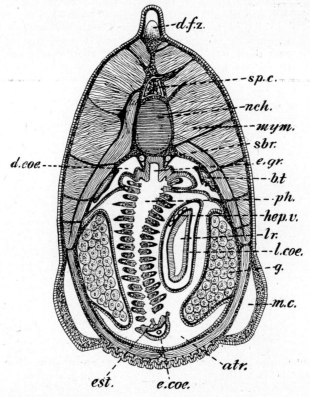

FIG. 308.—A transverse section through the pharyngeal region of *Amphioxus*.

atr., Atrium ; *b.t.*, brown tube ; *d.coe.*, dorsal cœlom ; *d.fr.*, dorsal fin ray ; *e.coe.*, endostylar cœlom, containing ventral aorta ; *e.gr.*, epipharyngeal groove ; *est.*, endostyle ; *g.*, gonad ; *hep.v.*, hepatic vein (here a plexus) ; *l.coe.*, cœlom around liver ; *lr.*, liver ; *m.c.*, metapleural canal ; *mym.*, myomere ; *nch.*, notochord ; *sbr.a.*, suprabranchial artery or paired dorsal aorta ; *sp.c.*, spinal cord.

length of the gut, and is placed in a portion of the body which is enclosed by the atrium. Its sides are pierced by the gill slits, which lie obliquely, their lower ends being

Alimentary System and Perivisceral Cavity.
behind the upper, so that a number of them are cut in a transverse section of the body. Each gill bar is covered with a deep columnar epithelium, ciliated except on the side towards

the atrium, and contains a skeletal rod. At the tops of the bars these rods fork and join one another over the arches. At the lower ends the rods of alternate bars fork

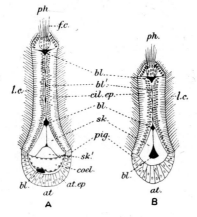

FIG. 309.—Transverse sections of gill bars of *Amphioxus.*
—Partly after Benham.

at., Atrial side ; *at.ep.,* atrial epithelium ; *bl.,* main blood vessels ; *bl'.,* capillaries ; *cil.ep.,* ciliated epithelium ; *coel.,* cœlom ; *f.c.,* frontal cilia ; *l.c.,* lateral cilia ; *ph.,* pharyngeal side ; *pig.,* ment cells ; *sW.,* skeletal rods ; *sk'.,* additional skeletal piece.

but do not join their neighbours, which are unsplit. The bars which contain forked rods are known as *primary bars,* the alternate bars, with unsplit rods, are *secondary bars,* or *tongue bars,* because they arise in development by the downgrowth of a tongue-shaped process from the top of a slit, thus dividing it into two secondary openings which become the permanent slits. This process may be seen in all its stages at the hind end of the pharynx, where new slits are continually being added as long as the animal is growing.[1]

[1] In the larva the primary slits correspond with the myomeres, but afterwards they become more numerous.

The rods of the primary bars are really double, consisting of two strips which lie side by side touching one another in the bar, but

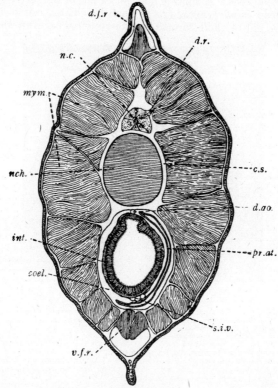

FIG. 310.-- A transverse section of *Amphioxus* in the region of the intestine.

c.s., Connective tissue sheath of the notochord; *coel.*, cœlom; *d.ao.*, dorsal aorta; *d.f.r.*, dorsal fin ray; *d.r.*, dorsal root; *int.*, intestine; *mym.*, myomeres; *n.c.*, nervecord; *nch.*, notochord; *pr.at.*, backward prolongation of the atrium; *s.i.v.*, subintestinal vein (here represented by several vessels); *v.f.r.*, ventral fin ray.

separate to form the forks above and below. The rods of the secondary bars are single, though each parts into two to become forked at its upper end.

The gill bars are connected by horizontal bars or *synapti-culæ*, of which two or three cross each slit. These contain skeletal rods. Along the mid-dorsal line of the pharynx is a deep *epipharyngeal groove* lined by ciliated cells. The mid-ventral wall is formed by a longitudinal bar with which

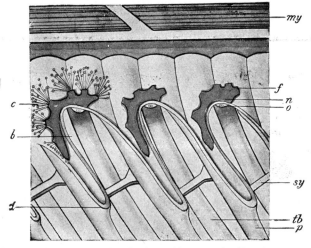

FIG. 311.—Nephridia of *Amphioxus*.—After Boveri.

A lateral view of the upper region of the pharynx, the body-wall being removed. The atrial chamber is laid completely open by the removal of its outer wall, which is cut through along its line of insertion. The result is to show that the chamber is prolonged dorsally into a series of bays (*b.*), which lie outside the tongue bars (*t.b.*). Into these bays the nephridia (*n.*) open by pores (*o.*), while they also project internally by blind funnels (*f.*), fringed by very large solenocytes (*c.*). The bays are separated by ridges (*d.*), formed by a downgrowth of the walls of the cœlom over the primary bars (*p.*); *my.*, a myomere; *sy.*, one of the synapticulæ connecting the pharyngeal bars

the lower ends of the gill bars are fused. This bar bears a groove known as the *endostyle*, lined by ciliated cells with two longitudinal bands of gland cells on each side. These cells secrete mucus which is passed outwards by the cilia. At the front end of the pharynx two peri-pharyngeal bands of long cilia connect the endostyle with the epipharyngeal groove. Each primary bar contains a narrow cœlomic canal. At the tops of the bars the cœlomic canals of each side join a longitudinal canal, known as the *dorsal cœlom*, which lies within the body-wall above the atrium. Below the bars the canals join a median longitudinal *subendostylar cœlom*. This arrangement is the remains of the originally continuous perivisceral cœlom of the pharyngeal region of the body, broken up into canals by the piercing of the walls by the gill slits. Behind the atrium, the perivisceral cœlom is a narrow but unbroken space and surrounds the alimentary canal, which runs straight back through it to the anus. Immediately behind the pharynx is a very short, narrow œsophagus, continuous with the epibranchial groove ; then comes a wider region known as the stomach. This gives off forward on its right side a pouch known as the *hepatic cæcum* or liver, which pushes before it the atrial wall and lies in the atrium beside the pharynx. Behind the stomach the gut narrows and is known as the intestine. The whole alimentary canal is lined by a columnar epithelium which contains gland cells and is ciliated in tracts.

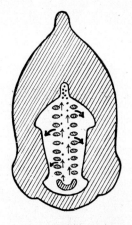

FIG. 312.—The outlines of a transverse section through the pharyngeal region of *Amphioxus*, with arrows to show the course of currents in the pharynx and atrium. Heavy arrows show the main current passing from pharynx to atrium, light arrows show the currents which transport to the epipharyngeal groove mucus containing the particles retained in the pharynx.

Amphioxus feeds on small organisms and other organic particles which it filters out of the water. A current enters the mouth, passes through the gill slits from the pharynx to the atrium, and leaves by the atriopore ; it is caused to flow by the action of the cilia on the sides of the gill bars (*lateral cilia*), which beat outwards. The cilia on the inner faces of the bars (*frontal cilia*) pass the mucus which is secreted by the endostyle upwards across

Feeding.

the pharynx wall, crossing the slanting clefts, to the epipharyngeal groove ; the peripharyngeal bands perform a similar function for the strip of pharyngeal wall in front of the clefts. As the water flows through the clefts the particles it contains are entangled in the mucus and carried up to the groove, where they are conveyed backwards by ciliary action to the œsophagus. The oral cirri and velar tentacles strain out coarse and unsuitable matter, and particles which eddy round under the hood are caught by the wheel organ, which entangles them with mucus and sends them backward to the pharynx. The mucus containing the food particles passes through the œsophagus as a sausage which by ciliary action is carried backward, rotating as it goes, to the anus. Digestion is performed by the secretions of the hepatic cæcum and gut, and absorption takes place in the intestinal region.

Microphagy. The resemblance between this procedure and the feeding of the mussels (p. 376) is very striking. In both water containing the food particles is made to flow through a meshwork by cilia on the sides of the meshes, the particles are retained upon the surface of the meshwork, and they are transported thence to the digestive organs by another set of cilia. The habit of feeding on organic particles (*microphagy*) is followed by many animals. Usually the particles are gathered by cilia, but among Arthropoda, which have no cilia, those that feed in this way do so by means of fine bristles. The mosquito larva (p. 346) is an example.

Excretory Organs. In the dorsal wall of the atrium, lying between the atrial epithelium and the dorsal cœlomic canals, is a series of short tubular structures, corresponding in number with the primary gill slits and opening into the atrium opposite the dorsal ends of the tongue bars. Each passes forwards round the top of the adjoining slit and gives off on its upper side several short branches. From each branch there projects into the cœlom a tuft of fibres known as *solenocytes*, which are fine, protoplasmic tubules, each ending blindly in a knob which contains a nucleus. The other end of the tubule opens into one of the branches of the main tube. Each tubule contains a long flagellum, which arises from the protoplasm round the nucleus and hangs into the main duct. These organs are nephridia, although they do not, like the nephridia of the earthworm, open into the cœlom. Their solenocytes recall the flame cells of the Platyhelminthes (p. 243). It has been shown that if the animal be fed with carmine the colouring matter is excreted through the nephridia. A single nephridium, *Hatschek's nephridium*, lies in a cœlomic cavity on the left side of the head and opens behind into the pharynx. A pair of funnel-shaped structures, known as *brown tubes*, which lie in the hinder part of the dorsal cœlom and open into the atrium at their wide posterior ends, have also been regarded as excretory.

The blood is colourless and contains **Vascular System.** white corpuscles. The vascular system is closed. There is no heart, but the larger vessels are contractile and set up a circulation. A *ventral* or *branchial aorta* in the subendostylar cœlom gives off to each primary gill bar a vessel which divides to take part in the formation of a rather complicated *branchial system* in the primary and secondary bars and synapticulæ. On each side the branches of this system are gathered up into a series of vessels, which open into a longitudinal *suprabranchial artery* (or *lateral dorsal aorta*) beside the epibranchial groove, some of the blood passing through *nephridial plexuses* on the way. Behind the pharynx the suprabranchial arteries unite to form a dorsal aorta, which runs back under the noto-

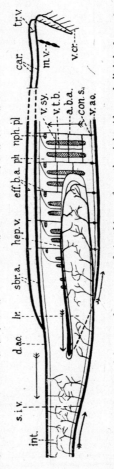

FIG. 313.—A diagram of the vascular system of *Amphioxus*, from the right side, and slightly from above.

a.b.a. Afferent branchial arteries; *ar.*, carotid continuations of the suprabranchial arteries; *con.s.*, contractile swellings on the afferent branchial arteries; *d.ao.*, dorsal aorta; *e* "*br.a.*, efferent branchial arteries; *hep.v.*, hepatic vein; *int.*, intestine; *lr.*, liver; *mv.*, "moniliform" branch of right carotid at base of velum; *nph.pl.*, nephridial plexus; *ph.*, pharynx; *s.i.v.*, subintestinal vein; *sbr.a.*, suprabranchial arteries; *tr.v.*, transverse vessel joining the carotids; *v.ao.* ventral aorta; *v.cr.*, vessels of cirri; *v.sy.*, vessels of synapticulæ; *v.t.b.*, vessels of tongue-bars.

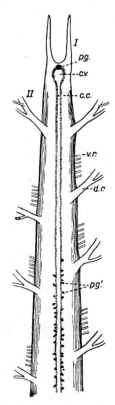

FIG. 314.—The front part of the nerve cord of *Amphioxus*, seen from above.

c.c., Central canal; *c.v.*, cerebral vesicle; *pg.*, anterior pigment spot; *pg'.*, pigment spots in the floor of the cord; *v.r.*, ventral root — the corresponding dorsal root lies immediately behind it; *I, II*, first two pairs of nerves.

chord, giving branches to the gut and body-wall. From these blood is collected by a *subintestinal vein*. This is for much of its course a plexus, but in front becomes a single vessel which runs to the liver and there breaks up again into a *hepatic plexus*. A hepatic vein, which is joined by a pair of vessels (*ductus Cuvieri*) from the body-wall, conveys the contents of this plexus to the ventral aorta. Comparison of this circulation with that of the dogfish, presently to be described, will show that the general course of the blood is similar in the two cases. It will be seen that the direction of flow in the ventral and dorsal vessels of *Amphioxus* is opposite to that in the worm and the same as that of the fish, that its gills are supplied in the same way as in the fish, and that there is in both a hepatic portal system.

The body contains a number of lymph spaces. Some of these (as those in the fins and certain spaces among the muscles) are of cœlomic origin. Others, such as the metapleural canals of the adult, may possibly be hæmocœlic.

Nervous System and Sense Organs. The position of the nerve cord has been described. It is roughly triangular in transverse section, being flattened on its under side, ends abruptly in front at the level of the first myomere, and behind tapers to a point over the hind end of the notochord. There is no ventral fissure, but a deep dorsal fissure, which is clearly due to the closure of a tube, part of which remains as the minute central canal. This tube is lined by an epithelium, and around it lie nerve cells, but there are no dorsal and ventral horns. The remainder of the cord is composed of non-medullated fibres. At the anterior end the canal widens out into a *cerebral vesicle*, which in the larva communicates by a pore with a ciliated funnel known as the *olfactory pit*, on the dorsal surface of the left side of the body. In the adult this opening is lost, though the pit remains. Whether it is sensory is doubtful. A ciliated depression of the floor of the vesicle perhaps corresponds to the infundibulum of a vertebrate animal. The first two pairs of nerves are specialised as cerebral nerves. The first pair arise from the lower side of the anterior end of the cord, the second pair from the dorsal surface behind the cerebral vesicle. These pairs are symmetrical. They are distributed to the epidermis of the snout and are sensory in function. The remaining nerves are not symmetrical, but alternate with one another on the two sides, in correlation with the alternation of the myomeres. Each corresponds to a dorsal or a ventral root of a spinal nerve of the frog, the ventral roots being placed in front of the dorsal. The roots do not join, the ventral, which are groups of slender rootlets, passing direct to the muscles, and the dorsal, which are compact, passing in the septa between the myomeres to the epidermis. The dorsal roots have no ganglia, their fibres being in the condition of the afferent fibres in a worm such as *Nereis* (Fig. 185, B), that is, having their nerve cells at the periphery of the body. They are said also to supply the alimentary canal. The sense organs are few and simple. Supposed tactile cells bearing short, stiff processes are scattered among the ordinary ectoderm cells, especially at the front end of the body and around the mouth. A mass of pigment which lies in the front wall of the cerebral vesicle is not sensitive to light, but small groups of pigmented organs which occur at intervals on the lower side of the canal in the cord appear to be so.

The sexes of the lancelet are separate, but show no differences save in the nature of the gonads. These are

27

cubical bodies, twenty-six on each side, placed in the wall
Reproductive Organs. of the atrium, into which they shed their germs by rupture of their walls. Each corresponds to one of the myomeres and consists of a closed cœlomic sac, whose cavity is known as the *gono-cœle* and on whose wall the germs arise, though they are actually derived, by a rather complicated process, from the epithelium of the embryonic cœlom of the myomere behind that in which they lie. The egg is minute, but contains yolk granules. The gametes are carried out by the current through the atriopore and fertilisation takes place in the water.

The lancelet is an example of a group of animals known
Chordata. as *Chordata*, which includes also the backboned or vertebrate animals and certain less familiar creatures. Chordate animals are cœlomate Metazoa distinguished by the possession of a notochord, a hollow, dorsal nerve cord, gill clefts (" visceral clefts "), and almost always a muscular hinder or " tail " region which contains no viscera and is used, either for driving or steering, in locomotion. In many members of the group, however, some or all of these features may be present during development and lost by the adult, as the adult frog has lost the notochord, gill clefts, and tail which were possessed by the tadpole.

CHAPTER XXI

THE DOGFISH

VARIOUS species of the small sharks known as Dogfish are
Habits.   found in British waters. One of the commonest
of them is the Lesser Spotted Dogfish or Rough
Hound, *Scyllium canicula*. Like other dogfish, it justifies
its name by travelling in packs and hunting by smell. It
lives usually near the sea bottom, and feeds largely upon
crabs, hermit crabs, and other crustaceans, though it also
often devours shell-fish, or small fishes, and will indeed
take most kinds of animal food, dead or alive. It is very
voracious and is a nuisance to fishermen by taking the
bait meant for its betters. Its flesh, though coarse, is used
for food.

The length of a well-grown rough hound is about two
External   feet. Its slender, sinister-looking body, well-
Features.   shaped for passage through the water, tapers
from before backwards, and, though it
shows no sudden differences in size, there may be recognised in it a head, trunk, and tail, the hinder limit of
the former being marked roughly by the hindmost
gill slit (see below), and that of the trunk by the vent. The
head is flat, and has a blunt-pointed snout, a wide,
crescentic mouth on the lower side, a pair of round nostrils
in front of the mouth and connected with it by *oronasal grooves*, and at the sides two slit-like eyes. Immediately behind each eye is a small, round opening, the
spiracle, while farther back and more towards the ventral
side is a row of slits which are the *gill slits* or *gill clefts*. The
spiracle and the gill clefts open internally into the pharynx.
Behind the head the body gradually changes its shape,
becoming flattened from side to side instead of from above

downwards. The vent or opening of the cloaca lies in a
deep longitudinal groove of the belly,
just before the middle of the body.
Into the same groove there opens at
each side one of the *abdominal pores*,
which lead from the body cavity. There
are two pairs of fins and four unpaired
fins. The *fore or pectoral fins*, corresponding to the arms of the frog, are a
pair of flat, triangular organs attached
by one angle to the sides of the ventral
surface not far behind the head. The
hinder or pelvic fins are smaller and
narrower structures of somewhat the
same shape, attached one on each side
of the middle line of the belly in front
of the vent. In the male, their inner
edges are fused and there projects backwards from the under surface of each a
rod, grooved along its inner side, known
as a *clasper*. The unpaired fins are
median structures in the tail. Two,
known as the anterior and posterior
dorsal fins, are on the back, one, the
ventral fin, is on the under side, and
another, the *caudal fin*, surrounds the
end of the tail. This fin has two lobes,
and the axis of the tail is turned upwards
and passes into the upper lobe.

Certain generalisations which we have
made in the course of the
General Internal Features. previous chapters enable us
to state in a few words a
good deal of information
about the anatomy of the dogfish. A

FIG. 315.--The Rough Hound.

Note mouth, eye, spiracle, lateral line, gill clefts,
pectoral and pelvic fins, dorsal fins, caudal fin,
ventral fin between caudal and pelvic fins.

c.f., Upper lobe of caudal fin; *c.f.*, lower lobe of the
same; *pl.f.*, right pelvic fin.

dogfish is a metazoan animal (p. 177). It is triploblastic
(p. 275). It has a large perivisceral cœlom (p. 275) and a
closed circulation (p. 306). It is bilaterally symmetrical
(p. 33). It is segmented (p. 277), though the primary
segmentation is best seen in the early stages of development and is represented in the adult only by the arrangement of the muscles of the body-wall, the segmentation
which is found in the backbone and nervous system arising

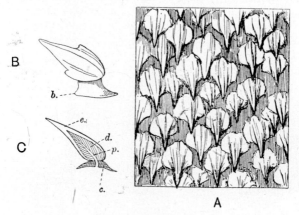

FIG. 316.—Placoid scales.

A. A portion of the skin of the rough hound as seen under a hand lens ; *B*, a single
scale removed from the skin ; *C*, the same in section (diagrammatic).

b., Base of the scale ; *c.*, the same in section ; *d.*, dentine ; *e.*, enamel ;
p., pulp cavity.

later. It is chordate (p. 418). Lastly, like the frog, it is a
backboned or *vertebrate* animal. This term implies more
than the possession of a backbone. The *Vertebrata* are a
large group of animals which have in common, besides the
features we have just mentioned, the following : (1) they
possess an internal skeleton of bone or cartilage, part of
which forms a skull and backbone ; (2) their central nervous
system, which is dorsal and hollow, consists of a spinal
cord and a complicated brain ; (3) the gill clefts, which they
all possess during some period of development, are few and

do not open into an atrium ; (4) they have a heart, which lies below the gut ; (5) most, though not all of them, possess two pairs of limbs and none has more ; (6) like *Amphioxus*, but unlike certain other Chordata, they are, though incompletely, segmented.

Skin. Upon the back and sides of the rough hound the skin is of a grey-brown colour with small spots of darker brown ; upon the belly it is whitish. It feels smooth to the hand if it be stroked from head to tail, but rough if it be stroked in the opposite direction. This is due to the presence of *scales*, which are not flat like those

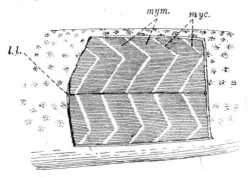

FIG. 317.—The hinder part of the trunk of a dogfish seen from the left side, with a piece of the skin removed.

l.l., Tube of the lateral line ; *myc.*, myocommata or septa of connective tissue ; *mym.*, myomeres.

of most fishes, but bear minute spines directed backwards. Such scales are said to be *placoid*. Each consists of a calcified basal plate embedded in the dermis, and a spine which is composed of dentine covered with enamel. A pulp cavity, containing highly vascular connective tissue, passes through the base into the spine. It will be seen that the general features of such a scale resemble those of the tooth of a frog (p. 57). In fact the teeth of the dogfish, though they are larger, have the structures of the scales, and we must regard teeth as modified scales.

In the body-wall (p. 35) the muscles are for the most part segmentally arranged, each muscle-segment being known as a myomere. The myomeres do not lie straight, but each is bent five times, so that it runs a zigzag

Muscles and Movements.

course from the middle of the back to that of the belly. In the muscles of the head, throat, and fins the segmental arrangement is not apparent. The myomeres are separated by partitions of connective tissue (myocommata), between which their fibres run longitudinally. In swimming, waves of curvature produced by contraction of the muscles (especially powerful in the tail, which is more than half the length of the body) pass alternately down the two sides. The leading (backward) face of each wave presses upon the water obliquely backwards and to one side, that of the next wave presses similarly backwards but to the other side, and so their net effect is by pressing backwards to drive the fish forwards. The tail fin (though in this respect less important than that of most fishes) adds to the propellant surface which is applied to the water

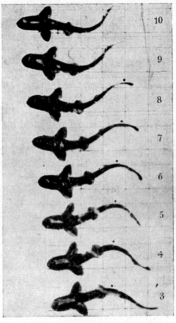

FIG. 318.—Successive positions of a dogfish during swimming.—After Gray.

The crest of a wave is marked by a black dot. Intervals between the photographs 0·10 sec.

when a wave reaches the end of the body. In turning, a strong contraction is sent down one side and turns the head to that side. The tail, owing to the resistance offered by its fin, stands firm as a fulcrum for the head-turn; afterwards it is swung into line with the head. As the tail is moved to and fro it is caused by the larger size of the lower lobe of its fin to rise, and it would therefore drive the snout downwards were it not counteracted by the pectoral fins. The function of these, and to a less extent of the pelvic fins, is, by acting like the wings of an aeroplane, to raise the forepart of the body. Thus the whole body is held up in the water without the air bladder which some fishes possess. The dorsal and ventral fins act like the keel of a boat in keeping the body upright.

The scales of the dogfish are a part of the skeleton which, being on the surface of the body, is known as the *exoskeleton*, and in the frog is represented only by the teeth. The *endoskeleton* of the dogfish corresponds to that of the frog in its main outlines, but differs from it in some important respects. (1) It is wholly cartilaginous, like that of the tadpole, containing nothing which corresponds either to the membrane bones or to the cartilage bones of the frog, though in places the cartilage is calcified. (2) The axial skeleton (p. 36) is traversed longitudinally below the central nervous system by a peculiar rod, the notochord, which consists of large vacuolated cells with stout walls, and is derived, in the course of development, from the roof of the primitive alimentary canal. A notochord is present in the tadpole, but in the adult frog is represented only by pads of tissue between the centra of the vertebræ. (3) There are no structures which represent any part of the sternum. (4) In correspondence with the difference in the form of the limbs, their skeleton differs entirely in the two animals. (5) Unlike that of the tadpole, the median fins are supported by rays.

Skeleton : General Features.

The backbone consists of about 130 vertebræ (p. 36), in each of which the centrum is pierced from end to end by a canal for the notochord. This canal is narrower in the middle of the vertebra, so that the notochord is constricted, and after its removal the centrum appears as a biconcave disc. On each side the centrum bears a pair of *ventrilateral*

Backbone.

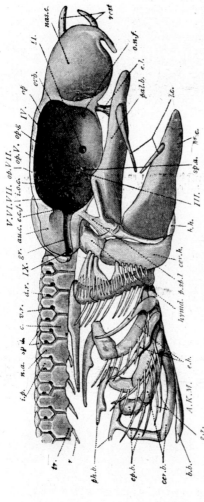

FIG. 319.—Skull and part of the backbone of a dogfish, seen from the right side. The skeleton of the visceral arches has been pulled a little downwards.

au.c., Auditory capsule; *b.b.*, basibranchial cartilage; *b.h.*, basihyal cartilage; *c.*, centrum; *cer.b.*, ceratobranchial cartilages; *cer.h.*, ceratohyal cartilage; *cer.b.*, ceratobranchial cartilages; *d.r.*, *v.r.*, foramina for the dorsal and ventral roots of a spinal nerve; *e.b.*, extrabranchial cartilages; *e.c.f.*, "external carotid" foramen; *ep.b.*, epibranchial cartilages; *e.l.*, ethmopalatine ligament; *gr.*, groove for vein which connects orbital and anterior cardinal sinuses; *gr.*, gill rays; *hyma.*, hyomandibular cartilage; *i.o.c.*, interorbital canal; *i.p.*, intercalary plate; *l.c.*, labial cartilages; *M.c.*, Meckel's cartilage; *nas.c.*, nasal capsule; *n.a.*, neural arch; *o.n.f.*, orbitonasal foramen; *op.V*, *op.VII*, foramina for ophthalmic branches of fifth and seventh nerves; *op'.*, foramen through which combined ophthalmic nerves pass from the orbit to the snout; *op.g.*, grooves for *ob.V.*, *VII.*; *orb.*, orbit; *p.sp.t.*, postspiracular ligament; *pal.b.*, palatine bar; *ph.b.*, pharyngobranchial cartilages; *r.*, rib; *rost.*, rostrum; *sp.a.*, foramen for spiracular artery; *spd.*, supradorsals (often miscalled neural spines); *tr.*, ventrilateral (so-called transverse) process.

Other views of these structures are given in Fig. 320.

processes.[1] In the trunk region these are directed outwards and bear short *ribs*, which lie beneath the muscles of the back ; in the hinder part of the body the processes are directed downwards and are known as *hæmal arches*, enclosing a *hæmal canal*, in which lie the caudal artery and vein. Towards the hinder end of the tail they fuse at their ends and bear a median *hæmal spine*. Between the neural arches of successive vertebræ are wide gaps which are closed by *intercalary pieces*. A series of flat median pieces of cartilage, the *supradorsals*, twice as numerous as the vertebræ, fill the gaps between the tops of the neural arches and intercalary pieces and roof in the vertebral canal.

The skull consists, like that of the frog, of a cranium which contains the brain, with a pair of nasal capsules in front, a pair of auditory capsules one at each side of the hinder end, and a visceral skeleton below. The nasal capsules are large, thin-walled structures, continuous with the cranium, widely open below, and separated by the cartilaginous *internasal septum* or *mesethmoid cartilage*. Three slender processes, one from the front wall of each capsule and one from the mesethmoid cartilage, project into the snout and are together known as the *rostrum*. At the junction of the cranium and the nasal capsules the roof of the skull shows a large gap, the *anterior fontanelle*. From the sides of the cranium large *supraorbital and suborbital ridges* project above and below the orbit. On the auditory capsules, which are continuous with the cranium, ridges mark the position of the semicircular canals. A pit on the roof between the auditory capsules receives on each side a canal, in which a tube, the *aquæductus vestibuli* (the ductus endolymphaticus, p. 101), runs from the ear labyrinth to a small opening above, by which the endolymph communicates with the sea water. There is no ear drum. At the hinder end, between two occipital condyles, is seen the notochord, which passes into the floor of the cranium for some distance. Numerous openings pierce the

Skull.

---

[1] These are often called transverse processes, but they do not correspond with the transverse processes of the frog, which belong to the neural arches.

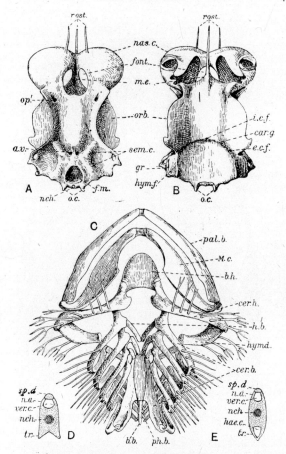

FIG. 320.—Parts of the skeleton of the dogfish.

A, The skull, from above ; *B,* the same, from below ; *C,* skeleton of visceral arches, not including the labial or extrabranchial cartilages; *D,* section of a trunk vertebra ; *E,* section of a tail vertebra.

a.v., Opening of tube from inner ear ; *b.b., b.h., cer.b., cer.h., e.c.f., gr., hymd., M.c., n.a., nas.c., orb., op′., pal.b., ph.b., rost., spd., tr.,* as in Fig. 300; *car. g.,* groove for carotid artery ; *e.c.f.,* foramen for orbital (" external carotid ") artery ; *f.m.,* foramen magnum ; *font.,* fontanelle ; *h.b.,* hypobranchial cartilage ; *hae.c.,* hæmal canal ; *hy,.f.,* facet for hyomandibular cartilage ; *i.c.f.,* foramen for internal carotid arteries ; *m.e.,* mesethmoid cartilage ; *nch.,* notochord ; *o.c.,* occipital condyles ; *sem.c.,* semicircular canals ; *ver.c.,* vertebral foramen.

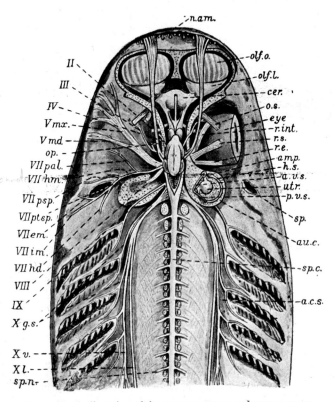

FIG. 321.—A dissection of the nervous system and sense organs
of a dogfish.

On the left : nerves labelled as in Figs. 336–340.
On the right : *a.c.s.,* anterior cardinal sinus ; *a.v.s., amp., h.s., p.v.s., utr.,* parts
    of labyrinth, labelled as in Fig. 55 ; *au.c.,* auditory capsule ; *cer., olf.l., o., ol., l.,*
    sp.c., as in Fig. 336 ; *n.am.,* neuromast ampullæ ; *os., r.e., r.int., r.s., s.p.,* as
    in Fig. 339.
The eye and part of the auditory capsule, which have been removed from the left-
    hand side, remain *in situ* on the right.   The cartilage of the skull and vertebræ
    is dotted, and the nerves are seen passing through the foramina shown in
    Fig. 319.

wall of the cranium. (1) On the roof lies the anterior fontanelle which we have already mentioned. (2) At the front end two large foramina put the cranial cavity in continuity with those of the nasal capsules. Through these the olfactory nerves pass from the surface of each olfactory lobe of the brain into the olfactory organ. (3) On each side wall numerous openings allow the passage of nerves and blood vessels to and from the orbit. The relative sizes and positions of these are seen in Fig. 319. (4) Just behind the auditory capsules, at the bottom of a deep pit, is the foramen for the ninth nerve, and on each side of the occipital condyles is a foramen for the passage of the tenth nerve. (5) On the under side there may be seen two shallow grooves, along which the internal carotid arteries run. Where these meet there is a small opening, through which the two arteries enter the cranium. At the outer ends of the grooves are the openings through which the orbital (so-called external carotid) arteries pass from the roof of the mouth to the orbits. (6) At the hinder end of the skull is the large foramen magnum. The *visceral skeleton* is a series of seven arches (p. 436), each consisting of several pieces, which lie at the sides of the mouth. The first of these is the *mandibular arch*, which forms the skeleton of the jaws. Each *upper jaw-bar* or *palato-pterygo-quadrate cartilage* is a rod which meets its fellow in front of the mouth and is there joined to it by a ligament. It is attached to the cranium in front of the orbit by the *ethmo-palatine ligament* and behind to the auditory capsule by a *postspiracular ligament*. Each half of the lower jaw is formed by *Meckel's cartilage*, which is a wide, flat bar, tapering forwards to a point, where it is joined with its fellow by a ligament. It articulates behind with the palato-pterygo-quadrate cartilage. Both the upper and the lower jaw bars are joined by ligament to the hyomandibular cartilage which forms their principal attachment to the skull. The second or *hyoid arch* consists of two pieces, the *hyomandibular cartilage*, which is a short, stout rod articulated with a large facet on the side of the auditory capsule, and a longer, more slender, *ceratohyal cartilage*, which passes forwards and inwards from under the hyomandibular to join a median plate, the *basihyal cartilage*, in the floor of the mouth. The remaining five arches are the *branchial arches*.

Each branchial arch contains above a flat, pointed *pharyngobranchial* which, starting beside the backbone, slopes forwards to join an *epibranchial* that lies at the side of the pharynx in a line with the hyomandibular cartilage. From the lower end of this the *ceratobranchial* runs forwards and inwards parallel with the ceratohyal and mandibular cartilages. The first four ceratobranchials are connected with *hypobranchials* in the floor of the pharynx. The first hypobranchial is small and joins the first ceratobranchial with the basihyal;

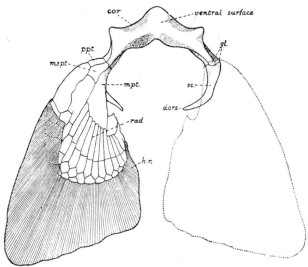

FIG. 322.—A ventral view of the skeleton of the pectoral girdle and pectoral fin of a dogfish.

cor., Coracoid region ; *dors.*, dorsal end of scapula ; *gl.*, glenoid facet ; *h.r.*, horny rays (dermotrichia) ; except on the outer border of the fin shown these have been cut away where they covered the cartilaginous rays ; *mpl.*, metapterygium ; *mspt.*, mesopterygium ; *ppt.*, propterygium ; *rad.*, cartilaginous rays ; *sc.*, scapula.

the three hinder are larger and directed backwards and inwards. The last two pairs of hypobranchials and the fifth ceratobranchials join a median *basibranchial plate*. The epibranchial, ceratobranchial, hyomandibular, and ceratohyal cartilages bear *gill rays* along their hinder borders. Outside the upper and lower jaws lie a pair of *labial cartilages*, and along the outer sides of the second, third, and fourth ceratobranchials are *extrabranchials*.

The median fins are supported by a skeleton consisting of several series of rays. The series nearest the body are cartilaginous rods known as *basalia* and are attached to the neural and hæmal spines. They are succeeded by a similar series known as *radialia*, and these by two rows of small, polygonal plates of cartilage which are overlapped at the sides by a double series of horny rays or *dermotrichia* that project beyond them. The dermotrichia, which belong to the dermis, are fine fibres composed of the same substance (*elastin*) as the elastic fibres of connective tissue. In the caudal fin the cartilaginous rays are not distinct from the supradorsals and hæmal spines.

The limbs are anchored into the body by girdles which

Limbs.
corre-
spond to those of the frog. The pec-toral girdle con-sists of two curved pieces of cartilage, at the sides of the body, of which the lower ends are fused in the mid-ventral line. To the hinder sides of these pieces are articulated the fins. The surface of articu-lation is the *glenoid facet*, the portion of the girdle above the facet being the *scapular region* and that below, the *cora-*

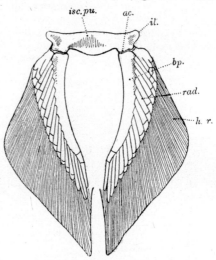

FIG 323.—The skeleton of the pelvic fins and girdle of a female dogfish

ac., Acetabular surface; *bp.*, basipterygium; *h.r.*, horny rays; *il.*, iliac process; *isc.pu.*, ischio-pubic region; *rad.*, cartilaginous rays.

coid. The scapula is rod-like; the coracoid is broad and flat and supports the floor of the pericardium. The pectoral fin articulates with its girdle by three basal cartilages, the *pro-*, *meso-*, and *metapterygia*, of which the former is the anterior and smallest, the metapterygium the hindmost and largest. Along the outer borders of these pieces are set a series of *radialia*. The pro- and mesopterygia each bear one stout ray, the metapterygium several, which are slender. To the end of these, smaller, polygonal pieces are attached, and these in turn bear a double series of horny *dermotrichia* which overlap them above and below and project beyond them. The pelvic girdle is a stout, straight bar of cartilage, placed athwart the belly and bearing a blunt knob at each end. The main part of the bar is the *ischiopubic region*, the knobs are the *iliac processes*, and the fins articulate with an *acetabular facet* upon the hinder border at the base of the iliac processes. The fin has a long inwardly-curved *basipterygium*, bearing a row of radialia along its outer side. In the male it also bears a long piece of cartilage which supports the clasper.

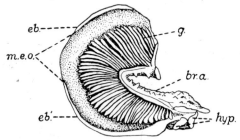

FIG. 324.—The hinder wall of a gill pouch of the dogfish.

br.a., Branchial arch, flexed because the pharynx floor is raised; *eb.*, *eb.'*, extrabranchials; *g.*, gill; *hyp.*, hypobranchials in section; *m.e.o.*, margin of external opening.

The perivisceral cavity (cœlom) is divided into two parts, the small pericardial cavity just in front of the pectoral fins, and the large peritoneal cavity behind it, between the two pairs of fins. The two cavities are divided by a membranous septum, but a narrow passage, the *pericardio-peritoneal canal*, leads from one to the other below the œsophagus. From the peritoneal cavity the two small abdominal pores lead to the exterior, one on either side of the vent. This cavity contains, like the pleuro-peritoneal cavity of the frog, among other organs, the whole of the alimentary canal with the exception of the mouth and pharynx. The gape of the mouth is edged with several rows of teeth,

Cœlom and Alimentary System.

which, as we have seen, are simply enlarged scales. These lie in a part of the skin which passes over the jaw and is tucked into a groove within it. They are not in any way

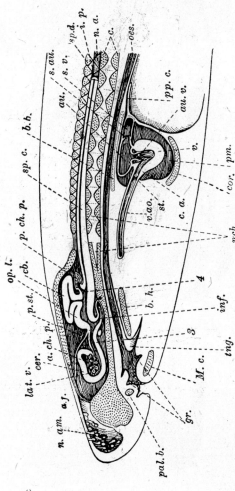

FIG. 325.—A semi-diagrammatic drawing of a longitudinal section through a dogfish, passing slightly to the right of the middle line.

a.ch.p., Anterior choroid plexus; *a.j.*, anterior ontanelle; *au.*, auricle; *au.v.*, auriculo-ventricular opening and valve; *b.b.*, basibranchial cartilage; *b.h.*, basihyal cartilage; *c*, centrum; *c.a.*, conus arteriosus; *c.b.*, cerebellum; *cer.*, cerebrum; *cor.*, coracoid region of the pectoral girdle; *gr.*, grooves in which the teeth are formed; *i.p.*, intercalary plate; *inf.*, infundibulum; *lat.v.*, lateral ventricle; *M.c.*, Meckel's cartilage; *n.a.*, neural arch; *n.am.*, ampullary sense organs; *n.h.*, notochord; *oes.*, oesophagus; *op.l.*, optic lobe; *p.ch.p.*, posterior choroid plexus; *p.st.*, pineal stalk; *pal.b.*, palatine bar; *p.m.*, pericardium; *pp.c.*, pericardio-peritoneal canal; *s.au.*, sinu-auricular opening; *s.v.*, sinus venosus; *sp.c.*, spinal cord; *sp.d.*, supradorsal cartilage; *sl.*, semilunar valves; *tng.*, tongue; *v.*, ventricle; *v.ao.*, ventral aorta; *3*, third ventricle; *4*, fourth ventricle.

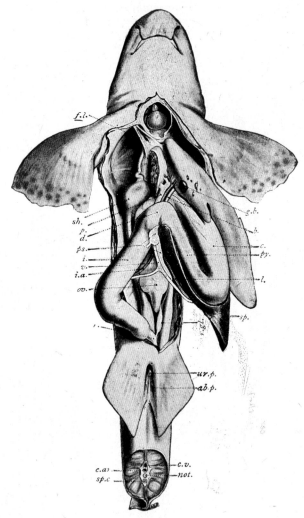

FIG. 326.—For legend see opposite.

attached to the jaw. As they wear away they are replaced by new rows which are constantly being formed in the groove and carried up over the edge of the jaw by the growth of the skin. Like those of the frog their function is only to hold the food, which is swallowed whole. The pharynx is only distinguished from the mouth cavity by possessing the inner openings of the spiracle and gill clefts. These are placed between the arches of the visceral skeleton, the first gill cleft lying between the hyoid and first branchial arches. The clefts do not pass straight outwards through the wall of the throat, but the outer opening of each is at some distance behind the inner, so that the cleft is a pouch which slants backwards and outwards from the pharynx to the exterior. The pouches are spacious cavities, being deep, and considerably taller than their openings at either end, though the inner opening is larger than the outer. On each wall of the pouch lie a number of folds which constitute a *gill*. These are highly vascular, and in fresh specimens have consequently a bright red colour. There is a gill on each side of each cleft except the last, which has no gill on the hinder side. The spiracle is a small cleft of the same series as the gill cleft, and bears on its front side a vestige of a gill, known as a *pseudobranch*. The regions between the clefts, and those immediately in front of the first cleft (the spiracle)

FIG. 326.—A female dogfish in which the abdominal and pericardial cavities have been opened from the ventral side, and the viscera somewhat displaced. The pericardium has been opened slightly to the left of the middle line, and the right lobe of the liver has been cut away.

ab.p., Abdominal pores ; *b.*, bile duct ; *c.*, cardiac limb of stomach ; *c.ar.*, caudal artery ; *c.v.*, caudal vein ; *d.*, bursa entiana ; *g.b.*, portion of gall bladder appearing on surface of left lobe of liver in which it is embedded ; *i.*, intestine ; *i.a.*, intestinal branch of anterior mesenteric artery ; *l.*, lienogastric artery ; *not.*, notochord ; *ov.*, ovary ; *p.*, portal vein lying beside hepatic artery ; *ps.*, pancreas with duct opening into intestine ; *py.*, pyloric limb of stomach ; *r.*, rectum, between hinder ends of oviducts, with rectal gland (*r.gl.*) attached to its dorsal side ; *s.l.*, suspensory ligament of liver, with internal opening of oviducts ; *sh.*, right shell gland on course of right oviduct ; *sp.*, spleen ; *sp.c.*, spinal cord ; *ur.p.*, urinary papilla ; *v.*, branch of portal vein formed by junction of intestinal and splenic veins.

Besides the above, note—nostrils ; oronasal grooves ; mouth ; pectoral and pelvic fins ; pericardial and abdominal cavities ; heart, consisting of sinus venosus (behind), ventricle, auricle (showing at sides of ventricle), and conus ; cloaca, and transverse section of tail, showing at the sides the myomeres, above the anterior dorsal fin, and in the middle the cartilage of the backbone enclosing spinal cord, notochord, and blood vessels.

and behind the last, are known as *visceral arches*, and named, in order, mandibular, hyoid, and first to fifth branchial. Each contains a skeletal arch, arteries, and a nerve (Fig. 345). The spiracle separates the mandibular and hyoid arches. The movements of the visceral arches, which carry out the processes of feeding and, as we shall see, of breathing, are brought about by muscles which run between the cartilages of the arches and the coracoid region of the shoulder girdle. From the pharynx the narrower œsophagus leads back through the cœlom to the stomach. This is sharply divided into a cardiac and a pyloric part. The former is a sac, in shape not unlike the stomach of the frog ; near its hinder end on the right side arises the narrow tubular pyloric division, which runs forwards beside the cardiac. At its front end a slight constriction marks the presence of the pyloric sphincter and divides it from the intestine. The main part of the intestine is the ileum, a long, wide sac which passes backwards towards the cloaca and has its internal surface increased by a spiral fold of the mucous membrane known as the *spiral valve*. Between this region and the pyloric sphincter lies a short, somewhat narrower region called the duodenum or *bursa entiana*, which is without a spiral valve and receives the ducts of the liver and pancreas. At its hinder end the ileum narrows and loses its spiral valve, thus becoming the rectum, this in turn ending in the wider cloaca, which receives the urinary and generative ducts and opens by the vent. There is no bladder. The liver is a very large organ, consisting of long right and left lobes united in front and slung by the *suspensory ligament* from the anterior wall of the peritoneal cavity. The gall bladder is embedded in the front part of the left lobe of the liver, but usually a part of it shows upon the surface. From it the bile duct runs backwards to open into the intestine, lying in the membrane or *omentum* which carries the hepatic artery and portal vein. The pancreas lies between the stomach and intestine ; it is long and narrow and has in front a rounded ventral lobe, from which its duct passes to the ventral side of the intestine. The *rectal gland* is a small, cylindrical structure which opens into the dorsal side of the rectum by a duct.

By a munching action of the floor of the mouth and
Respiration. pharynx the fish incessantly renews the water
that bathes its organs of respiration, the gills.
When the floor is lowered water is drawn in through the
mouth, while the flexible front edge of each gill cleft is
caused, by the lower pressure within, to flap back so as to
prevent the entry of water that way. When the floor is
raised the lips prevent the escape of water through the
mouth, contraction of the œsophagus keeps that also closed,
and the water, being under pressure, opens the clefts and
passes out over the gills. The shape
of the gill pouches must cause the
water to eddy about the gills as it
goes. Through the thin membrane
which is all that separates the
blood in the gills from the water,
the gases of respiration are exchanged.

The spleen must be mentioned
here, although it has no connection
with the alimentary canal. It is
attached by membrane to the hinder
end of the stomach as a triangular
lobe with a forward prolongation
along the right side of the pyloric
division.

FIG. 327.—Diagram of
spiral valve. — After
T. J. Parker.

The kidneys of the dogfish, like those of the frog
(p. 78), lie above the abdominal cavity, out-
Excretory and side the peritoneum, and are masses of tubules.
Generative
Organs. In the embryo the tubules correspond with
the muscle segments, but later more are
added to these primary ones. Unlike those of the frog,
many of the primary tubules keep a minute *peritoneal
funnel*, opening to the cœlom, which they had in the
embryo. The kidneys are relatively larger than the frog's,
and each consists of a wide part behind, which forms a
cushion-like swelling and is the principal excretory organ,
and a narrow part in front, which in the female is a mere
vestige, only to be found by removing the peritoneum, but
in the male is larger, and, with the Wolffian duct coiled upon
it, makes a ridge along the body cavity. The *Wolffian duct*

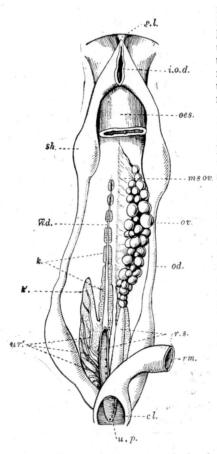

runs the whole length of the kidney, lying upon its ventral face and receiving the tubules of the narrow anterior part. In the female it is straight and its hinder end is widened to form a *urinary sinus*, which joins its fellow to open into the cloaca upon a median *urinary papilla*; in the male it is coiled and serves, as in the frog, for the vas deferens, its swollen hinder part being a vesicula seminalis. The tubules of the hinder part of the kidney join five or six ducts, which in the female open into the urinary sinus of their side but in the male unite to form a so-called *ureter*, which passes backwards to open separately

FIG. 328.—The reproductive organs of a female dogfish.

cl., Cloaca ; *i.o.d.*, internal opening of the oviducts ; *k., k'.*, anterior and posterior parts of right kidney ; *msov.*, mesovarium ; *o.d.*, oviduct ; *oes.*, œsophagus ; *ov.*, ovary ; *rm.*, rectum ; *s.l.*, part of the suspensory ligament of the liver ; *sh.*, shell gland ; *ur'.*, ducts of posterior part of kidney ; *u.p.*, urinary papilla ; *ur.s.*, urinary sinus ; *W.d.*, Wolffian duct.

from the vesicula semin-
alis into a median *urinogenital sinus*. This
has two forward horns
known as the *sperm
sacs*, which lie upon
the ventral faces of the
vesiculæ seminales,
and opens behind
into the cloaca by a
urinogenital papilla behind the anus. The
differentiation, in the
adult kidney, of a hinder
urine-forming part,
with its own duct,
from an anterior part,
vestigial in the female
and sperm-conducting
in the male, is carried
further in higher ani-
mals — reptiles, birds,
and mammals (as the
rabbit, p. 548), where
two such parts are
separated, the hinder
or actual kidney being
called the *metanephros*
and the anterior the
mesonephros.[1]

[1] The terms " meso- "
and " metanephros " sig-
nify " mid- " and " hind-
kidney," and the reason
for which they are applied
to the parts of the kidney
which bear them is that in
the embryo of every vertebrate (though very rarely
in the adult) there lies in
front of these parts a region
known as the *pronephros*.
or " fore kidney." That

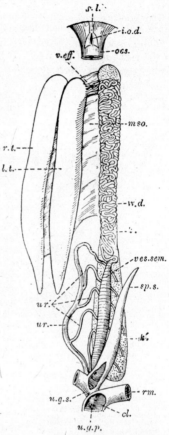

FIG. 329.—The reproductive organs of
a male dogfish.

cl., Cloaca ; *i.o.d.*, rudiment of internal opening
of oviducts ; *l.t.*, left testis ; *k.*, *k′.*, anterior and posterior parts of left kidney ;
mso., mesorchium ; *oes.*, œsophagus ; *r.t.*,
right testis ; *rm.*, rectum ; *s.l.*, suspensory
ligament ; *sp.s.*, left sperm sac ; *u.g.p.*,
urinogenital papilla ; *u.g.s.*, urinogenital
sinus ; *ur.*, ureter ; *ur′.*, ducts of posterior
part of kidney ; *v.eff.*, vasa efferentia ; *ves.
sem.*, vesicula seminalis ; *W.d.*, Wolffian
duct or vas deferens.

The principal end-product of nitrogenous metabolism is urea. Much of this, however, is retained in the blood (see p. 448).

There is a single ovary, which probably represents that of the right side of the frog. It hangs into the body cavity and varies in size and appearance with age. The ova are in different stages of ripeness, the ripest being very large and yolky. They are shed into the body cavity and passed forwards by contractions of the abdominal walls to the front of the peritoneal space where they enter the *internal opening of the oviducts.* The latter are large straight tubes, one on each side of the body, attached to the dorsal wall of the cœlom. They start from a common opening in the suspensory ligament, not far behind which each has a round swelling known as the *shell gland,* by which the shells of the eggs are secreted. At the hinder end of the trunk they enter the cloaca by a common opening just behind the anus. The testes are a pair of long organs slung by membranes from the dorsal wall of the cœlom. Each communicates at its front end with the kidney of its side by several small vasa efferentia, the sperm passing through these into kidney tubules and thence to the vas deferens or Wolffian duct, by which it is conveyed to the

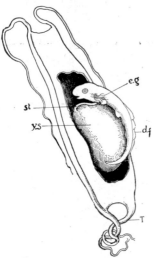

FIG. 330. —An embryo dogfish in its egg-case ("mermaid's purse") which has been cut open to show the contents.— From Thomson.

d.v., Dorsal fin fold; *e.g.,* "external" gills; *st.,* stalk of yolk-sac; *T.,* tendrils, prolongations of egg-case by means of which it is moored to seaweed; *y.s.,* yolk-sac.

part of the original kidney which lies behind the pronephros and in some animals is separated into meso- and metanephros receives, as a whole, the name *opisthonephros,* or "after kidney." In the dogfish, and in the frog, the adult kidney is the opisthonephros.

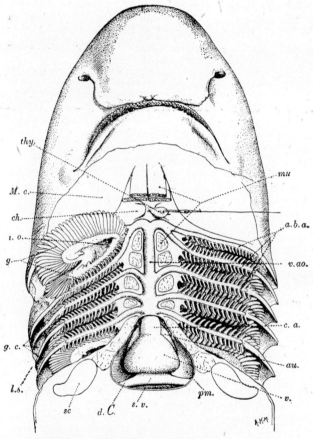

FIG. 331.—The forepart of the body of a dogfish, dissected to show the heart and ventral arterial system.

a.b.s., Afferent branchial arteries; *au.*, auricle; *c.a.*, conus arteriosus; *ch.*, cerotohyal cartilage; *d.C.*, ductus Cuvieri; *g.*, gills; *g.c.*, gill clefts; *i.o.*, internal opening of the first gill cleft; *l.s.*, line of section in Fig. 325, which should be compared; *M.c.*, Meckel's cartilage; *mu.*, muscles from coracoid region of shoulder girdle to various parts of visceral skeleton; *p.m.*, pericardium; *s.v.*, sinus venosus; *sc.*, scapula; *thy.*, thyroid gland (displaced); *v.*, ventricle; *v.ao.*, ventral aorta.

urinogenital sinus. A rudiment of the internal opening of the oviducts is found in the suspensory ligament of the male. Sperm is passed by the aid of the claspers into the cloaca of the female and fertilisation takes place within her.

It is possible that the sperm is washed out of the grooves of the claspers by sea water injected into them by the " siphon "—a muscular sac which lies under the skin of the ventral surface in the pelvic region and communicates by two channels with the grooves.

The eggs are laid in flat, oblong, brown shells whose angles are prolonged into tapering tendrils, which twine round seaweeds and thus anchor the egg. Protected by the shell, the young dogfish develops slowly at the expense of the yolk, which comes to be contained in a sac attached to its belly. At one stage long, vascular threads project from the gill clefts of the little fish. These are the so-called external gills, but they are covered with endoderm and thus differ from the true external gills of the tadpole.

Blood Vessels : Heart. The heart of a dogfish lies in the pericardium between the hinder gill-clefts of the right and left sides. It is a median structure with muscular walls, and consists essentially of an irregular tube, bent twice like an S (Fig. 325) and composed of four successive chambers. The hindermost chamber is the thin-walled sinus venosus, which is triangular as seen from below, and lies with its base against the hinder wall of the pericardium. In front of it comes the thicker walled auricle or atrium. This is also triangular, with its apex forwards, and has its hinder angles widened into pouches, but is not divided into two chambers like that of the frog. The S then curves downwards, as the very thick-walled, conical ventricle, which lies below and somewhat behind the auricle. From it the narrow conus arteriosus passes forwards through the front wall of the pericardium to become the ventral aorta, which is merely the foremost part of the single vessel whose thickening and twisting produces the heart behind. Thus the heart, or contractile blood-vessel, of the dogfish, like that of the frog and all other vertebrate animals, is ventral in position, whereas the principal contractile vessel of an invertebrate is generally

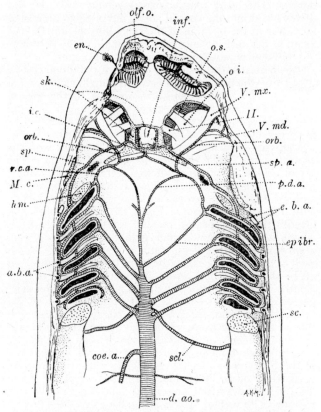

FIG. 332.—The forepart of a dogfish, dissected from the ventral side, to show the dorsal arterial system, the olfactory organs, and certain structures in the orbits. The middle part of the floor of the mouth has been removed.

a.b.a., Afferent branchial arteries; *cœ.a.*, cœliac artery; *d.ao.*, dorsal aorta; *e.b.a.*, efferent branchial arteries; *en.*, nostril; *epibr.*, epibranchial artery; *h.m.*, hyomandibular cartilage; *i.c.*, internal carotid foramen; *inf.*, infundibulum; *M.c.*, Meckel's cartilage in lower jaw; *olf.o.*, olfactory organ; *orb.*, orbital or "external carotid"; *p.d.a.*, prolongation of aorta; *r.c.a.*, carotid root; *sc.*, scapula; *scl.*, subclavian artery; *sk.*, skull; *sp.*, spiracle; *sp.a.*, spiracular artery; *V.md.*, *V.mx.*, mandibular and maxillary branches of fifth nerve; *II.*, optic nerve.

dorsal. The heart contracts from behind forwards, and drives blood into the ventral aorta, reflux being prevented by valves at the opening of the sinus into the auricle and again at the auriclo-ventricular opening, and by two rings of semilunar or watch-pocket valves in the conus.

Arteries. The ventral aorta lies in the middle of the throat, below the pharynx and between the gill clefts, giving off *afferent branchial arteries* to the fourth, third, and second branchial arches, and ending by dividing into two vessels, each of which again forks to supply the first branchial and hyoid arches of its side. There are thus five afferent branchial arteries. These, together with the ventral aorta, form the *ventral arterial system*. The thyroid gland, an organ of internal secretion (p. 62) which does not belong to the vascular system, lies below the anterior end of the ventral aorta as a pear-shaped body with the stalk forwards. From the afferent branchial arteries the blood passes into the capillaries of the gills, where it is oxygenated and gathered up into *efferent branchial arteries*. These form a complete loop round each of the first four clefts, the loops being joined fore and aft by short horizontal vessels at about the middle of their lengths. The last cleft, having no gill on its hinder side, has an efferent vessel on its front side only, and all the blood of this vessel passes by the horizontal vessel into that of the gill in front. From the dorsal end of each of the complete loops arises a vessel known as an *epibranchial artery*, which runs backwards and inwards on the roof of the pharynx to join the median dorsal aorta opposite to its fellow of the other side. From the dorsal end of the first efferent branchial artery, just outside the origin of the first epibranchial artery, arises the *root of the carotid artery*.[1] This runs forwards and inwards under the skull and is presently joined by a small branch from the dorsal aorta (see below), after which it becomes the carotid (internal carotid) artery. Behind the orbit it gives off forward an orbital branch which immediately passes through the opening we have mentioned (p. 429) and runs forwards along the floor of the orbit to supply the

[1] This is often called the " common carotid artery," but it does not correspond to the vessel of that name in the frog.

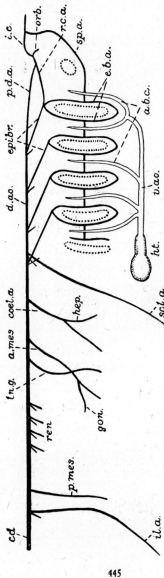

FIG. 333.—A diagram of the arterial system of a dogfish, seen from the right side.

a.b.a., Afferent branchial arteries; *a.mes.*, anterior mesenteric artery; *cd.*, caudal artery; *cœl.a.*, cœliac artery; *d.ao.*, dorsal aorta; *e.b.a.*, efferent branchial arteries; *epibr.*, epibranchial arteries; *gon.*, genital artery; *ht.*, heart; *hep.*, hepatic artery; *i.c.*, internal carotid artery; *il.a.*, iliac artery; *ln.g.*, lienogastric artery; *orb.*, orbital or "external carotid" artery; *p.d.a.*, prolongation of the dorsal aorta; *p.mes.*, posterior mesenteric artery; *r.c.a.*, root of carotid artery; *ren.*, renal arteries; *scl.a.*, subclavian artery; *sp.a.*, spiracular artery; *v.ao.*, ventral aorta.

445

upper jaw and the snout. This branch is often called the external carotid artery but does not correspond to the external carotid (lingual) of the frog. The carotid artery continues its course in the carotid groove, towards the middle line, where it unites with its fellow for a short distance, but separates again, passing through the internal carotid foramen into the cranium to supply the brain. Outside the carotid root yet another artery arises from the first efferent branchial vessel. This is the *spiracular artery*, which starts in a line with the horizontal vessels that join the loops, runs forwards to the spiracle, where it supplies the pseudobranch, crosses the orbital floor, enters the cranium by a small foramen in the inner wall of the orbit, and joins the internal carotid artery. The dorsal aorta ends in front by breaking into two small prolongations that curve outwards and join the carotid roots, forming the definitive carotid arteries. Just before the dorsal aorta is joined by the last pair of epibranchial vessels it gives off a pair of subclavian arteries, which pass backwards and outwards to the fore-fins. Behind the pharynx it runs backwards along the whole length of the body below the backbone, lying, in the tail, in the hæmal canal as the *caudal artery*. Besides paired vessels to the body-wall, it gives off to the viscera several median vessels, known successively as the cœliac (of which the hepatic is a branch), anterior mesenteric (of which the genital is a branch), lienogastric, and posterior mesenteric, and to the kidneys several paired renal arteries.

The sinus venosus receives the whole of the blood re-

Veins.   turning to the heart by a number of very large veins which are called *sinuses*, though, unlike the sinuses of the cockroach, they do not take the place of capillaries as well as veins in the circulation, but are merely enlarged parts of the veins. The blood from the liver returns direct to the sinus venosus by two *hepatic sinuses* which enter its hinder side. The rest of the blood is returned by two large precavals or *ductus Cuvieri* which join the sinus venosus, one on each side in the pericardium. Into these the blood from the region of the body in front of the fore-fins is conveyed by a pair of large dorsal *anterior cardinal sinuses* and two smaller *external* or *inferior*

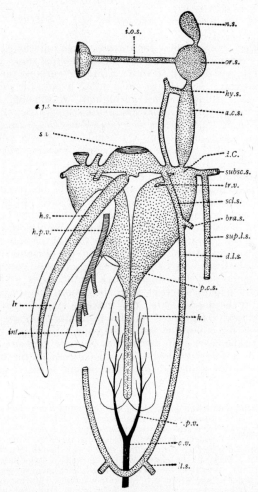

FIG. 334.—A diagram of the venous system of the dogfish.

a.c.s., Anterior cardinal (or internal jugular) sinus ; *bra.s.*, brachial sinus ; *c.v.*, caudal vein ; *d.C.*, ductus Cuvieri, or precaval sinus ; *d.l.s.*, deep lateral (abdominal) sinus ; *e.j.s.*, external or inferior jugular sinus ; *h.p.v.*, hepatic portal vein ; *h.s.*, hepatic sinus ; *hy.s.*, hyoidean sinus ; *i.o.s.*, interorbital sinus ; *il.s.*, iliac sinus ; *int.*, intestine ; *k.*, kidney ; *lr.*, liver ; *n.s.*, nasal sinus ; *or.s.*, orbital sinus ; *p.c.s.*, posterior cardinal sinus ; *r.p.v.*, renal portal vein ; *s.v.*, sinus venosus ; *scl.s.*, subclavian sinus ; *sub.c.s.*, subscapular sinus ; *sup.l.s.*, superficial lateral sinus ; *tr.v.*, transverse vessel joining subclavian sinuses.

iugular sinuses, below the throat.   Each anterior cardinal
sinus communicates in front with an *orbital sinus* around
the eye, and this in turn with a *nasal sinus* around the olfactory organ.   A *hyoidean sinus* in the hyoid arch joins the
anterior cardinal and inferior jugular.   At the outer end of
each ductus Cuvieri a *subscapular sinus* enters from the fore-
fin.   On its hinder side a very large *posterior cardinal sinus*
brings back blood from the trunk.   The two posterior
cardinal sinuses converge backwards, growing narrower,
and lie side by side between the kidneys, from which blood
passes into them by numerous renal veins.   On each flank
two *lateral sinuses* return blood from the body-wall, and
into one of these open vessels from the fins.   Blood from
the tail is returned by the *caudal vein* ;   this divides opposite
the hinder ends of the kidneys into two renal portal veins,
which run forwards along the outer sides of the kidneys and
supply them with blood.   Blood from the alimentary canal
and spleen is conveyed to the liver by a hepatic portal vein,
and thence, after passing through capillaries, is discharged
into the hepatic sinuses.   It will be noticed that the circulation of the dogfish (Fig. 335) makes a single circuit only,
the blood oxygenated in the respiratory organs being
carried directly to the rest of the body without first returning to the heart as in the frog (p. 76) :   the pressure of this
blood is therefore low.   The blood cells of the dogfish
resemble those of the frog.   The plasma is extremely rich
in urea.

By that fact hangs a surprising and interesting tale.   The solids in
the blood of most fishes give it a higher osmotic pressure
**Water
Regulation.**
than that of fresh waters and lower than that of sea
water.   Freshwater fishes are therefore liable to gain
by osmosis from their surroundings more water than is good for them
(p. 79).   They put the matter right by forming a very dilute urine :
the filtrate formed in the glomeruli is rendered more watery by the
abstraction of solids from it by the kidney tubules.   Marine fishes are
liable to the opposite danger of the loss of water.   Bony fishes counter
this by drinking sea water and excreting its salts through the gills
and kidneys, so that there is a net gain of water.   But the dogfish and
other cartilaginous fishes have adopted the remarkable expedient of
retaining much of the urea which results from their nitrogenous
metabolism, and so raising the osmotic pressure of their blood till
it is slightly above that of sea water.   As a result, a moderate amount
of water enters their bodies but this is got rid of through the kidneys

as in the freshwater fishes. The retention of urea is brought about by a special section of each kidney tubule, which re-absorbs it from the filtrate that is formed by the glomeruli.

The spinal cord of the dogfish resembles in most respects that of the frog (p. 84) and need not be described **Central Nervous System.** here. The brain, although in general features it is like that of the frog, shows considerable differences in detail. The foremost region in the middle line is the *cerebrum*, which corresponds to the

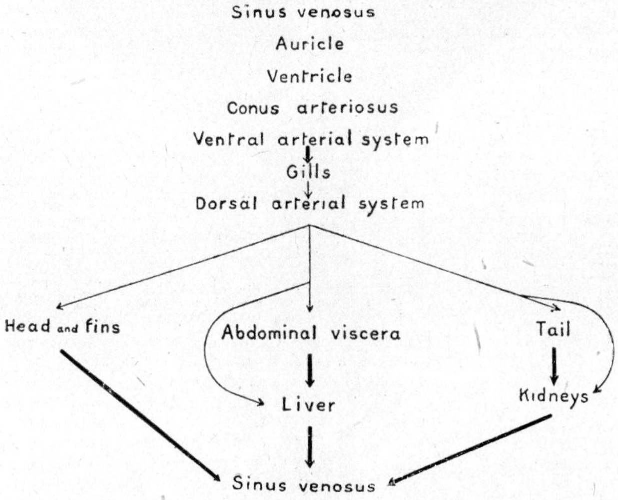

Sinus venosus

Auricle

Ventricle

Conus arteriosus

Ventral arterial system
↓
Gills
↓
Dorsal arterial system

Head and fins   Abdominal viscera   Tail

Liver   Kidneys

Sinus venosus

FIG. 335.—A diagram of the circulation of the blood in a dogfish. Thick lines indicate venous blood, narrow lines arterial blood.

cerebral hemispheres of the frog, but is single and some-what globular in shape ; its double nature is shown out-wardly by a shallow longitudinal groove and internally by the presence of two lateral ventricles. It has no cortex. The two olfactory lobes lie at the sides of the cerebrum, each arising from it by a short, stout stalk, which expands

29

into a large mass against the olfactory capsule. The lateral ventricles of the cerebrum are continued into the olfactory lobes. The cerebrum is followed by a long

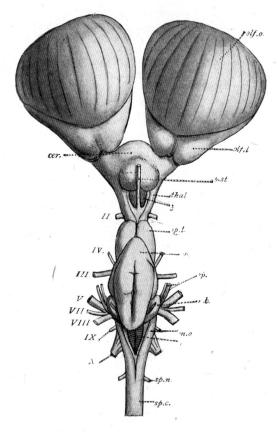

FIG. 336.—The brain of the dogfish, seen from above.

cb., Cerebellum ; *cer.*, cerebrum ; *m.o.*, medulla oblongata ; *olf.l.*, olfactory lobe ; *olf.o.*, olfactory organ ; *op.*, ophthalmic branches of fifth and seventh nerves ; *op.l.*, optic lobes ; *p.st.*, pineal stalk ; *r.b.*, restiform body ; *sp.c.*, spinal cord ; *sp.n.*, spinal nerve ; *thal.*, thalamencephalon ; 3, 4, third and fourth ventricles ; *II.-V., VII.-X.*, cranial nerves.

thalamencephalon, containing a spacious third ventricle
from the hinder part of whose thin roof arises the long,
hollow, slender pineal stalk, which runs forward over the

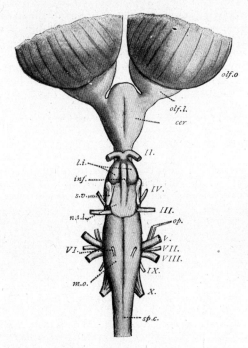

FIG. 337. —The brain of a dogfish, in ventral view.

cer., Cerebrum; *inf.*, return limb of infundibulum, constituting the ventral lobe of
the pituitary body; *l.i.*, lobi inferiores; *m.o.*, medulla oblongata; *n.s.l.*, neuro,
intermediate lobe of pituitary body; *olf.l.*, olfactory lobe; *olf.o.*, olfactory
organ; *op.*, ophthalmic branches of fifth and seventh nerves; *sp.c.*, spinal
cord; *s.v.*, saccus vasculosus; *II.–X.*, cranial nerves.

cerebrum to end in a small swelling below the membrane
which covers the anterior fontanelle. On the floor of the
thalamencephalon, the infundibulum bears at the sides a
pair of thick-walled *lobi inferiores* and behind these a

thin-walled, vascular expansion known as the *saccus vasculosus*, after which it expands as the *posterior (neuro-intermediate) lobe* of the pituitary body (p. 64) and then turns forward as the *ventral lobe* of that structure. The anterior lobe is present as glandular tissue applied to the upper side of the ventral lobe. The mid-brain, which succeeds the thalamencephalon, bears above the two optic lobes, which stand closer than those of the frog. The cerebellum behind them is much larger than that of the frog and oval in outline, with the long axis fore and aft, and overhangs the optic lobes in front and the thin-roofed fourth ventricle in the medulla oblongata behind it. The medulla is produced forward into a pair of wings, the *restiform bodies*, which lie at the side of the cerebellum.

The cranial nerves resemble in number and general

Nerves. distribution those of the frog, but the presence of the gills and other differences in the arrangement in the organs of the head causes the distribution to differ in detail. The olfactory nerves are groups of fine threads which pass into the olfactory organs from the adjoining olfactory lobes of the brain. The optic nerves pass from the lower surface of the thalamencephalon, each through the optic foramen of the opposite side, to the eyeballs, crossing in a chiasma below the brain. The third or oculomotor nerve of each side, arising from the ventral surface of the mid-brain, passes outwards through its foramen into the orbit of its own side, where it supplies the superior, inferior, and internal recti muscles of the eye by short branches and gives a long branch across the floor of the orbit to the inferior oblique. The slender fourth, trochlear, or patheticus nerve arises from the dorsal surface of the brain between the optic lobes and the cerebellum, and passes out through a special foramen to supply the superior oblique muscle of its side. The sixth or abducent nerve is also slender. It arises from the ventral side of the medulla and supplies the external rectus muscle, passing through the same foramen as the main branches of the fifth and seventh nerves. The latter two nerves, with the eighth, arise close together from the sides of the medulla below the restiform body. The fifth or trigeminal has three branches. Of these the first, or ophthalmic, parts at once from the rest of the nerve, turns forward within the skull, passes through a foramen in the side of the cranium above the recti muscles, and runs forwards along the outer side of the cranial wall, together with the similar branch of the seventh nerve, to leave the

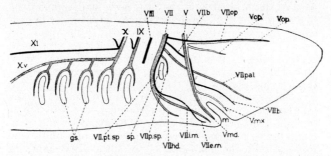

FIG. 338.—A diagram of certain cranial nerves in the dogfish. The nerves omitted (III, IV, VI) consist of motor fibres to the eye muscles. Those shown supply the visceral arches and certain other parts. They contain (*a*, shaded) visceral motor (autonomic) and visceral sensory fibres ; (*b*, black) fibres from the neuromast system (p. 458) and ear ; and (*c*, white), chiefly in V, some other somatic sensory fibres from the skin.

V.-X., Roots of the nerves ; *V.md.*, *V.mx.*, *V.op.*, mandibular, maxillary, and superficial ophthalmic branches of the ffifth nerve ; *Vop'.*, deep ophthalmic nerve, not mentioned in the text, inconspicuous in the rough hound, but large in many other fishes (p. 465) ; *VII.b.*, *VII. e.m.*, *VII.hd.*, *VII.i.m.*, *VII.op.*, *VII.pal.*, buccal, external mandibular, hyoidean, internal mandibular, ophthalmic, and palatine branches of the seventh nerve ; *VII.p.sp.*, *VII.pi.sp.*, pre- and post-spiracular divisions of hyomandibular branch of seventh nerve ; *X.l.*, *X.v.*, lateral line and main visceral branches of the tenth nerve ; *g.s.*, gill slits ; *m.*, mouth ; *sp.*, spiracle

orbit by a foramen above the nasal capsule and be distributed to the skin of the snout. The rest of the nerve leaves the cranium by a large foramen below the recti muscles and runs outwards across the orbital floor as a broad band, which divides into a maxillary branch to the upper jaw and a mandibular branch to the lower. The seventh or facial nerve has a complicated distribution : it possesses (i) an ophthalmic branch which, leaving the cranium by a foramen above the ophthalmic branch of the fifth, accompanies the latter ; (ii) a buccal branch, which joins the main branch of the fifth within the skull, crosses the orbit with it, leaves it before it divides, and is distributed to certain sense organs (neuromast organs, p. 458) of the side of the face ; (iii) a small palatine branch which runs across the floor of the orbit behind the fifth nerve and supplies the roof of the mouth ; and (iv) a large hyomandibular branch which runs outwards in the hinder wall of the orbit and passes down the hyoid arch. This branch gives off a small prespiracular branch to the anterior wall of the spiracle, after which it passes as the postspiracular nerve behind the spiracle and divides into three branches—an internal and an external mandibular, and a hyoidean. Of these, it is the internal mandibular which corresponds to the mandibular (chorda tympani) of the frog. The palatine and hyomandibular branches pass together through the same foramen with the main part of the fifth. The eighth or auditory nerve passes into the auditory capsule to supply the inner ear. The ninth or glossopharyngeal nerve arises from the side of the medulla behind and rather below the eighth, passes through a passage in the cartilage of the auditory capsule, emerges by its foramen behind the capsule, and turns down the first branchial arch, after giving off a small " pretrematic " branch to the hyoid arch. The tenth or vagus nerve arises by a number of roots immediately behind the ninth. It leaves the skull by a foramen beside the occipital condyle, and runs backwards along the anterior cardinal sinus, lying just median to that vessel, immediately against its lining, through which it can be seen if the vein be opened. It represents several nerves fused, and gives off across the floor of the sinus a branch to every branchial arch behind the first, each such branch bearing a pretrematic branch to the preceding arch. Shortly after leaving the skull the vagus gives off a lateral line nerve, which runs along the side of the body, rather deep among the muscles, and supplies an organ in the skin known as the lateral line, which will be mentioned later. After giving off the last of its branches to the branchial arches, the vagus passes downwards to supply the heart and other viscera (Fig. 321).

These nerves and their principal branches may be summarised as follows :

Name.	Function.	Distribution.
I. Olfactory . . .	Afferent	Nasal organ.
II. Optic	Afferent	Retina of eye.
III. Oculomotor . .	Efferent	1 oblique and 3 recti eye-muscles.
IV. Trochlear . . .	Efferent	Superior oblique muscle.
V. Trigeminal . . .	Mixed	
(a) Ophthalmic . .	Afferent	Snout.
(b) Maxillary . .	Afferent	Upper jaw.
(c) Mandibular . .	Mixed	Mandibular arch (lower jaw).
VI. Abducent . . .	Efferent	External rectus muscle.
VII. Facial . . .	Mixed	
(a) Ophthalmic . .	Afferent	Snout (neuromast organs).
(b) Buccal . . .	Afferent	Side of head (,,).
(c) Palatine . .	Afferent	Roof of mouth.
(d) Hyomandibular .	Mixed	Hyoid (and mandibular) arches.
VIII. Auditory . . .	Afferent	Ear.
IX. Glossopharyngeal . .	Mixed	1st branchial (and hyoid) arches.
X. Vagus	Mixed	
(a) Lateral line . .	Afferent	Lateral line sense organ.
(b) Branchial branches	Mixed	Branchial arches 2–5.
(c) Main visceral . .	Mixed	Viscera.

The comparison of the cranial nerves with dorsal and ventral roots of spinal nerves which was made with regard to the frog (p. 92) holds good for the dogfish and all other vertebrates. A feature of their distribution which was not obvious in the latter animal is that certain of them (V., VII., IX. and X.) give branches, whose function is chiefly visceral, to the arches. Each such branch gives off an afferent *pretrematic* branch to the arch in front of that which it chiefly serves (in the case of the fifth nerve this branch passes to the upper jaw). The *post-trematic* branch is efferent or mixed. The lay-out of the primary components of these nerves is shown in Fig. 338.

The spinal nerves of the dogfish are more numerous than those of the frog, but in their general structure and distribution resemble them. The dorsal and ventral roots by which each arises from the spinal cord pass through the wall of the neural canal by small notches in the hinder edges of the intercalary pieces and neural arches respectively. The sympathetic system is irregular and difficult of dissection in the dogfish, but in the main outlines of its plan it resembles that of the frog.

Each of the olfactory organs of the dogfish (Figs. 332 and
Sense Organs. 336) is a sac enclosed in the olfactory capsule
of its side of the body. It opens externally by
the nostril, but has no internal opening into the mouth.
Its walls are thrown into vertical folds covered with an
epithelium which contains sense cells. The eyes resemble in
all important respects those of the frog (p. 98), and need no.

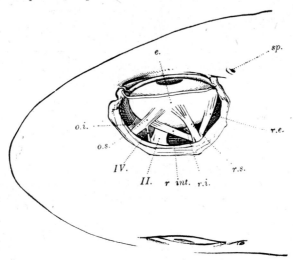

FIG. 339.—The head of a dogfish, seen from above with the right orbit
opened.

e., Eyeball ; *o.i.*, *o.s.*, inferior and superior oblique muscles ; *r.e.*, *r.i.*, *r.int.*, *r.s.*,
external, inferior, internal, and superior recti muscles ; *sp.*, spiracle ; *II.*, optic
nerve ; *IV.*, fourth nerve.

here be described. On account, however, of their larger size,
they are more suitable objects for the study of the eye
muscles. Like the eyes of the frog and those of all other
vertebrate animals, each is moved by six muscles, which
arise from the inner wall of the orbit. Four of these, known
as recti, arise together near the hinder end of the orbit and
diverge to be inserted into the eyeball at various points.
The *rectus superior* runs outwards and forwards and is in-

serted into the upper side of the eyeball. The *rectus inferior* runs a similar course below the eyeball to be inserted into its lower surface. The *rectus internus* or *medialis* runs forwards between the eyeball and the cranial wall and is inserted into the front side of the former. The *rectus externus* or *lateralis* runs outwards behind the eyeball, into whose hinder surface it is inserted. The remaining two muscles are

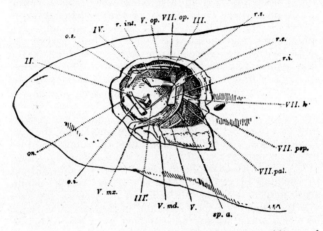

FIG. 340.—The left side of the head of a dogfish with the orbit opened and the eye removed.

on., Orbitonasal foramen ; *o.i.*, *o.s.*, *r.e.*, *r.i.*, *r.int.*, *r.s.*, eye muscles as in Fig. 339; *sp.a.*, spiracular artery ; *II.–VII.*, cranial nerves ; *III.*, third nerve entering the orbit and dividing to supply eye muscles ; *III.*, its branch to the inferior oblique muscle ; *V.md.*, *V.mx.*, *V.op.*, mandibular, maxillary, and ophthalmic branches of fifth nerve ; *VII.hm.*, *VII.op.*, *VII.pal.*, *VII.psp.*, hyomandibular, ophthalmic, palatine, and prespiracular branches of seventh nerve.

known as obliqui. They arise together near the anterior end of the orbit and pass outwards and backwards to their insertions into the eyeball. The *obliquus superior* is inserted into the dorsal surface of the eyeball just in front of the superior rectus ; the *obliquus inferior* is inserted in a corresponding position in front of the insertion of the inferior rectus upon the lower side of the eyeball. By the contraction of various combinations of these muscles the eyeball may be turned in any direction. The lower eyelid is movable. The structure of the internal ear is essentially similar to that of the frog (p. 100). Its communication with the external water and the absence of a drum have already been mentioned (p. 426). Besides these sense organs, which are found in all vertebrates, fishes possess a peculiar system, known as the *neuromast organs*, which are not found in any other adult vertebrates with the exception of certain newts. These consist of sensory patches of the epidermis containing sense cells, which bear short, stiff sense hairs, and supporting cells. In the dogfish the sense patches are placed at the bottom of tubes in the skin, which are filled with slime or mucus. The most conspicuous of these tubes runs along the side of the body, its position being marked by a rather indistinct *lateral line* (Figs. 315, 317). It opens upon the surface of the body at intervals. On reaching the head the lateral line divides into two branches, which pass above and below the eye, branch again, and rejoin in front upon the snout. Besides this branching system of tubes there are, upon the snout, others which pass straight inwards through the skin and end in swellings or ampullæ (Fig. 325, *n.am.*) which contain sense patches. These can be found by pressing the skin and thus squeezing the mucus out of them in little drops. The neuromast organs are supplied by a special set of nerve fibres, which join the same portion of the grey matter of the brain with which the fibres of the auditory nerve are connected, but enter the brain by various nerves (Fig. 338), of which the principal are the ophthalmic branch of the seventh and the lateral line branch of the tenth nerve. The function of these organs is the detection of vibrations in the water which are of too low a frequency to be detected by the ear. The latter must be regarded as a specially highly developed part of the same system as the neuromast organs.

Finally, we may note the condition of the ductless glands (p. 62) in the dogfish. With the thyroid and the pituitary body we have already dealt (pp. 444, 452). The thymus is present as lobed masses of glandular tissue above the gill clefts, from whose epithelium it arises during development,

Ductless Glands.

as in all vertebrates. The adrenal bodies are represented by two separate elements. Between the kidneys, an elongate structure, the *interrenal body*, derived from the cœlomic epithelium, represents the cortex of the adrenals of the frog and higher vertebrates ; on the course of the sympathetic chains a number of bodies of the same origin as the cells of the sympathetic ganglia represent the medulla of the adrenals. These bodies are the *suprarenals*, properly so-called, though that name is often applied to the entire adrenal bodies

CHAPTER XXII

COLD-BLOODED VERTEBRATA [1]

THE dogfish and the frog are examples of two of the principal classes of backboned animals—the **Vertebrates—Cold- and Warm-blooded.** Fishes, or *Pisces*, and the *Amphibia*. The members of these groups, unlike the Birds (*Aves*) and Suckling Animals, or *Mammalia*, which are the subjects of later chapters, are cold-blooded.[2] There exist two further classes of vertebrates, the *Cyclostomata* and the *Reptilia*, both of which are also cold-blooded. The cold-blooded vertebrates, other than the two which we have already studied at some length, deserve our attention both for their own sake and also because of the light which is thrown by their anatomy upon that of the examples we are studying in detail. We shall see that some of them link the frog to mammals, others bridge the gap between the frog and the dogfish and lead downwards from the latter to the lancelet, and yet others exhibit, well developed, organs which are lacking or insignificant in the dogfish and frog.

The Cyclostomes are a small group, of low organisation, **Cyclostomata.** whose members are fish-like but differ from all other Vertebrata in that their mouth has no jaws. Extinct members of this group (*Ostracoderms*) had a strong bony armour in the skin and probably lived a more active life than their existing representatives, the Lampreys and Hags, which are semiparasitic creatures,

---

[1] It has been assumed in writing this chapter that it will usually be studied after Chapter XXIV., but it is not necessary that this order should be observed.

[2] That is, in them the temperature of the body varies with that of its surroundings. See pp. 74 and 557. Invertebrate animals are also cold-blooded.

without limbs, scales, or bony tissue, that live on juices obtained from their prey through a circular, suctorial mouth. In place of the usual pair of nostrils, these

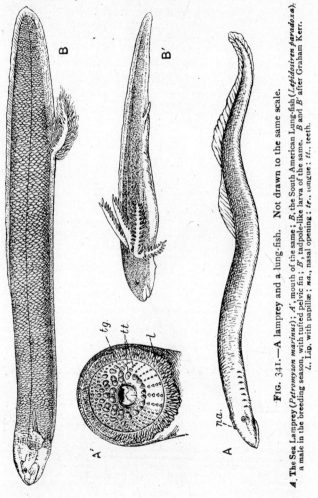

FIG. 341.—A lamprey and a lung-fish. Not drawn to the same scale.

A, The Sea Lamprey (*Petromyzon marinus*); *A'*, mouth of the same; *B*, the South American Lung-fish (*Lepidosiren paradoxa*), a male in the breeding season, with tufted pelvic fin; *B'*, tadpole-like larva of the same. *B* and *B'* after Graham Kerr. *l.*, Lip, with papillæ; *na.*, nasal opening; *tr.*, tongue; *tt.*, teeth.

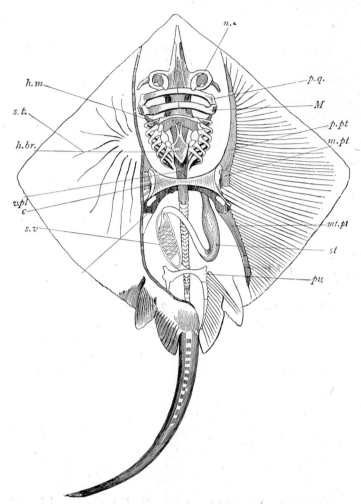

FIG. 342. — A skate, dissected to show its skeleton and the position of
the alimentary canal in its abdominal cavity. — From Thomson.

c., Coracoid region of pectoral girdle; *h.br.*, basibranchial cartilage; *h.m.*, hyomandibular cartilage; *M*, cartilage of lower jaw; *m.pt.*, mesopterygium;
mt.pt., metapterygium; *n.c.*, nasal capsule; *p.pt.*, propterygium; *p.q.*, cartilage of upper jaw (palato-quadrate); *pu.*, ischiopubic bar of pelvic girdle;
s.t., sensory tubules in the skin; *s.v.*, spiral valve; *sc.*, scapula; *st.*, stomach;
v.bl., fused vertebræ.

creatures, and some of their extinct forbears, have a single median opening which leads both to the olfactory organ and also to a sac belonging to the pituitary body. In the Lamprey (*Petromyzon*) this nostril is on the top of the head. The Lamprey has an interesting larva, the *Ammocœtes*, which feeds much as the lancelet does, the thyroid gland opening on the floor of the pharynx and, like the endostyle, secreting mucus, which is carried upwards by peripharyngeal bands and backwards along the roof of the pharynx to the gullet. In the scientific classification of the animal kingdom the Cyclostomata are separated from all other Vertebrata, which, from their possession of jaws, are known as *Gnathostomata*.

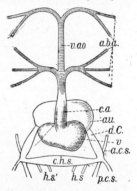

FIG. 343.— A semi-diagrammatic view of the heart and neighbouring vessels of a skate.

a.b.a., Afferent branchial arteries *a.c.s.*, anterior cardinal sinus; *au.*, auricle; *c.a.*, conus arteriosus; *c.h.s.*, common hepatic sinus; *d.C.*, ductus Cuvieri; *h.s'.*, hepatic sinuses; *p.c.s.*, posterior cardinal sinus; *v.*, ventricle; *v.ao.*, ventral aorta.

Fishes : Elasmobranchii : The Skate. Among fishes, three subclasses now exist (see p. 471), the Cartilaginous Fishes or *Elasmobranchii*, the Bony Fishes or *Actinopterygii*, and the Lung Fishes or *Choanichthyes*. The Elasmobranchii have no bones and no air-bladder, their gill clefts are uncovered, and they wear placoid scales (p. 422). Besides the dogfishes and sharks, skates and rays belong to this group. In a skate, the body is transformed by an immense development of the pectoral fins, which stretch forward to the end of the snout and spread outwards so that the width of the fish is much greater than its depth, and by a narrowing of the tail to a whip-like organ. The skate lives upon the ground, drawing its breaths of water through the large spiracles, which are upon the top of the head, whereas the gill clefts are on the smooth, white

under side with the mouth.   The spiracle is used for taking
in water in the dogfish also, but is there not of the same

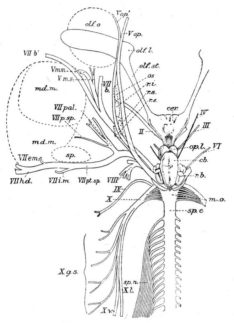

Fig. 344.—The central nervous system of a skate.

b., Cerebellum ; *cer.*, cerebrum ; *m.o.*, medulla oblongata ; *ma.m.*, mandibular
muscle ; *olf.l.*, olfactory lobe ; *olf.o.*, olfactory organ ; *olf.st.*, stalk of olfactory
lobe ; *op.l.*, optic lobe ; *os.*, superior oblique muscle ; *r.b.*, restiform body ;
r.e., *r.i.*, *r.s.*, external, internal, and superior recti muscles ; *sp.*, spiracle ;
sp.c., spinal cord ; *sp.n.*, spinal nerves (converging to form brachial plexus) ;
II.–X., cranial nerves ; *V.m.m.*, common stem of maxillary and mandibular
branches of fifth nerve ; *V.m.s.*, subsidiary branches in maxillary region ;
V.op., superficial ophthalmic branch of fifth nerve, with which is united that of
seventh nerve ; *V.op'.*, deep ophthalmic nerve ; *VII.b.*, inner buccal, *VII.b'*,
outer buccal, *VII.em.*, *VII.hd.*, *VII.i.m..*, *VII.p.sp.*, *VII.pal.*, *VII.pt.sp.*,
external mandibular, hyoidean, internal mandibular, prespiracular, palatine,
and postspiracular branches of seventh nerve ; *X.g.s.*, *Xl.*, *Xv.*, gill slit, lateral
line, and main visceral branches of tenth nerve (vagus).

importance, since the fish, not being flattened upon the
ground, can generally obtain most of its water through

the mouth. The arrangement of the principal blood-vessels of the Common Skate, which differs a little from that of the dogfish, is shown in Fig. 343. In the nervous system (Fig. 344) there will be seen to be two ophthalmic nerves, one of which—the *superficial ophthalmic*—passes above certain of the eye muscles (the internal and superior recti and the superior oblique), whereas the other—the *deep ophthalmic (ophthalmicus profundus)*—passes below them. The first of these nerves corresponds to the two ophthalmics which are conspicuous in the dogfish—the ophthalmic branch of the seventh cranial nerve and the (superficial) ophthalmic branch of the fifth—closely united. The deep ophthalmic, which is represented in the dogfish by an inconspicuous twig of the fifth nerve, sends branches to the eyeball and runs on to the snout.

Although it appears to arise from the fifth, this nerve is really the dorsal root of the nerve whose ventral root is the third (p. 92). The ophthalmic nerve of the frog is a deep ophthalmic, though the superficial ophthalmic, which does not appear as such, is perhaps united with it. The ophthalmic of a mammal divides not far from its origin into a nasal branch, which

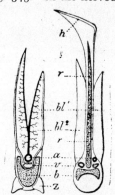

Fig. 345.—Transverse sections through gill arches of a dogfish (on the right) and a cod, showing how Elasmobranchii differ from Actinopterygii and Choanichthyes in respect of these organs.—From Sedgwick, after R. Hertwig.

a, Afferent, branchial artery; *b,* branchial arch of skeleton; *bl*[1] and *bl*[2], gill lamellæ; *h,* skin of the side of the body between the openings of two gill clefts in the shark; *r,* cartilaginous gill-ray supporting the septum between two gill pouches in the same; *v,* efferent branchial arteries, double in the shark, single in the cod; *z,* small tooth-like tubercle (in some Teleosteans elongated as a "gill raker"), one of a double row on the branchial arch of the cod.

represents the deep nerve, and a frontal, which may be the superficial nerve. The ophthalmic branch of the seventh nerve (together with the buccal and external mandibular branches of the same nerve and the lateral line branch of the vagus, which also supply neuromast organs) is lost, with the neuromast organs which it supplies, in the adults of animals higher than fishes.

30

Branches of the lateral line system extend on to the pectoral fins of the skate, and are connected with the exterior by rather long tubules (Fig. 342). The anterior vertebræ are fused into a continuous mass. Both ovaries are present.

Actinopterygii. The Actinopterygii are not the only fishes which have bone as well as cartilage in the skeleton, but they are the most bony. They have in the abdominal cavity an air bladder which is a hydrostatic organ, oxygen being secreted into or absorbed from it so as to alter the specific gravity of the fish ; a peculiar, thin, non-nervous roof (pallium) to the cerebrum ; and a bone-supported fold, the *operculum*, over the external openings of the gill clefts, which lead straight outwards through the sides of the throat, and do not slant backward through pouches like those of the Elasmo-branchii (p. 435). Thus the arches are narrow from within outwards, and cannot accommodate the full width of the gills, which project into the chamber under the gill cover (Fig. 345). The scales of the Actinopterygii are flat, bony plates, only in a few cases provided with small vestiges of enamel-capped spines of the placoid type, and are embedded in the skin, usually overlapping like tiles on a roof.

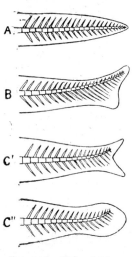

FIG 346.—Tails of fishes.

A, Protocercal (Cyclostomata and Dipnoi); *B*, Heterocercal (Elasmo-branchii and Ganoids) ; *C'*, *C''*, Paracercal (Teleostei).

"Ganoids." Certain small sections of the Actinopterygii, loosely known as " Ganoids," of which the Sturgeon (*Acipenser*) is an example, keep a varying number of the following features of Elasmobranchii : the spiracle, spiral valve, common vent or cloaca, muscular

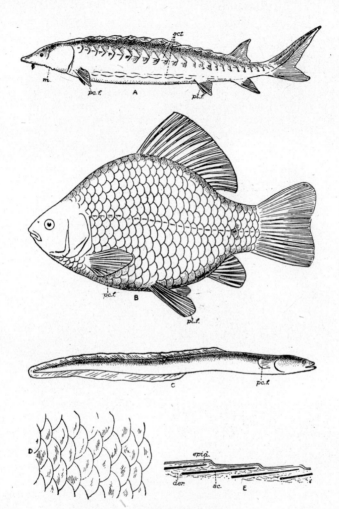

FIG. 347.—Actinopterygii.

A, The Sturgeon; *B*, the Crucian carp; *C*, the eel; *D*, scales on the skin of a whiting, in surface view; *E*, the same in section.

der., Dermis; *epid.*, epidermis; *m.*, mouth; *pc.f.*, pectoral fins; *pl.f.*, pelvic fins; *sc.*, scales; *sct.*, bony plates or scutes.

conus arteriosus (instead of a non-muscular " bulbus arteriosus "), and obviously unsymmetrical or " hetero-cercal " tail (the bony framework of the apparently sym-metrical " paracercal " tail of an ordinary fish is really unsymmetrical, except in certain cases, such as the cod, etc., where, by the absence of the upturned tip of the back-bone, it reaches a complete secondary symmetry). Most ganoids have for scales stout, bony armour plates, over which the epidermis wears away, very different from the thin rounded *cycloid* scales which clothe the majority of Actinopterygii.

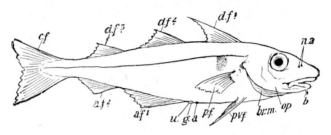

FIG. 348.—A diagram of the Haddock.—From Thomson.

a., Anus; *af*[1]., *af*[2]., anal fins; *b.*, barbule; *br.m.*, branchiostegal membrane (a continuation of the gill cover); *cf.*, caudal fin; *df*[1]–*df*[3]., dorsal fins ; *g.*, genital opening ; *na.*, nasal openings (double on each side) ; *op.*, operculum or gill cover ; *pf.*, pectoral fin ; *pvf.*, pelvic fin ; *u.*, urinary opening.

All these features, however, disappear in the great mass of ordinary bony fishes or Teleostei. The Whiting (*Gadus merlangus*), which, with its near kindred the Haddock (*G. æglefinus*) and Cod (*G. morrhua*), is often dissected in the laboratory,[1] is a typical Teleostean, both in the above respects and in the very large number of bones which compose its complicated skeleton (Figs. 544, 545). In it, as in many others, the pelvic fins have shifted forwards till they lie actually in front of the pectorals, and the air-bladder does not com-municate with the gullet. The Salmon, Herring, Carp,

**Teleostei :
The Whiting.**

[1] The student who wishes to study systematically one of these three fishes will find on pp. 750, 751 a summary of its anatomy with addi-tional figures.

and Eel resemble the ganoids in carrying their pelvic fins
in the normal position, and in that the air-bladder communicates with the gullet, which it does on the dorsal side.
Figs. 349 and 350 show the ventral and dorsal arterial
systems of the whiting. They should be compared with
those of the dogfish (Figs. 331 and 332), and the differences
noted, particularly the absence of an afferent vessel to the

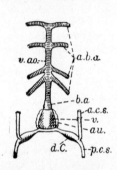

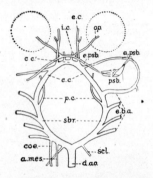

FIG. 349.—A semi-dia-
grammatic ventral view
of the heart and neigh-
bouring blood-vessels
of a cod.

a.b.a., Afferent branchial
arteries; *a.c.s.*, anterior
cardinal sinus; *au.*, auricle;
b.a., bulbus arteriosus;
d.C., ductus Cuvieri;
p.c.s., posterior cardinal
sinus; *v.*, ventricle; *v.ao.*,
ventral aorta.

FIG. 350 —A diagrammatic ventral
view of the dorsal arterial system
of a cod.

a.mes., anterior mesenteric artery; *a.psb.*,
afferent pseudobranchials; *c.c.*, carotids;
c.c'., anastomosis between the internal carotids which completes the *circulus cephali-
cus*; *coe.*, cœliac; *d.ao.*, dorsal aorta;
e.b.a., efferent branchial; *e.c.*, orbitonasal
or "external carotid"; *e.psb.*, efferent
pseudobranchial; *i.c.*, internal carotid;
op., ophthalmic; *p.c.*, orbital or "posterior
carotid"; *psb.*, pseudobranch; *sbr.*, suprabranchial; *scl.*, subclavian artery.

hyoid arch, which in the whiting carries no gill, but only a
vascular vestige or pseudobranch supplied from the efferent
system, and the replacement of the dorsal aorta in the gill
region by two suprabranchial arteries, which recall those
of *Amphioxus*. The whiting also reveals a feature in which
the Teleostei (and one or two ganoids) are unique among
Vertebrata—namely, that the oviducts are continuous
with the ovaries. The bony flat fishes (Soles, Plaice, etc.)
are related in general features to the whiting, but are

flattened—not, as is the skate, from above downward, but from side to side in a remarkable way. They lie on one side, which is white and has lost its eye, this being brought on to the upper, coloured side by a twist of the skull in the region of the orbits. The body is very tall— that is, in its present position, broad. The young are shaped like ordinary fishes.

At this point we may pause to consider a relevant and very interesting topic—the history of verte-
The History of Vertebrata. brate animals. There is good reason to believe that this began in inland waters. The fact that the body of the lower vertebrata is so built as to

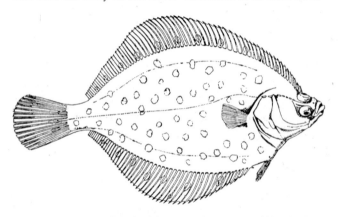

FIG. 351.—The Plaice (*Pleuronectes platessa*).—From Shipley and MacBride.

be a muscular, streamlined swimming machine suggests that it came into being where there were strong constant currents such as those of rivers ; and the glomeruli by which the kidneys of vertebrata are enabled to excrete water rapidly look like a defence against a peril which, as we have seen, besets freshwater animals—the danger of dilution of the body fluids. Moreover, the earliest remains of vertebrates are found in freshwater or estuarine deposits. The first vertebrates were probably cyclostomes, and a great advance was made when in some of them one of the gill arches came to strengthen the borders of the mouth and thus made biting possible. (This arch — the mandibular arch — was not the foremost: there appear to have been two clefts in front of the present position of the mouth.) Thus the true Fishes, the earliest gnathostomes, came into being. The first of them—the Sub-class *Aphetohyoidea*, long since extinct—had a full-sized cleft between the mandibular and hyoid arches, but before long this cleft became reduced so that it was possible for the jaws (the mandibular arch) to be held firm by ligaments attaching them to the hyomandibula. Thus the modern fishes arrived.

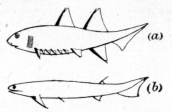

FIG. 352A.—Aphetohyoid Fishes. —From Swinnerton.

(a) *Climatius* (Devonian); (b) *Acanthodes* (Permian).
Both belong to the Order Acanthodi, which had a strong spine in front of each fin. *Climatius*, one of the oldest known fishes, has on each side a row of small fins from the pectoral to the pelvic, and this suggests that in other fishes the latter two fins are the remaining members of a longitudinal series, which perhaps arose by the break-up of an original longitudinal fin on each side like the long dorsal fin of some fishes.

Some of these passed into the sea and there, after a time, for some reason bone disappeared from their skeletons and they became Elasmobranchs—thoroughly marine creatures using the remarkable expedient, which we studied in the dogfish, of retaining urea in their blood so that they do not lose water to the medium around them. The fishes that remained in freshwaters became more bony, lost their gill pouches, and developed opercula.

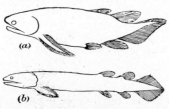

FIG. 352B.—Crossopterygian Fishes. —From Swinnerton.

(a) *Notoptychius*; (b) *Glyptopanus*. Note the stout central portions of the fins, containing skeleton and doubtless muscle, and thus having the makings of legs.

During the Devonian period freshwaters were subject to

periodic drying up, when much of that part of them which
continued to exist became foul and stagnant.   In such conditions some means of breathing air was essential.   Those
fishes that survived this ordeal did so by gulping air from
the surface and using it for oxygenating their blood in the
lining of a pouch which they developed from their gullets
and which, as it grew, presently came to lie under the
backbone, where, as the air bladder, it now is in modern
bony fishes.   Most of the fishes in which this happened
presently found another way out of the difficulty by going
down to the sea, where, when once they were acclimatised
to sea water, they found food plentiful and oxygen to be
had by their gills.   Their air bladder, however, did not
degenerate but became the hydrostatic apparatus which
it now is.   These fishes are the Actinopterygii.   Most of
them have lost the duct that connected the air bladder
to the alimentary canal, but some keep it, and of them a
few can still use the bladder for respiration.   These are
among those that, with the improvement of conditions in
freshwaters, have once more returned thither.

The fishes that remained to brave it out under the

Choanichthyes. unfavourable conditions of freshwaters in
Devonian times are known as the *Choanich-
thyes*.   The better to breathe air by thrusting their snouts
out of water they adopted a new device.   The oronasal
grooves which in the dogfish and its allies run from the
nostrils to the edge of the mouth are in Choanichthyes
closed over so that they have become tubes, and their
mouthward openings have shifted into the mouth, where
they become internal nares.   Thus air can be drawn
through the nostrils into the mouth and so into the air
bladder, which is, in fact, a lung or, where it is divided,
a pair of lungs.   The Choanichthyes fell into two groups—
the *Crossopterygii* and the *Dipnoi*.   Of these one crossopterygian and three dipnoans alone survive.   Both were
similarly adapted to breathing air, but the Dipnoi had a
peculiar configuration of the skull and teeth which enabled
them to crunch shellfish, and the fins of the Crossopterygii
were shorter and stouter.   Nothing is known of the internal
anatomy of the Crossopterygii but they probably shared
with the Dipnoi certain features that point forward to the

Amphibia, notably special arrangements in the heart and vessels to and from the lungs, paired cerebral hemi-

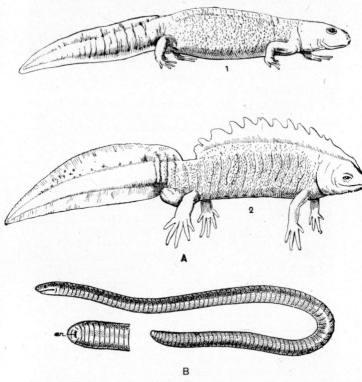

FIG. 353.—Amphibians.

A, The Warty newt (*Molge cristata*); 1, female; 2, male at the breeding season, showing the crest which is specially developed at that time; *B*, *Cœcilia*, one of the Gymnophiona. *an.*, anus, in an enlarged view of the underside of the hinder end. Note the absence of a tail.

spheres with roofs of nervous tissue, and a larva like the tadpole.

Towards the end of the Devonian period Crossopterygii began to invade the land. Their powers of breathing and their strong muscular fins, adaptable to a clumsy kind of crawling, made this possible. The new adventure was perhaps first undertaken when it became necessary to wander from a drying pond to better waters, and extended on account of the supply of food provided by the plant life which was then becoming plentiful on land and beginning to support a population of arthropods. Land life turned the Crossopterygii that adopted it into Amphibia, the first of the great group *Tetrapoda*—vertebrates that have legs and live on land.

The Amphibians differ from fishes and agree with higher

Amphibia. vertebrates in two important respects—their paired limbs are pentadactyle (p. 49), and if they have unpaired fins these are without fin-rays. They are also like the higher vertebrates in possessing lungs and an inferior vena cava, but the Dipnoi have what are at least very passable attempts at both of these. Like the fishes, however, Amphibia have only ten cranial nerves, lay eggs without shells, lack the metanephros and the embryonic membranes known as the amnion and allantois (p. 649), and start life as gilled larvæ.

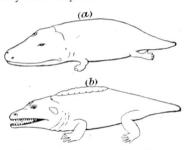

FIG. 354.—Stegocephalia.—From Swinnerton.

(a) *Mastodonsaurus* (Upper Trias) ; (b) *Cacops* (Permian).

Most modern Amphibia have no exoskeleton. The sturdy, long-legged, tailless animals, known as frogs and toads (*Anura*), and the long-bodied, short-legged, tailed Newts, or *Urodela*, are naked but the group also comprises the *Gymnophiona*— small blind, limbless, and tailless creatures, which live like earthworms in the soil of warm countries. The Gymnophiona have rings of small scales embedded in the skin, recalling those of the Teleostei, but probably really the last remains of a scaly armour that covered parts of the body of certain members of the earliest groups of

Amphibia (*Stegocephali*), now extinct. Upon the head of the Stegocephali as on that of the Crossopterygii the scales were replaced by bony plates that became a part of the skull, which was in other respects more highly developed than that of the frog. The skulls of modern Amphibia show a progressive simplification in Gymnophiona, frogs, and newts.

The reader will find on pp. 632–633 of this book an account of the fish-like arrangement of the arteries of a tadpole, and their relation to that of a frog. Here it may be added that in various newts more than one pair of aortic arches persists in the adult. In the Common Newt (*Molge*) the ductus arteriosus remains well developed, giving an additional pair of arches (the pulmonary) ; in the Salamander the missing third branchial arch, lying between the two that are persistent in the Common Newt, is also complete ; in other cases both ductus caroticus and ductus arteriosus remain open, and so on.

In the newts there is a distinction between two regions of the adult kidneys such as is found in the dogfish but not in frogs and toads (see Fig. 353).

The Amphibia are but amateurs at terrestrial life. **Reptilia.** Their not very efficient apparatus for breathing by forcing air into their lungs is supplemented by using the skin, which has therefore to be permeable, and consequently they lose much water through it when they are on land. What is even more important is that their eggs are laid as spawn, which must be kept wet, and that their gilled larvæ must live in the water. It is not surprising that such creatures are less numerous and successful than either the fishes, perfectly adapted to life in water, or the Reptilia, the next group of vertebrates to appear, which are thoroughly land-adapted animals. Reptiles [1] resemble Amphibians in being cold-blooded, lung-breathing, pentadactyle vertebrates, but they differ in a number of ways, in most of which they are the better fitted for a life on land. They have an impermeable exoskeleton of horny scales, with sometimes also bony plates ;

---

[1] The student who wishes to make a systematic study of the anatomy of a reptile will find assistance, with figures, in the practical directions, on p. 754, for the examination of a lizard.

their lungs are filled and emptied by a process of expansion and contraction which is more efficient than the injection procedure of the frog ; the heart and great arteries are better adapted to carry on the double circulation through the lungs and body ; their eggs are protected by a chalky shell, in which the embryo is saved from drying up by being enclosed in a sac of watery fluid, the *amnion,* and is provided with an organ (the *allantois*) by which it breathes through the porous shell ; they have no larval stage but by a great store of nourishment (yolk) in the egg are enabled to remain in the shell until they have taken on the adult form. They have twelve pairs of cranial nerves,[1] and their functional kidney is the metanephros (pp. 548, 636). Existing reptiles *crawl* with their bellies on the ground, like amphibians and unlike birds and mammals, which *walk* with bodies raised by their legs, since these are not only bent downwards at the middle joint (Fig. 359 A) but also have rotated inwards so as to stand under the flanks, parallel with the body. Certain extinct reptiles resembled birds and mammals in this respect.

FIG. 355.—A horse trotting. —From Pettigrew.

Walking. The paired limbs of vertebrates act as levers ; those of the pentadactyle type are compound levers composed of several segments jointed together, and are thus the better able to execute complicated movements and can lengthen by straightening. In walking they work essentially as follows : certain of them, being straightened, raise the body higher above the ground and tilt it onwards ; meanwhile the others, kept bent, moved partly by muscles, partly by the mere effect of gravity, swing forwards and take up a position in front of those that have remained upon the ground ; then those that have swung touch the ground, straighten, and in turn allow the rest to swing forwards. In four-legged animals it is usually the near fore leg and the off hind leg which work together (p. 56) ; in those which walk upon two legs the pair act alternately (Fig. 453).

The Reptiles supplanted the Amphibia as the dominant animals of the land, and many and various kinds of them

[1] Except in snakes.

came into existence, including some that flew and some that were as well adapted to marine life as the whales. But at the end of the mesozoic period they declined before the advance of two groups that arose from among them — the Birds and the Mammalia. These groups are quite unrelated ; indeed each of them resembles certain extinct reptiles more than it does the other ; but they have both solved a problem before which the reptiles failed. They are " warm-blooded " ; that is, by keeping the temperature in their bodies constant they ensure that their activity is neither slowed by cold nor disordered by excessive warmth. Thus in them one more of the major factors of the environment has been mastered. The existing members of the Reptilia are : Turtles, Crocodiles, Snakes, Lizards, and the Tuatara, a little lizard-like animal found in New Zealand.

The skulls of reptiles are complicated structures. They contain less cartilage than those we have dealt with as yet, and the arrangement of the bones is of interest in several ways. (1) In the occipital region, there are, as well as the exoccipitals at the sides,

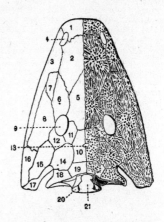

Fig. 356.—The skull of *Capitosaurus nasutus,* one of the Stegocephali. — From Reynolds, after von Zittel.

1, Premaxilla; 2, nasal; 3, maxilla; 4, anterior nares ; 5, frontal ; 6, prefrontal (*or* lachrymal); 7, lachrymal (*or* adlachrymal); 8, jugal ; 9, orbit ; 10, parietal ; 11, postfrontal ; 12, postorbital ; 13, interparietal foramen ; 14, supratemporal ; 15, squamosal ; 16, quadratojugal ; 17, quadrate ; 18, tabulare ; 19, postparietal ; 20, exoccipital ; 21, foramen magnum.

The sheet of membrane bones which forms the roof of this skull is a special development of the armour of bony scales which is found on other parts of the body of Stegocephali. It is not only the roof of the cranium, but stretches over the space between the cranium and the upper jaw (palato-pterygo-quadrate bar). In most other bony skulls, gaps (the fossæ, p. 440) appear between the bones of this dermal sheet.

a supraoccipital above and a basioccipital below, and (except in some extinct forms) a single occipital condyle underneath the foramen magnum replaces the two lateral ones of the frog. We shall see later that birds have one condyle, and mammals two. (2) The frontoparietals of the frog are usually represented here, as in most other vertebrates, by separate frontal and parietal bones. Prefrontals and postfrontals lie at the corners of the frontals. (3) In most cases (not in snakes) the forepart of the cranium is so compressed between the eyes that its hollow disappears, and it is replaced by a vertical sheet of membrane, the *interorbital septum*, so that in the dried skull the two orbits open widely into one another. The sphenethmoid of the frog is not found. (4) The quadrate cartilage of the frog is replaced by a quadrate bone, with which the lower jaw articulates. This bone is found in birds, but not in mammals, where the lower jaw articulates with the squamosal. (5) Except in turtles a *transpalatine bone* joins the maxilla to the pterygoid. (6) The true cranium is not large, but there is a scaffolding about it which

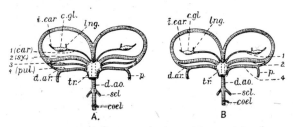

FIG. 357.—Semi-diagrammatic views of the arterial arches.

A, of a salamander ; *B*, of a common newt.

1–4, Vessels of the first to fourth branchial arches ; *c.gl.*, carotid gland ; *car.*, carotid arch ; *coel.*, cœliac artery ; *d.ao.*, dorsal aorta ; *d.ar.*, ductus arteriosus ; *i.car.*, internal carotid artery ; *lng.*, lingual artery ; *p.*, pulmonary artery ; *pul.*, pulmonary arch ; *tr.*, truncus arteriosus ; *scl.*, subclavian artery ; *sy.*, systemic arch.

supports the jaws, and upon which the skin of the head is stretched. This is the remains of a complete false roof of dermal bones found in the Stegocephali (p. 475), which is now under the skin. The more median of these bones form the roof of the cranium ; those at the sides, arching outwards to the upper jaw, enclose a cavity which is filled by the jaw muscles. The earliest reptiles had this roof complete and it is so in turtles, but in the remaining reptiles (and in all other land vertebrates) it is pierced by openings, known as *fossæ*, which give more room for the muscles. The scaffolding is most perfectly developed in the tuatara. Here there are two longitudinal bars or *arcades* strutted out from the skull by two transverse bars. The bars are composed as follows : (i) The *upper* or *supratemporal arcade*, parallel with the parietal region of the cranium, of the postorbital and squamosal (in other reptiles the postorbital becomes a part of the postfrontal) ; (ii) the *lower* or *infratemporal arcade*, below and outside the supratemporal, of the jugal and quadratojugal ; (iii) the *postorbital bar*, of the postfrontal, postorbital, and jugal ; (iv) the *post-temporal bar*, at the hinder end of the skull of the parietal and squamosal (with which is fused a

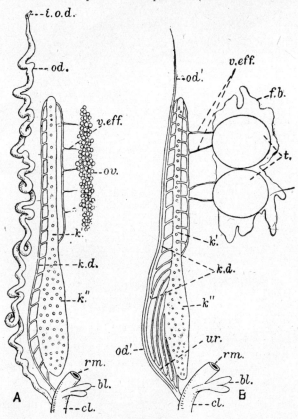

FIG. 358.—The urinary and generative organs of the right side in the Newt.

A, Female ; *B*, male.

bl., Bladder ; *cl.*, cloaca ; *f.b.*, fat body ; *i.o.d.*, internal opening of oviduct ; *k'.*, anterior part of kidney ; *k".*, posterior part ; *k.d.*, primitive kidney duct (Wolffian duct) ; *od.*, oviduct ; *od'.*, vestige of same in male ; *ov.*, ovary ; *rm.*, rectum ; *t.*, testis ; *ur.*, ureter ; *v.eff.*, vasa efferentia, or vestige of same in female.

A

B

FIG. 359.—Two English reptiles.—From Lindsay.

A, The Sand Lizard, *Lacerta agilis* B, the Viper, *Pelias berus.*

supratemporal, separate in lizards). The fossæ are : the *supra-temporal fossa*, between the cranium and the supratemporal arcade bounded by the postorbital bar in front and the post-temporal behind and the *infratemporal fossa*, similarly placed between the two arcades.

A similar arrangement is found in crocodiles, where, however, the bones are stouter and the fossæ smaller. In lizards there is a single fossa. Probably this is the supratemporal, the infratemporal arcade and fossa having disappeared owing to loss of the quadratojugal (Figs. 361 B and 549). In snakes (and some lizards) the supratemporal arcade and fossa also disappear. The result of these dispositions is that in crocodiles, turtles, and the tuatara the upper jaw is held rigid, in lizards it has a good deal more elasticity, and in snakes it is extremely elastic, so that the animal can swallow very large prey. The elasticity of the jaws of snakes is further increased by the absence in them of a process from the exoccipital which in other reptiles struts

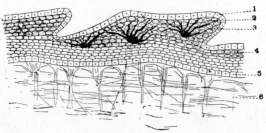

FIG. 360.—**A section through the skin of a lizard.**—From Shipley and MacBride.

1, " Epitrichial layer " of clear cells ; 2, heavily cornified cells forming the scale ; 3, pigment cell ; 4, ordinary cells of horny layer ; 5, innermost Malpighian layer ; 6, dermis.

the quadrate. If with these arrangements in reptiles we compare that in a frog, we shall find that the lower arcade is present, but that the absence of the upper arcade and the postorbital bar leaves one large fossa at the side of the cranium. The same is the case in birds. Mammals have an arcade, the zygomatic arch, composed mainly of an element, the jugal, which belongs to the lower arcade of the reptiles. Above this they have a single temporal fossa.

The heart of reptiles consists of sinus venosus, right and left auricles, and ventricle partly divided by an incomplete septum into right and left chambers, except in crocodiles, where the division is complete, so that there are two ventricles as in birds and mammals. There is no conus arteriosus, and the pulmonary artery and right and left systemic arches communicate with the ventricle each by an opening of its own, though the systemics may adhere outwardly to form a so-called truncus arteriosus. They cross at their bases, and

31

in crocodiles the right arch arises from the left ventricle and the left arch, with the pulmonary, from the right ventricle. The right is the

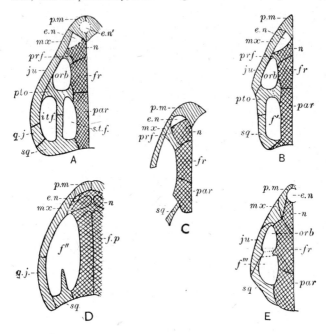

FIG. 361.—Diagrams of the arcades and fossæ of the skull.

A. In the tuatara and crocodiles ("diapsid" type); *B*, in most lizards; *C*, in snakes; *D*, in the frog; *E*, in mammals ("synapsid" type).

The bones of the cranium are shaded heavily, those of the arcades lightly.

e.n., External nares; *e.n'.*, the same in crocodiles; *f'., f"., f"'.*, the single fossa in lizards, frogs, and mammals, respectively; *f.p.*, fronto parietal; *fr.*, frontal; *i.t.f.*, infratemporal fossa; *ju.*, jugal; *mx.*, maxilla; *n.*, nasal; *orb.*, orbit; *par.*, parietal; *p.m*, premaxilla; *prf.*, prefrontal; *pto.*, postorbital with postfrontal; *q.j.*, quadratojugal; *s.t.f.*, supratemporal fossa; *sq.*, squamosal.
Compare Fig. 362.

more important channel of the two, and conveys the arterial blood. These dispositions foreshadow that of the birds, in which the right systemic arch alone persists. (The only complete aortic arch of a mammal is the left systemic.) In most lizards (Fig. 548) the ductus

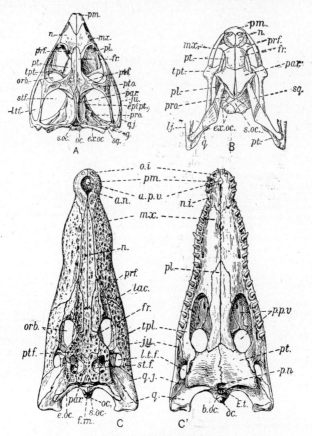

FIG. 362.—Skulls of reptiles.

A, Dorsal view of the skull of the tuatara (*Sphenodon*); *B*, the same view of the
skull of the grass snake (*Tropidonotus natrix*), with small portions of the lower
jaw; *C*, dorsal, and *C'*, ventral views of the skull of a crocodile.

a.n., Anterior nares; *a.pv.*, anterior palatine vacuity; *b.oc.*, basioccipital; *E.t.*,
common opening of Eustachian tubes; *epipt.*, epipterygoid; *ex.oc.*, exoccipital;
f.m., foramen magnum; *fr.*, frontal; *ju.*, jugal; *lj.*, portion of lower jaw;
l.t.f., lateral temporal fossa; *lac.*, lachrymal; *mx.*, maxilla; *n.*, nasal; *n.i.*,
notch into which fits the fourth tooth of the lower jaw; *o.i.*, opening into which
fits the first tooth of the lower jaw; *o.c.*, occipital condyle; *orb.*, orbit; *p.n.*, posterior nares; *p.p.v.*, posterior palatine vacuity; *par.*, parietal; *pl.*, palatine;
pm., premaxilla; *prf.*, prefrontal; *pro.*, prootic; *pt.*, pterygoid; *ptf.*, postfrontal; *pto.*, postorbital; *q.*, quadrate; *q.j.*, quadratojugal; *s.oc.*, supraoccipital; *sq.*, squamosal; *st.f.*, supratemporal foramen; *tpt.*, transpalatine.

For the lizard and turtle, see Figs. 549 and 366.

Note that the tuatara and crocodiles have both supratemporal and lateral temporal
fossæ, the lizard, being without quadratojugal, has no lateral temporal fossa, the
snake has neither arcade, and in the turtle there are no fossæ.

Compare Figs. 356, 361.

caroticus persists, and in turtles the ductus arteriosus. The venous
system of a reptile is much like that of an amphibian, and has a
renal portal system, which is lacking in birds and mammals.[1] The
red blood corpuscles are oval and nucleated, like those of other cold-
blooded vertebrates and birds, not like those of mammals. Turtles,
whose ribs are fixed by their shell (p. 486), breathe by movements
of the pectoral girdle, other reptiles breathe by movements of the
ribs like those of mammals (p. 547), but there is no midriff. (The
active movement in the breathing of a bird is that by which the air
is driven out.) There is no important difference between the reptilian
and amphibian nervous systems, but by the taking into the brain of
the hypoglossal, and the appearance of a nerve between it and the
vagus, the number of cranial nerves is raised to twelve. The functional
kidney of reptiles is the metanephros (p. 636). The mesonephros,
though it has quite lost its urinary function, persists in the male as a
body called the *epididymis* attached to the testis, and from it the vas
deferens leads. Thus here, as in all vertebrates except Cyclostomes
and Teleostei, the testis discharges its products through a part of the
original kidney, and uses as its vas deferens the original kidney duct
(Wolffian duct : see Fig. 415).

We will now briefly survey the surviving groups of
reptiles. Lizards (*Lacertilia*) and Snakes
Orders of Reptiles. (*Ophidia*) are closely related : indeed, it is
difficult to distinguish between them, for there
are lizards, like the Blindworm, which have no outward
trace of limbs, and snakes, like the Python, which have
vestiges of hind legs. The true snakes, however, may be
distinguished by the absence of any trace of a shoulder
girdle or urinary bladder. The shoulder girdle of lizards
(Fig. 550) shows a bony scapula, coracoid, and precoracoid,
with a cartilaginous epicoracoid, meeting a broad cartilaginous sternum, to which some of the ribs are usually
prolonged, as in birds and mammals, but not in amphibians. There are also clavicles and a long, median
interclavicle, which lies upon the sternum. Both snakes
and lizards have two penes—hollow sacs which open into
the hinder wall of the cloaca, and can be protruded by
being turned inside out.

A snake crawls or climbs by means of its ribs. These are
attached to broad scales on the belly (seen in Fig. 359 B).
which they raise in turn, and thus cause to grip the surface
over which the animal is moving. The backbone is enabled

[1] A comparison of the principal types of venous system found in
Vertebrata is given in Fig. 421.

to stand the strain of this process by the presence on each vertebra of two knobs, the *zygosphenes*, which fit into pits, the *zygantra*, on the hinder side of the preceding vertebra.

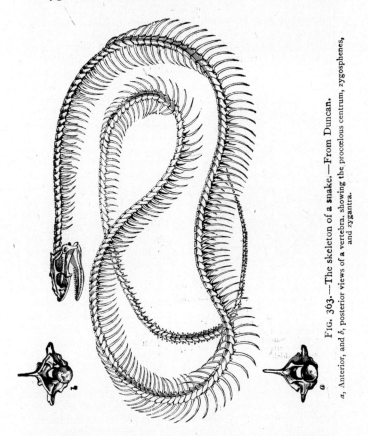

FIG. 363.—The skeleton of **a snake.**—From Duncan.

a, Anterior, and *b*, posterior views of a vertebra, showing the procœlous centrum, zygosphenes, and zygantra.

Turtles and tortoises (*Chelonia*) are characterised by having bony shields (*carapace* and *plastron*) on back and belly, the absence of a sternum, the peculiarities of their strong, toothless skulls, and the presence of a single penis. In the turtles the hands and feet are converted into paddles, in tortoises they are adapted for crawling. In some turtles the skeleton of the limbs shows all the bones of the typical pentadactyle limb (Fig. 24). The only other case in which this is found is that of the hind limb of certain newts. The sharp, bony jaws are covered with horny plates and are very effective both for feeding and as weapons, forming, as they do, part of a very rigid skull.

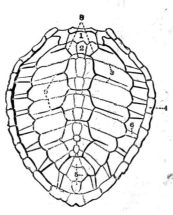

FIG. 364.—A dorsal view of the carapace of a turtle. — From Reynolds, after Owen.

1, Nuchal plate; 2, first neural plate; 3, second costal plate; 4, marginal plate; 5, pygal plates; 6, rib; 8 and 9, outlines of first vertebral and third costal epidermic shields.

The carapace is composed of a number of dermal bones, some of which are fused to parts of the endoskeleton. In the middle is a row of small *neural plates*, fused to the neural spines of vertebræ. On each side of this row is a set of *costal plates*, fused to the ribs. A ring of *marginal plates*, completed in front by a *nuchal plate*, outlines the whole, and some little *pygal plates* fill a gap at the hinder end of the neural series. Since the plates of the carapace are sutured together, the ribs and vertebræ which are fused to them are immovable. The plastron is also composed of dermal bones, some of which represent the clavicles and interclavicle of other reptiles. Over the carapace and plastron the scales are represented by large, horny, epidermal scales or shields of "tortoise-shell," arranged in a regular pattern but not corresponding to the underlying bones. Nerve endings give the tortoise-shell a certain sensitiveness. The two halves of the shell are strutted by a characteristic tripod-shaped shoulder girdle, in which the precoracoid has disappeared, its place being taken by a well-developed acromion process. We shall find this structure, small in the frog, to be well developed in mammals. No doubt the plastron makes a sternum needless.

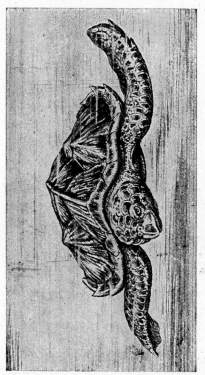

FIG. 365.—The Hawksbill Turtle (*Chelone imbricata*) swimming.—From Pettigrew, after Mützel.

Crocodiles, alligators, and gavials (*Crocodilia*) are lizard-shaped reptiles with bony dermal plates corresponding to the epidermal scales of the back, two arcades and a fixed quadrate in the skull, a palate separating nasal passages from the mouth, a sternum and pectoral girdle, one penis, no bladder, and completely separated ventricles. The palate is a structure we have not yet met with. It is supported by flanges of the premaxillæ, maxillæ, palatines, and pterygoids arching under the primary roof of the mouth and forming a secondary roof. A short partition of this kind, not involving the pterygoids, is found in turtles. In mammals there is a palate longer than that of the turtles, but not so long as that of crocodiles (see p. 539).

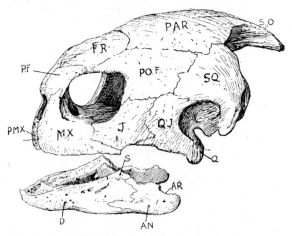

FIG. 366.—The skull of a turtle.—From Thomson.

AN., Angular; *AR.*, articular; *D.*, dentary; *FR.*, frontal; *J.*, jugal; *MX.*, maxilla; *PF.*, prefrontal; *PAR.*, parietal; *PMX.*, premaxilla; *POF.*, postorbital fused with postfrontal; *Q.*, quadrate; *QJ.*, quadrato-jugal; *S.*, surangular; *SO.*, supraoccipital; *SQ.*, squamosal.

The Tuatara (*Sphenodon*) is the only living representative of the *Rhynchocephalia*, a very ancient group of reptiles, lizard-shaped animals without bony armour, with two arcades and a fixed quadrate in the skull, no penis, and an incompletely divided ventricle. The pineal organ of *Sphenodon* is more highly developed than in any other existing vertebrate, and its distal part shows a striking resemblance in structure to an eye and lies in a foramen on the roof of the skull between the parietal bones.

The same arrangement is seen in lizards, but less well developed.

We have seen that two warm-blooded groups of animals took over from the reptiles the dominance of **Birds and Mammals.** the world. Both of them are warmly clad, one with feathers, the other with hair. Both owe their success to their activity and resourcefulness, but these characters are shown very differently by them. The Birds have an organisation which in almost every detail adapts them, directly or indirectly, to flight. Their behaviour shows a very high development of instinct—

FIG. 367.—The Tuatara (*Sphenodon punctatus*), a lizard-like reptile found only on some islets off the coast of New Zealand.

fixed conduct for particular emergencies. They have succeeded by specialisation. The organisation and behaviour of mammals are more plastic. Members of this group, though some of them can fly, are less efficient in the air than the highly adapted birds, but elsewhere they are dominant. This they have achieved partly by suitable modifications of their basic organisation but even more by their adaptable behaviour. Both they and the birds tend their young, but mammals do this more efficiently in that all of them provide a special food—milk—and nearly all give the ova protection and nourishment within the body of the mother during development. We shall now study a typical example of each of these groups.

CHAPTER XXIII

THE PIGEON [1]

THE many different kinds of domestic pigeons are familiar to every one. All of them—carriers, tumblers, **The Rock Dove.** fantails, pouters, etc. — have been bred, by selection continued for many generations, from the wild Rock Dove (*Columba livia*), a bird of strong flight which is found over a great part of Europe and Asia, building among

FIG. 368.—A pigeon wheeling in the air.—From Pettigrew.
The bird is steering to its left. Note the different positions of the wings and the spreading of the tail feathers.

high rocks or in ruins an untidy nest of sticks, in which two white eggs are laid. It feeds on seeds of various kinds.

The pigeon's boat-shaped body offers little resistance to the air, and to the same end has an even **External Features.** contour, due to the coat of feathers, which also affords a light and warm covering. A distinct head, neck, and trunk are present, but the tail is a mere

[1] It has been assumed, in writing this chapter, that the pigeon will usually be studied after the rabbit.

stump which bears a fan of long feathers. Since the fore-limbs are wings, the hinder—the legs—must support the whole weight in standing. We shall see that the skeleton is adapted to this necessity. The feet are naked and covered with scales, which are horny and epidermic like those of

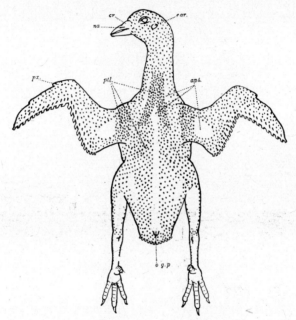

Fig. 369 —**A** plucked pigeon, seen in dorsal view.

apt.., Apteria ; *cr.*, cere ; *ear* ; *na.*, nostril ; *o.g.p.*, papilla on which the oil gland opens ; *ptl.*, pterylæ ; *px.*, thumb.

a reptile, not like those of a fish. There are four toes, which have a wide tread, the first being directed backwards and the other three forwards ; the fifth is wanting. The front or facial portion of the head is drawn out into a *beak* covered with horny skin. At its base above is a swollen, featherless patch of skin, the *cere*. The nostrils lie below the cere, the eyes behind it at the sides of the head, and the

ear openings below and behind the eyes, covered by
feathers. There are three movable eyelids (p. 33), and the
drum of the ear is at the bottom of a tube, but there is no
ear flap. There is a single cloacal opening, as a transverse slit below the tail, and above the tail is a knob **on**

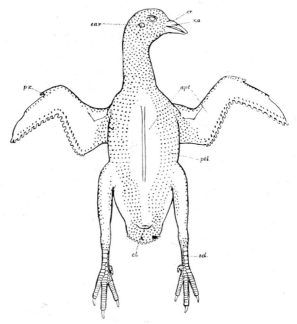

Fig. 370 —A plucked pigeon, seen in ventral view.

apt., Apteria; *cl.*, cloacal opening; *cr.*, cere; *ear*; *na.*, nostril; *ptl.*, pteryla; *px.*, thumb; *scl.*, scales on the foot.

which opens the *oil gland*, whose secretion is used in
preening the feathers.

The feathers are epidermal structures. When the bird
is plucked they are found to have been arranged
Feathers.   in certain tracts or *pterylæ*, leaving between
them bare *apteria* The feathers are of several kinds. The

quill feathers are found along the hinder edges **of the** wings and tail, those on the wings being *remiges*, those **on** the tail *rectrices*. The *contour feathers* cover the body. Those at the bases of the quill feathers are known as *coverts*. *Filoplumes* are little hair-like feathers among the contour feathers. The feathers are moulted

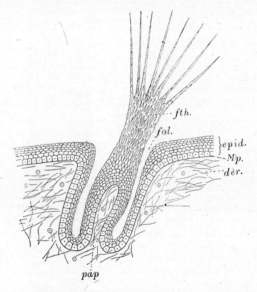

FIG. 371.—A diagram of a developing feather, highly magnified. —From Shipley and MacBride.

der., Dermis; *epid.*, epidermis; *fol.*, follicle; *fth.*, feather; *Mp.*, Malpighian layer of epidermis; *pap.*, papilla by the growth of whose epidermis the feather is formed.

every year and thus those damaged by use become replaced.

A quill feather consists of the following parts : The *stem* or *scapus* is divided into a lower, hollow part, the *calamus* or *quill*, and an upper, solid part, the *rachis*. The quill is embedded in a pit of the skin and has at its lower end an opening, the *inferior umbilicus*, through which a vascular papilla projects into the growing feather. At the junction of the quill and rachis is a minute opening known as the *superior umbilicus*. Close to this arises a small tuft known as the *aftershaft*. The rachis is the axis of the flattened part of the feather known as the *vexillum* or *vane*. This is composed of a series of elastic plates set along the sides of the rachis with their flat sides perpendicular to the plane of the vane. The plates are known as *barbs*, and they are held together by *barbules*, which are smaller processes that fringe the barbs. The barbules of one side of a barb (distal barbules) bear little hooks or *barbicels* which catch upon the barbules of the adjoining barb. Thus the whole vane is held together and forms a single surface for striking the air. The barbules of the contour feathers are less well developed than those of the quill feathers, so that the barbs separate more easily. The filoplumes consist each of a hair-like stem with a very rudimentary vane of a few isolated barbs at its apex.

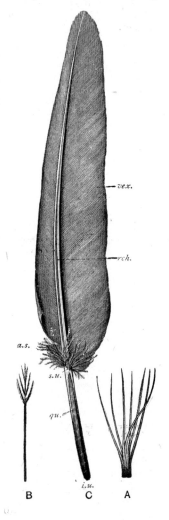

Wings and Flight.

In the wing of a plucked bird there may easily be made out parts corresponding to the upper arm, forearm, and hand. In the latter the thumb is the only digit that projects. A fold of skin known as the *propatagium* connects the shoulder with the forearm in

Fig. 372. —Feathers of a pigeon.

A, Down feather; *B*, filoplume; *C*, quill feather.

a.s., Aftershaft; *i.u.*, inferior umbilicus; *qu.*, quill or calamus; *rch.*, rachis or shaft; *s.u.*, superior umbilicus; *vex.*, vexillum or vane.

B   C   A

front, and a small *postpatagium* of the same kind lies across
the armpit. The greater part of the surface of the wing,
however, is provided by the row of twenty-three remiges
along the hinderside of the limb. The remiges borne
upon the hand are eleven in number and are known as
primaries. Those on the forearm are known as *secondaries*.
A tuft of feathers on the thumb is the *bastard wing*. In
flight, as the wing strikes downwards its strong front edge

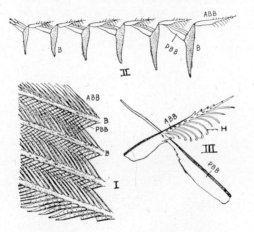

FIG. 373.—Parts of a feather.—After Nitzsch.

I., Four barbs (*B.*) bearing anterior barbules (*A.BB.*) and posterior
   barbules (*P.BB.*) ; *II.*, six barbs (*B.*) in section, showing interlocking of barbules ; *III.*, anterior barbule with barbicels (*H.*).

is twisted forwards so that the concave lower surface faces
back as well as down and thus the body is both propelled
and supported, much as we saw that of the cockroach to
be (pp. 327, 328). In rising flight the angle is altered so
that the wing presses more downwards. In gliding, the
wings are outspread and serve as those of an aeroplane.
The tail feathers can be spread out on one or both sides,
and are used for steering, and to check the " way " of the
bird, as in alighting. The downstroke of the wing is more
powerful than the upstroke, which is helped by the fall of
the body when the downstroke ceases to raise it.

FIG. 374.—Two positions in the flight of a pigeon.—
From Marey.

Below : shortly after the beginning of the downstroke.   *Above :* near the end of the
same stroke.

The pigeon is a backboned animal, and its structure is on the same general plan as that of the frog and dogfish.

FIG. 375.—The wing of a dove.—From Thomson.

c., Carpals; *h.*, humerus; *m.c.*, carpo-metacarpus; *p.f.*, primary feathers; *r.*, radius; *s.f.*, secondary feathers; *u.*, ulna.

It has a chest or thorax, walled by ribs and a broad breast-bone, but lacks the midriff or diaphragm of **Internal Organs: Skeleton.** mammals. It is of the pentadactyle type and its skeleton resembles in main outlines that of the frog. The bones are very light and spongy in texture, and most of them, except those of the

32

tail, forearm, hand, and hind-limb, contain air spaces. A
tendency to the fusion of bones is seen in various regions,

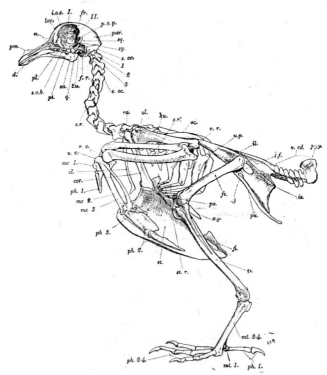

Fig. 376.—**The skeleton of a pigeon, seen from the left side.**

c.r., Fixed cervical rib; *c.r'.*, free cervical ribs; *cl.*, clavicle; *cor.*, coracoid; *d.*,
dentary; *Eu.*, Eustachian tube; *e.oc.*, exoccipital; *f.r.*, fenestral recess; *fe.*,
femur; *fi.*, fibula; *fr.*, frontal; *hu.*, humerus; *i.f.*, iliosciatic foramen; *i.o.s.*,
interorbital septum; *il.*, ilium; *is.*, ischium; *lac.*, lacrymal; *mc.* 1–3, metacarpals; *mt.* 1–4, metatarsals; *n.*, nasal; *o.f.*, obturator foramen; *pa.*, patella;
par., parietal; *ph.*, 1–4, phalanges; *pl.*, palatine; *pm.*, premaxilla; *p.o.p.*,
postorbital process of frontal; *pt.*, pterygoid; *pu.*, pubis; *pyg.*, pygostyle; *q.*,
quadrate; *r.c.*, radial carpal; *ra.*, radius; *s.o.b.*, suborbital bar; *s.oc.*, supraoccipital; *sa.*, supra-angular; *sc.*, scapula; *sq.*, squamosal; *st.*, sternum; *st.r.*,
sternal ribs; *ti.*, tibia; *u.c.*, ulnar carpal; *u.p.*, uncinate process; *ul.*, ulna;
v.cd., caudal vertebræ; *v.r.*, vertebral rib; *x.p.*, xiphoid process; *zy.*, zygomatic
process of the squamosal; *I., II.*, foramina for first two cranial nerves; 1–3,
first three cervical vertebræ.

and the proportion of cartilage is very small. The back-bone is divided into five regions : (1) The neck contains thirteen to fifteen cervical vertebræ, the commonest number being fourteen. The ends of the centra of these are of a peculiar shape known as *heterocœlous*. In front they are saddle-shaped, concave from side to side, and convex from above downwards : behind they have these curvatures reversed. The third to the eleventh or twelfth cervical vertebræ bear short ribs fused to the centra and trans-verse processes. The ribs of the last two are free, but do not reach the breastbone. (2) Behind these come five thoracic vertebræ, whose ribs reach the breastbone. Of these the first three are fused together, the fourth is free,

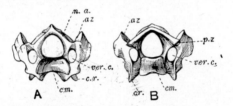

FIG. 377 —Cervical vertebræ of a pigeon.

A, From in front ; *B*, from behind.

az., Prezygapophysis ; *c.r.*, cervical rib ; *cm.*, centrum ; *n.a.*, neural arch ; *p.z.*, postzygapophysis ; *ver.c.*, foramen of transverse process.

and the fifth is fused with those behind it. (3) The next half-dozen vertebræ are known as lumbars and are fused in front with the last thoracic and behind with (4) the two sacral and (5) the first five caudals. Thus there is a long group of fused vertebræ, known as the sacrum, to which the pelvic girdle is attached. Then follow six free caudals and the *ploughshare bone* or *pygostyle*, which consists of four fused vertebræ and supports the tail. Each rib has a head or capitulum which articulates with the centrum of its vertebra and a tubercle which articulates with the transverse process. Those which join the sternum are bent forwards at an angle to do so, the part above the angle being known as the vertebral rib, that below as the sternal rib. Both parts are bony in the pigeon, whereas in the rabbit the sternal ribs are cartilaginous. On the hinder side of each of the free ribs, except those of the last pair, is an *uncinate process*. The skull is remarkable for the fusion of most of its bones. There is a short, wide cranium, lying mainly behind the large orbits, which are separated, not by the cranium, but by an *interorbital septum* (p. 478). A scaffolding of slender jawbones supports the beak.

The hinder part of the cranium is formed by two exoccipitals at the sides of the foramen magnum, a median basioccipital below and a

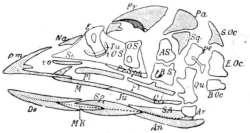

FIG. 378.—A diagram of a bird's skull, disarticulated.— After Gadow. Membrane bones shaded.

B.Oc., basioccipital; *E.Oc.*, exoccipital; *S.Oc.*, supraoccipital; *Pa.*, parietal; *Fr.*, frontal; *Na.*, nasal; *pm.*, premaxilla; *M.*, maxilla; *Ju.*, jugal; *Qj.*, quadrato-jugal; *Qu.*, quadrate; *P.*, palatine; *Pt.*, pterygoid; *pe.*, periotic; *Sq.*, squamosal; *AS.*, alisphenoid; *B.S.*, basisphenoid; *O.S.*, orbito-sphenoid; *Pr.Sph.*, presphenoid; *vo.*, vomer; *iO.S.*, inter-orbital septum; *E.*, ethmoid; *Se.*, nasal septum; *De.*, dentary; *Sp.*, splenial; *An.*, angular; *S.A.*, supra-angular; *Ar.*, articular; *MK.*, Meckel's cartilage.

median supraoccipital above. There is one median occipital condyle, formed mainly by the basioccipital. The roof of the cranium in the middle and foremost regions is formed by the parietals and frontals. In the region of the parietals the floor is formed by the basisphenoid, which lies in front of the basioccipital, but is covered in below by a broad membrane bone, the basitemporal, which perhaps corresponds to the crosspiece of the parasphenoid. The side of the skull in this region is formed mainly by the squamosal, from which a zygomatic process projects forwards, lying free. Below the squamosal the wall is derived in front from the alisphenoid and behind from the bones of the auditory capsule united with adjoining bones, but the limits of none of these can be made out. In the frontal region, the cranial cavity is greatly restricted by the presence of the interorbital septum, over which, however, it extends forward somewhat. The septum is formed by the union of mesethmoid with presphenoid and orbitosphenoid elements to form a single plate of bone with a thickened ventral edge, known as the rostrum, representing the blade of the parasphenoid. The frontal sends downward a postorbital process. The lacrymal of each side is a small, flat, curved bone, in front of and above the orbit. In the olfactory region, the nasals are a pair of thin bones in the roof, before the frontals. Their fore edges are deeply notched for the nostrils. The vomers (prevomers) of the pigeon are vestigial. In the common fowl they are represented by a slender median rod in front of the rostrum. In the upper jaw, the palatines are a pair of slender

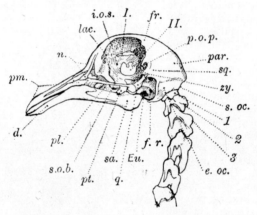

FIG. 379.—The skull and some of the cervical vertebræ of a pigeon, from the left side.

d., Dentary; *Eu.*, Eustachian tube; *e.oc.*, exoccipital; *f.r.*, fenestral recess; *fr.*, frontal; *i.o.s.*, interorbital septum; *lac.*, lacrymal; *n.*, nasal; *par.*, parietal; *pl.*, palatine; *pm.*, premaxilla; *p.o.p.*, postorbital process of frontal; *pt.*, pterygoid; *q.*, quadrate; *s.o.b.*, suborbital bar; *s.oc.*, supraoccipital; *sa.*, supra-angular; *sq.*, squamosal; *zy.*, zygomatic process of the squamosal; *I*, *II.*, foramina for first two cranial nerves; 1-3, first three cervical vertebræ.

bars placed lengthwise in the roof of the mouth. From the hinder end of each a short, stout pterygoid slopes outwards and backwards to join the quadrate, which is a strong, three-branched bone articulated above with the squamosal, in front with the pterygoid, and below with the lower jaw, whose suspensorium it forms. The premaxilla of each side is a large, triradiate bone with the main part directed forward and fused with its fellow to form the tip of the beak, while two other processes pass back to join the two forward processes of the nasal and thus enclose the nostril. The maxilla is a rod lying inside the lower backward process of the premaxilla and projecting backward beyond it. It gives off a plate of bone, the maxillopalatine process, on its inner side. A slender splint, the jugal, joins it to a third slip, the quadrato-jugal, which articulates with the outside of the lower end of the quadrate. Thus there is formed a fine suborbital bar. In the slender lower jaw, articular, angular, supra-angular, dentary, and splenial elements can be made out. There is a columella auris and a slender, mainly bony, forked hyoid apparatus.

The shoulder girdle contains narrow, sabre-like scapulæ, stout coracoids which slope down to join the sternum, and slender clavicles which unite to form the "merry thought." Where scapula, coracoid, and clavicle join, a small opening, the *foramen triosseum*, is left between them. The sternum is a broad plate, bearing below a conspicuous median keel for the attachment of the great wing muscles, behind two xiphoid processes, at the sides facets for the ribs, and in front surfaces for the articulation of the coracoid bones. In the wing skeleton there is a short, stout humerus,

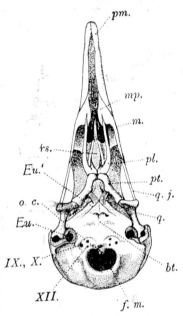

FIG. 380.—The skull of a pigeon, seen from below.

bt., Basitemporal ; *Eu.*, hinder opening of passage for Eustachian tube ; *Eu'.*, anterior opening of the same ; *f.m.*, foramen magnum ; *m.*, maxilla ; *mp.*, maxillopalatine process ; *o.c.*, occipital condyle ; *pl.*, palatine ; *pm.*, premaxilla ; *pt.*, pterygoid ; *q.*, quadrate ; *q.j.*, quadrato-jugal ; *rs.*, rostrum ; *IX., X., XII.,* foramina for cranial nerves.

a parallel radius and ulna, rather widely separated except at their ends, where they touch, only two free carpal bones, those of the second row having fused with the metacarpals, of which there are three, fused together, and three digits. The thumb has one joint, the first finger two, and the second one. In the pelvic girdle there is a long ilium, reaching a good way behind as well as in front of the acetabulum, and connected with the sacrum along nearly the whole of its inner side. This, together with the length of the sacrum, enables the trunk to be supported in a more or less horizontal position by the single pair of legs. The acetabulum is placed near the middle of the ilium. The ischium is a flat, backwardly directed bone. Its hinder part is fused with the ilium, but just after the acetabulum an oval opening—the *iliosciatic foramen* —lies between the two. The pubis is slender and also directed backwards. In many birds it has a small *prepubic process* in front. The obturator foramen is slit-like. There is no symphysis or ventral junction of the girdles. The hind-limb has a short, stout femur, a long tibia, a slender fibula, partly joined to the tibia below, no free tarsals, these bones being fused to the tibia and meta-tarsals, a single tarso-metatarsus formed by the union of the distal tarsals with the meta-tarsals (except the small, free, first metatarsal), and four toes, each of several joints.

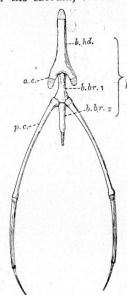

FIG. 381.—The hyoid apparatus of a pigeon.

a c., Anterior cornu; *b.*, body of the hyoid; *b.br.*1, *b.br.*2, basi-branchials; *b.hd.*, basihyoid; *p.c.*, posterior cornu.

The most conspicuous part of the muscular system is the great *pectoral muscles*. The *pectoralis major*, arising from the sternum and **Muscular Arrangements.** clavicle, is inserted on the under side of the humerus, which it pulls downwards, thus raising the bird and driving it forward by the wing-beat in flight. The smaller *pectoralis minor* arises from the sternum above the major and passes through the foramen triosseum and over the shoulder to its insertion on the upper side of the humerus, which it raises. The perching mechanism is also interesting. The flexor tendons which curve the

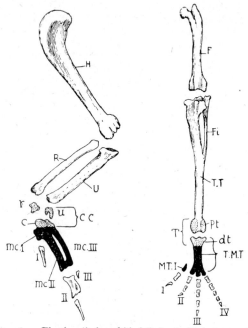

FIG. 382.—The fore-limb and hind-limb of a bird compared.
—From Thomson.

H., Humerus ; *R.*, radius ; *U.*, ulna ; *r.*, radiale ; *u.*, ulnare ; *C.*, distal carpals united to carpo-metacarpus ; *CC.*, the whole carpal region ; *MC.I.*, metacarpal of the thumb ; *I.*, phalanx of the thumb ; *MC.II.*, second metacarpus ; *II.*, second digit ; *MC.III.*, third metacarpus ; *III.*, third digit. *F.*, femur ; *T.T.*, tibio-tarsus ; *Fi.*, fibula ; *Pt.*, proximal tarsals united to lower end of tibia ; *dt.*, distal tarsals united to upper end of metatarsus, forming a tarso-metatarsus (*T.MT.*); *T .* entire tarsal region ; *MT.I.*, first metatarsal, free ; *I.–IV.*, toes.

toes round a branch are so arranged that they are tightened by the bending of the metatarsus on the tibia in perching, so that the bird does not fall even when it is asleep.

The mouth has no teeth, no true palate (false roof, pp.
Alimentary 488, 539), like the rabbit's, large posterior
System. nares partly hidden by soft palatal folds, a single
opening for the Eustachian tubes, and a sharp-
pointed tongue. The glottis is not protected by an epiglottis
as in the rabbit. The gullet widens into a thin-walled *crop*, in
which the food is stored. From the crop the gullet continues
to the *fore-stomach* or proventriculus, a glandular part of

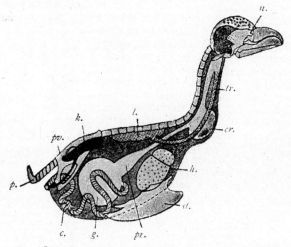

FIG. 383.—The position of organs in a bird.—After Selenka.

n., Nostrils; *tr.*, trachea; *cr.*, crop; *h.*, heart; *st.*, sternum; *pr.*,
  proventriculus; *g.*, gizzard; *c.*, cæca; *p.*, pygostyle; *pv.*, pelvic
  girdle; *k.*, kidney; *l.*, lung.

the stomach, where the gastric juice is secreted. This is
followed by the *gizzard*, a lens-shaped chamber with very
thick muscular walls and a horny lining, where the food is
ground up by the aid of small stones which have been
swallowed. It lies below the proventriculus, which opens
on its dorsal border, rather to the left side: on the right
side near the same spot is the opening of the duodenum.
This is a ∨-shaped loop, between whose limbs lies the
pancreas. The ducts of this gland are three, and all open

into the distal limb of the duodenum, two about the middle of its length, and one, which is longer than the others, near the end. There are two bile ducts, which run from the large, bilobed liver and join the duodenum, the wide left duct opening into the proximal limb and the narrower right duct into the distal limb near the first two pancreatic ducts. There is no gall bladder in the common pigeon. The ileum is a much-coiled tube about two and a half feet in length. The rectum is about an inch and a half long. Its beginning is marked by a pair of small *rectal cœca*; behind it opens by an anus into the cloaca. This has three regions separated by shelves of the wall. The first and largest is the *coprodæum* into which the rectum opens, the small middle division is the *urodæum* into which the urinary and generative ducts open, the third, larger, is the *proctodæum*; upon its dorsal surface there opens in the young a glandular sac, the *bursa Fabricii*, of unknown function.

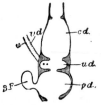

Fig. 384.—A diagrammatic section of the cloaca of a male bird.—After Gadow.

cd., Upper region of cloaca into which rectum opens; *ud.*, median region into which ureter (*u.*) and vas deferens (*vd.*) open from each side; *pd.*, posterior region into which bursa Fabricii (*B.F.*) opens.

The spleen is a small, red body, attached to the right side of the proventriculus.

Respiratory Organs. The glottis, behind the root of the tongue, opens into the voiceless larynx, from which the long trachea, strengthened with bony rings, leads back along the neck, lying at first below the gullet and then at its left side. At the base of the neck it divides into the two bronchi; these run outwards and backwards to the lungs, which lie against the dorsal walls of the thorax covered with peritoneum below only. The hinder end of the trachea is dilated and forms, with the beginnings of the bronchi, the *syrinx* or organ of voice. Sound is produced by the vibration of the *membrana semilunaris*, a delicate vertical fold of mucous membrane, extending forwards from the angle between the bronchi. The latter not only give off tubes which branch and form the

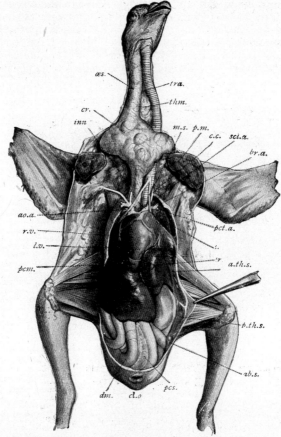

FIG. 385.—A pigeon opened from the ventral side to show the principal
organs in their natural positions.

a.th.s., Anterior thoracic air sac; *ab.s.*, abdominal air sac; *ao.a*, aortic arch;
br.a., brachial artery; *c.c.*, common carotid artery; *cl.o.*, cloacal opening;
cr., crop; *dm.*, duodenum; *inn.*, innominate arteries; *l.*, lung; *lv.*, left
ventricle; *lr.*, liver; *ms.*, muscles concerned in the movements of the syrinx;
æs., œsophagus; *p.m.*, pectoralis major muscle; *p.th.s.*, posterior thoracic air sac;
pcm., pericardium (torn open); *pcs.*, pancreas; *pct.a.*, pectoral artery; *r.v.*,
right ventricle; *scl.a.*, subclavian artery; *thm.*, thymus; *tra.*, trachea. The
gizzard is seen opposite the forceps which hold back the abdominal wall.

spongy lungs, but also pass right through these organs and are connected with a system of large *air sacs*, of which there are altogether nine, named, from behind forwards, the abdominals, posterior thoracics, anterior thoracics, interclavicular and cervicals. Certain of the air sacs are connected with air spaces in the bones. This arrangement adds some-

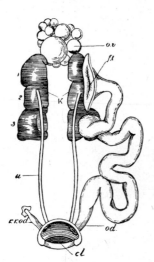

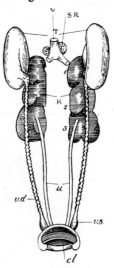

FIG. 386.—The urogenital organs of a female pigeon. — From Thomson.

K., Kidney (metanephros) with three lobes ; *u.*, ureter ; *cl.*, cloaca ; *ov.*, ovary ; *od.*, oviduct ; *ft.*, funnel at end of oviduct ; *r.r.od.*, rudimentary right oviduct.

FIG. 387.— The urogenital organs of a male pigeon. —From Thomson.

T., Testes ; *V.*, base of inferior vena cava ; *S.R.*, suprarenal glands ; *K.*, kidneys with three lobes (1, 2, 3) ; *u.*, ureter ; *v.d.*, vas deferens ; *v.s.*, seminal vesicle ; *cl.*, cloaca.

what to the lightness of the bird, but is probably of greater importance in raising the efficiency of its respiration by increasing the flow of the air through the bronchi. Respiration is brought about mainly by active expiration ; it is not due to a pumping in of air, as in the frog, or primarily to active inspiration, as in the rabbit. The movements of breathing consist in the rise and fall of the sternum, which

compresses and relaxes the air sacs and lungs. The air
passages in the lungs and air sacs of a bird are admirably
adapted to give the very efficient respiration which the
exertion of flight and the high temperature of the creature's
blood require. The fine branches of the bronchi end, not,
as those of a mammal do, in minute sacs in which the air
is stagnant, but in a network of *air capillaries* through
which the air circulates. At inspiration, air is drawn
through main branches of the bronchi into the great air

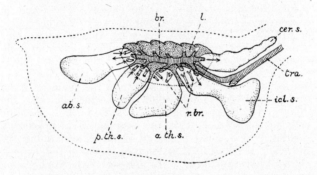

FIG. 388.—A diagram of a lung and its air sacs in the pigeon.

a.c.s., Anterior thoracic sac ; *ab.s.*, abdominal sac ; *br.*, bronchus ; *cer.s.*,
cervical sac ; *icl.s.*, interclavicular sac ; *l.*, lung ; *p.th.s.*, posterior
thoracic sac ; *r.br.*, recurrent bronchi ; *tra.*, trachœa. The arrows
show the direction of the air currents.

sacs ; at expiration it is forced from these through
recurrent bronchi into the system of air capillaries, and
from the latter through the bronchi to the exterior.

The kidneys are metanephric (pp. 548, 636). They lie in
the back under the sacrum as a pair of three-
lobed bodies. From the hinder lobe of each a
ureter runs back to the cloaca. There is no
bladder. Nitrogen is excreted as uric acid, not
urea. The urine is very concentrated and in the cloaca the
uric acid is precipitated and the water, with some salts, is
saved for the body by reabsorption as in the rectum of the
cockroach. The sexes are, of course, separate. The testes

**Excretory and
Reproductive
Organs.**

lie in front of the kidneys. From each of them the vas deferens, corresponding to the Wolffian duct of the dogfish and frog, runs back on the outer side of the ureter to end in a small swelling or seminal vesicle which opens into the cloaca. When it is full of ripe sperm the vas deferens is slightly convoluted. There being no penis, the sperm is passed in coition by the cloaca of the male being closely apposed to that of the female. The adult pigeon has only one ovary, that of the right side having atrophied early in life. The right oviduct also atrophies, but a small vestige remains attached to the cloaca. The ovary is covered with follicles which contain ova in various stages of ripeness. The oviduct is a wide, twisted tube, thin-walled in front and thick behind, opening into the body cavity by a long funnel just behind the ovary. When the ova are ripe they are shed into the body cavity and immediately caught by the opening of the oviduct. Each ovum is a large, round, yellow body which becomes the " yolk " of the egg (Fig. 487). It is a single gigantic cell, so full of yolk that the protoplasm is practically restricted to a small patch at one side, containing the nucleus. It is fertilised in the thin region of the oviduct, coated with white of egg in the first part of the thick region, and provided with a double membrane and a porous chalky shell in the hinder part. The eggs are hatched by the warmth of the body of the parents, who sit upon them in turns. The young, which emerge after sixteen days, are provided with a scanty yellow *down* and, unlike young chickens, are at first quite helpless, with closed eyelids. They are fed by their parents with a creamy fluid known as " pigeon's milk " formed by the breaking down of the epithelium of the crop. They are fledged at the end of three weeks, and after a few days' education in flight by their parents go out into the world for themselves.

The blood has a temperature of 42° C., which is higher than that of mammals. This fact is no doubt **Blood Vessels.** connected with the active life of the bird and the rapid metabolism which it necessitates. We have already seen how the respiratory organs provide the ample supply of oxygen which such metabolism demands. The

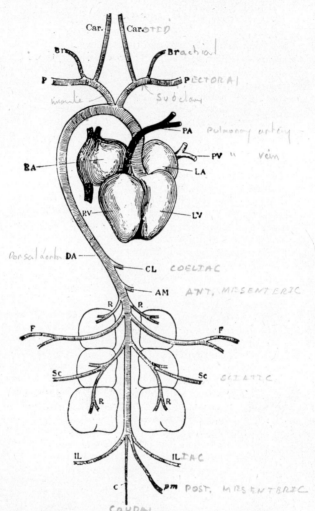

FIG. 389.—The principal arteries of a pigeon.—From Thomson.

A.M., Anterior mesenteric ; *Br.*, brachial ; *C.*, caudal ; *Car.*, carotid ; *CL.*, cœliac ; *D.A.*, dorsal aorta ; *F.*, femoral ; *IL.*, iliac ; *L.A.*, left auricle ; *L.V.*, left ventricle ; *P.*, pectoral ; *P.A.*, pulmonary artery ; *P.V.*, pulmonary vein ; *P.M.*, posterior mesenteric ; *R.*, renals ; *R.A.*, right auricle ; *R.V.*, right ventricle ; *Sc.*, sciatic.

red corpuscles are oval and nucleated. The heart has four chambers, two auricles and two ventricles, there being no sinus venosus or conus arteriosus. The impure blood returned by the venæ cavæ to the right auricle passes into the right ventricle through an opening guarded by a muscular valve without chordæ tendineæ. It is then driven by the pulmonary artery to the lungs, whence it returns by the pulmonary veins to the left auricle, passing thence through two membranous valves with chordæ tendineæ to the left ventricle, by which it is driven into the single aortic arch. The openings of the aorta and pulmonary artery are guarded each by three semilunar valves. The aortic arch bends over to the *right* side, giving off at its apex right and left innominate arteries, from each of which arise a carotid and a subclavian. The latter is exceedingly short, breaking up immediately into brachial and pectoral branches. The further course of the arteries is shown in the diagram on Fig. 389. The venous system is shown in Fig. 390. There are three venæ cavæ, as in the frog. Each superior vena cava is formed by the union of a jugular, a brachial, and a pectoral. The jugulars anastomose under the base of the skull. The inferior vena cava arises by the junction of two iliac veins in front of the kidney. Each iliac vein is formed by the union of a femoral, a renal and a big hypogastric which passes upwards through the kidney. Behind the kidneys the hypogastrics arise in the following way. The little caudal vein forks into two branches, each of which runs through one of the kidneys as a hypogastric. Each hypogastric is much larger than the caudal of which it is a branch, because at the bifurcation another vein, the coccygeo-mesenteric from the cloaca and large intestine, joins the caudal, and immediately after it has separated from its fellow the hypogastric receives an internal iliac vein. In its course through the kidney it receives several small renal veins and a sciatic. There is practically no renal portal system, though the femorals give a few small branches to the kidneys. A hepatic portal system exists as usual. A vein usually known as the epigastric takes blood from the great omentum, or sheet of fat which covers the abdominal viscera, to the left hepatic

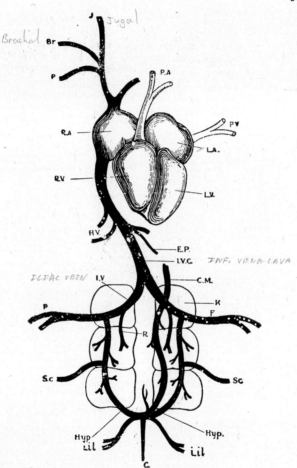

Fig. 390.—The principal veins of a pigeon.—From Thomson.

Br., Brachial ; *C.*, caudal ; *C.M.*, coccygeo-mesenteric ; *E.P.*, epigastric ; *F.*, femoral ; *H.V.*, hepatic ; *Hyp.*, hypogastric ; *i.il.*, internal iliac ; *I.V.*, iliac; *I.V.C.*, inferior vena cava ; *J.*, jugular ; *K.*, kidney ; *L.A.*, left auricle ; *L.V.*, left ventricle ; *P.A.*, pulmonary artery ; *P.V.*, pulmonary vein ; *R.*, renal; *R.A.*, right auricle ; *R.V.*, right ventricle ; *Sc.*, sciatic.

33

vein. It represents the anterior abdominal vein of the frog.

Nervous System and Sense Organs. The cerebral hemispheres of the brain are large, smooth, and rounded. The roofs of the lateral ventricles are relatively thin, though nervous, but the corpora striata are large; with this development is connected the elaborate but stereotyped behaviour of birds. The olfactory lobes are

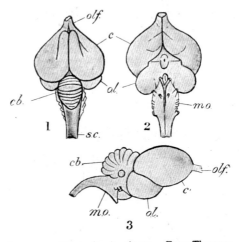

FIG. 391.—The brain of a pigeon.—From Thomson.

(1) Dorsal, (2) ventral, and (3) side view. *c.*, Cerebral hemispheres; *cb.*, cerebellum; *m.o.*, medulla oblongata; *o.l.*, optic lobes; *olf.*, olfactory lobes; *s.c.*, spinal cord.

very small. The cerebellum and cerebrum meet over the thalamencephalon, thrusting the round, hollow optic lobes to the sides. The cerebellum is ridged transversely. There are twelve cranial nerves, corresponding to those of the rabbit (p. 563). The sense of smell is not well developed. Hearing is acute, the labyrinth possessing the organ known as the cochlea which was quite rudimentary in the frog. Sight is very keen, and the eye is remarkable for the presence of a vascular pigmented organ, known as the *pecten*, which protrudes into the vitreous humour from the " blind spot " where the optic nerve enters.

Warm-blooded though they are, birds are more akin to reptiles than to mammals. This is expressed in many

FIG. 392.—*Archæopteryx macrura*, restored, about ⅙ natural size.

details of their anatomy—the structure and articulation of the lower jaw, various other features of the skull, the ankle joint, the organs of reproduc-tion, the preponderance of the right systemic arch, the nucleated red blood corpuscles, the scaly legs, etc. An interesting link between birds and reptiles is

Birds and Reptiles.

the extinct *Archæopteryx*, which is known only by two fossil specimens from the Upper Jurassic. This creature was, as far as is known, a bird in all essential features, but had, like a reptile, teeth, free fingers on the hand, and a long flexible tail of many vertebræ.

CHAPTER XXIV

THE RABBIT

THE Rabbit, *Lepus cuniculus*, is one of the animals that
Habits. have been introduced into Britain by man.
Its original home was in the countries at the
western end of the Mediterranean. Thence it has spread
or been carried by man throughout most of Europe and into
various other parts of the world, where its adaptability and
great fertility have enabled it to thrive to such an extent
that often, as notably in Australia, it has become a serious
nuisance. Its habits are well known. It is herbivorous, and
will eat a great variety of plants. It is gregarious, and digs
for itself burrows into which it retires to sleep or at the
approach of danger and to rear its young. On this account
it prefers districts where the soil is light and easily worked,
though it will live even in wet places if these bear
dense vegetation, in which it can form runs instead of
burrows. As befits its defencelessness, it is very wary, and
its habit of living in societies gives each individual a better
chance of receiving warning of the approach of an enemy.
Its custom of feeding chiefly at dusk has similar advantages
in enabling it to escape observation. It lives seven or eight
years and breeds four times, or oftener, in a year, beginning
to breed at six months old. As each litter contains from
five to eight young, its natural rate of reproduction is
enormous and enables it to pay the heavy toll taken by its
numerous enemies. It is readily domesticated, and various
fancy races have been produced by breeders.

The rabbit is covered with *fur*, which in the wild race
is of an inconspicuous, tawny-grey colour save
External on the under side of the short, upright tail,
Features. where it is white. When, on an alarm, the
animal scampers off to its burrow, the white patch on its

517

tail is conspicuous, and this, though no doubt it enables an enemy to follow the fugitive, has probably advantages to the species in guiding and warning other members of the society. The head is separated from the trunk by a distinct *neck*, a feature which we have not met with in the dogfish or frog. The long *external ears or pinnæ* are another new feature. The eyes have *movable upper and lower lids* with a few *eyelashes*, and a small third eyelid lies as a white membrane in the inner corner and is used in cleaning the cornea. This eyelid is rudimentary in man. The nostrils are two oblique slits at the end of the snout, and lead internally into the pharynx. We have seen that in the dogfish the nostrils do not open internally and in the frog they open into the front of the mouth. The upper lip is a "hare lip," cleft in the middle, the cleft being continuous with the nostrils and exposing the great front teeth. On the sides of the snout and round the eyes there are strong tactile hairs or *vibrissæ* which correspond to the so-called "whiskers" of the cat. There is *no cloaca*, the anus and urinogenital openings being separate, and the latter in front of the former, in the male on the end of a *penis*, in the female within a slit-like *vulva* which contains in front a small *clitoris* corresponding to the penis. Beside the penis in the male lie the *scrotal sacs*, into which the testes of the adult descend, but there is no hanging scrotum. Along the breast and belly of the female there are four or five pairs of *teats* on which open the milk glands of the *mammæ*, which we meet now for the first time. At the sides of the anus are a pair of hairless depressions, into which open the ducts of the *perineal glands*, to whose secretion is due the peculiar smell of the rabbit. The limbs have the same general shape as those of the frog and other land vertebrates, being of the type known as *pentadactyle* (pp. 47–49), though in the rabbit, while the fore-limbs have five digits, the hind-limbs have only four. The digits end in horny *claws*. The fore-limbs are shorter than the hind-limbs, and in running the animal does not tread upon the whole sole of the foot, carrying the heel above the ground.

The closely related Common Hare differs from the rabbit in its greater size, the greater length of the hind-limb, the black tips of the very long ears, the absence of

FIG. 393.—Races of the Rabbit.—From Romanes.

the burrowing habit, and the fact that the young, which are
Hares.   born in the open, are hairy, whereas those of the
              rabbit, born in the shelter of a burrow, are naked.
The hare is a native of Britain and other parts of Northern
Europe.   The Mountain Hare is more like the rabbit in
the shape of its body, but has black tips to the ears and
turns grey or white in cold weather.

The rabbit is a backboned animal, with all that we have
seen that to imply (p. 421). Its skin, like that of all Verte-

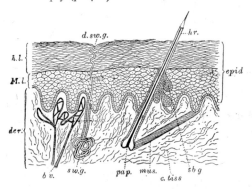

Fig. 394.   A diagram of a section through the skin of a mammal.
        Highly magnified.—From Shipley and MacBride.

b.v., Blood vessels ; *c.tiss.*, connective tissue of dermis ; *d.sw.g.*, duct of sweat gland ;
der, dermis or corium ; *epid.*, epidermis ; *h.l.*, stratum corneum or horny layer
of the same ; *hr.*, hair ; *mus.*, muscles by which the hair may be made to stand
on end ; *M.l.*, Malpighian layer ; *pap.*, hair papilla ; *sb.g.*, sebaceous gland ;
sw.g., sweat gland.

brata, is covered with a stratified epidermis.   There are no
               scales, but cellular outgrowths of the epidermis
General   form *hairs*, which are peculiar to the warm-
Anatomy and   blooded, suckling animals known as *Mammalia*.
Skin.   Each hair is embedded in a pit or follicle of the
epidermis, at the bottom of which it arises by the growth of
the epidermic cells which cover a vascular papilla.   The
bristles of the crayfish or of hairy caterpillars, and the chætæ
of the earthworm, are not true hairs, but cuticular structures
secreted by the epidermis.   The skin also contains *sweat*
or sudorific glands and *grease or sebaceous glands* which

secrete an oily substance into the hair follicles. The glands and follicles are parts of the epidermis, but project inwards into the dermis. Below the latter is a layer of fatty tissue. The muscles of the adult rabbit, as in the frog, show little trace of the segmentation which they have in the early stages of development. The general arrangement of the inte.nal organs resembles that of the frog, but a muscular partition, the *midriff* or *diaphragm*, separates off from the

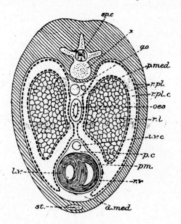

FIG. 395.—A diagram of a transverse section through the thorax of a rabbit.

a med., Ventral part of mediastinum ; *ao.*, aorta ; *i.v.c.*, inferior vena cava ; *l.v.*, left ventricle ; *œs.*, œsophagus ; *p.c.*, pericardial cavity ; *p.med.*, dorsal part of mediastinum ; *pm.*, pericardium ; *r.l.*, right lung ; *r.pl.*, right pleura ; *r.pl.c.* right pleural cavity ; *r.v.*, right ventricle ; *sp.c.*, spinal cord ; *st.*, sternum ; *v.*, vertebra.

peritoneal cavity of the abdomen a *chest* or *thorax* in the breast region, where lies the pericardium, with on each side a *pleural cavity*, into which the lung of its side projects. The lining of each pleural cavity is known as a *pleura*, and of course covers the lung as well as the inside of the thorax. The heart in its pericardium does not lie free in the cavity of the chest, as that of the frog does in the anterior part of the pleuroperitoneal cavity, but is fastened to the dorsal and ventral walls of the thorax by a double sheet of membrane, each sheet forming the inner wall of a pleural cavity. Between the sheets is a lymph-space known as the *mediastinum*. In the dorsal part of this space lie the aorta, certain other blood vessels, and the œsophagus ; its middle part is quite filled by the pericardium, with which its walls fuse ; and in its ventral part lies the thymus.

The skeleton of the rabbit in its main features, and to a considerable extent in its details, resembles that of the frog, but only in its broadest outlines can a correspondence with that of the dogfish be traced.

Skeleton : Backbone.

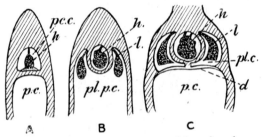

FIG. 396.—A diagram of the perivisceral cœlom : *A*, of the dogfish ; *B*, of the frog ; *C*, of the rabbit or man.

d., diaphragm ; *h.*, heart ; *l.*, lung ; *p.c.*, peritoneal cavity ; *pl.c.*, pleural cavity ; *pl.p.c.*, pleuroperitoneal cavity.

Like those of both the above-mentioned animals, it is composed of an *axial* part, consisting of the skull, the backbone of vertebræ, and the breastbone (sternum), which supports the head and trunk ; and an *appendicular* part, comprising the bones of the limbs and their girdles, which supports the limbs and anchors them to the trunk. The plan upon which the parts of the appendicular skeleton of the rabbit and other terrestrial vertebrate animals are built is shown in Fig. 48. Departures in the rabbit from this scheme are comparatively unimportant. The most considerable of them is the loss of most of the ventral region of the shoulder girdle. The structure of joints is described on p. 50.

The skeleton is almost entirely bony, though most of it is first laid down in cartilage, which persists upon the surfaces of the joints and elsewhere. The

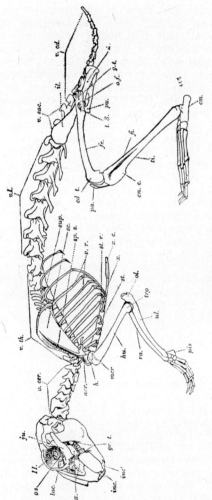

FIG. 397.—The skeleton of a rabbit.

ac., Acromion; *cd.t.*, condyles for tibia; *cm*, calcaneum; *cn.c.*, cnemial crest; *fe*, shaft of femur; *fi.*, fibula; *g.t.*, great trochanter; *gr.t.*, premolar and molar teeth; *h.*, head of humerus, fitting into glenoid cavity; *hu.*, shaft of humerus; *il.*, ilium; *inc.*, upper incisor teeth of the left side; *inc'.*, lower incisor tooth; *is.*, ischium; *ju.*, jugal bone; *lac.*, lacrymal bone; *mcr.*, metacromion; *mx.*, maxilla; *o.f.*, obturator foramen; *ol.*, olecranon process; *os*, orbitosphenoid bone; *pa.*, knee-cap; *pis.*, pisiform bone; *pu.*, pubis; *ra.*, radius; *sc.*, scapula; *sp.s.*, spine of scapula; *st.*, sternum; *st.r.*, sternal ribs; *sup.*, suprascapula; *t.3*, third trochanter; *ti.*, tibia; *tro.*, trochlea; *ul.*, ulna; *v.cd.*, *v.cer.*, *v.l.*, *v.sac.*, *v.th.*, caudal, cervical, lumbar, sacral, and thoracic regions of the backbone; *v.r.*, vertebral ribs; *x.*, xiphisternum; *x.c.*, xiphoid cartilage; *II*, foramen for optic nerve. The clavicle and hyoid are not shown. Enlarged views of the parts of the skeleton are given in the succeeding figures.

vertebræ [1] are much like those of the frog (p. 38), each of them being entirely bony and consisting of a body or centrum with two neural arches, which enclose above the centrum a vertebral foramen, surmounted by a neural spine or spinous process. As in the frog, each arch bears in front an upward-facing facet or superior articular process or prezygapophysis and behind a downward-facing inferior articular process or postzygapophysis which fits on to the corresponding prezygapophysis of the next vertebra, while at the side a transverse process projects, and at each end there is an intervertebral notch for the passage of a spinal nerve, the adjacent notches of two vertebræ enclosing an *intervertebral foramen*. Each end of each centrum, with the exception of the first two, is flat, and against it in the young rabbit is a thin bony disc or *epiphysis*, which fuses with it when growth is complete. There is more difference between the vertebræ than in the frog, the backbone being divided into five sections, the neck or cervical, chest or thoracic, loin or lumbar, hip or sacral, and tail or caudal regions. In the *cervical region* there are seven vertebræ, which may be recognised by the fact that apparently each of the transverse processes is pierced by an opening (its *foramen*): there is thus formed on each side a *vertebrarterial canal*, through which pass the vertebral artery and vein. This is due to the fusion with the vertebræ of short cervical ribs in such a way as to constitute a compound " transverse process " which encloses a space. The first vertebra, known as the *atlas*, is ring-shaped, with a very large vertebral foramen and no centrum. The ring is divided by ligament into an upper part, through which the spinal cord passes, and a lower part, into which fits a peg, the *dens* or *odontoid process*, projecting forward from the centrum of the second vertebra. This peg represents the centrum of the atlas removed from it and fused with the vertebra behind. The transverse processes of the atlas are very broad, and the front side of the vertebra has two very large articular surfaces for the occipital condyles. The second vertebra is known as the *axis* or *epistropheus*.

[1] The general characters of the vertebræ of the rabbit may be well studied in that known as the second lumbar (see below).

It has a long, crest-like neural spine and bears the odontoid process. The remaining cervical vertebræ are short and broad, with low neural spines, except that of the seventh. The *thoracic region* contains twelve or

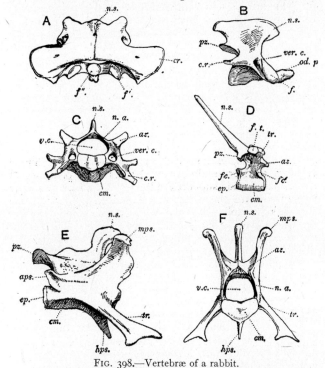

FIG. 398.—Vertebræ of a rabbit.

A, Atlas, from above; *B*, axis, from the right; *C*, one of the middle cervical vertebræ, from in front; *D*, fourth thoracic vertebra, from the right; *E*, second lumbar vertebra, from the right; *F*, the same from in front.

aps., Anapophysis; *az.*, prezygapophysis; *cm.*, centrum; *c.r.*, cervical rib, fused to transverse process and centrum; *ep.*, epiphysis; *f.*, facet on axis for articulation with atlas; *f'.*, corresponding facet on atlas; *f''.*, facet on atlas for odontoid process; *f.c.*, *f.c'.*, demi-facets for heads of ribs; *f.t.*, facets for tuberculum; *hps.*, hypapophysis; *mps.*, metapophysis; *n.a.*, neural arch; *n.s.*, neural spine; *od.p.*, odontoid process; *pz.*, postzygapophysis; *tr.*, transverse process; *v.c.*, vertebral foramen; *ver.c.*, foramen of transverse process.

See also Fig. 399, A and B.

thirteen vertebræ, which are characterised by bearing movably articulated ribs. The neural spines are tall, the transverse processes short and stout, and each, in the first nine vertebræ, provided on the under side with a facet or " costal pit " for articulation with the tubercle of a rib, presently to be described. The front end of the centrum (in the first nine the hinder end also) bears on each side a facet for the head of the rib. The hinder vertebræ of this set gradually become more like those of the *lumbar region*. These are usually seven in number. They are characterised by their large size and the great development of their processes, the prezygapophysis being borne upon the inner side of a large *metapophysis* and the hinder intervertebral notch being overhung by a small *anapophysis*. In the first two the centrum bears a median ventral *hypapophysis*. The lumbar vertebræ have no ribs. There is usually only one *sacral vertebra*, but sometimes two are found. These vertebræ are large and bear at the sides a pair of wing-like expansions, which support the hip girdle and are probably ribs fused with the vertebra. A certain number of the succeeding vertebræ are fused with the true sacral vertebra, the whole mass being known as the *sacrum*. The *caudal region* contains about eighteen vertebræ, of which the first three or four are fused with the sacral. They grow smaller from before backwards, losing their processes and becoming degenerate.

The *ribs* are present as independent elements only in the thoracic region. They are curved, bony rods, **Ribs and Breastbone.** articulated with the vertebræ. Those of the first nine pairs are connected at their lower ends with the breastbone by bars of calcified cartilage known as their *sternal portions* or as *sternal ribs*. The end which articulates with the vertebra has a knob known as the *head* or *capitulum*. The first nine pairs have a second facet on the dorsal side at a short distance beyond the head. This is for articulation with the transverse process of the vertebra ; immediately beyond it, for the attachment of ligaments, is a short projection, together with which it forms the *tuberculum*. The sternal portions of the first seven pairs articulate directly with the sternum ; those of the eighth and ninth are connected with the ribs in front of them. The last three pairs have no sternal portions and no tubercula. The breastbone or sternum is a long, narrow rod, divided into segments, and lying in the mid-ventral line of the thorax. The first segment is the *manubrium*. It is the

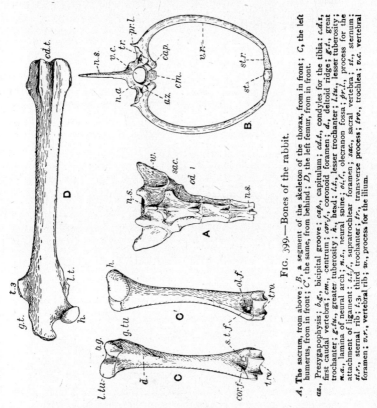

FIG. 390.—Bones of the rabbit.

A, The sacrum, from above; *B*, a segment of the skeleton of the thorax, from in front; *C*, the left humerus, from in front; *C'*, the same, from behind; *D*, the left femur, from in front.

az., Prezygapophysis; *b.g.*, bicipital groove; *cap.*, capitulum; *cd.t.*, condyles for the tibia; *c.d.1*, first caudal vertebra; *cm.*, centrum; *cor.f.*, coronoid foramen; *d.*, deltoid ridge; *g.t.*, great trochanter; *g.tu.*, greater tuberosity; *h.*, head; *l.t.*, lesser trochanter; *l.tu.*, lesser tuberosity; *n.a.*, lamina of neural arch; *n.s.*, neural spine; *o.l.f.*, olecranon fossa; *pr.l.*, process for the attachment of ligament; *s.t.f.*, supratrochlear foramen; *sac.*, sacral vertebra; *st.*, sternum; *st.r.*, sternal rib; *t.3*, third trochanter; *tr.*, transverse process; *tro.*, trochlea; *v.c.* vertebral foramen; *v.r.*, vertebral rib; *w.*, process for the ilium.

largest and is flattened from side to side. Behind it come four segments of equal size, then a very short segment, and finally the *xiphoid process* or *xiphisternum*, a long, slender rod, which bears behind a horizontal plate of cartilage. The ribs of the first pair articulate with the sides of the manubrium, and the succeeding six pairs between the segments.

Skull. The skull [1] contains the same regions that we have met with in the frog and dogfish, but it consists practically entirely of bones, which meet one another by jagged *sutures*.

The cranium or brain-case proper is relatively short, lies almost wholly behind the orbits, and is not in a line with the facial region, which is bent downwards at an angle of 60° upon it. Its bones are arranged in a series of three rings. (1) The *hinder or occipital ring* consists of four cartilage bones (p. 40). The *basioccipital* is a flat bone which forms the floor of the ring, including the lower edge of the fora.nen magnum and a small part of each occipital condyle. The *exoccipitals* make the sides of the ring, bounding the foramen laterally and forming the greater part of the condyles. The *supraoccipital* is a large, median bone which roofs the occipital ring. (2) In the *middle or parietal ring* there are both cartilage and membrane bones. It abuts on the occipital ring above and below, but at the sides is separated from it by the auditory capsules and squamosal bone. The floor of the cranium in this region is formed by a cartilage bone known as the *basisphenoid*, which lies in front of the basioccipital. It is triangular with the apex truncated and placed forwards, and upon its upper surface is a hollow, known as the *sella turcica*, which lodges the pituitary body. The *alisphenoids* are a pair of irregular cartilage bones which lie at the sides of the basisphenoid and form the lower part of the lateral wall of the cranium. The *parietals* are two large, square membrane bones upon the roof of the cranium, separated at the sides from the alisphenoids by the squamosals. The parietals meet in the middle line. Behind there is wedged in between them and the supraoccipital a small median *interparietal*. (3) The *foremost or frontal ring* contains a narrow median ventral cartilage bone known as the *presphenoid*, which lies in front of the basisphenoid and is connected with it by cartilage. With the presphenoid are fused at the sides a pair of cartilage bones known as the *orbitosphenoids*, which form the lower part of the lateral walls of the cranium in the orbital region. Above them the *frontals*, a pair of large, oblong, membrane bones, complete the side walls and form the roof, each bearing a large *supraorbital process*. (4) The front wall of the cranium is formed by a partition of cartilage bone, known as the *cribriform plate*, pierced by a number of holes, through which the olfactory nerves pass to the nasal capsules.

We have seen that the occipital and parietal rings are separated on each side of the cranium by a gap, in which stand the auditory capsule

---

[1] With the aid of Figs. 446 and 447, the following account may be applied to the skull of the dog, which is in some respects a more suitable example than that of the rabbit for a preliminary study of the mammalian skull. The most important differences are in the dentition (p. 583) and the conformation of the facial region.

and *squamosal*. The latter is a large membrane bone which abuts on the parietal, frontal, alisphenoid, and orbitosphenoid. From its outer surface there arises a stout *zygomatic process*, which bears on its under side the fossa for the articulation of the lower jaw and, beyond the

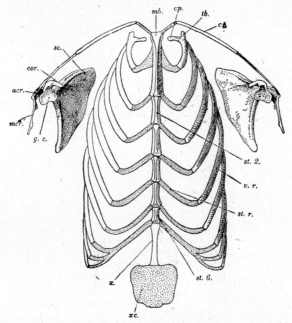

Fig. 400.—The breastbone and shoulder girdle of a rabbit, seen from below and somewhat from in front.

acr., Acromion ; *cl.*, clavicle ; *cor.*, coracoid process ; *cp.*, capitulum ; *g.c.*, glenoid cavity ; *mb.*, manubrium ; *mcr.*, metacromion ; *sc.*, scapula ; *st.r.*, sternal portion of a rib ; *st.2, st.6*, second and sixth sternebræ ; *tb.*, tuberculum ; *v.r.*, vertebral portion of a rib ; *x.*, xiphisternum ; *x.c.*, xiphoid cartilage.

See also Fig. 399 B.

facet, bends downwards to join another bone, the jugal, presently to be mentioned, thus forming the *zygomatic arch* or *cheek bone* (see p. 481). From the hinder border of the squamosal a slender *post-tympanic process* extends backwards. The auditory capsule consists of a large cartilage bone known as the *periotic*, which ossifies in development from three centres, one of which represents the prootic.

This bone fits loosely into a gap between the squamosal and the exoccipital. Its inner part is dense and known as the *petrous portion* : this encloses the auditory labyrinth. The outer part, which shows on the surface of the skull, is the *mastoid portion*. Against the lower part of the periotic is placed a thin membrane bone shaped like a flask with a gap on one side, the gap being turned towards the periotic. This is the *tympanic bone*. The body of the flask, or *bulla*, encloses the tympanic cavity, and the neck leads upwards and outwards from the drum to the ear opening, the passage it encloses being known as the *meatus auditorius externus*. At its inner end is a ring which marks the position of the drum in life. The inner wall of the tympanic

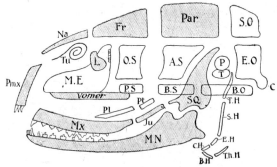

FIG. 401. —A diagram of the skull bones of a mammal (partly after Flower and Weber), the membrane bones shaded.

B.O., Basioccipital ; *E.O.*, exoccipital ; *C.*, condyle ; *S.O.*, supraoccipital ; *Par.*, parietal ; *Fr.*, frontal ; *Na.*, nasal ; *Pmx.*, premaxilla ; *M.E.*, mesethmoid ; *L.*, lachrymal ; *Tu.*, turbinal ; *P.S.*, presphenoid ; *O.S.*, orbitosphenoid ; *A.S.*, alisphenoid ; *B.S.*, basisphenoid ; *SQ.*, squamosal ; *P.*, periotic ; *T.*, tympanic ; *Pl.*, palatine ; *Pt.*, pterygoid ; *Mx.*, maxilla ; *Ju.*, jugal ; *T.H.*, tympanohyal ; *S.H.*, stylohyal ; *E.H.*, epihyal ; *C.H.*, ceratohyal ; *B.H.*, basihyal ; *Th.H.*, thyrohyal ; *vomer* ; *MN.*, mandible.

cavity is formed by the periotic bone, and on it may be seen two gaps, the *fenestra ovalis* and behind this the *fenestra rotunda*. In life a chain of three little cartilage bones, the *malleus, incus*, and *stapes*, connects the fenestra ovalis with the drum as the columella auris of the frog does, and like it transmits vibrations of sound (Fig. 427). These bones belong in reality to the visceral arches.

The part of the skull in front of the cranium is known as the *facial region*. It consists of the nasal capsules and certain of the bones of the upper jaw, and we have seen that it is bent downwards at an angle of 60° with the cranium. The *nasals* are elongated membrane bones which form the roof of the nasal cavities, uniting by a suture with the frontals behind. The *mesethmoid* is a median, vertical plate of cartilage extending forward from the cribriform plate and separating

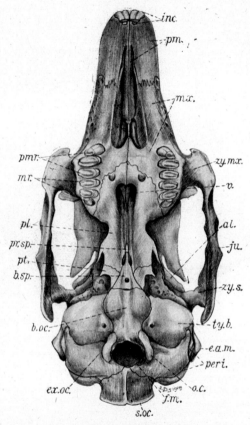

FIG 402.—A ventral view of the skull of a rabbit.

al., External process of the alisphenoid; *b.oc.*, basioccipital; *b.sp.*, basisphenoid; *e.a.m.*, external auditory meatus; *ex.oc.*, ex-occipital; *f.m.*, foramen magnum; *inc.*, incisors; *ju.*, jugal; *mr.*, molars; *mx.*, maxilla; *oc.*, occipital condyle; *peri.*, periotic; *pl.*, palatine; *pm.*, premaxilla; *pmr.*, premolars; *pr.sp.*, presphenoid; *pt.*, pterygoid; *s.oc.*, supraoccipital; *ty.b.*, tympanic bulla; *v.*, vomer; *zy.mx.*, zygomatic process of maxilla; *zy.s.*, zygomatic process of squamosal.

the nasal cavities. The *vomer* is not comparable with the " vomers " of the frog (prevomers). Its forepart is vertical and has on the upper side a trough that encloses the lower edge of the mesethmoid cartilage which supports the nasal septum (p. 539). Behind it sends out " wings " towards the sides of the nasal cavity, so as to form a horizontal partition, which separates an upper olfactory chamber from a lower narial passage (p. 539). The outer sides and floor of the nasal cavities are formed by the palatines, maxillæ, and pre-maxillæ presently to be mentioned. The surface of the cavities is increased by three pairs of thin and much-folded plates of cartilage bone known as the *turbinals* which project into them from their

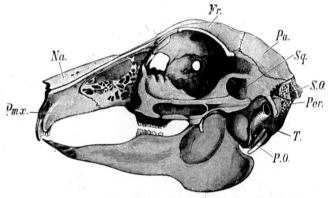

FIG. 403.—A side view of a rabbit's skull.—From Thomson.

Pmx., Premaxilla ; *Na.*, nasal ; *Fr.*, frontal ; *Pa.*, parietal ; *Sq.*, squamosal ; *S.O.* , supraoccipital ; *Per.*, periotic ; *T.*, tympanic (the reference line points to the bony external auditory meatus, beneath it lies the inflated bulla) ; *P.O.*, par-occipital process of exoccipital.

walls. In the upper jaw there may be recognised the same two series of bones as in the frog, the bones being membrane bones. The *pterygoids* are two vertical plates of bone attached to the lower side of the cranium at the junction of the basisphenoid with the alisphenoid bones. The *palatine bones* are a larger pair, which consist each of a vertical portion, attached above to the ventral side of the presphenoid and behind to the pterygoid, and a horizontal portion which meets its fellow in the median plane in the roof of the mouth (p. 539). There is no quadrate bone. The *premaxillæ* (*ossa incisiva*) are a pair of bones which form the front of the upper jaw and lodge the upper pair of large gnawing teeth. It has a nasal process, which passes backwards beside the nasal bone, and a palatine process, which, like that of the palatine bone, forms part of the floor of the

nasal passages. The *maxillæ* are two large irregular bones which lie
behind the premaxillæ in the facial region. The main part of each
bears the upper grinding teeth. From this arises a palatine process,
like those of the premaxillæ and palatine bones, which it connects so
as to form a floor to the narial passages, and a zygomatic process,
which passes outwards and backwards to form the front part of the
zygomatic arch. The zygomatic processes of the maxilla and squamosal are joined by a bar of bone known as the *jugal* or *malar bone*
or *zygoma*. The *lacrymals* are a pair of small bones which form
part of the front walls of the
orbits, lying between the frontals
and maxillæ.

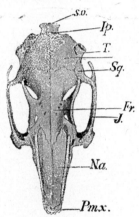

The lower jaw is composed
of membrane bone and represents the dentaries of the frog,
Meckel's cartilage, which is
present during development,
being absent in the adult.
The jaw articulates, not with
a quadrate but with the
squamosal bone (see p. 478
and Fig. 405). The *hyoid
bone*, lying in the floor of the
hinder part of the mouth,
represents part of the visceral
skeleton. It consists of a
median body, representing the
basihyal, and two pairs of
backwardly projecting cornua,
of which the hinder are the
larger. The anterior cornua
represent the hyoid arches,
and are completed by a series
of small separate bones, which

FIG. 404.—A dorsal view of a
rabbit's skull.—From Thomson.

S.O., Top of supraoccipital; *Ip.*, in
terparietal; *T.*, tympanic; *Pa.*,
parietal; *Sq.*, squamosal; *Fr.*,
frontal; *J.*, jugal; *Na.*, nasal;
Pmx., premaxilla.

connect the hyoid bone with the periotic region of the
skull. The posterior cornua represent the first pair of
branchial arches. The rest of the visceral skeleton is
represented by the jaws (mandibular arch) the ear ossicles
(hyomandibula, quadrate, and piece of mandible), and the
cartilages of the larynx (hinder branchial arches).

The following openings exist in the wall of each side of the skull:
(1) The *anterior nares*, at the front end of the nasal capsule, for the
nostril. (2) The *anterior* and (3) the *posterior palatine foramina*, a

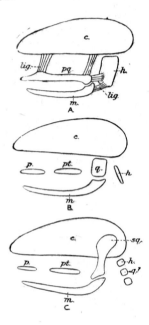

FIG. 405.—A diagram of the jaws of vertebrate animals.

A, The arrangement in the dogfish, in which the jaws are not at any point directly applied to the skull but are suspended by the hyomandibular which fits on to the skull (*hyostylic*); *B*, the arrangement in the frog, in which the lower jaw is suspended by the quadrate, which is directly applied to bones of the skull (*autostylic*); *C*, the arrangement in the rabbit, in which the lower jaw is suspended by the squamosal.

c., Cranium; *h.,* hyomandibular; *lig.,* ligaments; *m.,* lower jaw; *p.,* palatine; *pq.,* palatoquadrate bar; *pt.,* pterygoid; *q.,* quadrate; *q?.,* one of the ear ossicles, possibly representing the quadrate; *sq.,* squamosal.

In most fishes the jaws are hyostylic; in amphibians, reptiles, and birds they are autostylic.

large and a small opening in the palate for the passage of palatine branches of the maxillary nerve and blood vessels. (4) The *lacrymal foramen* between the lacrymal and maxillary bones, for the lacrymal duct which drains tears into the nose. (5) The *infraorbital foramen* in front of the zygomatic process of the maxilla, for the passage of a branch of the maxillary nerve from the orbit to the face. (6) The *optic foramen*, a large round hole in the orbitosphenoid for the optic nerve. (7) The *foramen lacerum anterius* or *sphenoidal fissure*, a vertical slit between the basisphenoid and alisphenoids for the third, fourth, sixth, and ophthalmic and maxillary branches of the fifth nerves. In the dog and most mammals the last-named branch passes through a separate opening, the *foramen rotundum*. (8) The *foramen lacerum medium*, an irregular opening on the under side of the skull between the alisphenoid and the periotic. Its anterior part represents the foramen ovale of the dog and other mammals and transmits the mandibular branch of the fifth nerve. (9) The *stylomastoid foramen*, a small opening behind the tympanic, through which the seventh nerve leaves the skull. (10) The *foramen lacerum posterius*, an irregular opening on the under side of the skull, between the occipital condyle and the tympanic bulla, through which the ninth, tenth, and eleventh nerves and the internal jugular vein pass. (11) The *carotid foramen*, which pierces the tympanic bone near its inner border, close to the occipital condyle, and transmits the internal carotid artery. (12) The *condylar foramina*, a couple of holes in the exoccipital, just in front of the condyle, through which the hypoglossal nerve passes in two divisions. In connection with the tympanic cavity there are two openings, the *Eustachian canal* at the anterior and inner angle of the tympanic bone, on the under side of the skull, behind the foramen lacerum medium, and the *external auditory aperture* at the end of the neck or spout of the tympanic flask.

Limbs. The shoulder girdle practically consists of one bone, the scapula, on each side. This is a flat, triangular structure, with the apex downwards and forwards, and bears a prominent external ridge or *spine*, which at its lower end becomes free as an acromion with a long, backward *metacromion*. At the apex is the shallow glenoid cavity for the humerus, in front of which a small hook or *coracoid process* represents the coracoid bone of the frog. Along the convex dorsal border lies a narrow cartilaginous suprascapula. The clavicle is a slender, curved bone, lying in a ligament between the acromion and the sternum. In mammals which move the forearm freely, as in man, it is well developed and articulates with acromion and sternum.

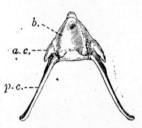

Fig. 406.—The hyoid bone of a rabbit, from above.

a.c., Base of the anterior cornu; *b.*, body; *p.c.*, posterior cornu.

The hip girdle is large, and each of its halves is known as an *os innominatum* or *os coxæ*. With the sacrum it forms a ring called the *pelvis*. In each os coxæ may be recognised a large dorsal ilium articulated with the sacrum, a posterior ischium, and a smaller, ventral and anterior pubis which unites with its fellow in a symphysis. The ischium and pubis are separated by a large *obturator foramen*, above and below which they meet. Above the obturator foramen all three parts of the os innominatum are continuous around the acetabulum, into which the head of the femur fits.

The limbs contain the same bones as those of the frog and other animals which have toes (Fig. 24). In the fore-limb the humerus has in front of the head a *bicipital groove* for the tendon of the biceps muscle, bounded by two roughened projections, on the inner side the *lesser tuberosity* or *small tubercle*, and on the outer side the *greater tuberosity* or *large tubercle*. At the lower end is a pulley-like trochlea, above which are two *supratrochlear fossæ*, the *coronoid fossa* in front and the *olecranon fossa*

behind, a *supratroch-lear foramen* putting the two into communi-cation. In the forearm the radius and ulna are distinct but not mov-able upon one another, the radius lying in front of the ulna. In man the lower end of the radius rotates round the ulna, so that the former lies in front of and obliquely across the latter when the palm faces downwards, but parallel with and out-side it when the palm is turned upwards. The position in which the palm is downwards is known as *pronation*, that in which it is up-wards as *supination*. In the frog the limb is

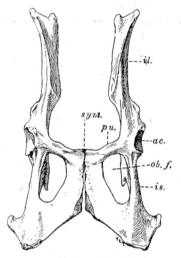

FIG. 407.—The pelvic girdle of a rabbit, from beneath.

ac., Acetabulum ; *il.*, ilium ; *is.*, ischium ; *ob.f.*, obturator foramen ; *pu.*, pubis ; *sym.*, symphysis pubis.

fixed half-way towards pronation ; in the rabbit it is fixed in the prone position. A large olecranon process of the ulna fits into the olecranon fossa. In the wrist all the nine bones of the typical plan are present, arranged, as usual, in a proximal and a distal row with a *central bone* or *centrale* between them. In the proximal row of three bones the radial is known as the *scaphoid* or *navicular*, the intermedi-ate as the *semilunar* or *lunate*, and the ulnar as the *cuneiform* or *os triquetrum*. In the distal row there are four distal carpals, the first on the inner side being known as the *trapezium* or *greater multangular*, the second as the *trapezoid* or *lesser multangular*, the third as the *os magnum* or *capitatum*, and the fourth, which represents

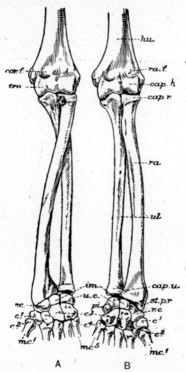

FIG. 408.—Bones of the left fore-limb of man.

A, In pronation; *B*, in supination.

c.[1], Os multangulare majus or trapezium; *c.*[2], multangulare minus or trapezoid; *c.*[3], capitatum or magnum; *c.*[4], hamatum or unciform; *cap.h.*, capitulum of the humerus, with which the radius articulates; *cap.r.*, capitulum of the radius; *cap.u.*, capitulum of the ulna; *cor.f.*, coronoid, fossa; *hu.*, humerus; *im.*, os lunare or semilunar; *mc.*[1], *mc.*[5], first and fifth metacarpals; *pi.*, pistoform; *r.c.*, os naviculare or scaphoid; *ra.*, radius; *ra.f.*, radial fossa; *st.p.r.*, styloid process of the radius; *tro.*, trochlea; *u.c.*, os triquetrum or cuneiform; *ul.*, ulna.

two fused, as the *unciform* or *os hamatum*. On the hinder
side of the wrist is a small *pisiform* bone. There are five
digits, of which the first is the shortest and the third the
longest. In the hind-limb, the femur has a prominent
head, below which are three rough prominences, the *greater*

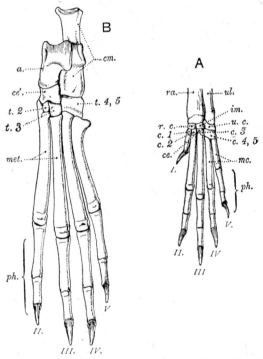

FIG. 409.—The skeleton of the left fore and hind feet of a rabbit.

A, Fore-foot ; *B*, hind-foot.

a., Astragalus ; *c.*1, first distal carpal or trapezium ; *c.*2, second distal carpal or
trapezoid ; *c.*3, third distal carpal or magnum ; *c.*4, 5, fused fourth and fifth
distal carpals or unciform ; *ce.*, centrale ; *ce.*, centrale of hind-foot or navicular;
cm., fibulare or calcaneum ; *im.*, intermedium or semilunar ; *mc.*, metacarpals ;
met., metatarsals ; *ph.*, phalanges ; *ra.*, lower end of radius with its epiphysis ;
r.c., radiale or scaphoid ; *t.*2, second distal tarsal or mesocuneiform ; *t.*3, third
distal tarsal or ectocuneiform ; *t.*4, 5, fused fourth and fifth distal tarsals or cuboid ;
u.c., ulnare or cuneiform ; *ul.*, lower end of ulnar with its epiphysis ; *I.-V.*, digits.

trochanter on the outside, the *lesser trochanter* on the inner
side, and the *third trochanter* below the great trochanter.
At the lower end of the bone are two large condyles for the
tibia. A *knee-cap* or *patella* covers the knee joint and is
connected by ligament with the tibia. The tibia and fibula
are fused at their lower ends only. The latter is a small
splint of bone outside the former, which is straight and
stout and bears in front a prominent *cnemial crest*. In the
ankle the bones, like those of the wrist, are arranged in two
rows with a central bone between them. The first row
contains, as in the frog, two bones, the astragalus or talus,
which corresponds to a fused tibiale and intermedium, and
the fibulare or calcaneum, which lies outside the astragalus
and projects backwards to form the heel. The central
bone is known as the *navicular*. The distal row consists
of three bones, that which corresponds to the missing first
digit being absent, and those which correspond to the
outer two digits being fused together. The innermost of
the remaining bones of the row is known as the *mesocuneiform*, the next as the *ectocuneiform*, and the third as
the *cuboid*. The metatarsals are long and there are four
digits.

The mouth differs from that of the frog in the possession
of mobile, muscular lips, and of a *palate*—an
Alimentary System : Mouth, Teeth, and Pharynx. inner roof which separates from the mouth a
narial passage. By this passage the approach
from the nostrils to the mouth is prolonged
backwards, so that the internal nares open
into the pharynx instead of into the forepart of the mouth
(Fig. 410). The first part of the inner roof is strengthened
by the horizontal processes of the premaxillary, maxillary,
and palatine bones (p. 532) and is known as the *hard
palate*; the hinder part is purely fleshy and is known
as the *soft palate*. The narial passage lies above the palate
and below the true olfactory chambers. Over the hard
palate it is not separated from these by any roof, and
the *nasal septum* between them comes down to divide
it into two (p. 532). Over the soft palate it is single, and
is separated from the olfactory chambers by a partition,
supported by the horizontal flanges of the vomer, representing the true roof of the mouth. Into this hinder part,

the *naso-pharynx*, open the Eustachian tubes. The *tonsils* are a pair of pits at the sides of the soft palate near its hinder border. The tongue is an elongate, muscular mass attached along most of its length to the floor

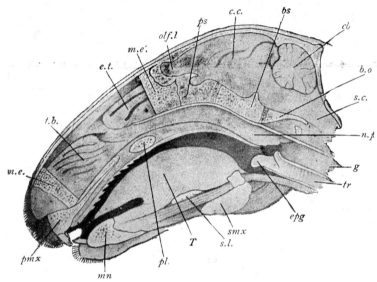

Fig. 410.—A vertical section through a rabbit's head.—From Thomson.

pmx., Premaxilla with incisors; *m.e.*, part of mesethmoid in front region, where narial passage is not separate from olfactory chamber; *m.e'.*, part of same in hinder region, where it divides from one another only the two olfactory chambers, which are here separated by a horizontal partition from the single narial passage (the intermediate part of the mesethmoid is cut away); *t.b.*, maxillary turbinals; *e.t.*, ethmoidal turbinal; *olf.l.*, olfactory lobe of cerebrum; *ps.*, presphenoid; *c.c.*, position of corpus callosum; *bs.*, basisphenoid with depression for pituitary body; *cb.*, cerebellum; *b.o.*, basioccipital; *s.c.*, spinal cord; *n.p.*, narial passage; *g.*, gullet; *tr.*, trachea; *epg.*, epiglottis; *smx.*, submaxillary salivary gland; *s.l.*, sublingual salivary gland; *T.*, tongue; *pl.*, transverse portion of palatine; *mn.*, anterior end of mandible.

of the mouth, but with a free tip in front. It bears papillæ of several kinds which subserve the sense of taste. The teeth differ from those of the dogfish and frog in that (1) they are not all alike, (2) they are inserted in sockets in the jaw, whereas those of the dogfish are embedded in the skin and those of the frog are fused to the jaw, (3) they are borne on the edges of the jaws only, and not on the roof of the mouth like the vomerine teeth of the frog, (4) instead of being continually replaced by the upgrowth of the skin from a groove as in the dogfish, or one by one as in the frog, they are in two definite sets, the *milk teeth* and the *permanent teeth*, of which the first is lost at an early age and replaced for life by the second. Unlike the teeth of most mammalia, those of the rabbit do not, when they have reached a certain size, narrow at their roots so as to form *fangs* and cease to grow, but continue to be added to below as fast as they are ground down at the top. The teeth do not form a continuous series as in man, but between the cutting-off teeth (*incisors*) in front and the grinders in each cheek is a wide gap (*diastema*) where most mammals have the holding (*canine* or dog-teeth), which, and others, the rabbit lacks. The upper jaw has two pairs of incisors, the first pair long, curved, and chisel-shaped, the second small and hidden behind the first; and six pairs of cheek teeth, which, like those of most herbivores, have broad, ridged crowns. The cheek teeth are much alike but are divided into two sets by the fact that the first three pairs, known as *premolars*, are preceded by milk teeth, while the rest, known as *molars*, are not. In the lower jaw there is only one pair of incisors; these are shaped like the first pair above, with which they work to gnaw off the food, which is munched fine by the grinders. This jaw has two pairs of premolars and three pairs of molars. It is usual to express the number and arrangement of the teeth of mammals by a *dental formula*. Thus, in the pig, which has a typical set of teeth, the formula is $i\,\dfrac{3}{3}\;c\,\dfrac{1}{1}\;pm\,\dfrac{4}{4}\;m\,\dfrac{3}{3}$, giving 22 on each side of the mouth, or 44 in all. With this we may compare the dentition of the rabbit, which is $i\,\dfrac{2}{1}\;c\,\dfrac{0}{0}\;pm\,\dfrac{3}{2}\;m\,\dfrac{3}{3}$, the total for both sides being 28. Four pairs of *salivary glands*, which are not found in the frog or dogfish, pour their secretion into the mouth. The *parotid gland* on each side lies behind the angle of the jaw, the *submaxillary gland* lies against its fellow between the angles of

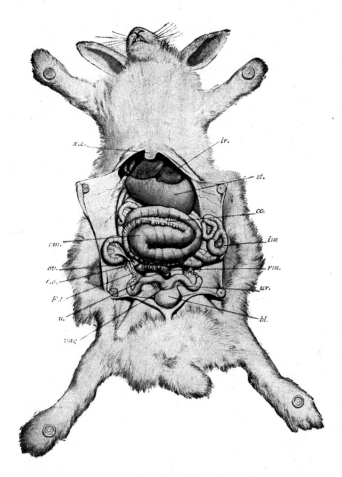

FIG. 411.—The body of a female rabbit with the abdomen opened, the organs being somewhat displaced so as to display them.

bl., Bladder; *cm*, cæcum; *co.*, colon; *F.t.*, Fallopian tube; *f.o.*, fimbriated opening of the oviduct; *im.*, ileum; *lr.*, liver; *ov.*, ovary; *rm.*, rectum; *st.*, stomach; *ur.*, ureter; *ut.*, right uterus; *vag.*, vagina; *x.c.*, xiphoid cartilage. Note also : regions of body (head, neck, chest, abdomen, tail), mouth, nostrils, hare lip, prominent incisor teeth, vibrissæ.

the jaw, the *infraorbital gland* lies below the eye behind
the cheek-bone, the *sublingual gland* lies along the
inside of the mandible. The saliva moistens the food and
contains an enzyme, known as *ptyalin*, which turns starch
into sugar. The pharynx receives in front the narial passage
and the mouth. Behind, it leads above (dorsally) into the
gullet and below into the glottis, which lies shortly behind
the tongue, covered by a flap, known as the *epiglottis*,
which is stiffened by a carti-
lage. Thus in the pharynx
there cross one another the
passages by which the food
passes to the alimentary canal
and the air to the lungs. In
swallowing, the soft palate is
raised and thus closes the
posterior nares, while the epiglottis protects the opening
of the windpipe, so that when
the food is thrust backwards
by the muscles of the tongue
and pharynx it passes only
into the œsophagus. That
tube, which is
longer and nar-
rower than those
of the frog and dogfish, runs
backwards through the neck
and chest, above the trachea.
Shortly after passing
through the diaphragm, the
œsophagus joins the stomach.

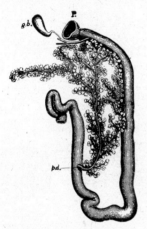

FIG. 412.—The duodenum of a
rabbit.—From Krause, in part
after Claude Bernard.

P., Pyloric end of stomach; *g.b.*, gall
bladder with bile duct and hepatic
ducts; *p.d.*, pancreatic duct.

Stomach and Intestine.

This is a wide sac, placed athwart the body cavity and
wider at the left or *cardiac end* than at the right or *pyloric
end*; it is curved, with the concave side turned forwards,
and the œsophagus enters at the bottom of the concavity.
The pyloric end communicates with the intestine by a small
opening, the *pylorus*, provided with a sphincter. The small
intestine is a narrow, much-coiled tube, seven or eight feet
in length. Its first section or duodenum runs from the pylorus
along the right side of the abdomen nearly to the hinder

end of the latter and then turns forward, forming a loop. In the mesentery between the two limbs of the loop lies the thin, diffuse pancreas, whose duct enters the returning limb of the loop about three inches behind the bend. The liver is a large, dark-red, lobed organ slung from the diaphragm by the falciform ligament ; in a groove upon its right central lobe lies the elongated, dark-green gall

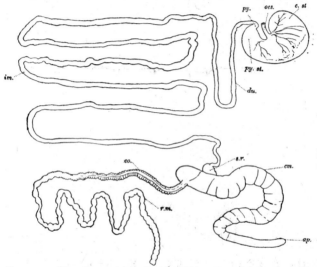

FIG. 413.—The alimentary canal of a rabbit removed from the body and spread out.

ap., Vermiform appendix ; *c.st.*, cardiac end of stomach ; *cm.*, cæcum ; *co.*, colon ; *du.*, duodenum ; *im.*, ileum ; *oes.*, œsophagus ; *py.*, pylorus · *py.st.*, pyloric end of stomach ; *rm.*, rectum ; *s.r.*, sacculus rotundus.

bladder, from which the bile duct runs backwards to open into the dorsal side of the duodenum shortly beyond the pylorus. The remainder of the small intestine is the ileum ; it ends in a round swelling known as the *sacculus rotundus*. The lining of the small intestine is beset with numerous minute processes or *villi*, by which its surface is increased. At the junction of the small and large intestine is placed a very large tube, the *blind gut* or *cæcum*, marked

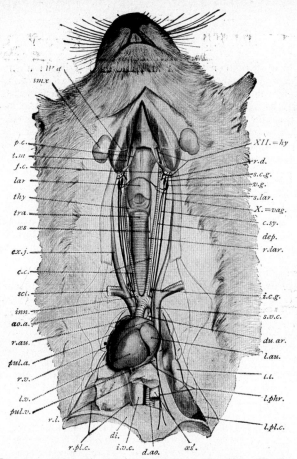

FIG. 414.—A dissection of the neck and thorax of a rabbit. The heart
has been displaced a little to the right, and the pericardium
and thymus removed.

ao.a., Aortic arch; *c.c.*, common carotid arteries; *c.sy.*, cervical sympathetic nerve;
d.ao., dorsal aorta; *dep.*, depressor nerve; *di.*, diaphragm; *du.ar.*, ductus
arteriosus; *ex.j.*, external jugular vein; *f.c.*, point at which the common carotid
divides; *hy.*, hypoglossal nerve; *i.c.g.*, inferior or posterior cervical sympathetic
ganglion; *inn.*, innominate artery; *i.v.c.*, inferior vena cava, lying in mediastinum; *l.au.*, left auricle; *l.l.*, left lung; *l.phr.*, left phrenic nerve; *l.pl.c.*,
left pleural cavity; *l.v.*, left ventricle; *lar.*, larynx; *œs.*, œsophagus in neck;
œs'., the same in mediastinum; *p.c.*, posterior cornu of the hyoid; *pul.a.*, pulmonary artery; *pul.v.*, pulmonary vein; *r.au.*, right auricle; *r.d.*, ramus descendens;
r.l., right lung, one part bulging into mediastinum; *r.lar.*, recurrent laryngeal
nerve; *r.pl.c.*, right pleural cavity; *r.v.*, right ventricle; *s.c.g.*, superior
cervical sympathetic ganglion; *s.lar.*, superior laryngeal branch of vagus;
s.v.c., superior vena cava; *scl.*, subclavian artery and vein; *smx.*, submaxillary
gland; *t.m.*, tendon of mandibular muscle; *thy.*, thyroid gland; *tra.*, trachea;
v.g., vagus ganglion; *vag.*, vagus; *W.d.*, duct of submaxillary gland (Wharton's
duct); *X.*, *XII.*, cranial nerves.

by a spiral constriction and ending blindly in a small, finger-like *vermiform appendix*. The sacculus rotundus opens into the cæcum about an inch from the end opposite to the vermiform appendix ; at the same end the large intestine starts. The cæcum is usually large in herbivorous mammals. In it the cellulose walls of plant cells are digested by bacteria which turn them for their own purposes into sugar, and thus make them available for the mammal. We have here an example of symbiosis (p. 217). Two regions may be recognised in the large intestine. The *colon*, which is not present in the frog or the dogfish, is a sacculated tube about a foot and a half in length where the greater part of the water in the intestinal contents is salved by being reabsorbed ; the rectum is a narrower tube about two and a half feet long, in which fæcal pellets can be seen. The digestion (p. 9) of the food of the rabbit resembles in general that of the frog (p. 61), but is complicated by the preparatory process in the mouth and by the conversion of cellulose in the cæcum. To provide for these, the alimentary canal possesses, as we have seen, features which are not found in the frog or dogfish.

The spleen is a narrow, crescentic, dark-red body lying close against the convex side of the stomach. **Ductless Glands.** The thymus is a soft, pink mass in the mediastinal space at the front of the thorax. The thyroid is a thin, red body consisting of two lobes, one at each side of the larynx, joined by a band across the ventral side of the latter. Adrenals and a pituitary body (pp. 548, 562) are present. (On ductless glands, see pp. 21, 63.)

For its active life and warm blood the rabbit needs a more elaborate respiratory apparatus than the **Respiratory Organs.** frog. The chest or thorax is a closed box whose side walls are formed by the ribs with the muscles between them, and its hinder wall by the diaphragm, which divides the main or pleuroperitoneal cœlom, parting two pleural cavities in front from a peritoneal cavity behind (p. 521). The windpipe comprises, besides the larynx, a long tube with rings of cartilage in its wall. This is the *trachea* or windpipe proper, which leads back along the neck and in the thorax divides into two bronchi which join the lungs. These are not mere sacks, like those of the frog, but spongy, because the bronchi break up into numerous *bronchioles*, which end in minute air sacs. The cavity of the thorax is enlarged from back to breast by an outward movement of the ribs and from head to tail by the movement of the diaphragm, which at rest is

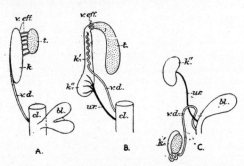

FIG. 415.—Diagrams of the male genital and urinary apparatus of :

A, The frog ; *B*, the dogfish ; *C*, the rabbit.
The animal is lying on its back, the organs of the right side are shown, and the bladder is turned to the left.
bl., Bladder ; *cl.*, cloaca ; *k.*, kidney ; *k'.*, anterior region of the same, which discharges through the Wolffian duct (*v.d.*) ; *k'.*, posterior region, which discharges through a duct of its own, the ureter (*ur.*) ; in the frog this region is not developed, though it is present in the newt. In the dogfish, the two regions remain continuous. In the rabbit, regions roughly corresponding to those of the dogfish become in the adult the " epididymis " (mesonephros) and " kidney " (metanephros) respectively. The " pronephros " or foremost region of the kidney of the embryo has in each case disappeared in the adult. Its history in the frog is described on pp. 635, 636 ; *t.*, Testis (that of the rabbit is not lettered) ; *ur.*, ureter ; *v.d.*, vas deferens (Wolffian duct) ; *v.eff.*, vasa efferentia.
The arrangement in reptiles is intermediate between types *B* and *C*, the mesonephros being reduced to an epididymis, though it and the testis remain in their original position, anterior to the metanephros.

convex towards the chest, but when it contracts flattens, thus increasing the size of the thorax. Since the pleural cavities are closed, their enlargement tends to set up a vacuum within them, and thus the lungs, which are not closed, expand to keep them full, drawing in air [1] through the glottis. When the inspiratory muscles relax air is

[1] That is, the air enters by its own pressure and expands the lungs when the pressure around them in the pleural cavity is lowered.

driven out by the collapse of the chest owing to the
elasticity of the lungs, but this can be aided by the contraction of certain other muscles, notably those of the
belly, which press the viscera against the diaphragm
from behind. (For respiratory regulation, see p. 21).

The kidneys of the rabbit are a pair of dark-red bodies,
convex on the outer side and concave on the
inner, which lie on the dorsal wall of the
peritoneal cavity, that on the left side farther
back than that on the right. Like those of
the dogfish and frog they consist of tubules, but these
even in the embryo have no cœlomic funnels. The tubules
resemble those of the frog (p. 79) but each has a long
additional hank known as the *loop of Henle*. As the
filtrate from the glomerulus passes down the tubule,
water is reabsorbed from it, possibly in the loop of Henle,
and so is saved for the use of the body. The principal
nitrogenous substance in the urine is urea (see p. 80).
It will be recalled that, whereas the kidney of the frog has
no distinction of regions, and discharges solely by the
Wolffian duct, that of the dogfish (like that of the newt)
has a narrow anterior region, which takes little part in the
secretion of the urine, and a larger hinder region, which
is the main urinary organ and in the male possesses a
duct of its own, the ureter. In the embryo of the rabbit
a somewhat similar condition is found. A strip of kidney
tissue—the mesonephros—lying in front of that which
becomes the kidney of the adult, is served by a Wolffian
duct. In the adult male the mesonephros becomes
attached to the testis and the Wolffian duct becomes the
vas deferens. In the female these structures are aborted.
The adult kidneys of both sexes represent only the metanephros or hinder part of the embryonic kidney, which,
instead of discharging through the Wolffian duct, has a
duct of its own, the *ureter*. From the concavity or *hilus*
the ureter runs back to open into the bladder. In the
early stages of development this organ joins the rectum
in a cloaca, but later the latter becomes divided, so that
the urinary and generative organs discharge by an
independent passage through the vulva or the penis.
Median to the kidneys lie two small, yellow, adrenal

(Excretory and Reproductive Organs.)

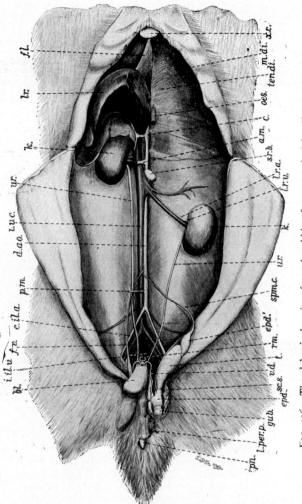

FIG. 416.—The abdominal cavity of a male rabbit, after removal of the alimentary canal.

a.m., *c*, *c.ila.*, *d.ao.*, *f.v.*, *i.v.c.*, *i.ilv.*, *k*, *l.r.a.*, *l.r.v.*, *p.m.*, *s.r.b.*, as in Fig. 420; *bl*, *epd*, *epd'*, *pn*, *rm*, *sc.s.*, *t.*, *ur.*, *vd.*, as in Fig. 417; *f.l*, falciform ligament; *gub*, gubernaculum; *lr*, liver; *l.per.p.*, left perineal pouch; *m.di*, *ten.di*, muscular and tendinous parts of diaphragm; *oes*, œsophagus; *spm.c.*, spermatic cord; *x.c.*, xiphoid cartilage. The uterus masculinus may be seen between bladder and rectum. but is not labelled.

glands. The testes are a pair of ovoid bodies which arise
in the course of development on the dorsal wall of the
peritoneal cavity near the kidney, but later becomes free
and pass backward into two pouches of the body-wall at the
sides of the penis known as the scrotal sacs. Each testis
remains connected with its original position by a *spermatic*

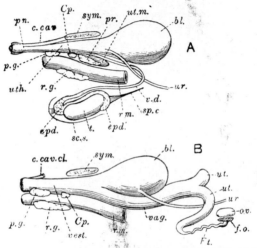

FIG. 417.—The reproductive organs of the rabbit. *A*, Male; *B*,
remale. In each case the dissection is made from the left side,
the animal lying on its back.

bl., Bladder; *c.cav.*, corpus cavernosum; *c.cav.cl.*, corpus cavernosum of the
clitoris; *Cp.*, Cowper's gland; *epd.*, cauda epididymis; *epd'.*, caput epididymis; *F.t.*, Fallopian tube; *f.o.*, fimbriated opening of the same; *ov.*, ovary;
p.g., perineal gland; *pn.*, penis; *pr.*, prostate; *r.g.*, rectal gland; *rm.*, rectum;
sc.s., scrotal sac; *sp.c.*, spermatic cord (cut short); *sym.*, symphysis pubis; *t.*,
testis; *ur.*, ureter; *ut.*, uterus; *ut.m.*, uterus masculinus; *uth.*, urethra;
v.a., vas deferens; *vag.*, vagina; *vest.*, vestibule.

cord, which consists of connective tissue with an artery
and vein. In passing backwards it carries with it the
mesonephros, which in the adult may be seen as the
epididymis, lying along the side of the testis and enlarged
at the front and hind ends into a *caput* and *cauda* respectively. The cauda epididymis is connected to the scrotal
sac by a short, elastic cord known as the *gubernaculum.*

Each epididymis consists of a mass of twisted tubules joining into a single, much-coiled tube which becomes continuous at the cauda with the vas deferens (or *ductus deferens*). This passes forwards out of the scrotal sac, curves over the ureter, and passes backwards again to open with the mouth of a small median sac known as the *uterus masculinus*, which lies above the neck of the bladder within the pelvic girdle. The uterus masculinus opens into the neck of the bladder, which is known after their junction as the *urinogenital canal* or *urethra*, and passes backwards into the penis, at the end of which it opens. Beside the uterus masculinus lie the *prostate glands* which pass their secretion into the urethra, and behind the prostate are *Cowper's glands*. The penis is situated behind the symphysis pubis and in front of the anus. It has spongy, vascular walls and is invested by a loose sheath of skin, the *foreskin* or *prepuce*. The ovaries are small, oval bodies attached behind the kidneys to the dorsal abdominal wall, and show on their surface little blister-like projections, known as *Graafian follicles*, each of which contains a microscopic ovum. The oviducts open into the abdominal cavity by wide, funnel-shaped *fimbriated openings* just outside the ovaries. When the ova are ripe the follicles burst and discharge the ova into the funnels, which at that time extend over them. The first section of each duct is narrow and gently sinuous and is known as the *Fallopian tube*. It runs backwards and enlarges into the *uterus,* a vascular-walled structure which joins its fellow in the middle line anteriorly to the bladder to form the *vagina*. This passes backwards within the pelvic girdle above the neck of the bladder, with which it presently unites to form the *urinogenital canal* or *vestibule*, which opens at the vulva. On its ventral wall lies the small, rod-like clitoris and on the dorsal wall two small Cowper's glands.

In most mammals the ripening of ova and their discharge, or *ovulation*, takes place at fixed intervals, and coition, usually, at the same periods. In the rabbit, however, ova are not actually discharged except after coition. The spermatozoa travel up the oviducts and fertilisation takes place at the upper ends of the latter. The ova pass down the oviducts, in which they segment. At

the end of the third day they reach the uterus. Here at
first they lie free. On the eighth day, however, they begin
to become attached to the uterine wall, and in the course
of the next few days there is formed in connection with

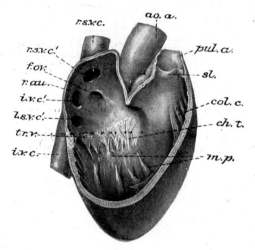

FIG. 418.— The heart of a rabbit, seen from the right side,
after the removal of the outer wall of the right auricle
and ventricle.

ao.a., aortic arch ; *ch.t.*, chordæ tendineæ ; *col.c.*, columnæ carneæ ;
f ov., fossa ovalis, the site of an opening through which in the
embryo there passed into the left auricle blood returning to the
heart by the inferior vena cava, much of which came from the
placenta and was therefore arterial (p. 66? · this blood was directed
by a fold of the auricular wall known as the Eustachian valve, lying
between the openings of the left superior vena cava and the inferior
cava, traces of which fold remain in the adult heart ; *i.v.c.*, inferior
vena cava ; *i.v c'.*, internal opening of the same ; *l.s.v.c'.*, internal
opening of left superior vena cava ; *m.p.*, musculi papillares ;
pul.a., pulmonary artery, cut open ; *r.au.*, wall of right auricle ;
r.s.v.c., right superior vena cava ; *r.s.v.c'.*, internal opening of the
same ; *sl.*, semilunar valve ; *tr.v.*, tricuspid valve.

each of them a special organ, known as the *placenta*,
in which blood vessels derived from the mother and the
developing young are in very close and extensive contact.
Through the thin walls of the two sets of blood vessels
interchange of fluid and gaseous contents takes place, and

in this way the nutrition and respiration of the young is provided for until birth, which takes place at the end of a month from fertilisation. Animals in which, as in the rabbit, a great part of development takes place within the body of the mother, so that the young when they are born are beyond the need of a shell or similar covering, are said to be *viviparous*.

The heart of the rabbit lies in the front part of the chest, enclosed in the thin pericardium, immediately behind the

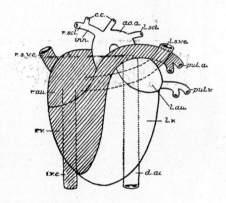

FIG. 419.—A diagram of the heart of the rabbit, in ventral view.

Lettering as in Figs. 414 and 418.
Parts containing venous blood are shaded.

soft, pink thymus. It has no sinus venosus or conus arteriosus, but there are two ventricles as well as **Blood Vessels :** two auricles (atria), so that four chambers **Heart.** are present. Three venæ cavæ corresponding to those of the frog open directly into the right auricle (Fig. 418), and two pulmonary veins lead by a common opening into the left auricle. The opening from the right auricle into the right ventricle is guarded by a threefold *tricuspid valve* (Fig. 418), with chordæ tendineæ, and a similar twofold *mitral valve* guards the opening between the chambers of the left side. The two sides do not communicate with one another. From the front end of the

right ventricle arises the pulmonary artery, and from the
front of the left ventricle, above the pulmonary artery,
arises the single *aortic arch*. The opening of each of
these vessels is provided with three semilunar valves. The
pulmonary artery divides to supply the two lungs, and the
arteries to the head and arms arise from the arch of the
aorta, which afterwards sup-
plies the trunk. In the beating of the heart, the auricles
contract simultaneously, and
the ventricles follow immediately afterwards ; then after
a short pause the auricles

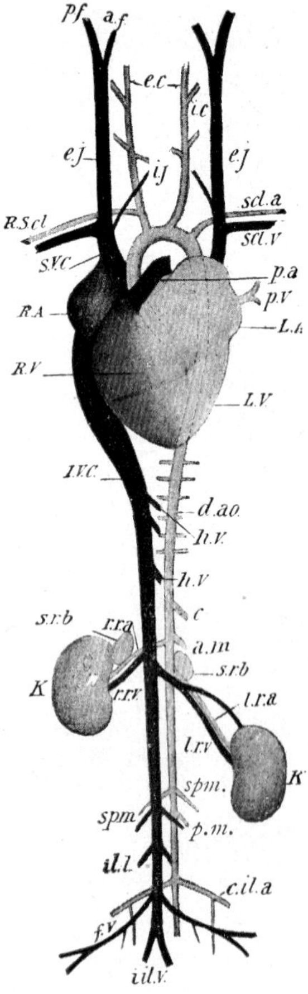

FIG. 420.—The circulatory system
of the rabbit.—From Thomson.

(*a*) Letters to right—
  e.c. External carotid artery.
  i.c. Internal carotid artery.
  e.j External jugular vein.
  scl.a. Subclavian artery.
  scl.v. Subclavian vein.
  p.a. Pulmonary artery (cut short).
  p.v. Pulmonary vein.
  L.A. Left auricle.
  L.V. Left ventricle.
  d.ao. Dorsal aorta.
  h.v. Hepatic veins.
  c. Cœliac artery.
  a.m. Anterior mesenteric artery.
  s.r b. Adrenal body.
  l.r.a. Left renal artery.
  l.r.v. Left renal vein.
  K. Kidney.
  p.m. Posterior mesenteric artery.
  spm. Spermatic artery (vein below).
  c.il.a. Common iliac artery.

(*b*) Letters to left—
  p.f. and *a.f.* Posterior and anterior
    facial veins.
  e.j. External jugular vein.
  i.j. Internal jugular vein.
  R.Scl. Right subclavian artery.
  S.V.C. Superior vena cava.
  R.A. Right auricle.
  R.V. Right ventricle.
  I.V.C. Inferior vena cava.
  r.r.a. Right renal artery.
  r.r.v. Right renal vein.
  s.r b Adrenal body.
  spm. Spermatic artery and vein.
  il.l. Ilio-lumbar vein.
  f.v. Femoral or external iliac vein.
  i.il.v. Internal iliac veins.

start another contraction. The venous blood which
reaches the right auricle from the capillaries of the
body is driven by the auricular contraction into the
right ventricle and thence in turn through the pulmonary
artery to the lungs. Returning oxygenated to the left

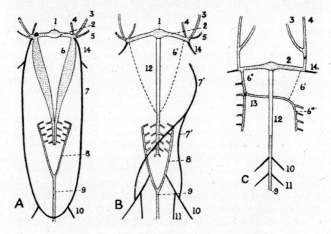

FIG. 421.—Diagrams of the venous system

A, of a dogfish ; *B*, of an amphibian ; *C*, of a rabbit.

The primary system in grey ; that of the lateral and anterior abdominal veins in
black ; the inferior vena cava in white. The hepatic portal system is omitted.

1, Entry to heart ; 2, left superior vena cava or precaval or ductus Cuvieri ; 3, left
internal jugular or anterior cardinal ; 4, left external jugular or inferior jugular ;
5, left subscapular ; 6, left posterior cardinal ; 6′, position of same in a newt ;
in the frog the posterior cardinals are absent ; in the rabbit the portion shown by
dots is wanting ; 6″, right azygos vein representing right posterior cardinal in a
mammal ; 6‴, left azygos vein ; 7, left deep lateral vein ; 7′, pelvic ; 7″, anterior
abdominal, representing both deep laterals fused ; 8, renal portal ; 9, caudal
(wanting in frog) ; 10, external iliac or femoral ; 11, internal iliac or hypogastric ;
12, inferior vena cava or postcaval ; 13, junction between azygos veins ; 14, left
subclavian.

auricle it is driven into the left ventricle, and thence
through the aorta to all parts of the body. There is thus
a double circulation, as in the frog, but the separation
of the ventricles and connection of the pulmonary artery
with one of them and the aorta with the other dispenses
with the elaborate apparatus of the truncus arteriosus.

The aortic arch bends over to the left and, as the dorsal
Arteries.   aorta, passes backwards under the backbone
through the chest and abdomen till it becomes
the small caudal artery. A ligamentous band, known as
the *ductus arteriosus* connects the aortic arch with the
pulmonary artery, just before the bifurcation of the latter.
At one stage in development this band is represented by
an open tube (p. 635). In its course the aorta gives off
numerous arteries, of which the following are the most
important : (1) The innominate, arising from the top of
the aortic arch and dividing into the right subclavian and
right common carotid, the latter passing up the neck and
forking opposite the angle of the jaw into external and
internal branches, (2) the left common carotid, arising from
the aortic arch immediately beyond the innominate,[1] (3)
the left subclavian, arising from the left side of the aortic
arch, (4) the cœliac, which arises from the dorsal aorta
shortly behind the diaphragm and divides into the hepatic
and the lienogastric, (5) the anterior mesenteric, shortly
behind the cœliac, (6) the renal arteries, (7) the genital
arteries, (8) the small posterior mesenteric, (9) the common
iliac arteries ; these last arise just before the hip girdle
and practically end the dorsal aorta, which after them is
diminished to the caudal artery.

Each superior vena cava is formed by the union of
Veins.   a subclavian vein from the shoulder and fore-
limb, an external jugular from the surface of
the head, and an internal jugular from the brain. The
right superior vena cava receives also an azygos vein from
the walls of the chest. The external jugular is larger than
the internal and lies nearer the surface in the neck. The
inferior vena cava is a large median vessel which lies beside
the dorsal aorta. It receives the following veins : (1) The
internal iliacs or hypogastrics from the back of the thighs,
(2) the external iliacs from the inside of the thighs, (3) the
ilio-lumbars from the hinder part of the abdominal walls,
(4) the genital veins, (5) the renal veins, (6) the large hepatic
veins from the liver, through which organ it passes on its
way to the heart. Blood from the stomach, intestines, pancreas, and spleen is carried to the liver by the portal vein,

---

[1] Sometimes from the innominate itself.

but there is no renal portal system. The general course of the circulation of the blood in the rabbit is shown in the table below.

Most of the lymphatic vessels are gathered up into a *thoracic duct* which opens into the left subclavian vein at its junction with the external jugular, but those of the right side of the head and neck and right fore-limb communicate with the venous system in the corresponding position on

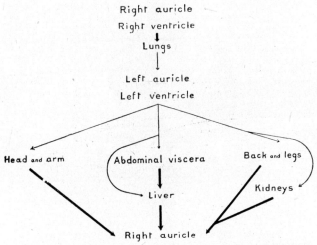

FIG. 422.— **A** diagram of the circulation of the blood in the rabbit. Thick lines indicate venous blood, narrow lines arterial blood.

the right side. (The arrangement of the main lymphatic vessels of man, which is substantially the same as that of the rabbit, is shown in Fig. 456.)

The blood of the rabbit differs from that of the frog and dogfish in two important respects. (1) The red **Blood and** corpuscles, instead of being oval in outline and **Temperature.** biconvex, with nuclei, are round and biconcave and have no nuclei. (2) The temperature of the blood, instead of rising and falling with that of the surrounding air or water, is almost constant at about 38° C. This is ex-

pressed by saying that the rabbit is a *warm-blooded* animal.
The heat is produced, not in the blood, but in the solid
tissues, particularly in the glands and muscles, its appearance accompanying the activity of the tissue. The circula-

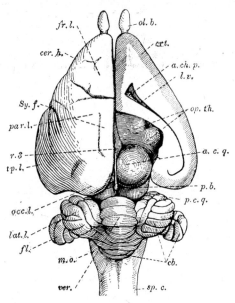

FIG. 423.—The brain of a rabbit, seen from above with part of the
right cerebral hemisphere cut away.

a.c.q., Anterior corpus quadrigeminum; *a.ch.p.*, anterior choroid plexus; *cb.*,
cerebellum; *cer.h.*, cerebral hemisphere; *crt.*, cortex; *fl.*, flocculus; *fr.l.*,
frontal lobe of cerebral hemisphere; *l.v.*, lateral ventricle; *lat.l.*, lateral lobe
of cerebellum; *m.o.*, medulla oblongata; *occ.l.*, occipital lobe of cerebral
hemisphere; *ol.b.*, olfactory bulb; *op.th.*, optic thalamus; *p.b.*, pineal body;
p.c.q., posterior corpus quadrigeminum; *par.l.*, parietal lobe of cerebral hemisphere; *r.3*, roof of third ventricle; *sp.c.*, spinal cord; *Sy.f.*, Sylvian fissure;
tp.l., temporal lobe of cerebral hemisphere; *ver.*, vermis.

tion of the blood, however, keeps the temperature of
different parts of the body nearly the same. The regulation of the temperature of the body as a whole is brought
about by alteration in the production of heat and in the rate
at which it is lost. The principal means of increasing the

production of heat is the activity of the muscles. Shivering is an example of this. Loss of heat is promoted by increased circulation in the skin and by sweating, which absorbs heat in the evaporation of the sweat. We have already noted that the power of maintaining a steady temperature

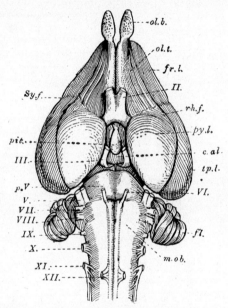

FIG. 424.—The brain of a rabbit from below.

c.al., Corpus albicans ; *fl.*, flocculus ; *fr.l.*, frontal lobe of the cerebral hemisphere ; *m.ob.*, medulla oblongata ; *ol.b.*, olfactory bulb ; *ol.t.*, olfactory tract ; *p.V.*, pons Varolii ; *pit.*, pituitary body ; *py.l.*, pyriform lobe ; *rh.f.*, rhinal fissure ; *Sy.f.*, Sylvian fissure ; *tp.l.*, temporal lobe of the cerebral hemisphere ; *II.–XII.*, roots of the cranial nerves.

has for those animals (the mammals and birds) which possess it the great advantage that their activity is not, like that of most creatures, closely dependent upon the external temperature. It is one of the ways in which higher animals have a greater mastery than lower ones over their surroundings.

The brain of the rabbit resembles that of the frog (p. 87) in the main outlines of its structure, but there **Nervous System.** are considerable differences in detail between the two. The most conspicuous part is the cerebrum, which consists of two very large cerebral hemispheres divided by a deep cleft or *median fissure*, at the bottom of which they are joined by a bridge known as the *corpus callosum*, composed of nerve fibres, nearly all of which run transversely. In the cerebrum the grey matter has migrated from around the central cavity to

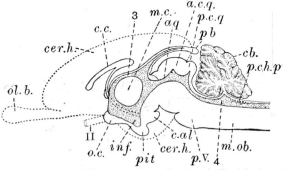

Fig. 425.—A semidiagrammatic, median, longitudinal section of the brain of a rabbit.

aq., aquæductus cerebri; *c.c.*, corpus callosum; *inf.*, infundibulum; *m.c.*, middle commissure, which connects the two optic thalami across the third ventricle; *o.c.*, optic chiasma; *p.ch.p.*, posterior choroid plexus; 3, 4, ventricles. Other lettering as in Figs. 423, 424.

the surface of the pallium, where it forms a good cortex (p. 89). It is almost smooth, but there can be seen on it faint indications of some of the furrows or *sulci* which in man are deep and numerous and divide the surface into *convolutions*. Midway at the side of each hemisphere is a shallow groove known as the *lateral* or *Sylvian fissure*, which separates a posterolateral *temporal lobe* from the *frontal* and *parietal lobes*. On the under side a longitudinal *rhinal fissure* marks off the frontal and temporal lobes from a region median to them known as the *rhinencephalon*, which consists of a *pyriform lobe* behind and the *olfactory lobe* in front. The latter consists of the *olfactory tract* and the *olfactory bulb*, which projects in front beyond the frontal lobe.

In each hemisphere the pallium with its cortex extends over the corpus striatum, where the grey matter remains internal. This

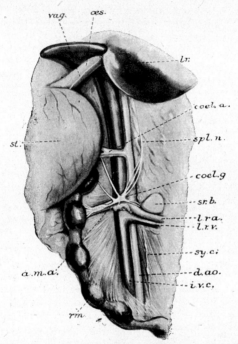

FIG. 426.—The solar plexus and neighbouring structures in a rabbit, exposed by opening the abdomen and drawing the stomach to the right.

a.m.a., Anterior mesenteric artery; *coel.a.*, cœliac artery; *coel.g.*, one of the cœliac ganglia; *d.ao.*, dorsal aorta; *i.v.c.*, inferior vena cava; *l.r.a.*, left renal artery (represented somewhat too large); *l.r.v.*, left renal vein; *lr.*, liver; *œs.*, œsophagus; *rm.*, rectum; *spl.n.*, left splanchnic nerve; *sr.b.*, suprarenal body; *st.*, stomach; *sy.c.*, sympathetic cord; *vag.*, left vagus.

disposition is due to a great expansion of an area (the *neopallium*) of the dorsal region of the pallium of lower vertebrates, which has thrust apart the lateral and median regions. These now occupy only small areas—the *pyriform lobe* on the ventro-lateral aspect, and

36

the *hippocampus*, which has been tucked in on the median side and is now mainly internal. With the development of the neopallium is connected the increased power of co-ordination possessed by the highest vertebrates, and the great extent of this region in mammals is accompanied by the ability to meet new situations intelligently.

The thalamencephalon is overhung and hidden by the cerebral hemispheres. Its thick sides form two large thalami, and from the hinder part of its thin roof the pineal stalk passes backwards to end in the pineal body

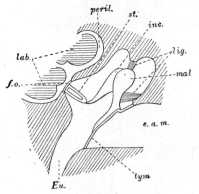

FIG. 427.—A diagram of the ear of a rabbit.

e.a.m., External auditory meatus; *Eu.*, Eustachian tube; *f.o.*, fenestra ovalis; *inc.*, incus; *lab.*, parts of the membranous labyrinth, containing endolymph; *lig.*, ligaments; *mal.*, malleus; *peril.*, perilymph; *st.*, stapes; *tym.*, tympanic membrane.

between the hinder ends of the hemispheres. The infundibulum is a funnel-like depression of the floor of the thalamencephalon, which enters the pituitary body. The latter, with the bottom of the infundibulum, is usually torn off in removing the brain from the skull, leaving a longitudinal slit which leads into the third ventricle or cavity of the thalamencephalon. A small, rounded, median swelling immediately behind the infundibulum is known as the *corpus mammillare* or *corpus albicans*. The mid-brain is almost covered by the cerebral hemi-spheres. Behind each of its optic lobes there is one of auditory function, so that four *corpora quadrigemina* or *colliculi* are seen. The crura cerebri are more prominent than in the frog. In the hind-brain, the cerebellum is very large and much folded and consists of a median lobe or *vermis* and two *lateral lobes*, each of which bears on its outer side a small lobe known as the *flocculus*. The lower side of the hind-brain is crossed in front by a wide flat band of transverse fibres, the *pons Varolii*, which connects the two halves of the cerebellum. The medulla oblongata, with the fourth ventricle in it, narrows backwards into the spinal cord. It is marked by a *ventral fissure* bordered by two longitudinal bands or *pyramids*.

There is no ventricle in the cerebellum, but small offsets of the aquæductus cerebri enter the corpora quadrigemina. The third ventricle is deep, but very narrow, and is crossed by a large *middle commissure*, which connects the thalami. The lateral ventricles are wide, shallow, and curved.

The cranial nerves are twelve in number. The first ten resemble those of the frog (p. 90) in origin and function, but differ in details : thus the olfactory nerves arise from the olfactory bulb as a number of fine threads which pass at once through the openings of the cribriform plate (p. 528). The seventh nerve, like that of the frog, has no ophthalmic branch. The *eleventh* or *accessory nerve* arises from the side of the medulla and spinal cord by a number of roots, the first of which is just behind the vagus and the last at the level of the fifth spinal nerve. It supplies certain muscles of the neck. The *twelfth* or *hypoglossal nerve* also arises by several roots ; these are situated on the ventral side of the medulla, outside the pyramid. Its course resembles that of the hypoglossal (first spinal) nerve of the frog. The spinal cord, its thirty or so nerves, and the sympathetic system resemble essentially those of the frog (pp. 86, 92). The sympathetic system has two ganglia on each side in the neck, twelve pairs in the thorax, and the same number in the abdomen. From the hinder thoracic ganglion there starts a *splanchnic nerve*, which passes backwards into the abdomen and ends with its fellow in a group of *cœliac ganglia* around the anterior mesenteric artery. These ganglia, with numerous nerves uniting and branching from them, constitute the *solar*

plexus (Fig. 426). A smaller plexus and ganglion of the
same kind lie around the origin of the posterior mesenteric
artery. A number of important nerves belonging to all
these series are found in the neck (Fig. 414). Among
them are the following : (1) The hypoglossal, curving
forwards round the angle of the jaw, with a backward
branch, known as the *ramus descendens*, which passes to
certain of the neck muscles ; (2) the vagus, running backwards outside the carotid artery and giving off a *superior
laryngeal* branch to the larynx, a *depressor* branch,[1] which
arises near the superior laryngeal and passes backwards
beside the main vagus, and a *recurrent* or *inferior laryngeal*
branch, which loops forward round an artery and runs
beside the trachea to the muscles of the larynx ; behind
this the vagus passes backwards along the œsophagus ;
(3) the *cervical sympathetic*, lying beside the vagus and
depressor ; (4) the spinal nerves, of which the third gives a
great auricular branch to the ear and the fourth and fifth
give off branches which join to form the *phrenic nerve* to
the diaphragm. The vagus bears its vagus ganglion just
before it gives off the superior laryngeal nerve, and the
sympathetic bears near the ends of the neck its two cervical
ganglia.

Sense Organs. The sense organs do not differ from those of the frog
(p. 98) enough to need special descriptions.
Besides the structures we have mentioned in
connection with the eye, there must be noticed
the *lacrymal* or *tear glands*, situated above the outer corner
of each eye, as well as Harderian glands corresponding
to those of the frog. There are no Harderian glands
in man. The secretion of the eye glands flows over the
conjunctiva and passes into the nose by the *nasal duct* at
the inner angle of the eye. The structures of the outer and
middle ear have been mentioned (p. 530 ; Fig. 427). In the

[1] This nerve, which runs to the beginning of the aorta, receives its
name on account of its function. It conveys from the aorta to the
brain afferent impulses, as a result of which, when the blood pressure
is too high, the central nervous system, acting through other nerves,
lowers the pressure of the blood by dilating the arterioles. In the
thorax, the main vagus sends branches to the heart. Through these
the beating of the heart is checked ; it is augmented through nerves
from the sympathetic system.

inner ear, there is present a large, spiral appendage of the
sacculus, known as the cochlea, which contains the endings
of those fibres of the auditory nerve which subserve the
sense of hearing. The ductus endolymphaticus ends in a
small saccus. In the nasal cavities (p. 539) the olfactory
epithelium is restricted to the upper part of the olfactory
chamber, the rest of the organ serving to warm and moisten
the air on its way to the lungs. Minute sense organs of
taste, known as *taste-buds*, are found in various parts
of the mouth, principally on certain elaborate papillæ of
several kinds on the tongue, and are supplied with fibres
which run in the glossopharyngeal and chorda tympani
nerves. The nature of the sense of taste in the rabbit,
though perhaps not in lower animals, may be inferred
from that of Man. In Man the only true "tastes" are
the perceptions of the qualities sweet, sour, bitter, salt,
and perhaps metallic and alkaline. Other so-called
tastes are aromas perceived by the organ of smell, to
which traces of the substances that give rise to them are
conveyed by air from the mouth through the posterior
nares.

CHAPTER XXV

MAMMALIA

THE rabbit is a member of a class of backboned animals which includes man himself, and is on that account usually regarded as the "highest" group in the animal kingdom, though it would be hard to show that its members are more highly organised than, for instance, the birds. They are

Mammalia : Prototheria, Metatheria, and Eutheria.

FIG. 428.—The Duckmole (*Ornithorhynchus*).—From Thomson.

known as Mammals or *Mammalia* from their possessing milk glands. They are warm-blooded, their skin bears hairs, the heart consists of two auricles and two ventricles and gives a single aortic arch, which curves to the left side, there are two occipital condyles, the lower jaw articulates with the squamosal bone, the sternum is segmented, and the kidney is a metanephros. One little group of mammals, found in Australia, Tasmania, and New Guinea and known as *Prototheria or Monotremata*, differs widely from the rest in that its members lay large, yolky eggs with shells, like those of reptiles and birds. Their temperature varies a good deal, and averages little above 25° C., whereas that of other mammals is pretty constant at about 39° C.[1] Their urinary, genital, and anal openings discharge into a common cloaca, and their shoulder girdle has well-developed precoracoids and coracoids which meet the breastbone. The Duckmole (*Ornithorhynchus*) is an example of this group. It is a

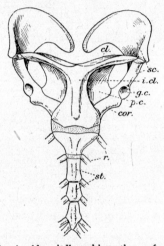

Fig. 429.—The shoulder girdle and breastbone of a duckmole.

cl., Clavicle ; *cor.*, coracoid ; *g.c.*, glenoid cavity ; *i.cl.*, interclavicle ; *p.c.*, precoracoid ; *r.*, ribs ; *sc.*, scapula ; *st.*, sternebræ.

small, aquatic animal with webbed forefeet and a horny bill, which lives in burrows in river banks in Australia. All other mammals have minute eggs, which are not laid, but undergo a great part of their development within the body of the mother, from which they receive nourishment. They have no cloaca or precoracoids, and the coracoids are small projections of the scapula. Among them the Pouched Mammals, *Metatheria*, or *Marsupialia*,

---

[1] The average temperature of man is about two degrees lower than that of most mammals.

stand apart from the rest.   Their young are born in a very
immature state and carried by the mother for some time
in a pouch under the belly.   They have a double vagina,
and the anus and urinogenital openings are surrounded
by a common sphincter.   They are found principally in
Australia, where they form almost the whole of the wild
mammalian population, including the Kangaroos, Wombats,

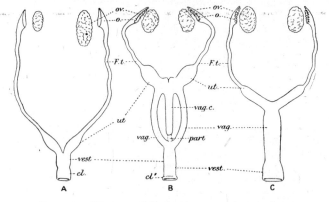

FIG. 430. — Diagrams of the female organs of generation :

A, of a duckmole (Monotremata); *B,* of a kangaroo (Marsupialia); *C,* of a rabbit
(Eutheria).

cl., Cloaca ; *cl'.,* vestige of cloaca represented by common sphincter around opening
of vestibule and anus; *F.t.,* Fallopian tube (oviduct); *o.,* internal opening of
oviduct; *part.,* position in which a passage breaks through for the birth of the
young; *ut.,* uterus ; *vag.,* vagina ; *vag.c.,* cæcum of vaginæ ; *vest.,* vestibule.

Note: in *A* no vagina, in *B* double vagina, in *C* single vagina.   A further
development is seen in man (Fig. 455), where there is a single uterus.   Note also
the progressive disappearance of the cloaca from A to C.

etc., but the Opossums of America also belong to this
group.   The remaining mammals, constituting most of the
class, are known as *Eutheria.*

The most aberrant of the Eutheria are the *Cetacea* or
Cetacea.　Whales and Dolphins—purely aquatic creatures
that live and breed in the water, to which they
are conspicuously adapted.   Their bodies are fish-like in
shape and hairless, save for a few sensory hairs on the
head, but are protected by a thick layer of fat, known as

FIG. 131.—The Killer Whale (*Orca gladiator*).—From Beddard, after True.

A

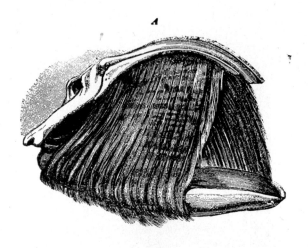

B

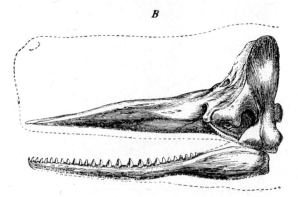

FIG. 432.—Skulls of two whales.

A, The Greenland Whale (*Balæna mysticetus*), a member of the Suborder
Mystacoceti, which are without teeth and capture their food by
means of a fringe of whalebone. In life the lower end of the fringe
is tucked in between the tongue and the jaw. *B*, The Sperm Whale
(*Physeter macrocephalus*), one of the Odontoceti. The dotted line
shows the outline of the soft parts of the head. The teeth of the
upper jaw are vestigial.

the blubber, under the skin. The fore-limbs are replaced
by paddles, in which, however, the bones of the arm and
hand can be made out, there are no hind limbs, the tail
bears a pair of fleshy flukes at the sides (not above and
below like those of a fish), and in some cases there is a
fleshy dorsal fin. The openings of the ears are relatively
minute and have no flaps, the eyes
are small, and the nostrils are placed
at the top of the head. This is in
connection with an arrangement by
which the end of the soft palate can
clasp the epiglottis and form a complete tube from the nostrils to the
lungs, so that the animals can feed
and breathe at the same time. Thus
whales breathe air like all mammals,
not water like fish. The so-called
spouting of whales is not the driving
out of water used in breathing, but
partly the getting rid of a little water
which has entered the nostrils and
mainly the condensation of steam in
the breath. Whales are carnivorous.
Some, like the Sperm Whale, have
teeth, which are numerous, simple,
and all alike. Others are toothless
and provided with strainers of the
horny substance known as "whalebone," by which they obtain for food
the countless small creatures which
swarm in the surface waters of the sea.

FIG. 433. — The left
fore-limb of *Balæ-
noptera*, a whale-
bone whale.—From
Thomson.

Sc , Scapula with spine
(*Sp.*); *H.*, humerus;
R., radius; *U.*, ulna;
C., carpals embedded
in matrix; *Mc.*, meta-
carpals; *Ph.*, phal-
anges.

Other aberrant groups of Mammalia, which can only be mentioned
here, are the Sea Cows or *Sirenia*,
aquatic animals which feed on water plants, and an assemblage of curious creatures, known as *Edentata*
because their teeth are defective or wanting,
comprising the Sloths, Armadillos, and Ant-
eaters. The rest of the Eutheria fall into three
great series : the Hoofed Mammals or *Ungulata*, which are
herbivorous ; the Nailed Mammals or *Primates*, which in

**Principal
Groups of
Eutheria.**

most cases lead an arboreal life and feed upon fruit, eggs,
or other food which they find in trees; and a less compact
assemblage of groups known as the Clawed Mammals or

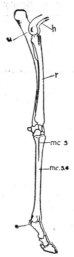

FIG. 434.— The
bones of the fore-
leg of a pig.—
From Thomson.

c., Cuneiform; *h.,*
h u m e r u s ; *l.,*
lunar (semilunar
or intermedium);
m., magnum; *r.*
radius; *s.,* sca-
phoid; *t.,* trape-
zoid; *u.,* unciform;
2–5, digits.

FIG. 435.—The
bones of the
right fore - leg
of a calf, from
the outer side.
—From Thom-
son.

h., End of humerus;
*mc.*3.4, cannon
bone (fused third
and fourth meta-
carpals); *mc.*5,
fifth metacarpal;
n., nodule; *r.,*
radius; *u.,* ole-
cranon process
of ulna.

Unguiculata, which are most often carnivorous in one way
or another. The broad distinctions between these groups
lie in the shape of their feet. The herbivorous ungulates
are comparatively defenceless and rely for their preservation

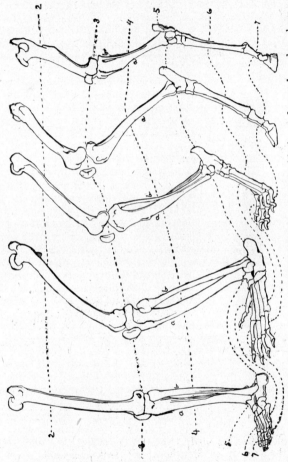

FIG. 436.—The bones of the hind limb of Man, compared with those of a monkey, dog, sheep, and horse.—From Romanes, after Le Conte.

from the attacks of carnivorous animals upon their turn of speed, which is attained partly by their walking, not upon the soles of their feet, but upon the tips of their toes, so that the power of their limbs is concentrated. This is expressed by the statement that they are *unguligrade*.

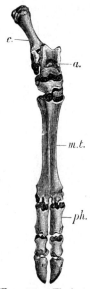

Animals which, like dogs and cats, walk upon the under surface of the toes and never place the palm or instep upon the ground are *digitigrade*. Those which, like bears and man, walk upon the whole sole of the foot are said to be *plantigrade*. Those which, like the rabbit, run upon the toes only, but when at rest apply the whole sole to the ground, are *subplantigrade*.

Ungulata. In Ungulata the metacarpal and metatarsal bones are lengthened, so that what seem to be "knees" are really the wrist and ankle joints, high above the ground. The first digit is wanting, and usually some of the others are also missing. The ends of those which remain are encased in the broad horny coverings known as hoofs. This does not apply to the elephants, which have five toes with short metacarpals and metatarsals. Hoofs are very broad nails, which cover the sides and part of the ends of the toes. Like other nails, they grow from above downwards. The part which covers the front and side of the last phalanx (the " coffin bone " of the horse) is formed by a thickened ring of skin above it, known as the "coronary cushion." That which covers the end of the digit (the so-called " sole ") is formed by the whole surface of the skin it covers. In correspondence with their diet, ungulates have broad grinding teeth, whose surfaces are generally ridged, though in the omnivorous pigs they are knobbed or *bunodont*. Ungulata fall into

Fig. 437.—The bones of the foot of an ox. —From Thomson.

a., Astragalus; *c.*, calcaneum; *m.t.*, cannon bone (fused third and fourth metatarsals); *ph.*, phalanges.

three main divisions: those of the even-toed forms or
Artiodactyla, comprising the pigs, cattle, antelopes, deer,

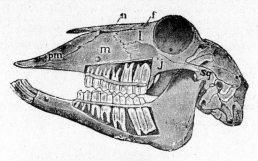

FIG. 438.—A side view of a sheep's skull, with the roots of the back
teeth exposed.—From Thomson.

f., Frontal ; *n.*, nasal ; *pm.*, premaxilla ; *m.*, maxilla ; *j.*, jugal ; *sq.*, squamosal ;
l., lachrymal.

and camels; the odd-toed forms or *Perissodactyla*, comprising horses, rhinoceroses, and tapirs: and the elephants
or *Proboscidea*.

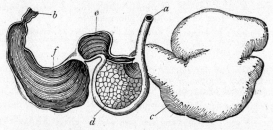

FIG. 439.—The stomach of a sheep.—From Leunis.

a., Œsopnagus; *c.*, rumen or paunch; *d.*, reticulum or honeycomb-bag;
e., psalterium or manyplies; *f.*, abomasum or reed; *b.*, beginning
of duodenum.

The Artiodactyla are distinguished by the fact that the third and fourth
digits of each foot are equally developed, and the line which halves the
foot runs between them. Thus they have cloven hoofs. The premolars
and molars are usually different. The stomach is often complex and

the cæcum is relatively small. The pigs and hippopotamuses, forming
the group *Suina*, are the least specialised of these animals. In correspondence with their habit of dwelling in marshes and forests, where the
ground is soft and a broad tread is needed, they have four well-developed
digits on each foot, though the middle two alone touch the ground, and their
metacarpal and metatarsal bones are not fused into "cannon bones." The
dental formula of the pig is $\frac{3, 1, 4, 3}{3, 1, 4, 3}$. The canines are large, grow
throughout life like the incisors of the rabbit, and in the male form
tusks; the grinding teeth are knobbed, not ridged, and the stomach has
not the complicated form of that of animals that chew the cud. Cattle,
with deer, giraffes, antelopes, sheep, and camels, form the *Ruminantia*.
Here only the third and fourth digits are complete, and the fused

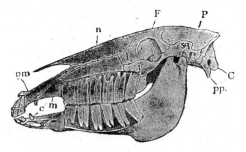

FIG. 440.—A side view of a horse's skull, roots of teeth exposed.
—From Thomson.

P., Parietal; *F.*, frontal; *n*, nasal; *pm.*, premaxilla; *m.*, maxilla; *j.*, jugal;
l., lacrymal; *sq*, squamosal; *pp.*, paroccipital process; *c.*, canine or
"tush"; *C.*, condyle.

metacarpals and metatarsals of these digits form "cannon bones."[1]
The fibula is represented only by a small nodule of bone attached to
the distal end of the tibia. Usually there are no front teeth in the
upper jaw, the dental formula being $\frac{0, 0, 3, 3}{3, 1, 3, 3}$. The ridges of the grinding teeth are crescentic and run fore and aft along the jaw. Such
teeth are called *selenodont*. The animals "chew the cud," and
in connection with this habit have a complicated stomach, with
four compartments shown in Fig. 439. The food when it is first
swallowed passes into the *rumen* or *paunch* at the left-hand end of the
organ, the walls of which are beset with small processes or villi. Here
it is kept till the animal is ready to chew it, becoming meanwhile
somewhat softened. It is then passed back into the mouth, chewed

[1] Vestiges of the second and fifth digits are found in deer.

up, and mixed with saliva. When it is swallowed again it passes along
a muscular groove on the upper side of the second division of the stomach,
known as the *reticulum* or *honeycomb-bag* from the pattern on its
mucous membrane, into the *psalterium* or *manyplies*. The folded
walls of this chamber, covered with papillæ, serve as a filter, through
which the food passes to the *abomasum* or *reed*, where the gastric juice
is secreted. Paired outgrowths of the frontal bones are common in
ruminants. In cattle, antelopes, sheep, and goats they are permanent and capped with hardened epidermis, the structures thus formed

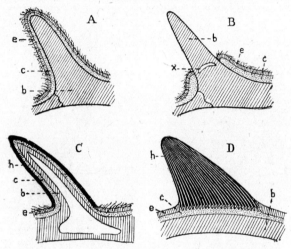

FIG. 441.— Diagrams of the structure of the horns of ungulata.

A., A growing antler; *B.*, the same fully grown; *C.*, the horn of an ox; *D.*, the
horn of a rhinocerus.

b., Bone; *c.*, cutis; *e.*, epidermis; *h.*, horn; *x.*, point at which bone is resorbed
in preparation for the shedding of the antler.

being known as *horns*. In deer they lose their skin and form purely
bony *antlers*, which are shed yearly. The horns of giraffes are short,
and, like antlers, are covered with skin, but this covering is permanent,
and the horns are not shed. (The horns of rhinoceroses are median
structures built up of epidermic fibres, and without a bony core.) The
camels and llamas have no horns, possess front teeth in both jaws, and
lack a psalterium in the stomach; and, by a well-known arrangement,
rows of little pockets, set like a honeycomb on the wall of the rumen,
serve to store water. The humps of camels contain a reserve of nutriment in the form of fat. The Bactrian camel of Central Asia has two

37

humps, the Arabian camel has one.   The dromedary is a swift race of the Arabian camel.

In the Perissodactyla the middle or third digit of each foot is larger than the others and symmetrical in itself, and may be the only complete digit.   The premolars and molars are alike and have broad, transversely ridged (*lophodont*) crowns.   The stomach is simple, the cæcum is large, and there is no gall bladder.   The rhinoceroses have three toes on each foot, immensely thick and very sparsely hairy skin, and one or two median horns, composed entirely of epidermic fibres adhering together. The tapirs have three toes on the hind foot and four on the fore foot, but the axis of each limb runs down the third digit, and not between the

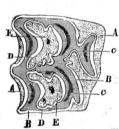

Fig. 442.—A transverse section of an upper molar tooth of a horse. — From Theobald, after Chauveau.

A, External cement; *B*, external enamel; *C*, dentine; *D*, internal enamel; *E*, internal cement.

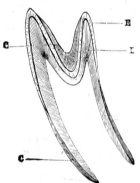

Fig. 443.—A vertical section of an incisor tooth of a horse. —From Theobald, after Chauveau.

C, Cement ; *E*, enamel ; *I*, dentine.

third and fourth as in the Artiodactyla.   The nose and upper lip are drawn out into a short but mobile proboscis.

Tapirs are found in two widely separated localities, in Malaysia, and South and Central America.   Horses, asses, and zebras belong to the genus *Equus*.   Here there is in each foot only one functional digit—the third—with splints representing the metacarpals and metatarsals of the second and fourth.   The wrist of the horse is known as the "knee," the ankle as the "hock."   The metatarsals and metacarpals are the "cannon bones," and the three phalanges of the single toe are the "pastern," "coronet" or "little pastern." and "coffin bone" respectively.   The latter bears the hoof.   The dental formula of the horse is $\frac{3, 1, 3, 3}{3, 1, 3, 3}$.   The ridges on the grinding teeth are complicated, some running along and some across the tooth.   The enamel on the

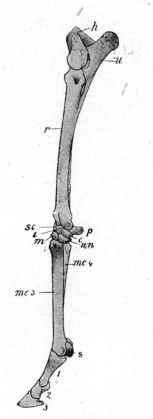

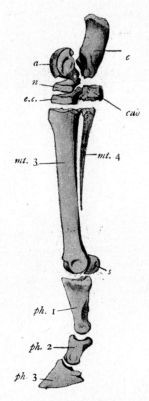

FIG. 444.—A side view of the lower part of a pony's fore-leg.—From Thomson.

h., Distal end of humerus; u., olecranon process of ulna; r. radius; sc., scaphoid; l., lunar; c., cuneiform; m., os magnum; un., unciform; p., pisiform; mc.4, splint of fourth metacarpal; mc.3, third metacarpal; s., sesamoid; 1, 2, 3, phalanges of third digit.

FIG. 445.—A side view of the ankle and foot of a horse.—From Thomson.

a., Astragalus; c., calcaneum; n., navicular; e c., external cuneiform; cub., cuboid; mt.3, third metatarsal; mt.4, splint of fourth metatarsal; s., sesamoid; ph.1–3, phalanges of third digit.

tips of the incisors is folded in, so as to form a pit. This gives rise to a marking which alters as the teeth wear down, and enables the age of the animal to be told.[1]

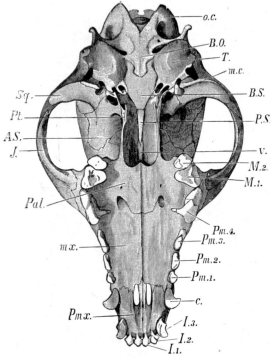

FIG. 446.   The lower surface of a dog's skull.—From Thomson.

o.c., Occipital condyle ; *B.O.*, basioccipital ; *T.*, tympanic bulla ; *m.c.*, postglenoid process behind fossa for condyle of mandible ; *B.S.*, basisphenoid ; *P.S.*, base of presphenoid ; *V.*, vomer ; *M.2*, second molar ; *M.*1, first molar ; *Pm.*1–4, premolars, the 4th the large carnassial ; *c.*, canine ; *I.*1–3, incisors ; *Pmx.*, premaxilla ; *mx.*, maxilla ; *Pal.*, palatine ; *J.*, jugal ; *A.S.*, alisphenoid ; *Pt.*, pterygoid ; *Sq.*, squamosal (the reference line points to the glenoid fossa).

[1] The dates of appearance and replacement of the teeth are also of use in judging the age of a horse. The incisors of the first pair are fully cut at one month, all three pairs at a little over one year. The first pair are replaced after two and a half years. The canines (tushes)

The *Proboscidea* or Elephants are generally classed with
Elephants. the ungulates. They have all the five toes. The
trunk is a muscular extension of the nose, with
the nostrils at the end. The tusks are the two upper incisors
and are composed of solid dentine or ivory. There are
no canines, but the six grinding teeth are very large and
transversely ridged, and are developed one at a time, so that

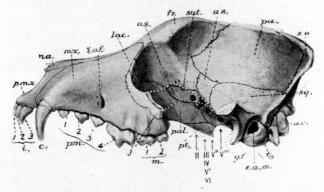

FIG. 447.—**The left side of a dog's skull, from which the zygomatic
arch has been cut away.**

as., Alisphenoid ; *c.*, canine tooth ; *e.a.m.*, external auditory meatus ; *fr.*, frontal ;
g.f., glenoid fossa ; *i.*, incisor teeth ; *i.o.f.*, infraorbital foramen ; *j.*, jugal ;
lac., lacrymal ; *m.*, molar teeth ; *mx.*, maxilla ; *na.*, nasal ; *o.c.*, occipital condyle (on exoccipital bone); *os.*, orbitosphenoid ; *pa.*, parietal ; *pal.*, palatine ;
pm., premolar teeth ; *pmx.*, premaxilla ; *pt.*, pterygoid ; *s.o.*, supraoccipital
(with which is fused an interparietal) ; *sq.*, squamosal ; *sut.*, line of dots marking
the suture between the jugal and squamosal on the removed zygomatic arch ;
t., tympanic ; *II.-VI.*, foramina for cranial nerves.

there is a succession of them, each being replaced as it
wears out. The testes do not descend into scrotal sacs.
The *Hyracoidea*, usually placed near the Elephants, are little
rabbit-like animals found in Palestine and Africa. *Hyrax*,
the " coney " of Scripture, is the best known example.

begin to show at four years, and are fully cut at five years, when all
the permanent incisors are level. At six years all the incisors show the
central enamel as a complete ring, and in the first pair the cement is
almost gone from within it. At eight years this pair shows the dentine
as a yellow line—the " star."

BAT·

·BIRD·

FIG. 448.—Diagrams to show the difference in construction between the wing of a bat and that of a bird. In the bat all the digits are present, four of them are very long, and the wing surface is provided by skin stretched from finger to finger and between the arm and the flank. In the bird there are only three digits, these are vestigial, and the wing surface is mainly provided by feathers in rows parallel with the axis of the limb.—From Romanes.

Among the other groups of Eutheria are : the *Rodentia*, to which belong rabbits, rats, mice, squirrels, etc., all characterised by two pairs of large incisors adapted for gnawing and by the absence of canines ; the *Insectivora*, to which belong moles, hedgehogs, and shrews, with sharp-cusped teeth and a long snout ; the *Chiroptera* or bats, in which the fore-limb becomes a wing by the lengthening of its digits and the formation of a web of skin between them and the side of the body ; and

Unguiculata.

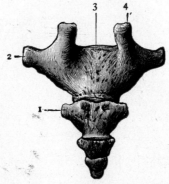

FIG. 449.—The Coccyx, or vestige of the caudal vertebræ of man.—From Cunningham.

1, 2, Transverse processes ; 3, for sacrum ; 4, cornu.

the *Carnivora*, to which belong dogs, cats, bears, and seals. These latter are generally bold, intelligent animals. They have claws, which in the cats are retractile. The canines are strong and sharp, and some of the back teeth are adapted by their narrow, blade-like crowns for cutting flesh. These are the four upper premolar and the first lower molar. The dental formula of the dog is $\dfrac{3,\ 1,\ 4,\ 2}{3,\ 1,\ 4,\ 3}$. Dogs and cats are digitigrade, and, like most of the other Carnivora, have five fingers and four toes. The clavicles are rudimentary.

The last group of mammals which we shall mention is

the *Primates*, which include monkeys and man, together
Primates.   with the lemurs, which link the monkeys to
other mammals. The Primates are plantigrade,
and either their thumb or their great toe—usually both—
can be opposed to the other digits so as to grasp objects.
There are well-developed clavicles, and the upper arm
and thigh are free, as in the elephants, not enclosed in

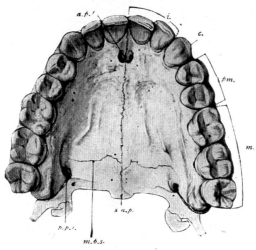

Fig. 450.—The bones of the hard palate and upper permanent
teeth of man.

a.p.f., Anterior palatine foramen, or *foramen incisivum*; *c.*, canine tooth; *i.*,
incisor teeth; *m.*, molar teeth; *m.p.s.*, suture between maxillary and palatine
bones; *p.p.f.*, posterior palatine foramen or *foramen palatinum majus*; *pm.*,
premolar teeth; *s.n.p.*, *spina nasalis posterior.*

the skin of the trunk, as in most mammals. The orbits
are turned forwards, not, as is usual, to the sides, and,
except in the lemurs, are enclosed behind by a complete
bony wall. The majority of these peculiarities are connected with an arboreal habit. It should be noted that in
most respects the Primates, and man with them, are not
highly specialised animals. In their limbs, in their teeth,
in the possession of clavicles, and in the alimentary canal

they present a type of organisation which is on the whole
below, rather than above, the average of specialisation in
the Mammalia.

Fig. 451.— The Dun-coloured Gibbon (*Hylobates entelloides*).—
From Flower and Lydekker.

Man. Man is related to a group of tailless, half-erect monkeys which includes
the gibbons, chimpanzee, gorilla, and orang-utan. From
these he differs far more strikingly by his mental attri-
butes than by his physical features, but the following points are of
interest. Man alone walks perfectly upright. His legs are longer than
those of the great apes, and the great toe is not opposable. He is less

hairy. He has a better command over his voice. His brain is twice
the size of that of the gorilla, which in this respect approaches him

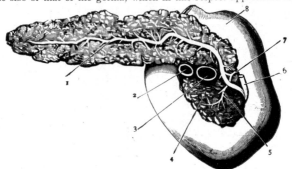

FIG. 452.—A dorsal view of the pancreas and duodenum of man,
   with the pancreatic duct exposed, showing its junction with the
   bile duct, and the accessory pancreatic duct.—From Cunningham.

1, Pancreatic duct; 2, superior (anterior) mesenteric artery; 3, superior mesenteric
   vein (branch of portal vein); 4, "head" of pancreas; 5, branch of accessory
   pancreatic duct; 6, bile duct; 7, accessory pancreatic duct or duct of Santorini,
   communicating both with duodenum and with main pancreatic duct; 8, first
   (superior) part of duodenum.

FIG. 453.—A man in the successive positions of walking.
   —From Marey.

Note how first the left leg is straightened and tilts the
   body forwards while the right leg swings to the front,
   and then the right is straightened and the left swung.
   See p. 476.

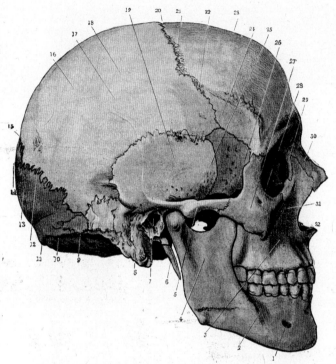

Fig. 454.—A human skull, seen from the right side.—From
Cunningham.

1. Mental foramen.
2. Body of the mandible.
3. Maxilla.
4. Ramus of mandible.
5. Zygomatic arch.
6. Styloid process.
7. External auditory
   meatus.
8. Mastoid process.
9. Asterion.
10. Superior nuchal line
    of occipital bone.
11. External occipital
    protuberance.
12. Lambdoid suture.
13. Occipital bone.
14. Lambda.
15. Obelion placed be-
    tween the two
    parietal foramina
16. Parietal bone.
17. Lower temporal line.
18. Upper temporal line.
19. Squamous part of
    temporal bone.
20. Bregma.
21. Coronal suture.
22. Stephanion.
23. Frontal bone.
24. Pterion.
25. Temporal fossa.
26. Great wing of sphe-
    noid.
27. Zygomatic bone.
28. Zygomatico - facial
    foramen.
29. Lacrymal bone.
30. Nasal bone.
31. Infra-orbital foramen.
32. Piriform aperture
    and anterior nasal
    spine.

most nearly, and his cerebral convolutions are more complex than those of the great apes. The cranial part of his skull is correspondingly enlarged. When the face looks forwards the foramen magnum opens downwards, instead of more or less backwards, as in most other mammals.

The dental formula is $\frac{2, 1, 2, 3}{2, 1, 2, 3}$, which is that of the great apes, but the small size of the canines and the absence of a gap between them

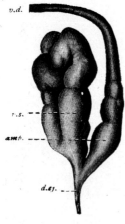

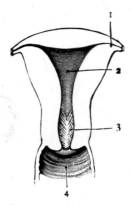

FIG. 455A.—The lower end of a vas (or ductus) deferens of man, with its seminal vesicle.—From Cunningham.

amp., "Ampulla" of vas deferens; *d.ej*, ductus ejaculatorius; *v.d.*, vas deferens; *v.s.*, vesicula seminalis.

FIG. 455B.—A diagram of the human uterus in longitudinal section. At the lateral angles the Fallopian tubes have been cut away.—From Cunningham.

1, Lateral angle of uterus; 2, cavity of body; 3, cavity of cervix; 4, vaginal cavity.

and the incisors are peculiar to man. The chin and the projection of the nasal bones to support the nose are also human features.

The essential facts of human morphology may be summed up as follows : Man is metazoan, triploblastic, chordate, vertebrate, pentadactyle, mammalian, eutherian, primate.[1] Excepting only the limb-skeletons, whose parts cannot be identified with those of animals lower than the Amphibia (p. 474), the main outlines of each of his

---

[1] See pp. 177, 275, 418, 421, 429, 566, 568, 584.

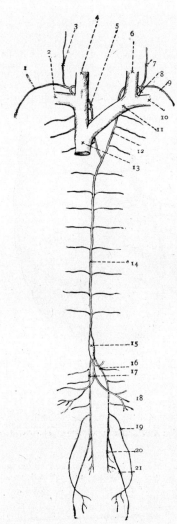

FIG. 456.—A diagram of the main lymph vessels, and of the branches of the superior vena cava of man. —From Cunningham.

1, Right subclavian lymph-trunk; 2, right subclavian vein; 3, right jugular lymph-trunk; 4, right internal jugular vein; 5, broncho-mediastinal (lymph) duct, represented as connected below with the thoracic duct, as it sometimes is; 6, left internal jugular vein; 7, left jugular lymph-trunk; 8, thoracic duct; 9, left subclavian lymph-trunk; 10, left subclavian vein; 11, left innominate vein; 12, thoracic duct; 13, superior vena cava; 14, thoracic duct; 15, cisterna chyli; 16, left lumbar lymph-trunk; **17,** right lumbar lymph-trunk; **18,** intestinal lymph-vessels; **19,** testicular lymph-vessels; **20,** lymph-vessels from pelvis; **21, lymph-vessels from leg.**

principal systems of organs may be traced back, like those of other mammals, to the fishes, as has been shown in the course of the foregoing chapters.[1] In comparison with the rabbit, the following features of his anatomy may be mentioned, in addition to those which have been stated in the last two paragraphs. His tibia and fibula are not fused ; the fore-arm is capable of pronation and supination (Fig. 408) ; there is no centrale in the wrist ; the bones of the adult skull show considerable fusions, there being a single " occipital bone " composed of basioccipital, exoccipitals, supraoccipital, and interparietal, a " sphenoid bone " composed of basisphenoid, alisphenoids, presphenoid, orbitosphenoids, and pterygoids, an

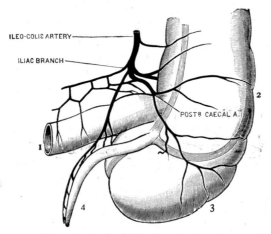

ILEO-COLIC ARTERY

ILIAC BRANCH

POSTR CAECAL A.

FIG. 457.—The cæcum and neighbouring structures in man.—From Cunningham.

1, Ileum ; 2, colon ; 3, cæcum ; 4, appendix.

" ethmoid bone " composed of mesethmoid, ectethmoids, turbinals and vomer, and a " temporal bone " composed of squamosal, tympanic, periotic, tympanohyal, and stylohyal ; small, irregular, additional bones (Wormian bones) may be found in the course of the sutures of the roof of the skull ; the pancreatic duct joins the bile duct near the entry of the latter into the duodenum ; the vermiform appendix is a good deal smaller and the cæcum very much smaller ;

---

[1] In making such comparisons the student will find of use, as summaries of the facts, the following diagrams, etc. : Figs. 396, 415, 421, 484, 486, the second and third paragraphs on p. 39, and Figs. 401, 405.

the left superior vena cava (or innominate vein) joins that of the right side before the latter enters the heart, forming thus a single superior vena cava ; the external and internal iliac veins of each side join to form a common iliac ; the fibres which form the depressor nerve of the rabbit are included in the main vagus nerve ; there is a single pair of mammæ, which are on the thorax ; the uterus is a single median structure ; the testes descend into an external scrotum ; a seminal vesicle opens into the hinder end of each vas deferens ; and the third eyelid is represented only by a slight, semilunar fold of membrane, the *plicæ semilunaris*.

CHAPTER XXVI

REPRODUCTION AND SEX

In the various animals which we have studied in the preceding chapters, we have come across a number **Reproduction: Sexual and Asexual.** of examples of reproduction, occurring in various ways and in different circumstances. It will be well at this stage to consider the process from a broad point of view. We have seen (pp. 13–16) that the essence of every act of reproduction is the origin, by fission from the body of an organism, of a reproductive body, and the development of the latter into the likeness of its parent, and that a process of reproduction is said to be sexual or asexual according as the reproductive body does or does not undergo the process known as syngamy before it develops. Reproductive bodies which differ thus in their behaviour have, with few exceptions, a corresponding difference in their constitution. This appears clearly on comparing the two kinds of reproduction as they occur in *Hydra*. Asexual reproduction is relatively a simple matter. It consists in the formation of a reproductive body known as a *bud* and its fission from the body and development, although in *Hydra* the structural part of the development is completed before fission takes place.[1] In the bud there are from the first both cells specialised for services within the body—the ectoderm and endoderm cells derived from the parent—and cells which are still undifferentiated and will later give rise to germs, for the bud will presently reproduce sexually. Thus the body

[1] Except in the case of longitudinal and transverse fission.

divides into two parts, but these are alike in composition, each containing both potential germs and differentiated body substance. Sexual reproduction is a more complicated process. It involves the formation of reproductive bodies which shall unite in syngamy before they develop. Since in syngamy two single nuclei unite, it can only be carried out by single cells, and these, since they are to reproduce the whole organism, must not be specialised for any function within the body (p. 150). Thus in the formation of the reproductive bodies of sexual reproduction we find a separation singly of cells which are not specialised for service within the body from those that are. A reproductive body which contains a single nucleus and is not specialised for body services, is known as a *germ*. Ova and spermatozoa are germs. Reproduction by means of germs involves a longer process of development, which, unlike asexual reproduction, brings into being radically reconstructed individuals with a completely new outfit of nuclei and cytoplasm.

In the Metazoa, sexual reproduction by means of ova and spermatozoa always takes place. In some **Reproduction of the Metazoa.** there is also asexual reproduction, as we have seen in Chapter XII., but this is never the case in the higher kinds, such as the frog. A number of Metazoa, however—various insects, crustaceaus, and worms—carry out a kind of reproduction which, while it resembles the sexual process in being effected by germs, is like asexual reproduction in not involving syngamy. This is *parthenogenesis* or the development of unfertilised ova. We have met with it in the liver fluke and the green-fly. In certain kinds of water-fleas and of the minute water animals known as rotifers fertilisation is not known ever to take place. An important deduction that may be drawn from the occurrence of parthenogenesis is that, though normally two sets of chromosomes are concerned in the development of an individual, one set by itself is competent to direct this process.

With the reproductive processes of Metazoa it is not difficult to compare those of the Ciliata. These animals, though they are not divided into cells, possess, as we have

38

seen, a body nucleus or meganucleus, and a germ
nucleus or micronucleus.   The ordinary fission

**Reproduction
of the
Protozoa.**

is asexual reproduction, each nucleus con-
tributing to both offspring.   The conjugation
of the Ciliata is an act of sexual reproduction,
consisting in the formation of germs, their union, and
a development of the zygote (p. 168).   The difference
between the germ formation of the Ciliata and that of the
Metazoa is due to the absence of body-cells in the former,
where only the body nucleus perishes, the rest of the
parent body becoming a germ, as does the portion
which separates from it.   Thus there arise two germs, of
which one has little if any cytoplasm and is a male
gamete, while the other, which keeps most if not all
of the cytoplasm of the parent, is a female gamete.   After
true syngamy, there takes place a process comparable to
the development of a Metazoon.   In the Sporozoa, also,
both sexual and asexual reproduction are found.   The
trophozoites give rise to a number of germs which unite
in syngamy to form the sporonts.   The latter give rise
asexually to the sporozoites, and from these; when they
have grown into trophozoites, there presently appear
sexual individuals again.   There is not in the germ
formation of Sporozoa any such obvious freeing of germ-
from body-substance as is found in Metazoa and Ciliata,
but there are reasons for believing that in the discarding
of the residual protoplasm such a separation occurs.   In
the Flagellata sexual reproduction is sometimes unknown
(*Trypanosoma*, etc.).   In *Polytoma* and *Copromonas*
syngamy occurs between ordinary individuals, and is
not part of an act of reproduction.   There is no visible
distinction between body- and germ-substance at any
stage, though it may be that matter which is comparable to the body-substance of the Metazoa is
destroyed before syngamy.   In *Amœba proteus* syngamy
is not known to occur.   At the same time, if, as
may well be, the multiple fission of *Amœba proteus*
resembles germ formation in that there is left behind
in the residual protoplasm something that corresponds
to the body-substance of Metazoa, then this process
has the essential features of parthenogenesis, for in

it bodies of the nature of germs develop without syngamy.

It will be gathered from what has just been said that, in respect of their reproductive processes, **The Problem of Sexual Reproduction.** animals present a series, in some members of which, as in certain *Amœbæ* and some flagellates, sexual reproduction is not known to occur, while in others it alternates more or less regularly with asexual reproduction, and in yet others, as in the frog, it replaces the latter entirely. We are faced with the question : " Why are there thus two modes of reproduction, and why does one come to replace the other as we pass from lower to higher animals ? " The facts may be partly explained as follows. Asexual reproduction is in two ways an easier process than sexual. (1) It is simpler, since it often can make use of tissues and organs already formed in the body of the parent, and always reaches its end by a less roundabout route than the development of an oosperm ; (2) it has not the handicap of requiring the union of two gametes, in bringing which about much energy is spent and loss sustained through failure. It is not surprising, therefore, to find asexual reproduction in animals whose tissues are not too specialised for it. That sexual reproduction also takes place in most of these animals can only be due to some necessity which imposes it upon the organism. In the higher animals, however, the cells which compose the tissues are so highly specialised that the production of a new individual from them is impossible, and thus asexual production is excluded and leaves the field to the sexual process or to parthenogenesis. It remains to inquire what may be the necessity which imposes the sexual process even upon animals which have asexual reproduction.

Sexual reproduction has two primary characteristics. One is, of course, syngamy ; the other is the **Reproduction from Germs.** formation of offspring from germs, that is, from protoplasm which is not specialised for services in the body. That this latter event occurs in the sexual reproduction of Metazoa is evident (p. 593). In Protozoa it is less so, since there it mainly affects the nucleus. In Ciliata and Sporozoa, however, there is, as we have seen, during gamete formation an observable discarding of nuclear matter which has been used for the life of the individual (*trophochromatin*), and there are indications that in all cases such chromatin is separable from the chromatin for the gametes (*idiochromatin*) and is destroyed at gamete formation, so that the gamete becomes a germ (p. 593) and the newly assembled nucleus of the zygote has its own way with the body. It must be in consequence of a need for one or both of these events—syngamy and reproduction from germs—that sexual reproduction occurs. Which, if either, is that whose necessity primarily imposes it ? Now reproduction by means of germs is very important. In most if not in all animals it is necessary to the continuance of the race, because protoplasm [1] specialised for processes in the body becomes effete (pp. 150, 238) and must be superseded by a fresh formation, and that is what happens in reproduction from germs. It has indeed been supposed that this is the goal of sexual reproduction, and that syngamy plays a secondary part, probably as a necessary stimulus to division (see below). But reproduction from germs does not come about only in the sexual process. It is also achieved in parthenogenesis and probably in various asexual processes in Protozoa (endomixis, some spore formations, etc.). Thus it does not, *per se*, necessitate sexual reproduction. It is syngamy that is the primary function of that process : that the reproduction should be performed by germs is incidental to the syngamy, whose zygote must be free from material that would hamper its development.

In itself syngamy is an act entirely distinct from repro-

Syngamy.

duction, and has a precisely opposite effect, since it lessens the number of individuals by fusion whereas reproduction increases them by fission. In a few Protozoa, as in *Copromonas* and sometimes in *Polytoma* (pp. 152, 155), it takes place between adult individuals (in which case it is known as *hologamy*), and then it has no connection with reproduction, but usually it takes place between germs specially produced for multiplication, and thus it becomes a part of the reproductive process, even though it halves the number of

---

[1] In Protozoa perhaps, sometimes nucleoplasm only.

adults that the germs could produce if they developed asexually.[1] So firmly, indeed, is it entrenched here that most germs perish unless they perform it. It seems clear from the very fact that it takes place in spite of the lessening in numbers which it causes, and also from the elaborate preparations which are often made for it, that it is in some way useful, and not merely brought about by certain circumstances without affecting the welfare of the being in which it occurs. The problem is to discover what is the use to the organism of this process which so often complicates reproduction. With regard to this several theories have been held.

(1) On account of the fact that the union of the germs of higher animals is followed by the rapid nuclear division which leads to the cell formation of development, it was at one time held that syngamy is primarily a *stimulus to nuclear division*, which is needed in certain cases. But if that were so the nuclear division in Protozoa ought also to be quickened by syngamy, whereas we find here that syngamy usually takes place *after* a period of frequent divisions and is often followed, as in *Polytoma*, by a period of rest in a cyst. Syngamy must meet some need other than the stimulation of division. In the Metazoa it comes, indeed, to act as a stimulus to division, but that is incidental. The occurrence of syngamy between the germs by which these animals reproduce is ensured by the germs being unable to divide without it. Union accomplished, however, the zygote undergo division to form the adult body. That this happens is ensured by the fact that the entry of the spermatozoon provides a centrosome which is lacking in the ovum and imparts to the zygote a stimulus to division, but this stimulus is not inherent in syngamy ; it accompanies it in these cases. Nor is it necessary for all ova. Those that are parthenogenitic can develop without it.

(2) Another theory of the meaning of syngamy supposes

[1] In the extreme case of *Paramecium*, where each parent forms only two gametes, the halving of numbers by syngamy brings it about that the zygotes are no more numerous than the parents, so that here sexual reproduction produces new individuals without increasing the total number, which grows only by asexual fission.

that *by its means the vitality of the protoplasm is renewed.*
We have already commented on the fact that the body
cells of a metazoon after a time become senile and die,
whereas an ovum and spermatozoon after their union
retain their vitality. It has been held that this is because
the zygote has been given a fresh lease of life by the
process of union of nuclei. Some observations upon
Paramecium and other ciliata were supposed to confirm
this view of the function of syngamy in the metazoa by
extending it to protozoa. But, as we have seen, this is a
mistake. The rejuvenating effects which often accompany
syngamy are due, not to the union of nuclei, but to
the previous freeing of the germs from the effete body
protoplasm.

(3) A third theory as to the meaning of this process
holds that its importance lies in the fact that it *combines
the hereditary characters of different individuals.* It is
well known that the individuals of a species of animal
differ from one another in respect of each of their characters. They are unlike in size, proportions, colour, intelligence, and so forth. It is also certain that many of
these differences are inherited ; the children of a tall man
will, for instance, be on the average taller than those of
a short man. In the sexually-produced offspring of
cross-fertilised animals these hereditary tendencies are
combined, so that the offspring are not exactly like either
parent. This happens in two ways. In many respects the
tendencies inherited from the two parents, when they
differ, do not counteract one another, but for a given
character of the animal in question, such as the size, or
shape, or colour, or texture, of any part of the body, one
or other of the parents is *dominant*, the legacy from the
other being latent or *recessive*, so that the offspring will
" take after " one parent. This dominance belongs to
one parent in the determining of some characters and
to the other in that of others, so that every syngamy
brings about a reshuffling of the characters, and the
young is not exactly like either parent. In respect of
other characters the tendencies inherited from the two
parents to appear to counteract one another in the
next generation, so that by syngamy these characters of

that generation become a mean of those of the parents. Here also there will be a difference between the two generations. Thus,[1] it comes about that no two members of a species are identical in their outfit of characters. It is held that a change in the conditions of life—as of food, temperature, enemies, and so forth—is thereby more likely to find individuals adapted—as by size, or clothing, or strength—to cope with it and continue the species, and this will clearly be of advantage. Now the hereditary tendencies of organisms are, of course, conveyed by the reproductive bodies—in fertilisation, for instance, by the ova and spermatozoa—and, as we have seen (p. 138), this is mainly effected by the nuclei. Syngamy, therefore, by the union of nuclei derived from different parents, maintains the unlikeness of individuals which is held to be desirable for the species, and this, according to the view we are discussing, is the function by which the process is beneficial. This view is supported by the elaborate preparations which, in the maturation of the gametes (p. 130 and Fig. 551), ensure that, as regards the nucleus, the parents make equivalent contributions to the zygotes which become the next generation. The occurrence in some hermaphrodite organisms (many plants, certain Protozoa, tapeworms, etc.) of self-fertilisation is an obvious obstacle to this theory, for the significance of syngamy in such cases clearly cannot be that it benefits the species by the combination of the characters of different parents. The difficulty, however, is not necessarily insuperable, for, in the first place, some self-fertilising organisms are occasionally cross-fertilised, and, in the second, it may be that self-fertilised organisms gain nothing by syngamy, but are compelled to retain the practice by the fact that it has become an inevitable step in the life-history.

In any case there can be no doubt that syngamy is a process of the highest importance to the organism. If by nothing else, this is shown by the fact that the whole mechanism of sex exists only for its sake. Sex is primarily *the differentiation of the individuals of a species into two kinds adapted to the*

Sex.

[1] But see p. 703.

production of two kinds of gametes, though the differentiation may extend to other functions, such as the part played by the parents in bringing about the union of the gametes or the nourishment and protection of the young. It is an example of the physiological division of labour between individuals. The basis upon which sex is established is the unlikeness or " dimorphism " of the gametes. In many protozoa, as, for instance, in *Polytoma* and some other flagellates, so far as observation shows, the gametes are identical (isogamous, p. 154). Nor is there any difference between their parents. In some species of *Monocystis* there is a dimorphism of the gametes together with a restriction of the production of each kind of them to certain individuals, which, however, show no further difference. We have here the simplest case of sex. The same thing is seen in some kinds of *Hydra* and in medusæ, where the sexes are alike in all respects both of structure and of behaviour, save that one produces only eggs and the other only sperm. In the frog the parents differ, not only in respect of the gametes which they form, but also in certain points of structure, such as the generative ducts and the pad upon the hand of the male, and conspicuously in their behaviour. One, the female, plays in coition the same passive part which the germs she forms play in syngamy. The other, the male, plays the active part in coition and forms germs which play the active part in syngamy. Throughout the animal kingdom it is the case that, so far as there is a difference between the sexes, the male is the active organism, the female relatively passive. It is the part of the female to lay up the surplus material that she manufactures in the formation of germs provided with the cytoplasm which the zygote will require, and stocked with yolk to serve as food in the early stages of development. Sometimes, as in mammals, she also nourishes the young formed from the zygote. The part of the male is freely to expend his substance in finding the female, while the germs that he forms are poor in cytoplasm, but actively motile to reach and enter the egg. In the highest animals his activity is directed also to the preservation of the female, for whom he fights and forages. It is in activity, not in size or strength or beauty, that the true difference between the sexes consists, though the female is perhaps generally the larger and the male relatively the stronger of the two, and the greater physiological vigour of the male is often accompanied, as in the peacock and the stag, by the possession of ornaments and weapons which are not found in the other sex, and which play a part in courtship and in the strife between males for the possession of females. Such features as these are known as *secondary sexual characters*. Sometimes, as in the newt (Fig. 353, A), they are developed at the breeding season only. From the existence of sex two benefits result. Firstly, a division of labour of the same kind that exists between the gametes becomes possible between the individuals that form them, one ensuring the union of the gametes, the other the nourishment of the zygote. Secondly, it is ensured that cross-fertilisation (p. 158) shall take place, since the germs formed by one parent, being all of the same kind, are unable to fertilise one another.

Hermaphroditism. Dimorphism of the gametes is not necessarily accompanied with the production of the two kinds upon distinct parents. It happens fairly often that both sorts are formed by one individual, which is then, of course, called a hermaphrodite. *Paramecium* presents such a case. Its gametes are dimorphous. The migratory pronuclei represent male gametes ; the stationary pronuclei represent female gametes. Each individual produces a gamete of each kind. Some kinds of *Hydra* also produce two sorts of gametes in one individual, though in them the gametes of one sort usually ripen before those of the other, so that the parent has a kind of temporary sex. Hermaphrodites are sometimes self-fertilised but usually, by such expedients as we have considered in earthworms and snails, are cross-fertilised. In *Vorticella*, as we have seen (p. 176), a curious imitation of sex is found. The parents are both hermaphrodites, but of two kinds, one active and the other passive, like parents which possess true sex.

The determination of sex. The question of what causes an individual to be a male or a female is an extraordinarily interesting and important one, but the answer to it is still in many ways doubtful. The difference between males and females is, in its essence, of the same nature as other differences between members of a species, and is known to be established in each generation according to the same " Mendelian " laws as such differences (see pp. 699, 701). But the working of these laws is complicated in the case of sex by quantitative phenomena, so that, *e.g.*, a certain " dose " of the male factor may be unable to overcome the female factor. One result of this is the occasional appearance of " intersexes "—abnormal individuals intermediate between the sexes, or gradually passing from one sex to the other, as a hen may with age come to resemble a cock or even to breed as one. These individual are of quite a different nature from hermaphrodites. The origin of hermaphroditism is at present quite obscure.

It will be seen that syngamy is usually cross-fertilisation, **Cross-fertilisation.** and that is caused to be so by various expedients, of which sex is one and mutual impregnation by hermaphrodites is another. This prevalence of cross-fertilisation might be explained upon the theory that the importance of syngamy to the

FIG. 458.—Sexual congress in the snail, a cross-fertilising hermaphrodite.

organism lies in its increasing variety by combining different strains of the species. On the other hand, it has often been held to indicate that for some physiological reason a certain degree of difference in the parentage of the gamete is necessary for the vigour of a zygote. At first sight the latter of these conclusions is supported by the facts that in some cases self-fertilisation of organisms which are normally cross-fertilised has been shown to give zygotes which either do not develop or become degenerate adults, and again that syngamy between gametes derived from near relatives, or *inbreeding*, is often found to be harmful—a fact which is well known to breeders, and is expressed in the marriage laws of many nations. But there are animals known in which self-fertilisation is the usual or the only kind of syngamy that occurs, and others in which inbreeding has no bad results whatever. The probable explanation of these facts is that near relationship of gametes is not harmful *per se*, and that the ill-effects which it usually has are due to its concentrating any deleterious tendencies which may exist in the race that is breeding in this way.

FIG. 459.—Secondary sexual differences in insects.

Above : the male (*A*) and female (*B*) of the Vapourer Moth, a species in which the
inactive habit of the female is exaggerated. Note her rudimentary wings,
heavy body, and small antennæ, and the large, well-feathered antennæ of the
male, with which he seeks her by scent.
Below : the male (with antler-like mandibles) and female of the Stag Beetle.

Stated in terms of Mendelism (p. 698), what happens is that the proportion of " recessive " characters, which are usually deleterious, increases with each generation of inbreeding. However, in a continuously inbred stock the weaklings may be removed by a selective death-rate and thus a strong race may result.

This theory is confirmed by breeding experiments. The virtue of cross-fertilisation thus appears to be that by affecting heredity it confers variety and weakens harmful factors—a conclusion which is in agreement with the theory that the function of syngamy is the modification of heredity.

Mules. While cross-breeding within a species usually has beneficial effects, gametes belonging to different species, if they will unite at all, nearly always produce a mule—a hybrid which, though it may in other respects be vigorous and hardy, cannot reproduce its kind. This is probably because, though their chromosomes can exist in the same nucleus, they do not form homologous pairs, and thus cannot give rise to gamete nuclei.

CHAPTER XXVII

EMBYROLOGY [1]

HITHERTO we have been concerned almost wholly with the anatomy and physiology of adult animals. We **Amphioxus : Early Stages.** must now give some attention to the process by which the adult arises from the fertilised egg. For this purpose we shall study first the development of the lancelet, which is relatively simple and easy to follow owing to the fact that the protoplasm of the ovum is not hampered with a large amount of yolk. The egg is about o·1 mm. in diameter, and covered with a slight *vitelline membrane*, which will become more distinct when the cytoplasm shrinks from it after fertilisation. Only the first polar body is found on it when it is laid ; the second is formed shortly after fertilisation. The ovum is one of a kind in which there can already be distinguished portions of the cytoplasm which are destined to form particular regions of the future body, though in Amphioxus these are not yet in position. Under the vitelline membrane is a layer of cytoplasm which is finely granular but free from yolk granules. Within this the cytoplasm contains yolk granules. A large nucleus (*germinal vesicle*) displaces it from a good deal of one side of the ovum. This is the *animal pole* ; the yolky side is the *vegetative pole*. The animal pole is usually spoken of as the upper side, but actually when the embryo is formed this side will be ventral and at the front end, while the vegetative side will be dorsal and behind. When the egg is fertilised certain changes occur. In preparation for the union of the two sets of chromosomes, one from each gamete

---

[1] In reading this chapter, the student should refer constantly to the figures.

nucleus, which takes place near the middle of the egg, the nuclear membrane of the germinal vesicle breaks down and a quantity of clear cytoplasm takes the place of the vesicle.

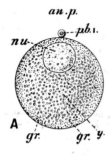

Meanwhile the granular cytoplasm which has covered the ovum flows to the vegetative pole and there becomes a crescent around the future posterior end. The clear cytoplasm which now forms the animal side of the egg will give rise to the ectoderm, the yolky cytoplasm on the vegetative side will give rise to the endoderm, and the crescent of granular cytoplasm between the two at the hinder end will give the mesoderm. The first cleavage (Fig. 461, 2) is vertical and forms two equal blastomeres (p. 137). The second is also vertical, at right angles to the first, the third nearly equatorial, dividing each blastomere into a rather smaller upper half and a rather larger lower half. The blastomeres do not meet in the middle, so that at this stage they form a ring. By repeated divisions, vertical and horizontal, there arises a sub-spherical (slightly pear-shaped) structure, known as the *blastula*, whose cavity is the *blastocœle*. Its wall consists of a single layer of cells, which differ somewhat in different regions. The ventral and anterior part is composed of small cells derived from the clear cytoplasm of the ovum, the dorsal cells are larger and more yolky, a crescent around the posterior end is made up of smaller cells with granular cytoplasm (Fig. 462, 2 and 3).

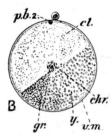

FIG. 460.—Ova of *Amphioxus*.

A, Unfertilised ; *B,* after fertilisation.
an.p., Animal pole ; *chr.,* chromosomes of the two pronuclei, which have met ; *cl.,* clear cytoplasm ; *gr.,* granular cytoplasm ; *nu.,* nucleus ("germinal vesicle") ; *p.b.*1, *p.b.*2, first and second polar bodies ; *v.m.,* vitelline membrane ; *y.,* yolky cytoplasm.

There now sets in a process known as *gastrulation*, by which the blastula is converted into a two-layered structure, the *gastrula* (Fig. 462). This begins by a flattening of the dorsal area of yolky cells. Next these are dimpled or *invaginated* into the blastocœle, forming a cup which, in spite of the difference in shape, may be compared with the body of a *Hydra*. The yolky cells—the endoderm or *hypoblast*—form the lining while the mouth or *blastopore*, which is as yet very wide, has a lip composed in front of small cells of the anteroventral area, now the ectoderm or *epiblast*, and at the sides and behind of the cells of the crescent. The process continues by a rolling in over these lips, so that in front ectoderm cells and at the sides the cells of the crescent become part of the lining of the cup. Meanwhile the embryo is lengthening, and the blastopore narrowing owing to the growth backwards of its anterior lip which, since it thus comes to cover the dorsal side, is known as the *dorsal lip*. The gastrula when it has thus been completed (Fig. 461, 1) is elongate, with a small blastopore at the hinder end of its flat upper side. Its cavity is lined below and at the sides by endoderm and has for its ceiling in the middle a strip of cells which rolled in over the dorsal lip and will form the notochord, and on either side of this a groove formed from the crescent cells. These

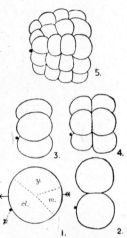

FIG. 461.—Early stages of the cleavage of the ovum of *Amphioxus*.

1., Fertilised ovum; *cl.*, clear cytoplasm which after cleavage will be situated in the ectoderm cells; *m.*, granular cytoplasm which will be in the mesoderm cells; *y.*, yolky cytoplasm which will be in the endoderm cells; 2., first cleavage—stage of two blastomeres; 3., four blastomeres; 4., eight blastomeres; 5., thirty-two blastomeres.

The figures are so posed that the side which will in the adult be dorsal is above and that which will be anterior is to the left : the horizontal axis of the adult is indicated by the arrow in No. 1. The animal pole of the ovum, indicated by the (second) polar body, is antero-ventral.

cells are the *mesoblast* or the rudiment of the mesoderm. The cavity of the gastrula is the *archenteron* : the blastocœle has been obliterated during the invagination. Meanwhile

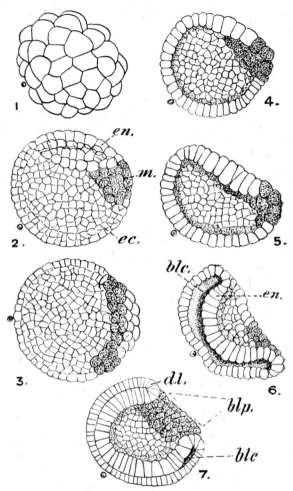

FIG. 462.—The gastrulation of *Amphioxus*.—After Conklin, with modification.

1, Sixty-four cell stage ; 2, completed blastula, from the left (and somewhat from the ventral side, so that the mesoderm appears rather more dorsal than it is) ; 3, approximately the same stage, from the ventral side and a little from behind ; 4, right half of the same viewed from within ; 5, beginning of gastrulation ; 6, later stage ; 7, late gastrula.

The figures are so posed that the side which will be anterior in the adult is to the left, and (except in No. 2, which is a ventral view) the dorsal side is above. The mesoderm cells are indicated by an arbitrary granulation.

the cells of the ectoderm develop cilia, by means of which the gastrula revolves within the vitelline membrane; and the cells of the flat dorsal side become more columnar and form a distinct strip known as the *neural or medullary plate*. The ectoderm at the sides of this plate now becomes detached from it and grows over it, enclosing a small space (Fig. 464). This process begins at the hinder end, so that the blastopore is covered and opens into the space in question (Fig. 463, 2*a*). The sides of the neural plate then fold upwards and meet above the space, so as to form a tube which will become the nerve cord. Its hollow is the *neural canal*, and the blastopore, which is now known as the *neurenteric canal*, leads from it to the gut. Eventually the neurenteric canal closes. An opening, known as the *neuropore*, long remains at the front end of the neural canal and puts it into communication with the animal's olfactory pit p. (417). While

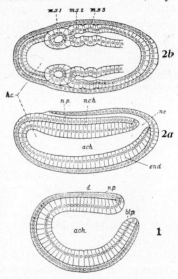

FIG. 463.—Longitudinal sections of embryos of *Amphioxus* at stages later than that represented by Fig. 462, 7.

1, Vertical section of the completed gastrula; 2*a*, vertical and 2*b*, horizontal sections of an early post-gastrula stage in which only the first mesoblastic somite has separated.

ach., Archenteron; *end.*, endoderm; *h.c.*, region which will become the anterior median pouch, or head cavity; *m.s.*, 1–3, mesoblastic somites; *n.p.*, neural plate; *nch.*, notochord; *ne.*, neurenteric canal.

these things are happening the ceiling of the archenteron gives rise to the notochord and to the mesoderm. The notochord is formed by a median longitudinal strip (Fig. 464, 2) which becomes grooved and separated from before backwards, its cells eventually rearranging

39

themselves to form a rod (Fig. 467) and becoming vacuolated. Its front end grows forwards to the end of the snout. The hind end is for a long time connected with the endoderm in front of the neurenteric canal. The mesoderm arises as hollow outgrowths (Figs. 463, 464, 467). One of these is median and unpaired in front. Behind it lies a pair of dorso-lateral grooves at the sides of the notochord. The median pouch soon separates from the gut, but the grooves, as fast as they close off in front, are prolonged backwards. As growth progresses the separated anterior part of the groove becomes segmented

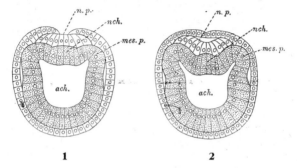

1   **2**

Fig. 464.—Transverse sections of embryos of *Amphioxus* at stages corresponding to Figs. 464, 1 and 2.—After Hatschek.

ach., Archenteron ; mes.p., pouch which will become first mesoblastic somite ; n.p., neural plate ; nch., rudiment of notochord.

into a series of pouches. These pouches are the *mesoderm segments* or *mesoblastic somites*. They will presently spread between ectoderm and endoderm and give rise to the mesoderm of the adult. When the notochord and mesoderm have separated, the dorsal edges of the endoderm close in under them to form a complete tube, the enteron, which will become the alimentary canal of the adult. The rudiments of all three layers of a triploblastic animal are now present. Ectoderm, endoderm, and mesoderm are known as the *germ layers*, and though, as we shall see, they arise in different ways in different cases, they are present at an early stage in the embryos of all

Triploblastica. Before these processes are complete, *hatching* takes place by the throwing off of the vitelline membrane, and the embryo becomes a larva (p. 32). Until the formation of the mouth the animal is sometimes called the "free embryo."

Hatching takes place about eight hours after fertilisation. About twenty-four hours later the mouth is formed as a small opening, which rapidly enlarges, on the left side of the forepart of the body. At the same time, by perforation from within outwards, the first gill-slit is formed as a median ventral opening which shifts upwards to the right side of the body. As we shall see, this slit belongs to the *left* side of the body of the adult. The anus is formed shortly after the first gill-slit, much nearer the hind end of the body than it is in the adult. Development henceforward takes place more slowly, the animal becoming adult in about three months. We will consider first the external features of its metamorphosis. More gill-slits are formed in the midventral line, and each in

Larva.

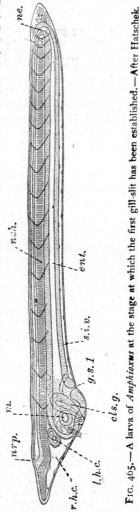

Fig. 465.—A larva of *Amphioxus* at the stage at which the first gill-slit has been established.—After Hatschek. *cl.g.*, Club-shaped gland; *ent.*, gut; *g.s.1*, first gill-slit; *l.h.c.*, left head cavity, now opening to the exterior; *m.*, mouth; *nch.*, notochord; *ne.*, neurenteric canal; *nrp.*, neuropore; *r.h.c.*, right head cavity; *s.i.v.*, subintestinal vein.

turn shifts on to the right side. They are primary slits, and each except the first acquires a tongue-bar. When fourteen of these slits have been formed, another series appears above them on the right-hand side. These are eight in number. Six of the first series of slits disappear, so that the number in the two series is the same. While the formation of the second series of slits is taking place both series shift downwards, the original series passing over to the left side of the body, while the second series remains on the right. At the same time the mouth also shifts to its adult position in the middle line. The slits at first open directly upon the surface of the body, but

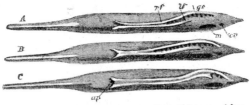

FIG. 466. —Three larva stages of *Amphioxus*.—After Lankester and Willey.

In *A* the metapleural folds are still separate; in *B* they are united behind; in *C* they are united along their whole length.

ap., Atriopore ; *co.*, ciliated pit derived from the left anterior cœlomic division of the cœlom ; *g.e.*, gill-slits ; *l.f.*, left metapleural fold ; *m.*, mouth ; *r.f.*, right metapleural fold.

at an early stage, when there are as yet only six clefts of the first series, two longitudinal ridges appear, one on each side of the slits. In correspondence with the position of the slits these ridges lie in front on the right side of the body, but behind curve down to the ventral side, where the new slits are forming. These ridges are the metapleural folds. From the inner face of each a secondary ridge grows inwards to meet its fellow and enclose a space below the body. This is the rudiment of the atrium. As the ridges do not meet behind, there is left an opening which becomes the atriopore. The closure of the atrium takes place from behind forwards as the folds shift downwards with the clefts, from the right side of the body to their permanent position (Fig. 466). The atrium is at first small, but enlarges so as to enclose the sides of the pharynx. The endostyle appears at the beginning of the larval period as a band of columnar ciliated cells on the right side of the anterior end of the pharynx above the first gill-cleft. It becomes folded as a V with the apex directed backward. When the two rows of clefts are established, the apex of this V grows back between them, the two limbs fusing to form a single strip. As the clefts move downwards the endostyle between them moves also. A structure known as the *club-shaped gland* is formed from the wall of the pharynx on the right side above the gill-clefts. It disappears while the second series of clefts is forming.

We must now consider the fate of the mesoderm rudi-
Mesoblastic Somites. ments. The median outgrowth divides into right and left halves, of which the right becomes a cœlomic cavity in the snout of the adult, while the left opens to the exterior and becomes Hatschek's pit in the wheel organ. Each of the somites of the first pair sends forward into the snout an outgrowth, which gives rise to a cavity in the head of the adult, while its walls form part of the mesoderm of the same region. The rest of the somite gives rise to other spaces in the neighbourhood of the mouth and by backward outgrowths to spaces in the metapleural folds. In the adult these latter spaces are represented by lymph canals of doubtful origin. The walls of the spaces give rise to mesodermal tissues around the mouth and in the metapleural folds, and to the first myomere. The remaining mesoblastic somites all behave alike. They extend downwards on each side (Fig. 467) till they meet below the gut. The outer or *somatic* wall of each lies against the ectoderm, together with which it is known as the *somatopleure* ; the inner or *splanchnic* wall lies against the endoderm and is known with it as the *splanchnopleure*. The longitudinal septum or ventral mesentery between the cavities of the two sides now breaks down, so that they become continuous. Meanwhile there has formed in each of them a horizontal septum which divides it into a dorsal half or *epimere* and a ventral half, the *hypomere* or *splanchnomere*. The

cavity of the ventral portion is known as the *splanchnocœle*.
The septa between the splanchnocœles break down so that
they form a continuous perivisceral cœlom, which afterwards becomes broken up in the pharyngeal region into a
series of tubes by the appearance of the gill-clefts (p. 406).
The cavities of the dorsal parts of the somites remain
separate and are known as *myocœles*. Their inner walls,

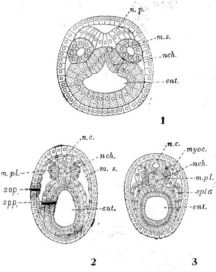

FIG. 467.—Transverse sections of embryos of *Amphioxus* at successive
    stages later than that represented by Fig. 462.—After Hatschek.

ent., Gut or enteron ; *m.pl.*, muscle plate ; *m.s.*, mesoblastic somit ; *myoc.*,
    myocœle ; *n.c.*, nerve cord ; *n.p.*, neural plate ; *nch.*, notochord ; *sop.*, somato-
    pleure ; *splc.*, splanchnocœle ; *spp.*, splanchnopleure.

against the notochord, become greatly thickened, each to
form a structure, known as a *muscle plate*, which gives
rise to a myomere in the adult, the walls between myocœles
giving rise to connective-tissue septa between the myomeres, and the outer walls of the myocœles to the dermis.
From the inner wall of each epimere, below the muscle
plate, an outgrowth burrows its way between the muscle
plate and the notochord and forms from its wall the

connective-tissue sheath of the notochord and nerve cord. This outgrowth is known as the *sclerotome*, the main part, which contains the muscle plate, being known as the *myotome*. Lastly, in the pharyngeal region the myotome grows down in the body wall, between the splanchnocœle and the ectoderm, and at its lower end forms an outgrowth, the *gonotome*, which forms a gonad.

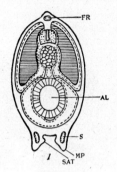

During the external and internal changes which **Habits of the Larva.** we have traced, the larval *Amphioxus* swims freely in the sea, usually at a depth of a few fathoms from the surface. As its metamorphosis reaches completion, it sinks to the bottom and takes up the burrowing habits of the adult (see p. 418).

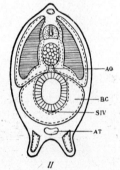

The ovum of the frog, its

FIG. 468.—The development of the atrial chamber in *Amphioxus*.—After Lankester and Willey.

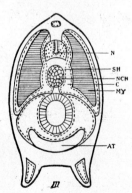

In I. the metapleural folds are seen sending a slight projection inwards. In II. the two projections have united and enclose a small space (*A T.*), which is the rudiment of the atrial chamber. In III. this space is enlarging at the expense of the cœlom. A comparison of this figure with the cross-section of the adult (Fig. 308) will show the relation of cœlom and atrial chamber.

FR., Cœlomic space within dorsal fin; *A L.*, gut; *S.*, cœlomic space of metapleural fold; *MP.*, metapleural fold; *SAT.*, projection which forms floor of atrial chamber; *AO.*, aorta; *B.C.*, cœlom; *S.I.V.*, sub-intestinal vein; *N.*, nerve cord; *SH.*, sheath of notochord; *MY.*, muscle plate; *C.*, cavity of sclerotome; *AT.*, atrial chamber. The dotted line indicates the mesodermic wall of the cœlom.

fertilisation, and the beginning of its cleavage have been described on pp. 136, 137. The first division of the cleavage forms two similar cells, each containing, like the ovum, an upper, black, pigmented portion and a lower, white, yolky portion. The second division is at right angles to the first and forms four similar blastomeres ; the third division is horizontal and separates four small, pigmented, upper blastomeres from four large, yolky, lower blastomeres. By succeeding divisions sixteen and then thirty-two blastomeres arise, after which cleavage becomes irregular, the pigmented cells dividing more rapidly than the yolky. The final result is the formation of a blastula (Fig. 470), in which the floor of the blastocœle is composed of large yolky cells and the roof of small pigmented cells. At the sides the upper cells merge gradu-

Frog : Segmentation.

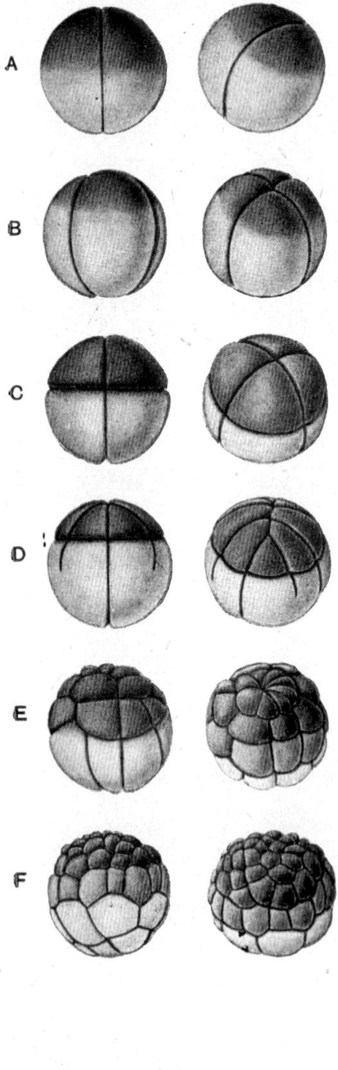

FIG. 469.—Stages in the cleavage of the frog's egg. Of each stage two views are given, one showing it from the side, the other obliquely from above. A–F show successively stages with two, four, eight, sixteen, thirty-two, and numerous blastomeres.

ally into the lower. The large cells are the future
endoderm, the small cells will give rise to the ectoderm
and mesoderm, and both regions differ from the corresponding parts of the blastula of
Amphioxus in being more than one
cell deep, though the floor is much
thicker than the roof. From this
blastula a gastrula is formed, not by
invagination of the yolky cells into
the cup formed by the small cells,
which would be impossible on
account of the relative amount of
the two layers, but by an extension
of the small cells over the yolk cells.

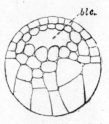

FIG. 470.—A vertical
section of a frog's
egg at the end of
cleavage.

blc., Blastocœle.

Gastrulation. When this process begins, the two kinds
of cells each form half the
outer surface of the blastula,
which floats with the black side uppermost.
The small, pigmented cells now start to
spread downwards, as a skin over the yolks cells, so that the
black area which the small cells form increases and the white area
where the yolk cells are exposed diminishes (Fig. 471). This process
is known as *epiboly*. If it took place all over the surface of the yolk

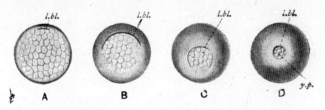

FIG. 471.—Stages in the gastrulation of the frog's egg. The egg is
seen from the lower, white pole, which faces in the direction of the
future hind end of the animal.

l.bl., Lip of the blastopore ; *y.p.*, yolk plug.

cells the result would be the formation of a close skin of small cells
over a solid mass of hypoblast without an enteron. But on one side
of the white surface, just below the boundary, on a greyish crescentic
area which arose there in the cytoplasm of the ovum when the
spermatozoon entered on the opposite side, there appears at this
time a small, shallow, crescentic slit, convex towards the black area

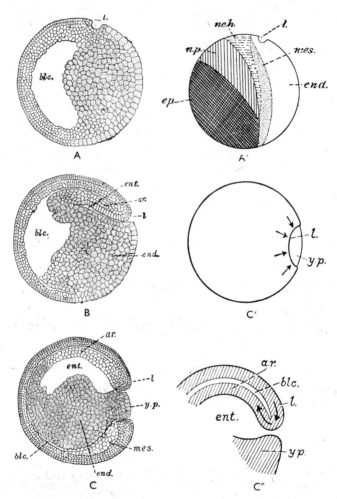

Fig. 472.—Gastrulation in the frog.

A, B, and *C,* are sections in successive stages corresponding roughly to *A, B,* and *D* of Fig. 471. *A′* is a plan of the presumptive areas in stage *A. C′* and *C″* show the rolling in of cells at the blastopore lip.

ar., Archenteron roof formed by growth of the lip ; *blc.,* blastocœle ; *end.,* endoderm ; *ent.,* gut ; *ep.,* epidermis ; *l.,* blastopore lip ; *mes.,* mesoderm ; *n.p.,* presumptive area of cells for neural plate ; *nch.,* cells for notochord ; *y.p.,* yolk plug in blastopore.

(Fig. 471, A, *l.b.l*). Where the advancing black area reaches this its further extension takes place in a different way, namely by the upper side of the slit growing out and thus projecting as a lip-like fold over the yolk cells on the other side. The result is that a narrow space is enclosed between the arched lip and the yolk cells (Fig. 472, B). This process, which may be compared to the narrowing of the blastopore of *Amphioxus* by growth of its lip (p. 607), is akin to invagination rather than to epiboly. The side on which it happens is the future dorsal side of the animal. The space enclosed is the archenteron. The cells on the outer side of the lip are of course continuous with the ectoderm. The cells of the lining of the lip form the roof of the archenteron, its floor being formed by the large yolk cells over which the lip is growing. As the lip extends, the rapid advance of cells on its outer (upper or dorsal) side causes that side to roll over at the edge, so that what was on the upper surface comes under to form the archenteron roof. The arrows in Fig. 472, C' and C", show the direction in which the cells move during this process. The cell material thus transferred from the outside to the inside of the roof of the archenteron during the formation of the gastrula is, as we shall see, the material for the mesoderm and notochord. When it was external it was not distinguishable from the epiblast, but could be shown by staining methods to lie in strips (*presumptive areas*) across the dorsal surface. As the small cells advance, these areas converge upon the lip and turn in over it. The lip is the upper border of the blastopore, which faces backwards : the rest of the border is as yet indefinite and represented by the limit of the advancing ectoderm all round the egg.

All this time the shape of the crescent is changing by its two ends lengthening and curving towards one another till at last they meet to form a circle. By that time the edge of the ectoderm has reached this circle all round its circumference, so that all the yolk is covered except that within a circular area, the definite blastopore, bordered by a continuous lip and filled by a *yolk plug* consisting of yolk cells which have not yet been covered. At this stage the embryo, which has hitherto floated with the white pole downwards, begins to rotate so that that pole moves upward around the aspect on which the dorsal lip grew down. Towards this aspect will be directed the future hinder end of the animal, and the remnant of the exposure of the white cells—the yolk plug—comes, before it disappears (in the way described below), to lie in the dorsal region of that end. By the same rotation the region formed by the growth of the dorsal lip moves up into the position of the dorsal side of the animal. The lip continues to grow over the yolk plug, thus narrowing the blastopore. The narrowing, however, takes place not by equally rapid ingrowth of the lip all round, but by a faster growing together of the sides of the circle in its hinder part. At last the plug is covered and the blastopore is a mere slit. Then the middle part of this slit closes completely, its sides coming together, but leaving at its ends two small openings. Of these the upper remains open, the last vestige of the blastopore, and becomes later the neurenteric canal (p. 622), while the lower, though it closes, leaves in its place a pit of

ectoderm—the proctodæum—in which the anus eventually breaks
through. Where the sides of the slit meet, between anus and
neurenteric canal, there remains a seam in the form of a groove—
the *primitive groove*—under which lies a band of cells—the *primitive
streak*—in which ectoderm, endoderm and mesoderm meet and fuse.
During this process an inward movement of the yolk cells has
obliterated the blastocœle and enlarged the enteron, which was at
first a mere slit, so that it becomes a spacious cavity, which communicates with the exterior by a slit between the dorsal semicircle
of the blastopore lip and the yolk plug. It is this change of site of

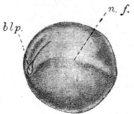

FIG. 473.—The embryo of a frog shortly after the
completion of gastrulation, seen from the
right side and somewhat from behind.

blp., Blastopore; *n.f.*, neural folds.

the principal cavity in the embryo that, by shifting the centre of
gravity, causes the rotation mentioned above.

At the end of gastrulation the archenteron is a large
cavity whose very thick ventral wall has arisen
Formation of Mesoblast. from the yolk cells, while the thinner dorsal
wall has been formed by the growth of the
blastopore lip. From the walls of the archenteron the
endoderm proper (epithelium of midgut, p. 625), notochord, and mesoderm arise as follows.

At each side the floor grows up within the roof as a
sheet which eventually meets its fellow in the mid-dorsal
line and so shuts off the roof from the cavity. The complete lining of the gut which is thus formed from the yolky
cells is the endoderm proper. The layer, now outside it,
formed by lip growth, becomes in the mid-dorsal line the
notochord and at the sides the mesoderm, which lies as
a mantle around the endoderm. Because of the way in
which the lip which formed it was completed, the meso-

derm mantle, which in front is dorsal only, behind
completely surrounds the endoderm. By growth of its
fore-edge it spreads forwards and downwards between
ectoderm and endoderm, forming a layer all over the
embryo, except in the mid-dorsal line, where the notochord
lies. It will be seen that the mesoderm first arises in the
position in which the mesodermal grooves arise in
Amphioxus ; moreover, as in *Amphioxus*, the cells which
constitute it were from the first distinct from the endoderm
and reached their position later, by rolling in over the
blastopore lip. On each side of the notochord the meso-

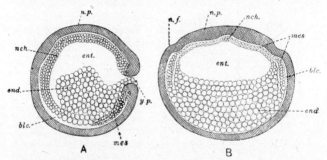

Fig. 474.—Sections of an embryo at about the stage of Fig. 473.

A, Vertical longitudinal; *B*, transverse.
blc., Blastocœle ; *end.*, yolky cells of endoderm; *ent.*, gut; *mes.*, mesoderm ;
n.f., neural fold ; *n.p.*, neural plate ; *nch.*, notochord ; *y.p.*, yolk plug.

derm is thicker than elsewhere, forming the *segmental
plate*. A split, the rudiment of the cœlom, appears and
separates an outer or somatic layer from an inner or
splanchnic layer (Fig. 477 A). This split does not extend
far into the segmental plate, from which it soon disappears.
The segmental plates now divide into a series of blocks,
the epimeres—usually, though incorrectly, called " mesoblastic somites "—separating from the *lateral plates*, which
do not segment. The lateral plates correspond to the fused
hypomeres of *Amphioxus* (pp. 613, 614). The epimeres
form from before backwards, but the head region is not
segmented in the embryo of the frog, though it is so in the
embryo dogfish.

Meanwhile external changes have been taking place.

External Features of Embryo. The embryo at the end of gastrulation was still roughly spherical, the blastopore marking the future hind end. In front of this the future dorsal ectoderm flattens to form the pear-shaped neural plate. The edges of this rise up owing to the incipient formation of folds—the *neural folds*, which are continuous in front, and behind join the side lips of the blastopore. On either flank of the anterior end of the neural plate appears a thickening which becomes divided by a furrow into a *gill plate* and a *sense plate* which joins with its fellow of the opposite side. A *neural groove* appears along the middle of the neural plate, while the neural folds grow taller, approaching one another and deepening the neural groove, bend over, and meet so as to enclose a space, the neural canal, uniting first about the middle of their length (Figs. 475, 477 A, 480 A). Since they enclose the blastopore vestige, the latter comes to lead from the gut to the neural canal and gives rise to a neurenteric canal, but this soon disappears. The neural canal separates from the ectoderm above it, formed by the outer sides of the neural folds, whose inner sides become the wall of the neural canal. Before the folds have united in front, the open canal between them is divided into three swellings, the rudiments of the fore-, mid-, and hind-brains. It will be seen that in the frog, as in the lancelet, the central nervous system arises by the sinking in and folding of a strip of the epidermis of the back. This process is found in all Chordata, and is of the highest importance in the drawing of comparisons between them and other animals. During the formation of the central nervous system the

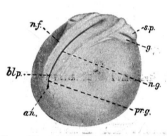

FIG. 475.—An embryo of the frog at a later stage.

an., Proctodæum (invagination which will form anus); *blp.*, last vestige of blastopore; *g.p.*, gill plate; *n.f.*, neural fold; *n.g.*, neural groove; *pr.g.*, primitive groove; *s.p.*, sense plate.

body has been elongating and other structures appearing. Below the blastopore, in the area which it occupied before its contraction, there appears, as we have seen, a pit known as the *proctodæum*, and an opening piercing through from this to the gut forms the anus. From anus to blastopore runs a slight groove, the *primitive groove*. Above it a knob grows out to form the tadpole's tail. Grooves appear on each gill plate marking out the visceral arches, and upon the first two branchial arches branched *external gills* grow out. Below the head, where the sense plates joined, a median pit of ectoderm forms the *stomodæum*, which will eventually break through to the enteron and become the mouth. Below the stomodæum is a horseshoe-shaped sucker; above, a pit in each of the sense plates gives rise to the olfactory organ. When these changes are complete the animal hatches. This happens about a fortnight after the eggs are laid.

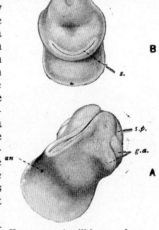

FIG. 476.—A still later embryo.
A, From behind and above; *B*, from in front.
an., Proctodæum; *g.a.*, gill arches; *s.*, sucker; *s.r.*, sense plate.

External Features of Larva.

In the external development of the tadpole (Fig. 11) the following changes take place. A third pair of external gills is formed, and the mouth opens and is provided with a pair of horny jaws, which are eventually lost. Meanwhile four gill-clefts open, and the external gills wither, being replaced by new gills on the walls of the clefts. The latter represent the first to fourth branchial clefts of the dogfish, the external gills standing on the first three branchial arches. Shortly after the appearance of the clefts a fold of skin grows back from each side of the head so as to cover them.

The folds are the *opercula*; they meet ventrally, and
presently their hinder edges fuse with the body everywhere,
except in one spot on the left side, where an opening is left

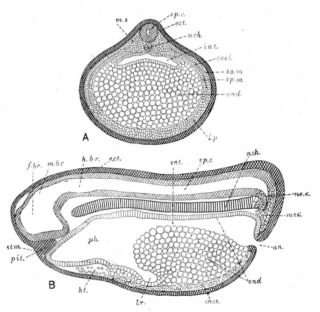

Fig. 477.—Sections of an embryo frog at about the stage of Fig. 476.

A, Transverse; *B*, longitudinal.

an., Anus *cœl.*, cœlom; *ect.*, ectoderm or epiblast; *end.*, endoderm or hypoblast
f.br., fore-brain; *h.br.*, hind-brain; *ht.*, rudiment of heart; *int.*, intestine,
l.p., lateral plate of mesoblast; *lr.*, rudiment of liver; *m.br.*, mid-brain; *m.s.*,
mesoblastic somite; *mes.*, mesoblast; *mes'.*, mesoblast continuous with epiblast
of neural canal and hypoblast of notochord in region of primitive streak; *ne.c.*,
neurenteric canal (closing); *nch.*, notochord, *ph.*, pharynx; *pit.*, rudiment of
pituitary body; *so.m.*, somatic mesoblast; *sp.c.*, spinal cord; *sp.m.*, splanchnic
mesoblast; *stm.*, stomodæum.

for the discharge of the water used in breathing. The
sucker now begins to degenerate. Shortly afterwards,
rudiments of the hind-limbs appear at the base of the tail,
as a pair of small knobs, which increase rapidly and
become first jointed and then divided into toes. The

fore-limbs arise at the same time as the hind-limbs, but as they are covered by the opercula they are not seen till a later stage. About the end of the second month the lungs which have been forming come into use and the gills start to degenerate, and a fortnight later the tadpole begins to turn into a young frog. The outer layer of the skin and the horny jaws are thrown off, the mouth enlarges and changes its shape, the fore-limbs appear, that on the left being pushed through the gill opening, that on the right breaking through the operculum, the gill-clefts close, and finally the tail shortens and is absorbed, and the metamorphosis is complete.

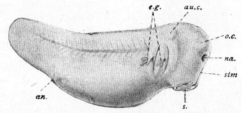

FIG. 478.—A frog embryo at the stage of hatching.

an., Proctodæum ; *au.c.*, slight swelling over the rudiment of the ear ; *e.g.*, external gills on gill arches ; *na.*, invagination to form nasal capsule ; *o.c.*, slight swelling over the rudiment of the eye ; *s.*, sucker ; *stm.*, stomodæum (invagination which will form the mouth).

Germ Layers. We have traced the internal development of the embryo up to the establishment of the three layers of the body of a triploblastic animal. From the embryonic ectoderm arise the epidermis, nervous system, sense organs, and lining of the mouth and cloacal opening ; from the embryonic endoderm arises the lining of the greater part of the gut, the lungs, liver, pancreas, and thyroid ; from the embryonic mesoderm arise the skeleton, connective tissues, vascular system, muscles, excretory organs, and generative organs. The skeletal tissues and unstriped muscle arise from a loose kind of mesoderm, known as *mesenchyme*, formed mainly of cells which break away from the compact layer around the cœlom (chiefly by a break-up of the sclerotome), but also of cells which

40

migrate from the ectoderm and endoderm. The mass around the cœlom is known as *mesothelium*, and from it arise all the remaining mesodermal tissues.

The origin of the central nervous system has already been described. Owing to the shape of the surface of the egg upon which the neural plate is formed, the fore brain is bent sharply downwards round the anterior end of the notochord (Fig. 477 B). This is known as the *cranial flexure*. The

Nervous System and Sense Organs.

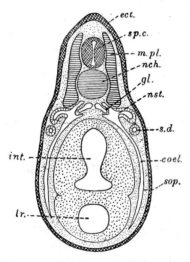

Fig. 479.—A diagram of a transverse section of the frog embryo at the hatching stage.

cœl., Cœlom; *ect.*, ectoderm; *gl.*, glomus, receiving a branch from one of the two suprabranchial arteries which a little further back join to form the dorsal aorta (cf. Fig. 485 A); *int.*, intestine; *lr.*, liver; *m.pl.*, muscle plate; *nch.*, notochord; *nst.*, nephrocœlomostome; *s.d.*, segmental duct; *sop.*, somatopleure; *sp.c.*, spinal cord.

dorsal roots of the nerves are formed as growths from structures known as the *neural crests*. These are a pair of internal ridges which project from the sides of the neural plate, near the tops of the neural folds, before the latter have met. The parts of the crests which do not become nerve roots are converted into mesenchyme and form, among other things, the visceral skeleton. The ventral roots arise later, as outgrowths from the side of the central nervous system, and those of the spinal cord become connected with the corresponding dorsal roots. The formation of the olfactory organs has been mentioned. The posterior nares arise from the olfactory chambers as downgrowths which break through into the mouth. The labyrinth of the ear is formed from the deeper layer of the ectoderm as an ingrowth which forms a vesicle, but does not open to the exterior. It gradually takes on the shape of the labyrinth by the formation of septa which grow into it and divide it up. The eye has a more complicated origin. The retina and the pigmented epithelium arise from a pair of outgrowths of the fore-brain, known as *optic vesicles*, which grow out towards the sides of the head soon after the closure of the neural tube. Each takes on the form of a hollow bulb on a hollow stalk. The stalk gives rise to the optic nerve. The outer half of the bulb becomes thickened and then folded back into the inner half, as a hollow india-

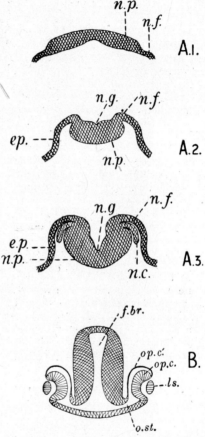

FIG. 480.—Diagrams to illustrate the formation of the central nervous system of the frog.

A, The folding off of the neural canal (cf. Figs. 473–476); *ep.*, future epidermis ; *n.c.*, neural crest, growing out to form a dorsal root ; *n.f.*, neural fold ; *n.g.*, neural groove ; *n.p.*, neural plate.

B, transverse section of the fore-brain at the hatching stage; *f.br.*, fore-brain; *ls.*, lens ; *op.c.*, inner wall of optic cup, which will form retina proper ; *op.c'.*, outer wall, which will form pigment layer; *o.st.*, stalk of optic vesicle.

rubber ball may be folded when it has been punctured
(Fig. 480 B). The two-layered cup which thus arises is
known as the *optic cup*. The thick layer which lines it
is the retina, the thin layer on the side towards the stalk is
the pigment layer. From the deeper layer of the epiblast
there arises a thickening which projects into the mouth of
the cup, separates from the ectoderm, and becomes the lens,
after passing through a stage in which it is a hollow vesicle.

Alimentary Canal. The alimentary canal arises from three rudiments :
the stomodæum (p. 623) or fore-gut, which
is of ectodermal origin and forms the mouth ;
the mesenteron or mid-gut, which is endodermal (p. 620) and forms the greater part of the
canal ; and the ectodermal proctodæum (p. 623) or hind-
gut, which forms the cloacal opening. The pituitary body
arises by an outgrowth from the roof of the mouth, meeting
the brain-floor (p. 64). The gill-slits are formed by outgrowths from the endodermal pharynx, which meet and
perforate the skin. The first of them, corresponding to
the spiracle of the dogfish, never opens, but forms the
tympanic cavity and Eustachian tube.[1] Between, in front
of, and behind the clefts mesodermal thickenings constitute the visceral arches, in which skeletal and vascular
structures corresponding to those of the dogfish arise.
The liver, pancreas, and lungs arise as ventral outgrowths
from the gut. The thyroid body starts as a median
longitudinal groove on the floor of the pharynx. This
gives rise to a solid mass of cells which separates from
the pharynx and divides into two. The intestine of the
tadpole, when the yolk in its ventral wall has been absorbed,
becomes for a time more coiled than that of the adult frog,
probably in correspondence with the vegetable diet.

Mesoblastic Tissues. We have seen (p. 621) that the body cavity or cœlom is
developed as a split in the mesoderm sheets.
Those cells of the splanchnic and somatic layers
which face towards this form the cœlomic
epithelium. The greater part of the cœlom becomes the
abdominal (pleuroperitoneal) cavity, surrounding the gut

[1] This is strictly true of many vertebrates (for instance, of birds and
mammals), but in the tadpole the first cleft disappears and where it
stood the Eustachian tube subsequently develops.

on all sides except in the mid-dorsal line, where the mesentery is left. A forward ventral prolongation of the cœlom becomes the pericardial cavity. The muscles of the gut are formed from the splanchnic layer, the body muscles from the myotomes, which, with sclerotomes (p. 615), have arisen from the epimeres ("mesoblastic somites"), though they are displaced in the adult. The skeleton arises from mesenchyme, mainly from sclerotomes: most of it is at first laid down in cartilage, which in places becomes replaced by bone and in places is reinforced by membrane bones (p. 40). The first rudiment of the cranium has the form of a pair of curved longitudinal bars, the *trabeculæ*, lying below the brain, and soon continued back as a pair of *para-chordal plates* at the sides of the front end of the notochord, which projects into the floor of the tad-pole's skull as it does into that of the dogfish. In most vertebrates, the chick included, the para-chordals are at first separate from the trabeculæ. The trabeculæ fuse with one another, leaving at first a median space or "fossa," in which lies the pituitary body, and with the cartilaginous nasal and audi-

FIG. 481.—A diagram of the rudiment of the skull in a tadpole.

au.c., Auditory capsule ; *l.c.*, labial cartilage ; *nch.*, noto-chord ; *p.f.*, pituitary fossa ; *p.p.q.*, palato-pterygo-quadrate bar ; *pch.*, para-chordal ; *trb.*, trabecula.

tory capsules ; and upgrowths from them form the sides and eventually the roof of the cranium. The pituitary opening presently closes. The continuous palato-pterygo-quadrate bar of cartilage, which forms a part of the cartilage of the mandibular arch, is at first the only skeleton of the upper jaw. The hyoid apparatus of the adult is the remains of the skeleton of the hyoid and the basal parts of some branchial arches of the tadpole. The remainder of the visceral skeleton forms the cartilages of the larynx.

The heart appears some time before hatching. It is at
Blood Vessels. first a straight tube, which arises below the pharynx. Subsequently the tube is thrown into an S shape (see p. 442) and becomes divided by partitions

into its several chambers. The endothelium or pavement epithelium which lines the heart arises by the rearrangement of some scattered mesenchyme cells between the splanchnic layer of mesoderm and the ventral endoderm of the gut, and the muscular tissue is formed by a folding of the splanchnic layer itself (Fig. 482). The space between the splanchno-

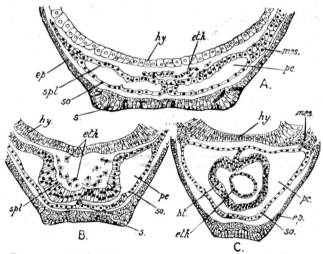

FIG. 482.—*A, B,* and *C,* transverse sections through the ventral wall of the throat of frog embryos of different ages, showing successive stages in the development of the heart.—From Bourne.

ep., Epiblast ; *hy.,* hypoblast ; *mes.,* mesoblast ; *eth.,* endothelial lining of heart ; *ht.,* heart ; *pc.,* pericardial cavity ; *s.,* sucker ; *so.,* somatic layer of mesoblast ; *spl.,* splanchnic layer of mesoblast.

pleure and somatopleure in the region of the heart forms the pericardial cavity. At this time it is continuous with the rest of the cœlom : later, communication between the pericardial and abdominal cavities is abolished by the formation of the great veins. The veins and arteries arise, by separation of cells of the mesoderm, as irregular spaces which join up to form blood vessels. The earliest vessels to appear are the *vitelline veins,* one on each side of the yolk mass in the splanchnic mesoderm. These join the sinus venosus and carry to the heart the food matter derived from the yolk. The venous system is at first arranged on the same plan as in the dogfish, with two ductus Cuvieri and anterior

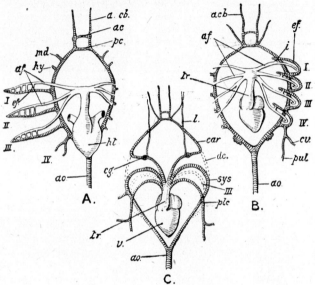

FIG. 483.—Diagrams of the heart and chief arteries of a tadpole.— From Bourne.

A, The vessels of a tadpole at the stage when three external gills are present ; *B,* the arrangement when secondary gills are in use ; *C,* the adult arrangement.

a.c., Anterior commissural vessel ; *a.cb.,* anterior cerebral artery ; *af.,* afferent branchial arteries ; *ao.,* dorsal aorta ; *car.,* carotid artery ; *c.g.,* carotid gland ; *cu.,* cutaneous artery ; *d.c.,* ductus caroticus ; *ef.,* efferent branchial arteries ; *ht.,* heart ; *hy.,* efferent hyoidean artery ; *i.,* connecting vessel ; *l.,* lingual artery ; *md.,* efferent mandibular artery ; *p.c.,* posterior commissural vessel ; *pl.c.,* pulmo-cutaneous arch ; *pul.,* pulmonary artery ; *sys.,* systemic arch ; *tr.,* truncus arteriosus ; *v.,* ventricle ; *I.–IV*, branchial aortic arches.

and posterior cardinal veins. Subsequently the posterior cardinal veins disappear and are replaced by the inferior vena cava, the ductus Cuvieri becoming the superior venæ cavæ, and the anterior cardinals the internal jugulars (Fig. 421). The vitelline veins are transformed into the

hepatic portal system and hepatic veins. The arterial
system of the tadpole closely resembles that of a fish. The
conus arteriosus leads into a long ventral aorta, from
the end of which arise four vessels to the branchial
arches.[1] From the gill capillaries there arises in each
arch an efferent vessel which discharges into a longitudinal suprabranchial artery. The two suprabranchial
arteries, which are the earliest arteries to appear, are at

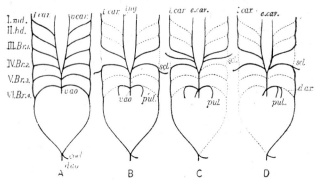

Fig. 484.—Diagrams showing how the arterial systems of adult vertebrates are related to that of the embryo. The vessels are shown
from the ventral side.

A, Theoretically complete system of arches, not found in this form in any vertebrate,
adult or embryonic ; *B*, the system of the adult frog ; *C*, that of the adult bird ;
D, that of the adult mammal.

I.-VI., Visceral arches ; *Br.1–Br.4*, branchial arches ; *cœl.*, cœliac ; *d.ao.*, dorsal
aorta ; *d.ar.*, ductus arteriosus ; *e.car.*, external (=ventral) carotid ; *hd.*, hyoid
arch ; *i.car.*, internal (dorsal) carotid ; *lng.*, lingual, or external (=ventral)
carotid ; *md.*, mandibular arch ; *pul.*, pulmonary ; *scl.*, subclavian ; *v.ao.*,
ventral aorta ; *v.car.*, ventral carotid.

first entirely separate, but presently join behind to form
the dorsal aorta. In front they are continued as the
internal carotids. In the presence of a single efferent
vessel in each arch and of the two suprabranchial arteries,
the tadpole, while it differs from the dogfish, resembles
certain other fishes (p. 469). When the lungs are formed, a
vessel to supply each of them arises from the fourth efferent

[1] There are traces of similar vessels in the hyoid and mandibular
arches.

branchial vessel of the same side. Before the gills are lost, direct communication is established between the afferent and efferent vessels, so that when the gill capillaries disappear blood can pass direct from ventral to dorsal aorta through four continuous aortic arches. After the loss of the gill capillaries certain parts of the four arches disappear, while other parts persist and become the great arteries of the adult. The first branchial arch becomes

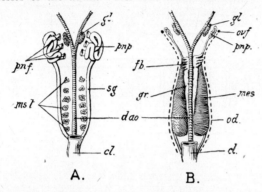

A.   B.

FIG. 485.—Diagrams of the development of the excretory system of the frog.—From Bourne.

A, The system of a tadpole about 12 mm. long, showing the pronephros and origin of the mesonephric tubules ; *B*, the system at the end of metamorphosis. The broken line represents approximately the position of the strip of peritoneal epithelium which gives rise to the oviduct.

cl., Cloaca ; *d.ao.*, dorsal aorta ; *f.b.*, fat body ; *gl.*, glomus ; *g.r.*, genital ridge ; *m.s.*, mesonephros ; *ms.t.*, mesonephric tubules ; *od.*, oviduct ; *ovf.*, position of oviducal opening ; *pn.f.*, pronephric funnels ; *pnp.*, pronephros ; *sg.*, segmental duct (the line points to the part which becomes the Wolffian duct).

The pronephros is shown diagrammatically in transverse section in Fig. 626.

the carotid. The portion of the suprabranchial artery which connected it with the arch behind it is usually obliterated, but sometimes there remains a trace of it known as the *ductus caroticus*. The second branchial arch becomes the systemic arch. The third branchial arch disappears altogether. The fourth branchial arch becomes the pulmo-cutaneous. It loses its connection with the aorta save for a vestige in the form of a ligament in most adults, but sometimes, as always in the newt, an

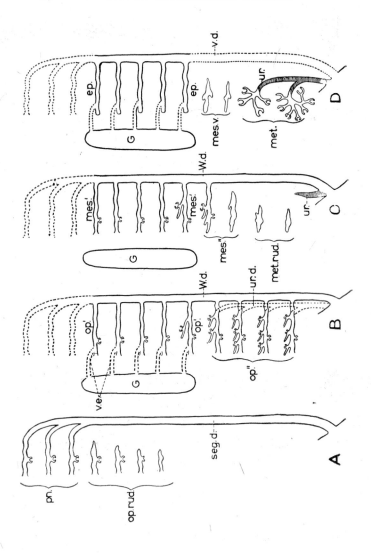

open connection persists, and is known as the *ductus arteriosus.*[1] We have seen (p. 556) that it is present also during the development of the rabbit, where a vestige remains in the adult.

Excretory and Generative Organs. The rudiment of the excretory system arises before hatching, as a longitudinal thickening of the somatic mesoderm on each side at the front end of the cœlom, immediately below the myotomes. The mesoderm here is the *intermediate cell mass.* In many animals it is composed of *nephrotomes*, one for each myotome. Its front part gives rise to the pronephros (p. 439), which consists of three twisted tubules each opening into the cœlom (*nephrocœle*) of the intermediate cell mass. Opposite the openings (*nephrocœlomostomes*) a sacculated outgrowth of the splanchnic layer appears. It is known as the *glomus* [2] and becomes filled with blood from the systemic arch. The outer part of the thickening for the kidney becomes a longitudinal tube, the *segmental* or *archinephric duct*, into which the pronephric tubules open at their outer ends. This duct grows backwards and at the time of hatching opens into the cloaca. Later the adult frog's kidney ("mesonephros," see p. 636) arises as a series of paired masses of cells in the kidney rudiment along the inner side of the segmental duct, behind the pronephros. The part of

---

[1] The term *ductus Botalli* is often applied both to the ductus caroticus and to the ductus arteriosus.

[2] This is exceptional. Usually each tubule has its own *glomerulus*, enclosed in a nephrocœle so as to form a Malpighian capsule (p. 78).

FIG. 486.—A diagram of the kidney tubules and ducts of vertebrata.

A., Condition in larva of fishes and amphibians (pronephric tubules shown with separate glomeruli). *op. rud.*, Developing rudiment of opisthonephros ; *pn.*, pronephros ; *seg.d.*, segmental duct. *B.*, Condition in adult fishes and amphibians. *G.*, gonad ; *op'.*, part of the opisthonephros which in the male is connected with the testis ; *op".*, part of the opisthonephros which is purely urinary in both sexes ; *ur.d.*, urinary duct of male dogfish and newt ; *v.e.*, vasa efferentia ; *W.d.*, Wolffian duct. *C.*, Condition in the embryos of reptiles, birds, and mammals, after the degeneration of the pronephros. *G.*, gonad ; *mes'.*, part of the mesonephros which in the male becomes connected with the testis ; *mes".*, rest of mesonephros ; *met. rud.*, rudiment of metanephros ; *ur.*, rudiment of ureter ; *W.d.*, Wolffian duct. *D.*, Condition in the adult of reptiles, birds, and mammals. *ep.*, in male, epididymis, in female a vestige known as epoophoron ; *G.*, gonad ; *mes.v.*, vestige of hinder part of mesonephros, known in male as paradidymis, in female as paroophoron ; *met.*, metanephros (possibly formed by the branching of one tubule only) ; *ur.*, ureter ; *v.d.*, vas deferens (in male only).

the segmental duct in this region is now called the Wolffian
duct. Each of the cell masses develops into one of the
kidney tubules, having at one end an opening to the
Wolffian duct, and at the other a Malpighian capsule
(secondary nephrocœle) with a glomerulus, and beyond the
capsule a " peritoneal funnel " which opens to the main
cœlom. In later stages this funnel loses its connection with
the tubule and acquires instead a communication with a
vein which it retains in the adult.[1] Outgrowths from
certain Malpighian capsules to the testis form the vasa
efferentia.

The frog, as we have seen, lacks the hind-kidney or metanephros
which reptiles, birds, and mammals possess, and which in them
forms alone the kidney of the adult (see pp. 439, 547, 548). In
the latter classes of animals the set of kidney tubules which constitute
the metanephros develop in a portion of the kidney rudiment which
lies behind the mesonephros, form no connection with the testis,
do not at any time open by a funnel to the cœlom, and discharge,
not by the Wolffian duct, but by a special duct, the ureter. This
duct arises by growing forward from the hinder end of the Wolffian
duct, branches to join the metanephric tubules, and eventually loses
its hindward connection with the Wolffian duct, and comes to open
independently into the cloaca (or bladder). Strictly speaking, what
we have called the mesonephros of the frog is an opisthonephros
(p. 440, footnote), corresponding to both the meso- and metanephros of animals which possess the latter. All the tubules of
the frog's kidney, however, have the connections of those of a
mesonephros.

Just before metamorphosis the pronephros and the front
part of the segmental duct degenerate. The oviduct arises
as a structure called the *Mullerian duct*, which is present
in the late tadpole in both sexes, but degenerates in the
male, leaving only a minute vestige. It is formed as a
longitudinal tract of the peritoneal epithelium outside the
kidneys, which becomes converted into a canal, the
front part by being grooved and then closing in, the
hinder part by hollowing out. Part of the groove does
not close, but remains as the internal opening of the
oviduct. The gonads are formed as thickenings of the

---

[1] In this condition of the peritoneal funnels, frogs are unique. It
is probably, like the lymph-hearts, an expedient for facilitating the
return to the blood vessels of lymph, which in the frog is copious and
less confined in vessels than that of higher vertebrata.

cœlomic epithelium, one on either side of the mesentery, on the dorsal wall of the peritoneal cavity. No distinction between the sexes can be seen until the metamorphosis takes place.

The difference between the mode of cleavage of the ovum of the lancelet and that of the ovum of **Kinds of Segmentation.** the frog is due to the presence in the latter of a considerable quantity of yolk or food material stored to provide for the nourishment of the embryo during the early stages of development. This yolk, lying on one side of the egg, hampers the relatively scanty protoplasm there, which therefore divides more slowly, and, as we have seen, forms fewer and therefore larger cells than the other side. In the dog-fish and in birds there is no food-procuring, larval stage of development, but the embryo is nourished within the egg until it has substantially the features of the adult. Accordingly the yolk is still more plentiful, with the result that the portion of the egg in which it is stored never divides at all,

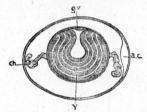

FIG. 487.—A diagrammatic section of the egg of a bird.—From Thomson.

a.c., Air chamber; *ch.*, twisted cords in the white known as "chalazæ"; *g.v.*, "germinal disc," a small patch of protoplasm, comparatively free from yolk, in which lies the "germinal vesicle" or nucleus; *y.*, yolk, in alternate layers of yellow and white substance. The yolk is surrounded by the "white of egg." Note the two membranes underlying the shell and separating to enclose the air chamber.

but remains as an inert mass until it is surrounded by the growth of the small protoplasmic region or *germinal disc*, which containing the nucleus, lies originally at one pole (Fig. 487), and segments to form the cells of the embryo. The cleavage of the ovum of the lancelet is *complete* or *holoblastic* and almost *equal*; that of the ovum of the frog is holoblastic and *unequal*; that of the dogfish and birds is *incomplete* or *meroblastic*.

The egg of a bird—for instance, that of the common fowl (Fig. 487)—consists of an immense ovum, the so-called "yolk," with certain coverings. The ovum

owes its size to being swollen, as we have just seen,
Development of the Chick : Early Stages. by a great quantity of nutritive material, the yolk proper, which pushes the bulk of the protoplasm to one side as the germinal disc. It is covered, first by its closely-fitting vitelline membrane ; then by the " white," which is a solution of proteins and salts, representing the jelly around the frog's ovum ; then by a double membrane, whose two layers, when the egg has been laid for some time, part at the broad end and so enclose an air-space ; and finally by a porous, chalky shell. The white provides an additional store of nutriment, but its principal function is to serve as a store of water, without

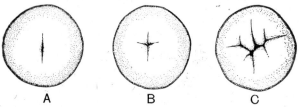

| A | B | C |

FIG. 488.—Views of the young blastoderm of the chick in three successive stages of cleavage.

A, Two-cell stage.   *B,* Four-cell stage.   *C,* Eight-cell stage.

which the embryo could not develop on dry land. Thus birds and reptiles are freed from that dependence upon a watery medium during their early stages which exists for the frog. Cleavage (Fig. 488) begins with the formation across the germinal disc of a furrow which does not reach to the disc's edge. This is soon crossed by another furrow, and then more appear till the disc is divided into a mosaic of small irregular segments (Fig. 490, 1). Sections of the disc show that at the same time a horizontal cleft is forming by which the segments become separated from the underlying yolk (Fig. 489, B). By a further series of horizontal clefts the disc becomes two or three cells deep (C). In that way, shortly before the laying of the egg, a cap of cells known as the *blastoderm* is formed. Between it and the yolk is a space known as the *subgerminal cavity.*

The cells at the surface now become fitted regularly together and form an *upper layer*, one cell deep, separated by a chink, the *blastocœle*, from the rest, which are rounded, and form an irregular stratum, the *lower layer* (Fig. 491, D). The upper layer will give rise to the ectoderm (epiblast) and to the primitive streak ; the lower layer is the endoderm (hypoblast) and will give rise to the lining epithelium of the gut and of the various organs which will form as outgrowths from that (p. 625). The subgerminal cavity will

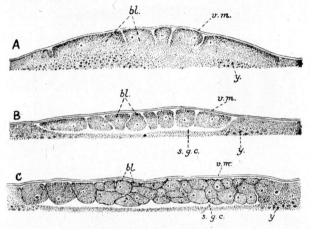

FIG. 489.—Sections through the young blastoderm of the chick in three successive stages, of which the first (*A*) is that of Fig. 488, *c*, and the second (*B*) a little later than that of Fig. 490, 1. Slightly diagrammatic.

bl., blastomeres ; *s.g.c.*, subgerminal cavity ; *v.m.*, vitelline membrane ; *y.*, yolk.

become the hollow of the gut. Around the edge the lower layer cells are more closely packed, and rest on the yolk, which in this region contains nuclei derived from them and is known as the *germinal wall* (Fig. 490, 2, g.w.). At this stage the egg is laid, and the low temperature outside the body of its mother brings its development to a standstill. When, however, the mother begins to sit, or the egg is put into an incubator, so that the temperature rises, changes take place rapidly. The blastoderm spreads

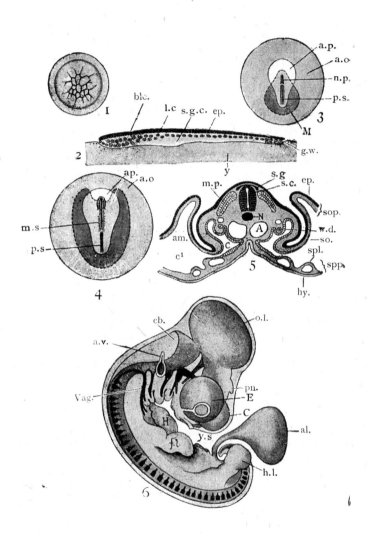

over the yolk, chiefly owing to the addition to its margin of cells formed around nuclei of the germinal wall, which recedes, by growing on the outside while it forms blastoderm on the inside. In a surface view of the blastoderm there is now a dark, translucent *area pellucida* (light in Fig. 490) over the subgerminal cavity, and a whiter *area opaca* where the blastoderm rests on the yolk. It is in the area pellucida that the body of the chick will be

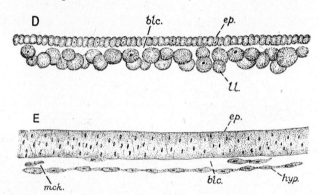

FIG. 491.—Sections through the blastoderm of the chick in two stages (D, E) which succeed that of Fig. 489, C, slightly diagrammatic.

blc., blastocœle ; *ep.*, ectoderm ; *hyp.*, endoderm ; *l.l.*, lower layer cells ; *mch.*, cells which will join the mesenchyme.

FIG. 490.—Stages in the development of a chick.—After Marshall.

1. Segmentation ; superficial view of blastoderm. 2. Longitudinal vertical section of later blastoderm ; *blc.*, Blastocœle ; *ep.*, ectoderm ; *g.w.*, germinal wall ; *l.c.*, lower layer of cells ; *s.g.c.*, sub-germinal cavity ; *y.*, yolk. 3. Diagrammatic surface view, a little later ; *a.p.*, area pellucida ; *a.o.*, area opaca ; *n.p.*, neural plate ; *p.s.*, primitive streak ; *M.*, mesoderm spreading from primitive streak, seen through ectoderm. 4. Diagrammatic surface view of later stage (end of the first day) ; *a.p.*, area pellucida ; *a.o.*, area opaca ; *m.s.*, mesoblastic somites ; *p.s.*, primitive streak. The dark border shows the spreading of the mesoderm over the yolk. 5. Cross-section behind the heart, at the end of the second day ; *A.*, one of the vessels which join to form the dorsal aorta ; *am.*, amnion fold ; *c.*, cœlom or pleuro-peritoneal cavity of the embryo ; *c'.*, extra-embryonic cœlom ; *ep.*, ectoderm ; *hy.*, endoderm ; *s.c.*, spinal cord ; *s.g.*, dorsal root ganglion forming from neural crest ; *so.*, somatic mesoderm ; *sop.*, somatopleure ; *spl.*, splanchnic mesoderm, with blood vessels ; *spp.*, splanchnopleure ; *N.*, notochord ; *m.p.*, myotome ; *W.d.*, Wolffian duct, with rudiment of kidney tubule adjoining. 6. Embryo at the end of the fifth day ; *a.v.*, auditory vesicle ; *al.*, allantois ; *C.*, cerebrum ; *cb.*, cerebellium ; *E.*, eye ; *f.l.*, fore-limb ; *H.*, heart ; *h.l.*, hind-limb ; *o.l.*, optic lobe ; *pn.*, pineal body ; *y.s.*, remains of stalk of cut-off yolk sac ; *vag.*, vagus.

41

formed. As the blastoderm continues to spread, a change comes over the lower layer cells of this area, most of which become flattened and adhere by their edges to form a continuous layer (Fig. 491, *hyp.*), the definitive endoderm for the gut. The endoderm in the area opaca is formed, from the lower layer cells there, somewhat later ; its cells are cubical and have the function of taking up yolk and passing it to the blood vessels which form in the mesoderm above them (p. 653). A few lower layer cells remain in the blastocœle and will join the mesenchyme (loose mesoderm, p. 625).

The above account of the formation of the endoderm of the chick is still the best substantiated of several that have been given. A more recent description of the process states that the endoderm of

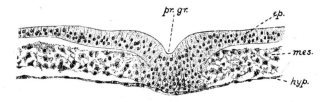

FIG. 492.—A section across the primitive streak of a chick embryo.

ep., ectoderm ; *hyp.*, endoderm ; *mes.*, mesoderm ; *pr.gr.*, primitive groove.

the area pellucida arises by a migration inwards and forwards of cells from a region of the surface of the blastoderm at what will be the hinder end of the embryo.

While the gut endoderm is forming, the area pellucida is becoming pear-shaped, with the broad end forwards (Fig. 490, 3). As this happens, there appears in the narrow end an opaque strip, the *primitive streak* (*p.s.*), and along this a *primitive groove* develops. Sections show (Fig. 492) the primitive streak is due to an immigration of cells from the upper layer, which presently reaches and fuses with the endoderm. The history of the primitive streak of the frog (p. 620) shows that this streak represents the blastopore. As we shall see, the cells which enter by it, like those which enter at the lip of the frog's blastopore, form the notochord and mesoderm.

Before their immigration these cells lie in " presumptive areas " of the surface in the same way as the corresponding cells of the frog's embryo. The cells which will form the lateral plate mesoderm are the first to immigrate; those which form the epimeres follow; those for the notochord enter last and form, at the anterior end of the streak, a swelling, the *primitive knot*, which recedes (see below) as it forms the notochord.

Gastrula. There are now present in the bird's embryo all the parts of a gastrula (p. 607) — ectoderm, endoderm, archenteron (subgerminal cavity), blastocœle, and blastopore, though the layers do not form a sac, and though they have arisen neither by invagination, as in the lancelet, nor by overgrowth (epiboly), as in the frog, but by division of a single layer of cells (*delamination*). It should be noted, however, that in the chick there is at no time a true blastopore, leading from the exterior to the enteron, and that the latter is formed in a manner quite different from the invagination by which it starts in *Amphioxus* and the frog.

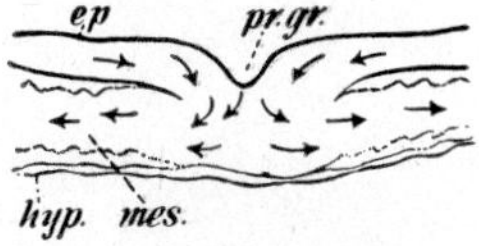

FIG. 493.—A diagram of a section across the primitive streak of a chick embryo with arrows showing the direction of the immigration of the cells which form the mesoderm.

Lettering as in Fig. 492.

Mesoderm and Notochord. The notochord and mesoderm of the embryo are formed from the primitive streak, which in its axial part becomes the notochord (not yet formed at the stage of Fig. 492), and laterally grows out between ectoderm and endoderm as sheets of mesoderm (*mes.* in Fig. 492 ; bounded by a dotted line in Fig. 490, 3 and 4). This transformation of the primitive streak happens at the front end ; meanwhile the hinder part lengthens correspondingly, and so the streak recedes. A split which forms in the mesoderm sheets gives rise to the cœlom (Fig. 497, A), with splanchnic layer of mesoderm within (below) it and somatic layer without (above). As in the frog (p. 621), each mesoderm sheet gives rise along its median side to a row of epimeres ("mesoblastic somites") visible chiefly as myotomes, sclerotomes being indistinct, and laterally to an unsegmented lateral plate.

By the end of the first day of incubation there are four or five pairs of epimeres.

From the germ layers thus laid down the organs of the chick arise essentially in the same way as those of the frog. But the course of development is much modified in detail, and has new features added to it, owing to the differences between the eggs of the two animals. The protected and well-provisioned egg

Folding off.

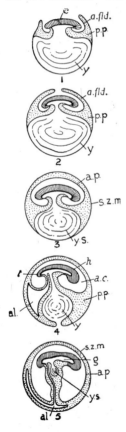

of a bird (or reptile) has great advantages in that it avoids the perils and delay of the larval stage of an amphibian and the necessity of visiting waters at the breeding season ; but, as we have just learnt, it entails forming the embryo, from a thin blastoderm, which must enclose the yolk in the course of the development, and it also makes necessary the provision of special apparatus for the retention of water, for respiration, and for storing excreta. These things are accomplished in the processes of the *folding off of the embryo* and the formation of the *embryonic membranes* which are found in reptiles, birds, and mammals (Fig. 494). The blastoderm continues to extend until, at a late period

Fig. 494.—The origin of amnion and allantois.—After Balfour.

1. Rise of amniotic folds (*a. fld.*) around embryo (*e*) ; *p.p.*, pleuro-peritoneal cavity or cœlom ; *y.*, yolk.
2. Further growth of amniotic folds (*a.fld.*) over embryo and around yolk.
3. Fusion of amniotic folds above embryo ; *a.p.*, amnion proper; *s.m.*, false amnion or serous membrane ; *y.s.*, yolk sac.
4. Outgrowth of allantois (*al.*) ; *a.c.*, amniotic cavity ; *h.*, head end ; *t.*, tail end.
5. Complete enclosure and reduction of yolk sac (*y.s.*) ; *s.m.*, serous membrane ; *a.p.*, amnion proper ; *al.*, allantois ; *g.*, gut of embryo.

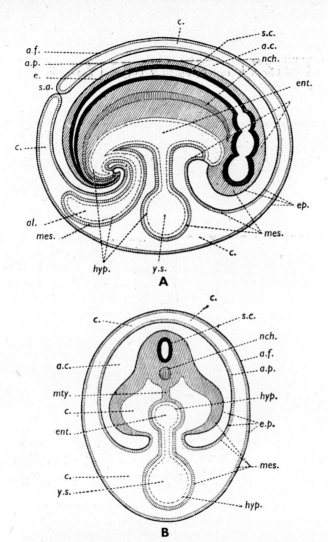

FIG. 495.—Diagrammatic sections of the chick embryo to show the relations of layers and folds. A, longitudinal; B, transverse.

a.c., Amniotic cavity; *a.f.*, false amnion; *a.p.*, true amnion; *al.*, allantois; *c.*, cœlom; *e.*, embryo; *ent.*, enteron; *ep.*, ectoderm; *hyp.*, endoderm; *mes.*, mesoderm; *mty.*, mesentery; *nch.*, notochord; *s.c.*, spinal cord; *s.a.*, sero-amniotic connection; *y.s.*, yolk sac.

in incubation, it has completely enclosed the yolk. As development proceeds, there appears in the area pellucida a furrow that surrounds a central region in which the embryo is forming. The furrow begins in front, in a region, called the *proamnion*, which does not yet contain

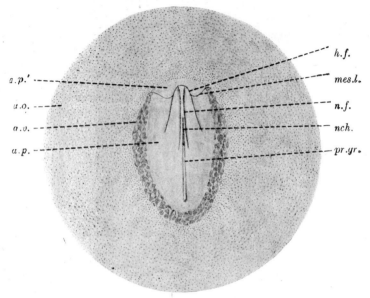

Fig. 496.—A diagrammatic dorsal view of the blastoderm of a fowl's egg towards the end of the first day (between Figs. 3 and 4 in Fig. 490).

a.o., Area opaca ; *a.p.*, area pellucida ; *a.p.'*, part of area pellucida into which mesoderm has not penetrated (proamnion) ; *a.v.*, area vasculosa ; *h.f.*, head fold ; *mes.l.*, anterior limit of mesoderm ; *n.f.*, neural folds ; *nch.*, notochord ; *pr.gr.*, primitive groove.

mesoderm, as the crescentic *head fold*, and is completed by a *tail fold* behind, which joins the head fold at the sides. These folds deepen, and pinch off the little embryo proper from the rest of the blastoderm and the yolk around which the latter is growing. The splanchnopleure, as it folds inwards (Fig. 497 B), comes to form in the body a

tube lined by endoderm. This tube is the rudiment of the
gut. In the hinder part of the head where, as we shall see,
the rudiments of the heart are forming, the splanchnopleure folds in more rapidly than the somatopleure, so
that the cœlom between them is very spacious, forming

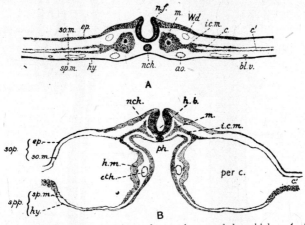

FIG. 497.—Transverse sections of an early second day chick. *A.* A
little behind the middle of the embryo, in the region in which
folding off has not yet taken place. *B.* Further forward, where
the splanchnopleure is folding in under the gut and is bringing
together the two tubes whose union will form the heart.

a.o., one of the pair of vessels which will join to form the dorsal aorta ; *bl.v.*, blood
vessels in the splanchnopleure ; *c.*, cœlom of the embryo ; *c'.*, cœlom in the
blastoderm outside the embryo ; *ep.*, ectoderm ; *eth.*, endothelial lining (endocardium) of the heart ; *h.b.*, hind brain ; *h.m.*, future heart muscle ; *hy.*, endoderm ; *i.c.m.*, intermediate cell mass (nephrotome) from which the kidney
tubules and duct will be formed ; *m.*, myotome ; *nch.*, notochord ; *per.c.*, pericardial cavity ; *ph.*, pharynx ; *so.m.*, somatic mesoderm ; *sop.*, somatopleure ;
sp.m., splanchnic mesoderm ; *spp.*, splanchnopleure ; *Wd.*, position of Wolffian
duct in a somewhat later embryo.

a chamber which will be the pericardial cavity. In the
middle of the body where the splanchnopleure folds have
not yet met, the gut communicates by an ever-narrowing
stalk with a sac, the *yolk sac*, which is the extra-embryonic
part of the splanchnopleure enclosing the yolk. The yolk
sac is separated from the somatopleure by a space
(c' in Fig. 490, 5 ; *p.p.* in Fig. 494) which is part of the

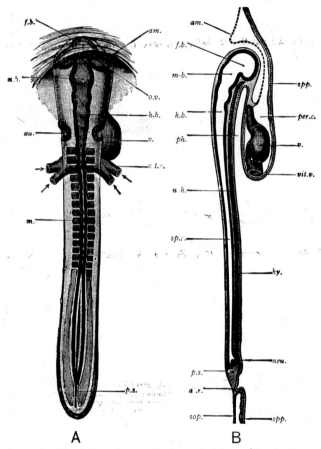

A   B

FIG. 498.—The chick embryo at the thirty-sixth hour of incubation.—
From Marshall and Hurst, *Junior Course of Practical Zoology.*

A, A dorsal view ; *B,* a diagram of a median longitudinal section.
a.r., Rudiment of the outgrowth of the future wall of the gut which will form the
  allantois ; *am.*, amnion, beginning to cover the head ; *au.*, pit which will form
  auditory vesicle ; *f.b.*, fore brain ; *h.b.*, hind brain ; *hy.*, endoderm ; *m.*, myotome ; *m.b.*, mid brain ; *nch.*, notochord ; *neu.*, pit representing the neurenteric
  canal ; *o.v.*, optic vesicle ; *p.s.*, primitive streak ; *per.c.*, portion of cœlom
  which will become pericardial cavity ; *ph.*, pharynx ; *sp.c.*, spinal cord ; *spp.*,
  splanchnopleure ; *sop.*, somatopleure ; *v.*, ventricle ; *vit.v.*, vitelline vein.

cœlom, continuous with the cœlom of the embryo proper, as is seen in Fig. 490, 5. As the embryo grows and lessens the yolk by absorbing it, the yolk sac becomes smaller than the embryo.

The *amnion* is a peculiar membrane which envelops the embryo. It arises in the following way.

Amnion and Allantois. At a time when the splitting of the mesoderm into somatic and splanchnic layers has progressed some way outwards from the embryo over the yolk there appear, starting in the proamnion, upward folds (am. in Fig. 490, 5 ; *a.fld.* in Fig. 494) parallel with the downward folds which formed the embryo, but consisting of somatopleure only. The folds on all sides of the embryo arch upwards and unite above, forming a dome over the embryo. When their tops unite, the inner limbs of the folds form the *true amnion* (Fig. 494, *a.p.*), the outer limbs form the *false amnion* or *serous membrane* or *chorion* (Fig. 494, *s.m.*).

At the point where the folds finally meet their fusion is incomplete and the inner and outer limbs remain connected (*sero-amniotic connection*).

The cavity bounded by the true amnion contains a fluid which bathes the outer surface of the embryo ; that between the true and false amnions is lined by mesoblast and is continuous with the cœlomic space between the yolk sac and the overlying somatopleure. As the split between the layers spreads round the yolk sac, the outer layer it forms continues the false amnion, which finally surrounds the sac. Meanwhile the folding off of the embryo has narrowed the connection between it and the rest of the blastoderm, so that the amniotic cavity encloses the embryo except in the region of this narrow *umbilical stalk* in the middle of the belly. The amnion provides a bath for the embryo, which is no more able to stand drying up than an amphibian larva is, and, as a cushion, protects it against injury when the egg is moved. While the amnion is being formed, a sac known as the *allantois* (Fig. 494, 4, *al.*) grows out from the hinder part of the gut of the embryo, in the position in which the urinary bladder stands in the adults of those vertebrate animals which possess it. This

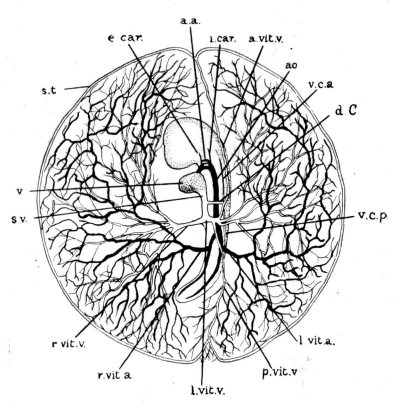

FIG. 499.—A diagram of the circulation of the chick at the end of the third day.

The blastoderm is viewed from below. The arteries are black, the veins in outline.

a.a., second, third, and fourth arterial arches (the first has degenerated ; *a.vit.v.*, *p.vit.v.*, veins from sinus terminalis to left vitelline vein ; *ao.*, dorsal aorta ; *d.C.*, ductus Cuvieri ; *e.car.*, *i.car.*, external and internal carotides ; *l.vit.a.*, *r.vit.a.*, left and right vitelline arteries ; *l.vit.v.*, *r.vit.v.*, left and right vitelline veins ; *s.t.*, sinus terminalis ; *s.v.*, sinus venosus ; *v.*, ventricle ; *v.c.a.*, *v.c.p.*, anterior and posterior cardinal veins.

The right anterior vitelline vein, which is not always present, has, if it existed, disappeared in the dwindling of the right side of the system.

sac, like the gut from which it grows out, is lined with endoderm and covered with splanchnic mesoderm, and projects into the body cavity. It grows down the umbilical stalk and spreads out between the true and false amnions, fusing by its mesoderm with the latter. In the end it completely lines the shell. It becomes very vascular, and by its means the embryo breathes through the porous shell, the urine is passed into it and uric acid deposited and retained in it, and it absorbs for the embryo water and protein from the white.

The formation of the organs of the chick resembles in broad outline that of the frog (compare Fig. 479 and No. 5 in Fig. 490). A neural (medullary) plate (Fig. 490, 3, n.p.) appears in the ectoderm in front of the primitive streak : its sides grow up as neural folds (Figs. 496, 497, *n.f.*) which presently, as in the frog, meet above the back to form the central nervous system. The neural folds lengthen backwards, and their lengthening keeps pace with the transformation of the primitive streak just mentioned, so that the streak is always behind the folds. By the end of the first day the medullary folds have met in the region of the hind brain. On the second day the front of the head begins to bend down, setting up a cranial flexure like that of the frog, by which the fore brain is bent down at right angles to the parts behind it. (Fig. 498, *f.b.*) The further development of the nervous system takes place in practically the same manner as in the frog (pp. 622, 626).

Organogeny : Nervous System.

The alimentary canal, like that of the frog, arises in three sections. (*a*) The greater part is lined by endoderm and is known as the mesenteron. It arises by a folding of the splanchnopleure in a manner which has been described above (p. 646). Five visceral clefts, which do not bear gills and of which the hinder two pairs do not break through, arise in its anterior portion (pharynx). (*b*) A small section which forms part of the mouth is lined by ectoderm and known as the stomodæum. It arises by outgrowths which form the jaws, surrounding a shallow depression. A hollow diverticulum from its roof forms the hypophysis (p. 64). (*c*) Another small section at the hind end, which forms the procto-

Alimentary Canal.

dæum, is also lined by ectoderm. The stomodæum breaks
through to the mesenteron at the end of the third day,
and proctodæum not until the fifteenth day.

The renal organs begin to be formed during the second
half of the second day. They arise, in the
Kidneys and Gonads. three sections which we have already mentioned
—pronephros (p. 439, footnote), mesonephros,
and metanephros (p. 636)—as groups of tubules formed

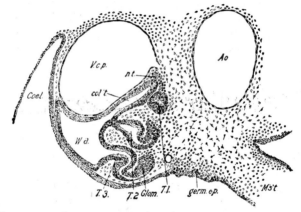

FIG. 500. —A transverse section through the middle of the
mesonephros of a chick embryo of 36 hours.—From Lillie.

Ao., Aorta; *cœl.,* cœlom; *col.t.,* collecting tubule; *germ.ep.,* germinal epithelium
(rudiment of gonad); *glom.,* rudiment of glomerulus; *mst.,* mesentery; *n.t.,*
nephrogenous tissue from which tubules are formed; *T.1, T.2, T.3,* tubules in
three stages of formation; *V.c.p.,* posterior cardinal vein; *W.d.,* Wolffian duct.

from the *nephrotome* or *intermediate cell mass* (*i.c.m.*
Fig. 497) which unites the epimere (" mesoblastic somite ")
to the lateral plate. The pronephros is never functional.
The outer end of each of its tubules turns backwards and
joins the next one, so that there is formed a longitudinal
duct, the archinephric or segmental duct, which grows
back to join the cloaca. The mesonephric tubules come
to open into this duct, and then, from the point where the
first of them joins, it is known as the Wolffian duct. The
ureter grows forwards from the hinder end of the Wolffian

duct to receive the tubules of the metanephros (Fig. 486).
Rudiments of the gonads appear on the fourth day on the
peritoneum at the base of the mesentery (Fig. 500). At
about the seventh day sexual differentiation begins to
appear in them. Eventually the foremost part of each
mesonephros becomes in the male the epididymis and in
the female a vestige known as the epoophoron, while the
Wolffian ducts become the vas deferens in the male and
degenerate in the female. The oviducts (Mullerian ducts),
of which a pair appear but that on the right degenerates,
begin, on the fourth day, as a thickened strip of peritoneum
overlying the mesonephros. The anterior part of the duct,
is formed by the folding in of the strip. Its end then grows
back under the peritoneum till it reaches the cloaca.

Concerning the skeleton and muscles we shall not here
add anything to what has been said about the formation
of these organs in the frog (p. 629).

Blood vessels arise during the latter half of the first day
Blood Vessels. in the loose mesoderm (mesenchyme) just
above the endoderm of the area opaca, where
they cause the region over which the mesoderm has extended to be distinguished, as the *area vasculosa*, from
the region outside it (Fig. 496). They arise by clumps of
mesenchyme cells hollowing out to form *blood islands* in
which some of the cells become corpuscles. Later the
islands join into a network and in this presently larger
vessels differentiate. The formation of blood vessels
spreads over the area pellucida into the embryo. The area
vasculosa soon becomes bounded by a ring vessel, the
sinus terminalis. A little later there is differentiated a pair
of *vitelline veins*, which are continued into the embryo,
and bear thither the nutriment absorbed from the yolk.
In the embryo these join, as we shall see, below the throat
to form the rudiment of the heart; vessels (Fig. 499,
a.vit.v., *p.vit.v.*) drain the sinus terminalis into them.
When the body turns to lie on its left side (p. 657) the
right half of this venous system dwindles.

The heart appears first at the beginning of the second
day. It is formed from a pair of longitudinal tubes in
the splanchnic mesoderm, each continuous behind with
one of the two vitelline veins which run in from the yolk

sac (p. 653).   As the splanchnopleure folds in under the
gut, the tubes join from before backwards, the
Embryonic Circulation. junction eventually proceeding for some distance along the vitelline veins.   As in the frog
the heart-tube is thrown into an S, constrictions mark
out the chambers, and partitions separate them.   At first
there is a sinus venosus, but this later becomes merged in
the right auricle.   Like that of the tadpole, it receives a
venous system with cardinal veins like that of a fish, and
posteriorly is entered by the common trunk of the vitelline
veins (*ductus venosus*) (Fig. 501, B).   Later the posterior
cardinals disappear, and the anterior part of the system
models itself into that of the adult.   The ductus venosus
is joined on the fourth day by the *allantoic vein*, and a
little later by the *inferior vena cava* (Fig. 501, D).   Towards the end of development the vitelline and allantoic
veins, having no further function, dwindle and disappear,
and the inferior vena cava becomes the great vein of the
hinder part of the body.   The portal system is developed
from the ductus venosus behind the junction of the
inferior vena cava.   As the heart forms there appear a
pair of dorsal aortæ and then two *vitelline arteries*
from the aortæ to the yolk sac.   Late on the second
day the dorsal aortæ fuse midway (Fig. 501, A), and
thereafter the junction extends backwards, bringing
together the vitelline arteries, which unite.   Though
there are no gills, aortic arches grow from the front
of the heart to join the dorsal aortæ.   The system they
form changes into vessels of the adult as shown in Fig.
484, C.   The blood which the allantois receives comes
from the dorsal aorta by a pair of *allantois arteries*
(Fig. 501, C *al.a.*).   After being oxygenated in the organ
this blood passes by the *allantoic vein* (Fig. 501, D, *al.v.*),
through the portal system into the inferior vena cava.   In
the heart, so long as the chick is breathing by its allantois,
the blood brought to the right auricle by the inferior vena
cava is not sent into the right ventricle but, by a crescentic
fold—known as the *Eustachian valve*—of the auricular
wall, is directed through the *foramen ovale*, an opening in
the partition between the auricles.   Thus the arterialised
blood from the allantoic vein, mixed, it is true, with some

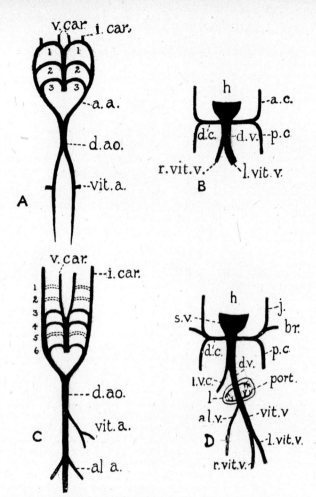

FIG. 501.—Plans of vascular systems of chick embryos. The vessels are shown as from the ventral side. Those which are indicated in outline have disappeared by the fifth day.

A, Arterial system on the third day ; *B*, venous system on the third day ; *C*, arterial system on the fifth day ; *D*, venous system on the fifth day.
a.a., Left root of the dorsal aorta, formed by the union of the aortic arches of its side ; *a.c.*, left anterior cardinal vein ; *a.la.*, left allantoic artery ; *al.v.*, allantoic vein ; *br.*, left brachial vein ; *d.ao.*, dorsal aorta ; *d.c.*, ductus Cuvieri (superior vena cava) ; *d.v.*, ductus venosus ; *h.*, heart ; *i.car.*, internal (dorsal) carotid artery ; *i.v.c.*, inferior vena cava ; *j.*, jugular vein ; *l.*, liver ; *l.vit.v.*, left vitelline vein ; *p.c.*, posterior cardinal vein ; *port.*, portal system ; *s.v.*, sinus venosus ; *v.car.*, ventral (external) carotid arteries ; *vit.a.*, left vitelline artery ; *vit.v.*, common vitelline vein.

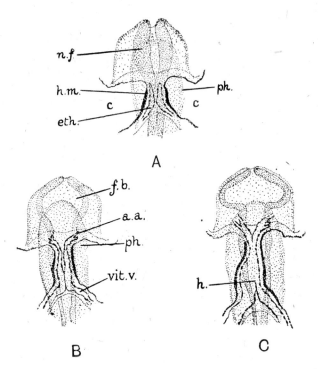

FIG. 502.—Semidiagrammatic views of the process of formation of the heart in the chick. Partly after Patten.

A. Two separate endothelial tubes with thickenings of the adjacent cœlomic wall for the heart muscles. B. The endothelial tubes are brought together, and aortic arches begin to grow out from their anterior ends (around the pharynx to join the dorsal aorta). C. The tubes unite (the muscle rudiments join around them) and thus the heart is formed. Indications of its S flexure (p. 654) are already visible.

a.a., Aortic arches; *c.*, cœlom; *eth.*, endothelial lining (endocardium) of heart; *f.b.*, fore brain; *h.*, heart; *h.m.*, muscular wall of heart; *n.f.*, neural folds; *ph.*, future pharynx; *vit.v.*, left vitelline vein; Compare Fig. 497.

venous blood from other constituents of the inferior vena cava, reaches the left or arterial side of the heart and is consequently distributed where it is needed. When the chick begins to use its lungs the allantois shrivels up, the foramen ovale closes, and the now wholly venous blood of the inferior vena cava takes the same course as the rest of that which enters the right auricle.

During development the posture and proportions of the body undergo changes (Fig. 503). The pre-
Posture. cocious development of the central nervous system is probably responsible for some of these. It causes the head to be at first disproportionately large, the head to suffer the cranial flexure (p. 626), which is permanent, and the whole body to assume a temporary ventral curvature which brings head and tail towards one another. As the embryo is raised above the yolk, first the head and then the whole body roll over to lie with the left side downwards.

Development lasts for three weeks, and during it the white is taken up as additional nutriment by
Hatching. the embryo, being reduced by the abstraction of water to a solid mass, which is then absorbed by the allantois. Finally, on the twentieth day of incubation, the beak pierces its way into the air chamber which exists at one end of the egg between the two shell-membranes, and the animal begins to breathe by means of its lungs. The shrivelling of the allantois now takes place (the yolk sac has already been absorbed), and the chick breaks its way out of the egg.

In all mammals except the little group of Monotremata the egg is minute and undergoes complete and
Development of Mammals. nearly equal cleavage. Its development, how-ever, is very different from that of the similar-looking egg of *Amphioxus*. Instead of producing a hollow sphere of cells which invaginates, cleavage nearly always results in a solid, spherical mass or " morula "; and there is never an invagination, though a stage com-parable to the gastrula arises by the establishment of differences between layers of the cells, and possesses, in the primitive streak, the trace of a blastopore. The later course of development resembles in the main that of a

42

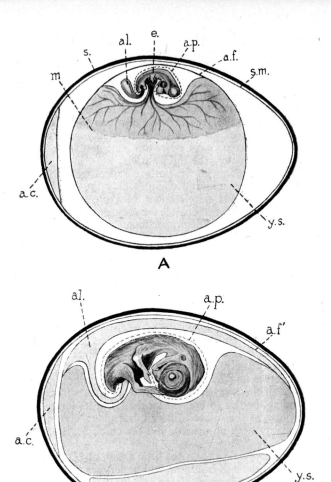

FIG. 503.—Chick embryos in the egg.—After Marshall. The
embryo, which actually lies with its left side on the yolk sac, has
been lifted into a vertical position for the sake of clearness.

A, Egg and embryo at the end of the fifth day of incubation ; *B*, the same at the end
of the ninth day.
a.c., air-chamber ; *a.f.*, false amnion, united with vitelline membrane ; *a.f′*, the same,
further united with allantois ; *al.*, allantois ; *a.p.*, amnion proper ; *e.*, embryo ;
m., site of the sinus terminalis ; *s.*, shell ; *s.m.*, shell membrane ; *w.* white ;
reduced to a semi-solid mass ; *y.s.*, yolk sac.

bird, a yolk sac (which, however, contains no yolk), an amnion, and an allantois being formed.

The details of the early stages and of the formation of the embryonic membranes differ a great deal in different mammals. In the rabbit they take place as follows. The

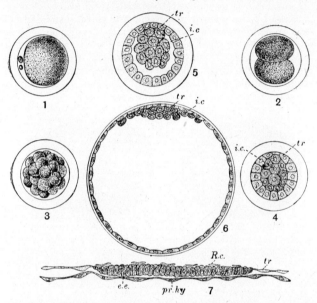

FIG. 504.—Early stages in the development of the Rabbit.—After various authors.

1. Ovum with polar bodies ; 2, two-cell stage ; 3, morula ; 4, section of a later stage ; 5, section of the young blastocyst ; 6, section of an older blastocyst ; 7, section of the embryonic area after differentiation of two layers.
e.e., Embryonic ectoderm ; *i.c.*, inner cells ; *pr.hy.*, primitive endoderm ; *R.c.*, Rauber's cells ; *tr.*, trophoblast.

Early Stages of Mammals. ovum has no vitelline membrane, but is enclosed in a relatively thick striated membrane, the *zona radiata*, and has outside that a coat of albumen secreted by the oviduct. The morula (Fig. 504, 3) lies in the uterus, which is reached (p. 552) at the end of segmentation. It is covered by a single layer of

cells which are rather smaller and more transparent than
those within. This layer is known as the *trophoblast*
(Fig. 504, 4, *tr.*), and will form a part of the ectoderm—
that part, namely, which covers the false amnion, but not
the ectoderm of the embryo proper nor that which lines
the amnion. It now begins to absorb water and nutriment
secreted by the wall of the uterus and to be distended, so
that it separates from the inner mass of cells, except at
one side, where they remain sticking to it, at first as a
knob (Fig. 504, 5), which afterwards (Fig. 504, 6) flattens
out upon the inner side of the trophoblast, forming a
circular patch, known as the *embryonic plate* (or *shield*,

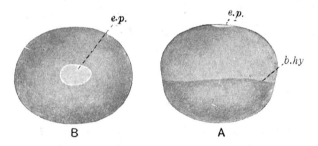

FIG. 505.—The blastocyst on the seventh day.—After Kölliker.

A, From the side ; *B*, from above.
b.hy., Boundary of the endoderm ; *e.p.*, embryonic plate.

or *area*). This afterwards becomes oval, and will give rise
to the embryo. The bladder-like structure which has
thus arisen is known as the *blastodermic vesicle* or *blastocyst* (Fig. 505). As it grows, its trophoblast cells stretch
and become thinner and flatter (Fig. 504, 7, *tr.*). Meanwhile the inner mass cells begin to differentiate into two
layers, an outer, columnar layer of ectoderm, and an inner,
flattened layer of endoderm. The endoderm starts to
grow round the blastocyst, lining the trophoblast beyond
the embryonic ectoderm. Over the latter, the trophoblast
cells (here known as " cells of Rauber ") become separated
and disappear, leaving bare the embryonic ectoderm,
which at its edges becomes continuous with the tropho-

blast, so that the vesicle remains unbroken. The blasto-cyst is now practically in the condition of the early blastoderm of the chick, though instead of the immense mass of yolk of the bird's egg there is only the fluid of the blastocyst, and the ectoderm (including the tropho-blast) already forms a complete vesicle. In the embryonic plate a primitive streak and groove (where cells immigrate from presumptive areas of the surface), medullary folds, mesoderm, head and tail folds (separating embryo from yolk-sac), amnion, and allantois now arise in succession (Fig. 507). The mesoderm, however, never extends to the ventral side of the yolk sac, whose endoderm is therefore, in that region, covered only by ectoderm (trophoblastic) : eventually the ventral wall thus formed

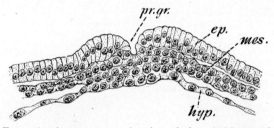

FIG. 506.—A transverse section through the primitive streak.

ep., Ectoderm ; *hyp.*, endoderm ; *mes.*, mesoderm ; *pr.gr.*, primitive groove.

breaks up and disappears. Meanwhile, outgrowths or " villi " of the trophoblast burrow into the wall of the uterus. These are especially numerous over a thickened, horseshoe-shaped patch of trophoblast which surrounds the hinder part of the embryo, in the region (*tr'.*) in which the placenta (p. 552) will arise. After the establishment of the membranes the embryo is known as a *fœtus*.

The early stages of the embryonic development of Man are im-perfectly known, but the process appears to belong to a type which resembles that of the chick less than the development of the rabbit does. In it the trophoblast over the embryo does not disappear, and the amnion is formed very early, as a cavity in the embryonic ecto-derm, which arises as a mass of cells, not as a layer. In the floor of this cavity the embryo is formed.

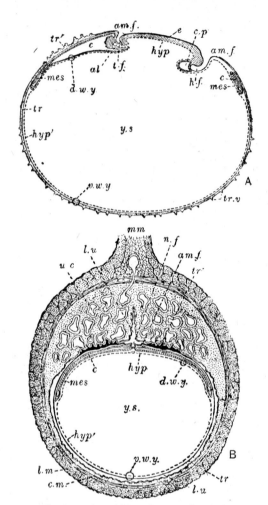

Fig. 507.—Sections of a rabbit embryo on the ninth day.—After
various authors.

A, Longitudinal section through a blastocyst removed from the uterus ; *B*, transverse section of the uterus and of a blastocyst *in situ.*—Partly after Marshall.
al., Allantois ; *am.f.*, amnion fold ; *c.*, cœlom ; *c.p.*, pericardium ; *c.m.*, circular
muscles of uterus ; *d.w.y.*, dorsal wall of yolk sac ; *e.*, embryo ; *h.f.*, head fold ;
hyp., endoderm of embryo ; *hyp'.*, endoderm of yolk sac ; *l.m.*, longitudinal
muscles of uterus ; *l.u.*, lumen of uterus ; *mes.*, mesoderm ; *mm.*, mesometrium
of uterus ; *n.f.*, neural folds ; *t.f.*, tail fold ; *tr.*, trophoblast (grey in *A*, black in
B) ; *tr'.*, thickened region of same in which will arise placenta ; *tr.v.*, villi of trophoblast ; *u.c.*, uterine capillaries ; *v.w.y.*, ventral wall of yolk sac ; *y.s.*, yolk sac.

For a while the yolk sac of mammals forms a union with
The Placenta. the uterine wall and through trophoblastic
villi is the main organ of nutrition and
respiration but in this it is soon replaced by the
allantois, which, as in the chick, spreads out under the
false amnion or *subzonal membrane* and fuses with it.
The organ thus formed is the placenta, and from it out-

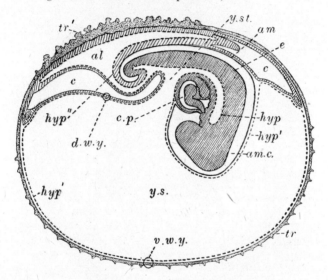

FIG. 508.—Longitudinal section of a rabbit embryo on the tenth day.

am., Amnion ; *am.c.*, amniotic cavity ; *hyp"*, endoderm of allantois ; *y.st.*, stalk
of yolk sac. Other letters as in Fig. 507.

growths penetrate into the uterine wall, expanding the
original villi of the trophoblast and obtaining nourishment and exchanging gases with the maternal blood in
lacunæ which are formed around them by the breakdown of blood vessels in the wall of the uterus. Thus, as
in the chick, the blood in the allantoic vein is arterial,
though it has here also an important function as the
vehicle of nourishment during the greater part of embryonic life. The arrangement, resembling that in the

chick (p. 654), by which this arterial blood is directed into
the left auricle, leaves traces in the heart of the adult

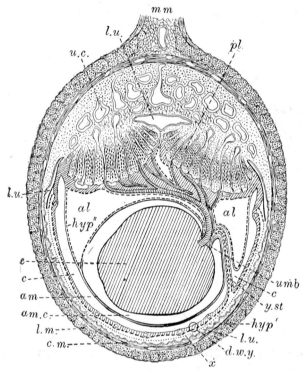

Fig 509.—Transverse section of the uterus of a rabbit with an embryo
of the nineteenth day.—Partly after Marshall. The placenta and
membranes are now attached only by a narrow stalk to the embryo, which lies on its side.

pl., Placenta ; *umb.*, umbilical stalk ; *x*, dotted line indicating position of vanished
ventral wall of yolk sac. Other letters as in Figs. 475, 476.

(Fig. 418 and its legend). The navel of the adult marks
the site of the *umbilical cord*, in which the stalks and
blood vessels of the yolk sac and allantois entered the
body. The urinary bladder is formed from a remnant of

the stalk of the allantois. The amnion is the " caul," and the placenta is shed as the " afterbirth."

The resemblance between the development **Nourishment of Young Stages.** of the minute, yolkless eggs of most mammals and that of the bird's egg, which is large and yolky, is a remarkable fact. It suggests that the ancestors of these mammals had yolky eggs as the Monotremata still have, that they acquired the habit of retaining them within the body, and that there the allantois, which in the bird's egg serves principally for the respiration of the embryo, enabled the mother to make complete provision for the nourishment

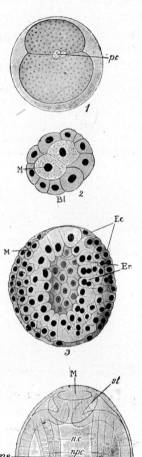

Fig. 510.—Stages in the development of an earthworm.—After Wilson.

1. Stage of two blastomeres; *p.c.*, polar bodies (*not* pole cells).
2. Blastula; *M.*, primary or pole cell of mesoblast.
3. Gastrula in ventral view; *Ec.*, ectoderm or epiblast; *En.*, endoderm or hypoblast; *M.*, mesoblast.
4. Late gastrula in ventral view, showing the bands of cells known as " germ bands " : the blastopore has narrowed, and what remains of it is now the mouth: *M.*, mouth; *m.*, primary mesoblast cells (pole cells); *ms.*, mesoderm bands; *N.*, nephridioblasts, large cells derived from the ectoderm which add to the bands of nephridial cells as the embryo lengthens; *Nb.*, neuroblasts, similar cells at the ends of the bands of cells which form the nerve cords; *n.c.*, nerve cords; *np.c.*, cells which will form nephridia; *st.*, stomodæum.

as well as for the respiration of her offspring, and with that the yolk disappeared. The Chordata whose embryology we have been studying exemplify well the several ways in which animals are nourished during their development. The lancelet obtains its own food as a larva. The frog during its early stages, and the bird throughout development, subsist upon yolk with which the ovum was stocked by the mother. Birds are provided also with nutriment (the " white ") around the ovum in the shell. Mammals are nourished directly from the mother's body both before and after birth.

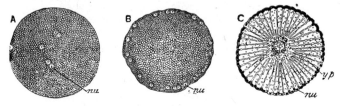

FIG. 511.—Three stages in the segmentation of the egg of the crayfish.—From Parker and Haswell.

nu., Nuclei ; *y.p.,* " yolk-pyramids."

With the embryology of invertebrata we can only deal very briefly.[1] The development of *Hydra* and *Obelia* has already been described (pp. 220 and 228). It includes complete and equal cleavage of the ovum, a hollow blastula, the conversion of this into the two layered (gastrula) stage by the immigration,[2] of some of the cells of its wall, the origin of the enteron as a split in the mass of endoderm, and the shaping of the gastrula into the adult by a simple process. In the starfish cleavage is complete and equal and ends in the establishment of a blastula, not unlike that of the lancelet, from

Development of Invertebrates.

[1] The external features and habits of the larvæ and other young stages of invertebrata have been described with those of the adults.
[2] Compare p. 643. The modes of formation of the gastrula ("gastrulation") of animals are : invagination or " emboly," epiboly, delamination, and immigration.

which by invagination a gastrula is formed. The mesoderm arises from the anterior end of the archenteron, as a
pouch whose cavity gives rise to the cœlomic spaces.

In the earthworm (Fig. 510) and swan mussel cleavage of
the ovum is complete but unequal, and forms a hollow
blastula, which invaginates to give rise to a gastrula.
The mesoderm arises along the ventral side as two bands,
each formed by the division of one of a pair of *pole cells* at
the hind end which are derived from a cell " determined "

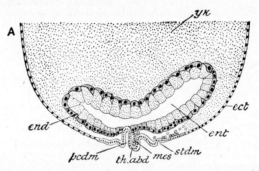

FIG. 512.—Part of a longitudinal section through the egg of a crayfish after the enteron has been established and the blastopore has
closed.—From Parker and Haswell, after Reichenbach.

ect., Ectoderm; *end.*, endoderm; *ent.*, enteron; *mes.*, mesoblast; *pcdm.*, procto
dæum (for hind gut); *stdm.*, stomodæum (for fore gut); *th.ab.*, rudiment from
which abdomen and part of thorax arise; *yk.*, yolk, lying at this stage in what
is morphologically the blastocœle.

for their formation during cleavage, and in the earthworm
each band subsequently divides into a row of mesoblastic
somites. These as they form become hollow, and the
cavity of each unites with that of its fellow on the other
side of the body to become the cœlom of one of the segments of the adult. In the crayfish the cleavage (Fig. 511)
is incomplete, but, as will be seen from the following
account, it is of a different kind from the incomplete
cleavage of the ova of the chick and dogfish. The nucleus
divides till a number of daughter nuclei are formed, and
these migrate to the surface, where they are at first

embedded in a continuous sheet of protoplasm which
encloses a central mass of yolk (" centrolecithal " cleavage).
Afterwards this protoplasm divides into cells which
constitute a one-layered blastoderm enclosing the yolk
mass.   Thus there arises a sort of blastula which has no
blastocœle, but contains yolk.   A shallow invagination
on one side of this, pushing into the yolk, gives rise to a
gastrula with a small enteron (Fig. 512).   The mesoderm
arises as two ventral bands, though pole cells are not
found :   it forms mesoblastic somites, whose cavities
afterwards disappear, save in the segment of the antenna,
where they become the end-sacs of the green glands.   The
later development of these animals cannot be followed
here, but it may be stated that it is quite unlike that of
the Vertebrata.

A comparison of the processes that have just been
von Baer's Law. described shows two facts of importance.
(1) They all have certain features in common.
(2) The animals which are more alike as adults resemble
one another longer in development.   This generalisation is
known as *von Baer's Law*.   All animals have at one stage
a single nucleus.   All Metazoa pass later through a gastrula
stage of two layers only.   When the Triploblastica acquire
the third layer, Annelida, Arthropoda, and Mollusca have
in common a process in which it starts as ventral bands,
while in Chordata it arises (after immigration) upon the
dorsal side of the primitive gut.   All Chordata have also
at one stage a notochord, a hollow dorsal nervous system
formed by the folding of a neural plate, and visceral clefts.[1]
All Vertebrata have at a later stage a cartilaginous
skeleton and a circulatory system like that of a fish.   At
a later stage still, the frog, bird, and mammal have
pentadactyle limbs and the rudiments of lungs.   The
embryo of a rabbit is at one stage much like that of
many other mammals, then it takes on the features of a
rodent, finally it shows those of its own species.   At the
same time it must not be overlooked that von Baer's law
holds good only in a very general sense.   The resemblance
between the young stages of related animals is never exact,

[1] The term " gill-clefts " should not be applied to these unless, as
in fishes and tadpoles, they bear gills.

and is often greatly obscured by disturbing factors, such as variations in the amount of yolk present or the precocious development of certain organs. Thus, for instance, the two-layered stages of the lancelet, frog, and chick (Figs. 462, 472, 490, 2) are extremely unlike on account of differences in the amount of yolk they contain ; and again amnion and allantois, which are peculiar to reptiles, birds, and mammals, are developed at an exceedingly early stage, when the embryo is only beginning to take on the features which are common to all chordate animals.

From the preceding pages of this chapter, the student will have learned what a complicated process **Regulating Factors :** is the development of the ovum into the **i. Chromo-** adult individual. As to how this process **somes and** is caused to pursue truly its intricate course, **Cytoplasm.** we have as yet very incomplete information, but in the main it appears to be regulated in the following way. The fact that the fertilised ovum grows into the likeness of its parents is due in the first place to the possession by its nucleus of *chromosomes* derived from each of them, and often, perhaps always, also to certain qualities of the *maternal cytoplasm* in it. But, in the divisions by which the cells of the body are formed, each cell receives a complete set of chromosomes, and has therefore, so far as chromosomes are concerned, the potentiality of assuming the features peculiar to any part of the body. Sometimes, though by no means always, the cytoplasm appears to be equally indifferent. What is it that decides which potentialities shall be realised in each of the cells ?

In the mass of cellular raw-material certain external factors establish the main lines of the *lay-out* **ii. Factors in** *of the body*. The principal axis, which in **the Lay-out.** bilateral animals lies fore and aft, is usually set up in the ovum before it is fertilised, by influences to which it is subjected in the ovary of the mother. In the frog, for instance, the anterior end is located on that side of the ovum which is towards the surface of the ovary, and, as in many other cases, the yolk is laid down in the hinder part, leaving in the anterior part unencumbered protoplasm for the formation of the delicate nervous and sensory organs.

The nucleus, though it can only form frog nuclei, has in it the potentialities of all the nuclei of a frog. The cytoplasm is not only predetermined to be frog cytoplasm, but is already under the influence of factors which decide that part of it shall be head-end cytoplasm and part tail-end cytoplasm. The dorsal and ventral sides are most often determined at fertilisation ; in the frog, for instance, the side opposite to the point of entry of the spermatozoon becomes dorsal.

Other factors, limiting the capabilities of the cells in the several regions, determine the nature of the organs to be formed in each locality of the body.

iii. Organising Factors.

(*a*) In some cases these factors have already arisen in the ovum, where parcels of cytoplasm sometimes distinguishable by colour, exist, and are marshalled by the divisions of cleavage until they come to lie in the regions whose capacity for organ-formation they determine. It is even possible, for instance, in certain molluscs, to cut off portions of the ovum and to find in consequence certain parts of the normal body missing in the larva. Regions so predestined in the ovum are held to contain specific *organ-forming substances*. Naturally in these cases the blastomeres into which the ovum is cut up at cleavage contain different complements of organ-forming substances, and are thus already specialised for forming certain organs and incapable of giving rise to others. The cleavage of such an organ is called *determinate cleavage*. It is found, for instance, in annelids and molluscs and in *Amphioxus*, but not in echinoderms and only to a limited degree in vertebrates. (*b*) In animals in which the cleavage is *indeterminate*, there is at first no limitation of the organ-forming potentialities of the cells. Each cell can assume any form proper to the species, according to its circumstances. If the first two blastomeres of an amphibian be separated, each will form a complete half-size embryo. This means, of course, that portions of each blastomere which under normal conditions would have formed certain organs actually give rise to quite different structures. This is shown very strikingly in the formation of partial twins by incompletely separated blastomeres, part of each first blastomere behaving normally and part abnormally.

When cleavage is completed, groups of cells transplanted, for instance, from the position of the eye and grafted into the side of the trunk will there give rise to ordinary epidermis. But at a later stage determination sets in,

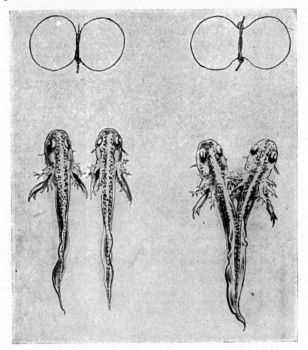

FIG. 513.—Potentialities of the blastomeres of Amphibia.

Left: Result of separating the first two blastomeres by a fine hair; two larvæ are produced. *Right*: Result of partially dividing a segmenting ovum; a two-headed monstrosity is produced.—From Wells, Huxley, and Wells, *The Science of Life*, after a drawing by L. R. Brightwell.

and now the fate of any group of cells is unchangeable. The eye rudiment, or that of a leg, if transplanted, will give rise to an eye or a leg and to nothing else, wherever it be placed and however useless it would be in its new position. This determination takes place under the in-

fluence of an entity known as an *organiser*. In amphibia
the dorsal lip of the blastopore assumes this function. By
an influence which is not fully understood but is probably
exercised by the emission of chemical substances, it limits
the potentialities of the hitherto indeterminate cells of
the embryo in accordance with a plan which is that of the
future body. It will exercise this influence even if it be
grafted into another embryo, so that the latter comes to
contain a second set of organ rudiments (Fig. 514). Its
dominance of the body recalls that which we have noted in the apex of a hydroid colony (p. 233). Some of the rudiments established by the primary organiser will develop without further external influences ; the optic cup is an instance of this ; such rudiments are said to be *self - differentiating*. Much differentiation, however, is dependent upon secondary organising influences exercised

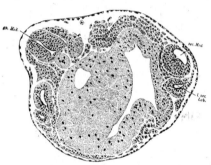

FIG. 514.—A section through a frog embryo into which has been grafted the dorsal lip of the blastopore of another embryo, and which has consequently developed a second set of organ rudiments.

br.Med., proper nerve cord of the larva ; *sec.Med.*, brain induced by the graft ; *l.sec.lab.*, left induced ear-vesicle.—From Haldane and Huxley.

by rudiments already established ; thus, for instance, the
lens of the eye is caused by the optic cup to develop from
the overlying ectoderm.

The developing rudiments, if they are to form normal
iv. Function. organs, require the stimulus of function. The
effect of use and disuse upon the size and
efficiency of organs in post-embryonic organisms is well
known. This effect, which is most familiar in the case of
muscles but is exercised equally elsewhere, is a very
important factor in securing the normal development of

organs in the early stages of life. Nervous, muscular, glandular, and particularly the skeletal tissues are susceptible to it, and their response affects the organs they compose.

Finally, the development of the several parts of the body in proper proportions and at the right times is largely due to the liberation of hormones and to the specific reactions of the rudiments to them. The anterior lobe of the pituitary body produces

v. Hormones.

FIG. 515.—Two dogs of the same litter: from that on the left the anterior lobe of the pituitary body was removed at the age of eight weeks; that on the right was allowed to grow up normally.—From Schäfer.

a hormone which, among other functions, stimulates the growth of bone. Excess or defect of it produces giants or dwarfs. The substance thyroxin which is secreted by the thyroid gland and has a stimulating effect on metabolism (p. 63) is of great importance to the development of vertebrates. Lack of it, owing to imperfection or removal of the glands, produces defective individuals. Human children of this kind are known as *cretins*. They are stunted, pot-bellied, ugly, and of imperfect intelligence. This condition can be completely cured by

43

administering extracts of the thyroid gland. In the amphibia, the metamorphosis of the tadpole is brought on by the secretion of the thyroid. If the thyroids of a tadpole be cut out, the larva will not turn into a frog, though it continues to grow and reaches a large size (Fig. 33). On the other hand, feeding young tadpoles

A   **B**

FIG. 516.—Thyroid action.

A, A cretin, 23 months old. *B,* The same child, 34 months old, after administration of sheep's thyroids for 11 months.—From Starling, after Osler.

with thyroid tissue brings on early metamorphosis and produces minute frogs. The testes and ovaries of verte-brate animals produce hormones which bring about the development of the secondary characters of sex. The effect of the lack of male hormones in castrated animals such as oxen and capons is well known. By means of hor-mones various organs of the body time one another during development.

CHAPTER XXVIII

CLASSIFICATION

THE animals that we have examined in the foregoing chapters have been chosen with a view to their serving, among other things, as examples of the principal kinds of creatures that constitute what is known as the Animal Kingdom. Explicitly or implicitly, the study of different objects of any kind must always proceed by a recognition of their resemblances and differences, but the number of different kinds of animals is so enormous that it is quite impossible to study them without arranging them in an orderly classification according to their degrees of likeness. We have seen that no two individual animals are wholly alike. The offspring of any parent are always unlike it and unlike one another. Even so-called " identical twins," which deserve that name at their birth, become to some degree different by the different action of their surroundings upon them as they grow up. Heredity, in fact, does not produce absolute resemblance, but is qualified by what, using the term in its widest sense, we may call *variation*, whether it be due to an unlikeness in the offspring at birth or acquired by the impress of the surroundings during their lifetime. At the same time, the likeness between the offspring of any parent is, on the average, greater than their likeness to individuals descended from other parents, and in this fact we find the first degree of resemblance between animals. For practical purposes however, the resemblance between members of a family (in the ordinary sense of the word) is useless in classification, on account of the vast number of small divisions it gives and the impossibility of identi-

*Classification :
Species.*

fying them. A more practicable basis is found in the fact
that animals which are closely alike will breed together and
give fertile offspring, whereas those which are less alike
will not. Thus the offspring of two horses is fertile, but
that of a horse and an ass is not, while breeding between
horses and oxen is impossible. The primary groups of
zoological classification consist of individuals which breed
together, but not with individuals outside the group. to
give fertile offspring, or of which it is concluded from
their likeness that they do so. Such a group is known as
a *species*. We have seen examples of the kind of differences
which separate species in the case of the hares and rabbits
(p. 520), of the crayfishes (p. 287), of the Hydras (p. 208),
and of the *Entamœbæ* (p. 179). It is believed that all the
members of a species are united by blood kinship ; that
is to say, that they are all in the long run the descendants
of one pair or several related pairs of parents, so that their
relationship is only an extension of that which exists
between offspring of the same parents. Thus the exclusive
resemblance between the members of a species depends on
two things : (1) their community of descent, (2) the fact
that their common inheritance is not weakened by interbreeding with unlike kinds of animals. At the same time
it must not be overlooked that upon the average, two
members of a species differ in more respects than two
children of one parent.

Although the things that are denoted in Biology by the term
" species " are natural entities, the term is hard to define. A species
is a group of individuals which (*a*) have in common morphological
or physiological features (and usually both) which they do not share
as a whole with other groups, (*b*) are fully fertile *inter se*, (*c*) do not
produce fully fertile offspring and usually produce none, with individuals outside the group. Two groups, each possessing the
requisite resemblances *inter se* and fertile *inter se*, may normally
have the third requirement for specific distinctness—that they do
not breed together—but be capable in certain circumstances
(*e.g.* in captivity) of breeding together to produce fully fertile offspring.
In such a case, the lack of interbreeding may be due to one of several
causes—to difference of breeding seasons, to psychological factors,
to ecological, or to purely geographical separation. Whether two
such forms are to be regarded as distinct species or as subspecies of
a single species depends upon the judgment of systematists, which
will usually be based on the degree of difference between them.

Species are grouped together by zoologists into divisions of a higher grade known as *genera*. A genus **Higher Groups.** consists of several species which resemble one another closely, but its limits are determined by convenience only, and are not natural, like those of a species. To every species there is assigned a Latin name consisting of two words, of which the first denotes the genus to which the species belongs, while the second is peculiar to the species. Thus the generic name of the rabbits and hares is *Lepus*, the specific name of the rabbit is *cuniculus*, the common hare is *Lepus timidus*, the mountain hare *L. variabilis*. The names of the species of *Astacus*, *Hydra* and *Entamœba* have already been given. The Latin names of many species are arbitrary, and some are even misleading, but they have the advantage of providing a generally recognised, international nomenclature. In the foregoing pages the Latin name of each species has been given. Above the genus are many divisions of the same nature, but higher rank. Genera are grouped into *families*, these into *orders*, orders into *classes*, classes into *phyla*, and in many cases it has been found necessary to institute additional grades of division, such as subclasses, subphyla, etc. The systematic position of the frog will serve as an instance of this arrangement. The frog is the Species *R. temporaria*, of the Genus *Rana*, Family *Ranidæ*, Order *Anura*, Class *Amphibia*, Subphylum *Vertebrata*, Phylum *Chordata*, Grade *Triploblastica*, and Subkingdom *Metazoa*. The following Table shows the main lines of the classification of the animal kingdom :—

I. Subkingdom PROTOZOA.

> Animals whose bodies have not a cellular structure.

> Contains only the :

Phylum PROTOZOA.

a. Class MASTIGOPHORA.

> Protozoa which move by means of flagella.

>> e.g. *Chlamydomonas, Polytoma, Euglena, Peramena, Copromonas, Trypanosoma, the Choano-flagellata.*

b. Class SARCODINA.

Protozoa which move by means of pseudopodia.

e.g. *Amœba, Entamœba, Pelomyxa.*

c. Class CILIATA.

Protozoa which move by means of cilia and have usually nuclei of two kinds.

e.g. *Opalina, Paramecium, Balantidium, Nyctotherus, Vorticella, Carchesium.*

d. Class SPOROZOA.

Protozoa, usually with no external organs of locomotion, which are always internal parasites and form numerous spores.

e.g. *Monocystis, Plasmodium.*

II. Subkingdom PARAZOA.

Animals whose bodies are composed of semi-independent cells, some of which are choano-cytes.   Contains only the :

Phylum PORIFERA.

e.g. *Sycon, Leucilla, Euspongia.*

III. Subkingdom METAZOA.

Animals whose bodies contain specialised and subordinate cells, none of which are choano-cytes.

A. Grade DIPLOBLASTICA.

Metazoa in whose bodies there are only two protoplasmic layers, ectoderm and endo-derm.   Contains only the :

Phylum CŒLENTERATA.

Radially symmetrical, diploblastic animals. The most important members of this group are :

Class HYDROZOA.

Polyps and medusæ with ectodermal gonads and no vertical partitions in the enteron.

e.g. *Hydra, Obelia.*

Class SCYPHOZOA (ACALEPHÆ).

Medusæ with endodermal gonads and with vertical partitions in the enteron of the polyp stage when the latter exists.

e.g. *Aurelia.*

Class ANTHOZOA.

Polyps without a medusoid generation and with endodermal gonads, a gullet, and vertical partitions in the enteron.

Here belong Sea Anemones and Corals.

B. Grade TRIPLOBLASTICA.

Metazoa in whose bodies a third layer, the mesoderm, lies between ectoderm and endoderm and usually contains spaces known as the hæmocœle and cœlom.

1. Phylum PLATYHELMINTHES.

Flat, worm-like Triploblastica without anus, blood vessels, or (in the adult at least) body cavity, with an excretory system formed of branched tubes ending in flame cells, and with a complicated, usually hermaphrodite system of reproductive organs.

a. Class TURBELLARIA.

Free-living, ciliated Platyhelminthes.

e.g. *Planaria.*

b. Class TREMATODA.

Parasitic Platyhelminthes with a cuticle, a forked gut, and no proglottides.

e.g. *Distomum, Schistosoma.*

c. Class CESTODA.

Parasitic Platyhelminthes with a cuticle, no gut, and proglottides which break off from the body.

e.g. *Tænia.*

2. Phylum NEMATODA.

Bilaterally symmetrical, unsegmented Triplo-blastica, with an anus, an intracellular body cavity, a stout cuticle, and no limbs.

e.g. *Anguillula, Tylenchus, Filaria, Trichinella, Ascaris, Oxyuris*, etc.

The following phyla and others which possess a cœlom are known as CŒLOMATA.

3. Phylum ANNELIDA.

Bilaterally symmetrical, segmented Triplo-blastica, with a closed blood-vascular system, a well-developed cœlom, nephridia, a double ventral nerve cord, parting in front to enclose the gut, and a thin cuticle.

a. Class OLIGOCHÆTA.

Annelida without parapodia, with chætæ.

e.g. *Lumbricus.*

b. Class POLYCHÆTA.

Annelida with parapodia and numerous chætæ.

e.g. *Nereis, Arenicola.*

c. Class HIRUDINEA.

Annelida without parapodia or chætæ, with two suckers, and with canalicular cœlom.

e.g. *Hirudo.*

4. Phylum ARTHROPODA.

Bilaterally symmetrical, segmented Triplo-blastica, with an open blood-vascular system, a very restricted cœlom, a double ventral nerve cord parting in front to enclose the gut, a thick cuticle, and paired jointed limbs, some of which serve as jaws.

a. Class CRUSTACEA.

Aquatic Arthropoda, with two pairs of antennæ, and usually with gills.

e.g. *Astacus, Cyclops.*

b. Class HEXAPODA or INSECTA.

> Land Arthropoda without gills, but with internal air tubes for breathing, with one pair of antennæ, three pairs of legs, and usually two pairs of wings.

> The characteristic features of the following groups of insects and examples of their members are given in Chapter XVI.

>> Sub-class AMETABOLA (APTERYGOTA).
>> Sub-class HETEROMETABOLA.
>>> Orders : ORTHOPTERA, ODONATA, HEMIPTERA.
>> Sub-class HOLOMETABOLA.
>>> Orders : COLEOPTERA, HYMENOPTERA, DIPTERA, APHANIPTERA, LEPIDOPTERA.

c. Class MYRIAPODA.

> Land Arthropoda without gills but with internal air tubes, with one pair of antennæ, numerous pairs of legs, and no wings.

> Centipedes and Millipedes.

d. Class ARACHNIDA.

> For the most part land Arthropoda without gills, but with internal air spaces ; and all without antennæ and with four pairs of legs.

i. Order SCORPIONIDA.

> Arachnida with segmented abdomen, bearing a poison sting in the telson, chelate pedipalpi, lung-books, and no spinnerets.

> Scorpions.

ii. Order ARANEIDA.

> Arachnida with unsegmented abdomen, poison glands in the cheliceræ, pedipalpi not chelate, lung-books and spinnerets.

>> e.g. *Epeira, Tegenaria* (the House Spider).

iii. Order ACARINA.

> Arachnida with unsegmented abdomen, pedipalpi not chelate, and no lung-books or spinnerets.

>> e.g. *Demodex, Sarcoptes, Ixodes.*

5. Phylum MOLLUSCA.

> Bilaterally symmetrical, unsegmented Triploblastica with an open blood-vascular system, a perivisceral cœlom of moderate size, a nervous system which encircles the forepart of the gut, a shell, but no cuticle, a mantle fold, and a ventral, muscular foot.

a. Class LAMELLIBRANCHIATA.

> Mollusca with bivalve shell, compressed body and foot, plate-like gills, and no head or radula.
>
> > e.g. *Anodonta.*

b. Class GASTROPODA.

> Mollusca with shell, if present, in one piece, depressed body, twisted visceral hump, flat-soled foot, feather- or comb-like gills, a head, and a radula.
>
> > e.g. *Helix, Buccinum* (a whelk).

c. Class CEPHALOPODA.

> Mollusca with shell usually internal or absent, if present always in one piece, body appressed from before backwards, foot converted into a funnel and tentacles round the mouth, feather-like gills, a head, and a radula.
>
> > e.g. *Octopus, Sepia, Nautilus.*

6. Phylum ECHINODERMATA.

> Radially symmetrical, marine Triploblastica without true blood vessels, with a spacious, complicated cœlom, and with calcareous plates in the dermis.
>
> > *Asterias*, Sea-urchins, Sea-lilies, etc.

7. Phylum CHORDATA.

> Bilaterally symmetrical, usually segmented Triploblastica, with a closed blood-vascular system, a spacious cœlom, a hollow, dorsal central nervous system, a notochord, and gill-clefts (visceral clefts).

A. Subphylum CEPHALOCHORDA.

Chordata with a notochord which runs from end to end of the body and lasts throughout life, an atrium, and very numerous gill-clefts provided with tongue-bars ; without definite brain, and without heart, limbs, or skeleton of bone or cartilage.

e.g. *Amphioxus.*

B. Subphylum VERTEBRATA.

Chordata in which the notochord does not reach the front of the head and is usually reduced or lost in the adult, without atrium, with few visceral clefts, which are without tongue-bars and are often lost in the adult ; with well-developed brain, heart, usually two pairs of limbs, and always an internal skeleton of bone or cartilage.

a. Division CYCLOSTOMATA.

Vertebrata without jaws, whose hypophysis retains its opening.

e.g. *Petromyzon.*

β. Division GNATHOSTOMATA.

Vertebrata with jaws, whose hypophysial opening closes.

a. Class PISCES.

Cold-blooded Gnathostomata with paired fins, bony scales, rays in the median fins, persistent gill-clefts, and no lungs, amnion, or allantois.

i. Subclass APHETOHYOIDEA.

Extinct fishes in which the mandibulo-hyoid cleft was not reduced, the jaws were autostylic, and the skeleton contained bone.

ii. Sub-class ELASMOBRANCHII.

Cartilaginous fishes with reduced mandibulo-hyoid cleft, without an air-bladder.

e.g. *Scyllium, Raia.*

iii. Sub-class ACTINOPTERYGII.

Fishes with reduced mandibulo-hyoid cleft, bone in the skeleton, an air-bladder not used as a lung, and no internal nares.

(1) " Ganoid " Orders (p. 466).

(2) Order TELEOSTEI.

Actinopterygii without spiracle, spiral valve, cloaca, or conus arteriosus.

e.g. *Salmo, Gadus, Pleuronectes,* and most fishes.

iv. Sub-class CHOANICHTHYES.

Fishes with reduced mandibulo-hyoid cleft, bone in the skeleton, internal nares, and air-bladders used as lungs.

(1) Order CROSSOPTERYGII.

Choanichthyes with normal upper jaw and separate teeth on jaw margins.

(2) Order DIPNOI.

Choanichthyes with strong crushing bite owing to fusion of upper jaw bar with cranium and union of teeth into compound structures on the palate.

e.g. *Lepidosiren.*

b. Class AMPHIBIA.

Cold-blooded Vertebrata with pentadactyle limbs, usually no scales, no rays in median fins, lungs, shell-less eggs, no amnion or allantois, and a tadpole larva with gill-clefts which are usually lost in the adult.

i. Order STEGOCEPHALI.

Extinct amphibians, with a complete covering of dermal bones on the skull and often a dermal armour on the body.

e.g. *Capitosaurus.*

ii. Order GYMNOPHIONA.

> Amphibians of worm-like habits, without girdles, limbs, or tail, and with rings of small scales in the dermis.
>
> > e.g. *Cæcilia.*

iii. Order URODELA.

> Amphibians with girdles and usually short limbs, with tail and no exoskeleton.
>
> > e.g. *Molge, Salamandra.*

iv. Order ANURA.

> Amphibians with stout bodies, long legs, no tail, and no exoskeleton.
>
> > e.g. *Rana.*

c. Class REPTILIA.

> Cold-blooded Vertebrata with pentadactyle limbs, horny scales, no median fins, lungs, large, heavily yolked eggs laid in calcareous shells, no larva, an amnion and an allantois in the embryo, and the visceral clefts never provided with gills.

> The characteristic features of the following Orders of Reptilia and examples of their members are given in Chapter XXIV.

> LACERTILIA, OPHIDIA, CHELONIA, CROCODILIA, RHYNCHOCEPHALIA.

d. Class AVES.

> Warm-blooded Vertebrata with pentadactyle limbs, of which the first pair are wings, feathers, horny scales on the legs, no median fins, lungs, large, heavily-yolked eggs laid in calcareous shells, no larva, an amnion and an allantois in the embryo, and the visceral clefts never provided with gills.
>
> > e.g. *Columba.*

e. Class MAMMALIA.

> Warm-blooded Vertebrata with penta-dactyle limbs, hair but no scales, median fins only in some whales, where they have no rays, lungs, eggs almost always minute, developing within the mother, milk-glands, no larva, an amnion and an allantois in the embryo, and the visceral clefts never pro-vided with gills.

> The characteristic features of the following groups of mammals are stated and examples of the members mentioned in Chapter XXV.

   i. Sub-class PROTOTHERIA.
       Order MONOTREMATA.
  ii. Sub-class METATHERIA.
       Order MARSUPIALIA.
 iii. Sub-class EUTHERIA.
       Order CETACEA.
       Order EDENTATA.
       Order SIRENIA.
       Order UNGULATA.
        Sub-order PROBOSCIDEA.
        Sub-order HYRACOIDEA.
        Sub-order ARTIODACTYLA.
         Tribe SUINA.
         Tribe RUMINANTIA.
        Sub-order PERISSODACTYLA.
       Order RODENTIA.
       Order CARNIVORA.
       Order INSECTIVORA.
       Order CHIROPTERA.
       Order PRIMATES.
        Sub-orders: LEMUROIDEA, ANTHROPOIDEA.

CHAPTER XXIX

EVOLUTION

FROM the earliest days of the science two theories have
been current as to the origin of the differences
between the several kinds of animals. One
contented itself with the statement that each species has
come into being independently by a process of *special
creation*, whose method it did not attempt to explain.
The other, which is now held by all zoologists, alleges
that every species has sprung from some other species
that was in existence before it, by a process known as
evolution, which starts from some of the differences
("variations") which exist between parents and their
offspring, and that the differences upon which the zoologist
founds genera and higher groups are due to the unlikeness
between species being increased by the same process. The
theory of evolution may be stated, in the words of Charles
Darwin, as follows : " All the living forms of life are the
lineal descendants of those which lived long before the
Cambrian epoch ; we may feel certain that the ordinary
succession by generation has never once been broken."
Darwin adds : " There is a grandeur in this view . . . that,
from so simple a beginning, endless forms most beautiful
and most wonderful have been evolved." Evolution is an
alteration of the average characters, either of the whole of
a species or of a certain group of its members, from generation to generation in a constant manner, by which they
become so different from what they were at first that a new
species arises. If it take place only in a group of the
members of a species, the other members continuing to
propagate their kind unchanged, or if it proceed in different

Evolution.

Charles Darwin.

Born 1809, died 1882.

[Fig. 517.]

directions in several groups at the same time, and be attended by infertility between the groups, then the number of species will be increased. The dying out of a species, which sooner or later practically always happens, removes the link which unites any descendant species it may have had, both to one another and to the ancestral species from which the parent species was itself descended. Thus the existing species of living beings are like the live tips of the branches of a tree which is being killed from the root upwards. The general tendency of evolution is to increase complexity of organisation, that is, to produce higher organisms from lower ones, though sometimes, notably in the production of parasites, it brings about simplification.

The theory of evolution is based upon several classes of evidence. (1) It is supported by the facts upon which *classification* is based. Species, genera, families, orders, etc., are like the branches of a genealogical tree, and when they are arranged as such suggest strongly that they have arisen by modification, each from the preceding grade. By the alteration in different directions of groups of members of a single species, the several species of a genus would arise. As each of these pursued its own line of evolution it would become more unlike its congeners until it reached the rank of a genus, by which time it would generally have given rise to species of its own, and so forth. Every attempt to classify animals results in an arrangement which to some extent suggests the evolution of its members, but in modern zoology classifications are expressly so constructed as to show what are believed to have been the lines of evolution which animals have followed. Each of the groups of such a classification represents an original species, from which all the sub-divisions of the group are supposed to have arisen by descent with modification in various directions. As an illustration of this, the several groups of the classification of the Mammalia given in Chapter XXV. may be arranged in the form of a genealogical tree as in Fig. 518.

Evidences of Evolution : Classification.

(2) The facts of *morphology* also support the theory of evolution. In our survey of a series of types of animals

44

we have seen how organs which serve different functions
Morphology.   are often built upon the same general plan,
which is modified in different directions in
the several instances. Thus the fore limbs of a frog, a
rabbit, a man, a horse, a whale, and a bird are all built

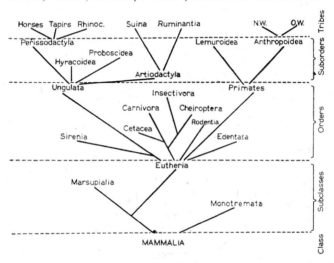

FIG. 518.—The classification of the Mammalia arranged in the form
of a genealogical tree. The Ungulata are arranged according
to the usual, but rather old-fashioned, classification adopted in
the text (p. 575). It would be more correct to make the artio-
dactyle branch start from the base of that which bears the Carnivora. The Sirenia should be nearer to the Proboscidea. N.W.
and O.W. in the top line stand for the New-world and Old-world
groups of monkeys.

upon the pentadactyle plan (p. 49), though the parts are
of different shapes in the several cases, and certain of the
bones may be missing or fused. It is difficult to find any
satisfactory explanation of this except the evolution of
the animals in question from a common ancestor whose
fore limbs were of the type which they share. Organs
which are believed thus to have arisen by modification

of identical organs in an ancestral animal are said to be *homologous*.[1] Thus the wings of a bird and a bat are homologous with one another and with the hands of a man and the paddles of a whale. Organs which have

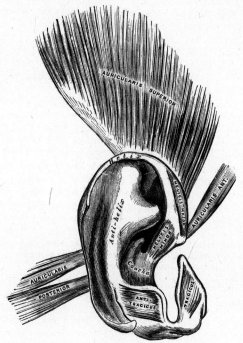

FIG. 519.—A dissection of the human ear to show the useless vestigial muscles.—From Gray.

the same function, but have arisen independently, are called *analogous*. The wings of a bird and an insect or

---

[1] The term is extended to include the case of members of a series in one individual, such as the nephridia of an earthworm or the legs of a cockroach, which are said to be *serially homologous* because they are built upon the same plan, so that the repetition of structure which is seen in them appears to be of the same nature as the repetition of the structure of an ancestor in its descendants.

the legs of a rabbit and a crayfish are analogous, since they perform similar functions but are built upon radically different plans. In the same class of evidence we may place the existence of *vestigial organs*, such as the remains of the pelvic girdle of whales, and the tail-bones and ear muscles (Figs. 449, 519) of man, which can only be satisfactorily explained on the supposition that they were functional in an ancestor.

(3) The facts of *embryology* suggest evolution. We have seen that different animals pass through **Embryology.** similar stages, and that animals which are more alike resemble one another longer during development. All animals have at one stage a single nucleus for all purposes, all Metazoa have at a later stage two layers only, all Vertebrata at a still later stage have visceral clefts and a notochord, all mammals at a later stage yet are five-fingered, and so forth (see p. 668). The simplest explanation of these facts is that it is due to the repetition during the development of an animal of characters which appeared during the development of its ancestors, the varying duration of resemblance during development being due to various degrees of relationship by descent.

This explanation of von Baer's Law was formerly known as the *theory of recapitulation*, in the belief, now discarded, that development directly represents *adults* at successive stages in the history of the race. They may, however, be inferred from it.

(4) The facts of *the distribution of animals* are yet another support for the theory of evolution. **Zoogeography.** It is found that the animal populations or *faunas* of various parts of the world differ, even when they inhabit regions in which the conditions of life are so similar that animals native in one will flourish if they be introduced into the other ; and that the difference between local faunas increases with their inaccessibility from one another and with the length of time during which the regions have been separated. For instance, between the fauna of Great Britain and that of the adjoining parts of Europe the differences, though they exist, are very slight, but distant New Zealand, though British animals and plants will flourish there, has a very different fauna ; it has no snakes, only two bats and a frog represent

mammals and amphibia, it has a number of peculiar
flightless birds (Moa, Kiwi, Ground Parrot, etc.) of various
families, and in fishes, insects, molluscs, worms, etc., it
lacks groups that are common in Britain and possesses
others that are not represented here.   Again, while the
fauna of Borneo resembles closely that of the adjacent parts
of Asia, 350 miles away, Madagascar, an older island, has a
fauna which differs greatly from that of Africa, only 250
miles distant.   It lacks the great mammals of Africa—
apes, lions, zebras, rhinoceroses, elephants, giraffes, etc.—
and most rodents, and has many peculiar lemurs, reptiles,
and birds.   Only by evolution can this connection between

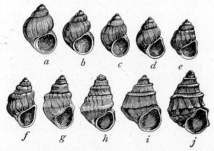

FIG. 520. — The gradual transition between *Paludina neumayri*
(*a*), the oldest form, and *Paludina hœrnesi* (*j*).—From
Neumayr.

isolation and peculiarity of fauna be explained.   It must
be due to the fauna of each district having had an evolutionary history different from those of the others.   The
chief cause of this difference is held to be that the faunas
have lived under different conditions.   However alike the
physical conditions may be in two districts, they are
never identical, and often they have been more dissimilar
in past times ;   moreover, unless the faunas and floras of
two districts were at one time identical, which will seldom
have happened, each member of either fauna will also
have an organic environment—enemies, food organisms,
and competitors—peculiar to its district.   The longer the
separation has lasted, the greater will be the evolutionary

divergence of the faunas. The more inaccessible the districts have been from one another the more opportunity there has been for any organism that may have reached one from the other, or both from a third, to be modified on the way by evolution.

(5) The facts of *palæozoology* (or the geological history **Palæozoology.** of animals) are also in favour of evolution.

It is clear that this is the only direction in which we could look for a complete *proof* of the theory, since all

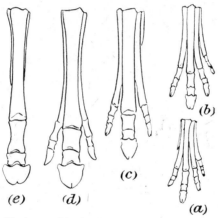

FIG. 521.—The bones of the forefoot of a horse compared with those of earlier members of its family.—From Swinnerton.

(a) *Eohippus* (*Hyracotherium*) (Lower Eocene); (b) *Orohippus* (Middle Eocene); (c) *Mesohippus* (Lower Oligocene); (d) *Hypohippus* (Lower Pliocene); (e) *Equus* (Upper Pliocene to Present).

the other evidence does no more than enable us to infer past history from present facts. Unfortunately, owing to what is known as the *imperfection of the geological record*, such complete proof is impossible. The unsuitability of the bodies of many animals for preservation, owing to the absence of hard parts, the destruction, during the history of the earth, of immense layers of rocks, and the small proportion of those which remain that can be examined, bring this about. But it is established that throughout geological history, there is a continual change in the types of animal life, leading up to those that exist at the present day, and in a few rare cases, particularly among Mollusca (Fig. 520), it is possible to trace fully the evolution of species, while in others, such as those of horses (Fig. 521) and of elephants, the origin of higher groups can be followed in the appearance of successive genera.

The horses are a classical case of the tracing of the evolution of a group of animals by means of fossils. Starting in Eocene times with *Hyracotherium (Eohippus)* of the size and proportions of a fox terrier, with four toes on the fore feet and three on the hind, and knobbed (bunodont) teeth, there is known, from successive strata a series of creatures which became larger and, owing to the lengthening of the feet, relatively taller, while their side toes dwindled to splints and the knobs on their teeth became grinding ridges with cement between them. Finally, in the Pleistocene, modern horses appeared. The fossils are the remains, not of actual forbears and descendants, but of animals whose features lead to the conclusion that each is a little off this direct line of descent. This evolution went on during, and was no doubt brought about by, a change in foothold and in food, due to upheaval of the land, in which marshy and forest conditions with succulent vegetation gave place to plains with firmer surface and harsher herbage.

Even where, as is generally the case, great gaps exist in our knowledge of the history of groups of animals, there are sometimes known fossils which enable us in theory to bridge the gulf. Such a case is that of *Archæopteryx* (p. 516), pointing backwards from birds to reptiles. We have traced in Chapter XXII. the history of the gradual adaptation of vertebrate animals to life on land.

Though zoologists have long been satisfied that evolution takes place, there has been, and still is, much conflict of opinion as to how it is brought about. To solve this problem it is necessary to know (1) how heritable differences between related organisms arise, and (2) how such differences increase, so that species and higher groups come into being. To answer the first of these questions, we must now take note of certain principles of heredity known as *Mendelism* after their discoverer, Gregor Mendel, Abbot of Brünn, who published them in 1866.

The Mode of Evolution : Heredity.

We have already seen (p. 598) that, in many cases, when two individuals between which there is a heritable difference

Gregor Mendel, Abbot of Brunn.
Born 1822, died 1884.

[FIG. 522.]

in any respect breed together, their peculiarities in this respect do not blend, but the peculiarity of one parent is " dominant " in the offspring, while that of the other is latent or " recessive." For instance, the offspring of a wild grey rabbit and one of the black variety are all grey. Thus the dominant variety remains distinct and is not weakened by crossing. If, however, the offspring of such a cross be bred together, it will be found that the recessive variety has also not been extinguished, for on the average a quarter of the generation will throw back to the recessive grandparent (in this case, the black rabbit). Further, when the peculiarities of parents in respect of any feature do blend in the first generation, it is found that, of a second generation produced by inbreeding between the brothers and sisters, only half the members exhibit the blended feature, while a quarter throw back pure to each of the grandparents. Thus it comes about that both varieties remain unimpaired within the species. This separating out of a pair of contrasted characters is known as *segregation.*

In the following genealogical table G represents the wild (pure or " homozygote ") grey rabbit, B the black, and (G) the cross-bred (" heterozygote ") grey, and, in order to represent the results of various kinds of matings, it is supposed that in the second generation a brother and sister breed together, and in the third there is one union of brother and sister and two with homozygote members of other stocks.

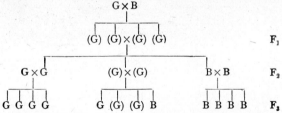

If the case had been one in which the tendencies inherited from the two parents blended their effects, instead of either of them dominating the other, it could be represented by the same table, but then (G) would stand for an individual of a colour which arose from the blending of those of the parents. Fig. 523 shows such a case.

These facts are explained as follows. Each germ, as
Mendelism. we have seen, contains in its set of chromosomes all the factors [1] that are necessary to
bring about the development of an individual of its species.
These factors are known as *genes*, and the presence of

FIG. 523.— To illustrate the results of crossing two pure-bred (homozygote) races of Andalusian fowls.—From Morgan.

P_1, the parents, one splashed-white and the other black ; F_1, the first hybrid generation, all individuals of which are alike, of a bluish-black shade due to the blending of the colours of the parents ; F_2, the second hybrid generation, bred by
mating F_1 individuals together.   One quarter resembles each of the parents
and the remaining half are like F_1.

[1] In making this statement we ignore for the sake of simplicity,
the facts that the action of the factors in the chromosomes depends
upon the qualities of the cytoplasm, and that a few characters appear
to be inherited through factors in the latter.

each of them is known by the appearance in the individual of some character which it evokes. Thus the grey and black colours of rabbits are due to a pair of genes (or, as it is sometimes said, two forms of a gene).[1] For each character, syngamy has given the individual two genes. If they were alike the zygote they formed is called a *homozygote* and develops the character they both bore. If they were unlike the zygote is called a *heterozygote* and one gene usually dominates over the other in the development. At the reduction division when the zygote forms gametes, the genes again separate, because, it is held, the two members of each of the pairs of genes which are alike in the homozygote and unlike in the heterozygote are carried one member in each of a pair of homologous chromosomes and these separate at the reduction division to go into different germs. In regard to the character in question, the gametes of a homozygote will all be alike, those of a heterozygote will be unlike, consisting of equal numbers of both kinds. When heterozygotes breed together, on the average half the offspring will be formed by the union of unlike germs—that is, will be heterozygotes like their parents. Half the remainder will be homozygotes formed by the union of gametes bearing the dominant gene ; half will be homozygotes formed by the union of those bearing the recessive gene. All the dominant homozygotes and all the heterozygotes will develop the dominant character. All the recessive homozygotes will develop the recessive character. Thus three-quarters of the offspring will have the dominant character, one-quarter the recessive character. The recessives, if bred with recessives, will all breed true. Of the seeming dominants only one-third—those which are pure dominants—will breed true ; the rest—the heterozygotes—will on inbreeding continue to throw one-quarter of pure recessives.

The members of a pair of characters which behave in a Mendelian way on crossing are known as *allelomorphs*. Parents may differ in

---

[1] The term gene is rather loosely used, to mean *either* an entity which exists (in one form or another) at the same locus in the same member of every chromosome set of a species, *or* the particular case of such an entity which exists at the locus in question in an individual chromosome.

respect of a number of such pairs, each inherited separately. The constitution of their offspring (that is, the average constitution of the offspring of a number of similar matings) can then be calculated from the facts we have learnt. Thus when parents are crossed which differ in two pairs of allelomorphs the hybrids of the first generation (F_1) will all be alike, exhibiting the dominant character of each of the two pairs, while the generation (F_2) produced by mating such hybrids consists on the average of nine which show both dominants to three which show one dominant and one recessive, three which show the other dominant and the other recessive, and one which shows both recessives. We may represent these results as follows : writing A and B for the genes which are dominant and *a* and *b* for their recessives,

Gametes AB × *ab* give the heterozygote AB*ab*

The gametes of the heterozygote will be, in equal numbers,

AB, A*b*, *a*B, and *ab*.

The zygotes from such gametes should be in equal numbers of the following sixteen combinations :

ABAB	ABA*b*	AB*a*B	AB*ab*
A*b*AB	A*b*A*b*	A*ba*B	A*bab*
*a*BAB	*a*BA*b*	*a*B*a*B	*a*B*ab*
*ab*AB	*ab*A*b*	*aba*B	*abab*

It will be seen that nine of these contain both dominants, three have each of the dominants alone, and one has neither.

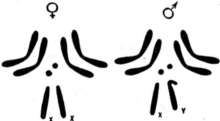

Fig. 524.—The chromosomes of the body cells of Fruit Flies (*Drosophila*).—After Morgan and others. Here there are only eight chromosomes, and the members of each of the pairs which separate at the reduction division can be recognised by their shapes and sizes.

♀, The chromosomes of the female ; ♂, those of the male ; *X*, x-chromosomes ; *Y*, a chromosome which forms a pair with the single x-chromosome of the male, but is distinguishable from the latter by having a hooked end.

One more case must be considered. In a cross between parents of which one is a heterozygote in respect of a given character and the other a recessive homozygote for the same character, the off-spring will be divided equally between the dominant and recessive allelomorphs, as the following diagram shows :

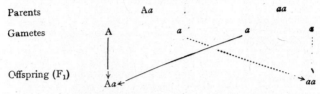

Parents	A*a*		*aa*

Gametes   A   *a*   *a*   *a*

Offspring (F₁)   A*a*   *aa*

That is, two kinds of individuals, breeding together, produce, on the average, equal numbers of each. Now this is what **Sex a Mendellian Character.** usually happens in respect of sex, and the inference that sex is a Mendelian character has been justified by research, though the case proves not to be so simple as that which has just been stated. The probable explanation of the facts is as follows. One sex is a homozygote and the other a heterozygote in respect of a factor which in double dose (the homozygote) confers sex of one kind, but in single dose (the hetero-zygote) is ineffective ; and in the latter case the individual is of the opposite sex.[1] The heterozygous sex is sometimes (Birds, Lepidoptera) the female, sometimes (other insects, mammals) the male. The chromosomes which carry the sex-factor in question (x-chromo-somes) can often be distinguished, and then it is found that two are of that kind in the cells of the homozygote sex and only one in those of the heterozygous, and that accordingly the gametes of the homo-zygote have each an x-chromosome, while only half of those of the heterozygote possess one. If *a* be taken to represent an x-chromo-some, and *A* the absence of one, the above diagram represents these facts.

From considerations into which we cannot enter here, it appears that the genes have each a definite position in a chromo-**Genes.** some and are there arranged in linear order, the genes for allelomorphs standing in the same position in homologous chromo-somes. Characters whose genes are in the same chromosome will usually be inherited together—thus in *Drosophila* black colour and curved wings are generally found in the same individual. This connection is known as *linkage*. Owing to crossing over it is not invariable. What the nature of genes may be is unknown, but it is clear that their action is dependent upon circumstances. The pre-sence of one of them is often betrayed by the existence of a particular character in the organism, but its production of this character is dependent (*a*) upon external conditions—for instance, pigmentation is in some cases only effected by the gene concerned if the temperature

---

[1] By the action, probably, of an independent factor, which is present in all individuals, but is countervailed by the double dose of the sex-factor of the homozygote just mentioned.

be favourable—(*b*) upon interaction with other genes. The genes in any organism make up a *gene complex* in which they react with one another to produce the characters of the organism. The effect of each gene depends upon the presence of several others, and each gene affects other processes than the production of the conspicuous character (if any) by which its presence is recognised. Thus a gene which gives white eyes in *Drosophila* also changes the colours of the testis sheath and the shape of the spermatheca.

Mutation.

The mechanism of heredity being what it is, heritable differences between related organisms can only arise by the origin of new genes or the re-combination of existing ones. The origin of new genes is known as *mutation*. It is due to a change occurring in a chromosome at the site of a pre-existing gene. For instance, in a race of water fleas which had been found to thrive best at a temperature of 20° C. and to die at 26° C., there suddenly arose by a change of this kind a strain which flourished best at 27° C. and died if the temperature fell to 20° C., in the same way, there appeared in the Fruit Fly *Drosophila melanogaster* individuals of a black colour instead of the ordinary grey. Though mutations have chiefly been studied in laboratories it is known that they occur in wild nature. Mutations may have obvious and considerable effects, or be so small as to be detectable only by close examination. At their first appearance they are usually recessive and also deleterious, by disturbing the gene-complex and so weakening the constitution and sometimes by altering the relation between the animal and its environment—making it, for instance, conspicuous, or weakening its defence. It seems, however, that an unfavourable mutation usually becomes recessive and a favourable one dominant. Probably this is due to the effect on the gene-complex of selection (see below). The larger the mutation the more likely it is to be harmful. It is believed that evolution usually takes place by the accumulation of small, favourable mutations. How mutations arise is not known. It has been supposed that alterations brought about in the body of an individual by circumstances (" acquired characters ") affect the germ cells so as to be inherited—that is, cause mutation—but this, as we shall see, has never been proved to occur. It has been supposed that the germ cells have an inherent tendency to mutate (and that, according to some authorities, continuously in certain directions) but this also has not been proved. Experiments have shown that mutations may arise in consequence of the influence of external factors upon the germ cells : thus by the effect of x-rays heritable modifications have been brought about in fruit flies ; but there is no evidence that any of the agencies so used in the laboratory are the normal ones in nature.

Recombination of genes takes place in two ways—by the union of different sets of chromosomes in sexual reproduction, and by the exchange of genes between chromosomes of different sets through crossing over at meiosis. It does not produce such novelties as mutation does, but it reassorts them, making new combinations of characters—as between colour and length of hair. Moreover, by altering the gene complex it alters the effects of individual genes, one gene, for instance, increasing or diminishing the effect of another—as by deepening or enlarging patches of colour. Any of these effects may be valuable or detrimental to the animal, and the existence of the species will accordingly be affected by the persistence in it of certain combinations of genes. Generally speaking the plasticity of feature which recombination gives is valuable in providing an assortment of kinds of individuals to meet the vicissitudes of the environment.

Recombination.

For the second part of the problem of evolution—how heritable differences between individuals are increased, so that species result and diverge until genera and higher groups appear—various solutions have been propounded. They are of three kinds. One of these supposes that the modifications which arise in each individual in the course of its life, by the action of its surroundings upon it, by its activity in response to the stimuli it receives from its surroundings or by the dwindling of certain of its organs from lack of use, are inherited in some degree by its offspring, and that the accumulation of such small modifications produces at length a different kind of animal. Thus, since it is known that one effect of cold upon a mammal is to increase the growth of its hair, the

Theories of Evolution : Lamarckism.

Jean-Baptiste de Lamarck.

Born 1744, died 1829.

[Fig. 525.]

long fur of species which live in cold countries might be supposed to be due to the inherited effect of the climate. Again, the effect of use upon muscles is to increase their size, and in this way the great size of the wing muscles of birds of strong flight might be supposed to have been brought about in the course of many generations. On the other hand, the dwindling which is undoubtedly caused in the organs of individuals by disuse might in time bring about permanent degeneration, such, for instance, as that which is found in the eyes of animals which live in dark caves. This hypothesis is known as the *Lamarckian theory*, from the name of its greatest exponent. It is rejected by most zoologists at the present day on account of the lack of satisfactory evidence that modifications which are produced in the course of the life of an individual are transmitted by it to its offspring. Such modifications are known as *acquired characters* and over the question of their inheritance discussion is still rife. The obstacles to belief in their transmissibility lie not only in the fact that numerous experiments and observations have hitherto failed to prove such transmission but also in the difficulty of conceiving any way in which modifications in other parts of the body can so affect the germ-cells as to be handed on to the offspring.

Many experiments have been made upon this point. In most of them the "acquired" character, whether produced crudely, as by cutting off the tails of mice, or more naturally, as the effects of altered nutrition upon the shells of water-fleas, is not inherited. There are some of which the result has been claimed to prove the inheritance of such a character, but all these are, for one reason or another, inconclusive.

Another hypothesis as to the way in which evolution is **Darwinism.** brought about is the *theory of natural selection*, known as *Darwinism* after the great naturalist by whom it was formulated. It supposes that the transformation of species is caused by a greater destruction by adverse circumstances of certain kinds of individuals in each generation before they can breed.[1] The result of

[1] Of course the eliminated individuals would not always be killed before they could breed. In some cases the reproductive period would merely be cut short so that the number of offspring was lessened.

OXFORD-DOWN
RAM.

HIGHLAND RAM.

COTSWOLD.

CHEVIOT RAM

LINCOLN RAM.

N.S.H.

FIG. 526.—British breeds of sheep.

Showing various races established by breeding from selected individuals.

this will be that the peculiar features of these individuals are inherited by fewer of the next generation and therefore gradually cease to appear in the species, or in that group of its members which has been subjected to the circumstances in question. Thus in a cold country those members of a species of mammals which had not thick fur would be more liable to die of cold or be so enfeebled that they could not compete with the rest for food or mates, or in a herd of wild horses pursued by wolves the slowest would be killed, so that the next generation would be descended from those members of the species which were best clad or swiftest, as the case might be, and would of course inherit their peculiarities. The result of this process would be the selection by Nature of certain individuals to breed, just as a breeder selects sheep with thick wool or without horns, or rabbits with long ears or fur, and, breeding from these in preference to the rest, alters his breed of sheep or rabbits. (See Figs. 526 and 393.)

Evolution by natural selection depends upon three factors : variation, the struggle for existence, **Factors in Darwinian Evolution.** and heredity. (1) We have seen that all animals are *variable*. It is true that variations which are produced during the lifetime of the individual by the action of the environment upon it or by its use or disuse of organs are probably not transmitted by it, but, as we have seen, there are other characters which are its birthright, being due to the make-up of the fertilised ovum which produced it, and these are inherited by some or all of its offspring, so that selection of them will affect the next generation. Some species are more variable than others and will therefore offer more scope for selection. Species often appear unable to vary in certain directions—thus roses are never blue—but apart from this variation is at random ; for evolution to take place direction has to be imposed upon it by the sifting action of selection. It is often urged that variations are too small to give an effective advantage in the struggle for existence, but on the one hand they may be of considerable magnitude, and on the other it has been shown that quite a small advantage is in the long run effective (p. 709). (2) The *struggle for existence* involves, not merely reaching a certain standard of fitness to cope with the surroundings, but a competition between individuals, because, while the offspring are always more numerous than the parents, the total number of individuals in the species does not as a rule increase, being already as many as the conditions of food, enemies, etc., will allow. A pair of robins will produce ten or more young in a year, yet, since the number of robins does not increase, only two of these can survive. This is an exceptionally small death-rate. Many animals produce thousands of offspring : the blow-fly, for instance, gives rise to a progeny of 20,000. Now it is impossible to believe that the destruction which this involves is altogether haphazard. Some of the individuals will be feebler, or slower, or less cunning, or less protectively coloured, or less warmly clad than the rest, and it is certain that these will as a rule be the first to be destroyed, and that the survivors will generally be above the average of the previous generation in regard to the characters in which selection has taken place.

The objection that much destruction is indiscriminate, as when spawn is eaten by fishes or minute sea animals by whales, is not valid, since what remains is sufficient in quantity and contains a fair sample of all the varieties for selection.

It should be noted that selection is not only an innovating but also a conservative force. It tends to destroy all new characters that are detrimental to the relation of the species with its environment. Thus it maintains existing species as well as, upon occasion, moulding new ones. It is the lack of selection maintenance that, by non-suppression of degenerative effects of mutation, brings about the degeneration of useless organs, which is sometimes regarded as a difficulty for the theory of natural selection.

(3) The alteration which is thus made in the average characters of the species will be maintained by the action of *heredity*. It has been alleged as an objection to the theory of evolution by natural selection that any large variation in a favourable direction, though it may lead to the survival of the individual in which it occurs, will nearly always be weakened in the next generation by what is known as the " swamping effect of intercrossing." That is to say, the exceptional individual will probably mate with an average member of the species and their offspring will be intermediate between them, and thus in a

few generations the favourable variation will have become so slight as to give no effective advantage in the struggle for existence. This difficulty, however, disappears when it is recognised that characters due to genes may temporarily vanish if the gene be recessive, but are not abolished or weakened.

Another objection which is dispelled by a knowledge of Mendelism is that the numerous variations which are necessary to constitute even a fairly simple organ are unlikely to occur together. Genes can persist in a recessive condition till there occur others in combination with which they give at least a minimally effective rudiment.

Natural Selection at Work. Natural selection has been observed actually in process in certain cases. Thus certain of the insects known as water boatmen (Corixidæ), which resemble in their colouring the background of the pond in which they live and are thus rendered inconspicuous, have been found to be selectively captured for food by fishes, which take a heavier toll of those that are least like their backgrounds. Again, it was observed in America that after a severe storm sparrows whose wings were unusually large or small had been killed in greater numbers than the others. Calculations have been made of the rate at which such selection would alter a species. Obviously this depends upon the number of individuals in which the new character appears and upon its effectiveness in the struggle for existence. It has been shown that a mutation which was a Mendelian dominant, if it appeared in 1 per cent. of the members of a species and gave only a 1 per cent. advantage to its possessor, would after 500 generations be present in half the population, and after 1658 generations be possessed by 99 per cent.

Orthogenesis. In the course of our discussion of natural selection we have dealt with various objections which have been raised against that theory. There remains one of considerable importance. Palæozoology reveals the fact that not only has evolution in many groups of animals proceeded in the same direction for long periods of time (as, for example, it did in horses), but in some such cases its course appears to have been of no advantage to the animals and eventually to have become disadvantageous, thus, for instance, the extinct group of mammals known as *Titanotheres*, as their size increased, evolved disproportionately large and, it is alleged, unwieldy horns ; and in the bivalve mollusc *Gryphæa* the shell curved to one side till it could not open properly. In such cases it is argued, selection cannot have been the directing factor, and it is therefore supposed that mutation in a definite direction was caused by some force in the organism. From this some authorities have proceeded to suppose that a similar force has played a major part in all evolution, with selection as a merely subsidiary limiting factor. Evolution of the kind alleged by this theory is known as *Orthogenesis*. Most zoologists, however, are unwilling to admit the existence of any such mysterious directive force as it involves. Nearly all the facts upon which the theory is based are susceptible of explanations compatible with natural selection (as by the connection of useless with useful characters, by " sexual selection," and so forth) and it is held that similar explanations will be found for the residue.

Selection Overrides. As against either of the theories that suppose evolution to take place by directed mutation—Lamarckism or Orthogenesis—the theory of Natural Selection from among random variations has the advantage that selection would undoubtedly override any directed mutation that can reasonably be supposed to occur. The intrinsic mutation upon whose direction orthogenesis is held to depend takes place at a rate which is insufficient to override selection. It has been shown that a reduction in viability of one-tenth of one per cent. as the result of a mutation would result in adverse selection which would override mutation at the highest rate ever observed in nature ; a mutation which increased viability by 0.1 per cent. would be spread by selection. The heritable changes upon which Lamarckism depends would certainly be similarly overridden, since they must be so small as hitherto to have escaped detection.

CHAPTER XXX

THE ANIMAL IN THE WORLD

OUR survey of zoology is drawing to a close. We began by observing that an animal is an organism and, in general terms, how and to what end its organisation functions. We went on to examine a series of animal organisms and to investigate the modes in which they have come into being both as individuals and as kinds of individuals. It remains for us to survey briefly the relations in which such beings stand to other material things.

Animals as Objects in Nature.

The outstanding fact about an animal, as about a plant, is its relation to its surroundings, or, as they are collectively called, its *environment*. We have seen that its life consists in adjustment to these, in avoiding the dangers and taking advantage of the opportunities which they present. Four principal factors are concerned in this relation—the ground or *substratum*, if any, upon which the organism stands, the *medium* (water or air) which bathes it, the heat and light which it receives from or can lose to its surroundings, and other organisms. Of these factors, the substratum has in most cases comparatively little importance, and we shall not consider it farther.

The Environment.

The medium, on the contrary, is very important. It exerts pressure all over the organism, supports it, may transport it from place to place, affects its movements, and controls all exchange, whether of matter or of energy, between it and the world around it. The medium of the first organisms must have been water : in dry surroundings protoplasm could never

The Medium.

have originated. Water is a factor of the first importance to living beings. Within the organism, it is essential as a constituent of protoplasm, and in higher organisms as a means of internal transport. When it is the medium, it has both advantages and dangers. On the one hand, it is then at hand in plenty, may carry food and other needful substances, inorganic or organic, in solution or suspension, and affords support. On the other hand, according as the concentration of salts in the watery medium be greater or less than that within the organism, water or dissolved substances will tend to pass by osmosis to or from the body, in which their proportions may thus be dangerously altered. It is for this reason, for instance, that marine organisms usually cannot live in fresh waters, and vice versa. We have noted, in several of the animals that we have studied, how when dangers of this kind exist for an animal in its normal environment protection against them is provided by lowered permeability of the surface of the body and by the excretion of water or solids according as one or the other threatens to be in excess. When the medium is air, the animal organism encounters a different set of difficulties. It spends more energy to obtain water and is liable to lose water by evaporation and hence, save in very moist places, needs an even less permeable covering than fresh-water creatures. It can rarely obtain food from the medium, cannot entrust its gametes to the latter and must, therefore, have internal fertilisation, cannot stand up above the substratum without a strong skeleton, must have respiratory organs adapted to the use of the more mobile medium, and, as we have seen (p. 80), has to adopt various chemical expedients to avoid being poisoned by its nitrogenous excreta.

The relations between an animal and other organisms are, of course, not only relations with other **Relations between Organisms.** animals. There are included among organisms many other creatures, of which the best known are the plants, though some cannot rightly be said to belong either to the animal or to the vegetable kingdom. We have already observed the differences between animals and plants and noted that their modes of nutrition differ and are complementary.

The fact must not be overlooked that intermediate organisms are
Organisms intermediate between Animals and Plants. known. These are not such creatures as polyps, which are true animals with the habit of remaining fixed in one spot, or the fungi, which are probably true plants that have lost their chlorophyll and consequently modified their mode of nutrition, so that they require somewhat more complex food materials. The real intermediate organisms are such creatures as *Chlamydomonas* and *Polytoma*, which have the power of locomotion like animals, but possess like plants either chlorophyll or starch or both. They are classed by zoologists as flagellate Protozoa (Mastigophora) and by botanists as Algæ. Their existence is a reminder that, fundamentally, all living beings belong to the same stock.

In this connection must be mentioned the *Bacteria*, which are minute, rod-like or spherical organisms often classified with the plants, but of which it is perhaps more true to say that they are neither plants nor animals, but a third kind of living beings.

Here must also be mentioned some special kinds of metabolism
Special Metabolisms. which differ greatly, though not in principle, from those of ordinary plants and animals. We have already seen (pp. 4, 367) that various organisms, of which *Ascaris* and other internal parasites are examples among animals, and the yeast fungus and many bacteria among plants, are able to live without

FIG. 527.—Bacteria of decay.

a, Bacillus vulgaris, the principal bacterium of decaying flesh;
b, Bacillus subtilis, very common in decaying plant tissues;
c, Bacillus coli, the commonest bacterium of dung.

free oxygen. Such organisms obtain their energy by the decomposition of oxygen-bearing molecules of organic substances. Thus the minute fungi of which yeast consists decompose grape sugar into alcohol and carbon dioxide with the evolution of so much energy in the form of heat that the temperature of the surrounding solution rises. This is the process of fermentation employed in the manufacture of alcoholic liquors, and from it the term *fermentation* has been applied to other processes, such as the souring of milk or wine, and the putrefaction of dead bodies by bacteria (p. 725), in which an organism brings about a change in a mass of matter which is very great compared with that of its own body. It has been shown that in many such cases there is formed by the organism an enzyme (p. 61) which brings about the fermentation without itself being destroyed in the reaction. Such an enzyme has been found in the protoplasm of yeast. Quite a different class of fermentation is found in certain bacteria which obtain energy by the oxidation of inorganic substances, such as sulphuretted hydrogen, sulphur, ferrous salts, and ammonia. The energy is used in building up organic from inorganic substances (*chemosynthesis*), as the energy of the sun's rays is used by green plants in photosynthesis. It is by an oxidation of this class that ammonia compounds derived from the bodies of organisms are converted into nitrates and thus made available for the higher plants (p. 30).

The Balance of Nature. The fundamental difference in nutrition between animals and plants has, as we saw, very important consequences in their relation with the rest of nature and with one another. In their action upon the inorganic world these two kinds of organisms bring about precisely opposite changes, and do so in such a way that each sets up conditions favourable to the activity of the other. Plants provide food and oxygen for animals; while animals, destroying this food, provide for the use of plants carbon dioxide and simple nitrogen compounds (though the latter are usually not available for the use of plants till they have been altered by the action of bacteria in the way mentioned above). The result is a *circulation of carbon and of nitrogen* through the bodies of organisms. It will be seen that this

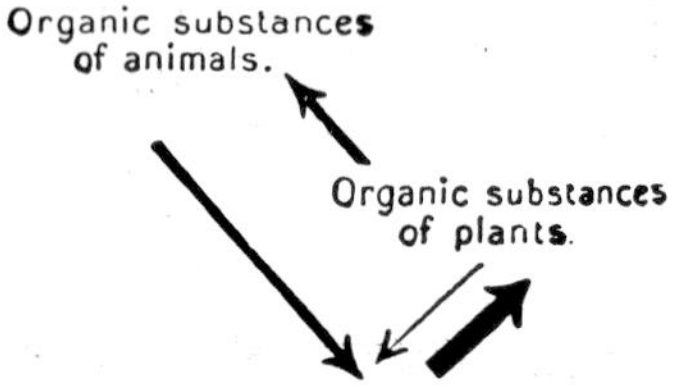

Organic substances of animals.

Organic substances of plants.

FIG. 528.—A diagram of the circulation of matter through the bodies of organisms.

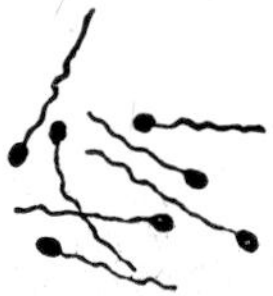

FIG. 529.—*Nitrosomonas*, a bacterium which performs the first stage of the oxidation of ammonia to nitric acid.

circulation of matter is accompanied by a transference of energy. The whole of the energy of the life both of plants and of animals is derived in the long-run from the energy of the sun's rays stored by plants in the complex substances they manufacture. It is stored by plants : most of it is not set free till it reaches the bodies of animals. There is, of course, no circulation of energy. That which is set free from the bodies of organisms is lost to them, and has to be replaced by the fixing of more energy from the sun's rays by plants when they work up the excreta of animals. The whole animal kingdom may be regarded as a vast complex system which, by means infinitely more subtle than those which are possible in the inorganic realm, disposes of the material and energy accumulated by plants.

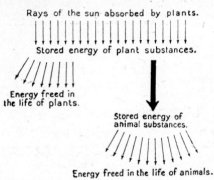

FIG. 530.—A diagram of the energy of organisms.

The relations between the different kinds of animals are almost all based in the long-run upon nutrition. **Relations between Animals based upon Nutrition.** Only between members of opposite sexes of the same species are there relations of another kind, namely those which are based upon reproduction. For the rest, either animals compete for the common supply of food which is derived directly or indirectly from plants, or some of them serve others for food, or in rarer cases they assist one another in the quest for food or in defence against enemies which would use them for food. We may class animals according to their food as omnivorous, herbivorous, and carnivorous, or according to their method of obtaining it as free-living, parasitic, symbiotic, and commensal. Most of these classes need no further comment. We have seen instances of the ways in which omnivorous, herbivorous, and carnivorous animals are nourished. We have dealt with parasitism and symbiosis. Under the head of *commensalism* a large number of curious instances of co-operation between animals is known. One of these must suffice here. The hermit crabs are crustaceans related to the crayfish, with the abdomen soft, owing to the thinness of its cuticle, and twisted so that it will fit into the empty shell of molluscs like the whelk. They search for such shells, often fighting one another for possession, so that they are sometimes called soldier crabs, and they anchor themselves into their shells by means of the limbs of the sixth abdominal segment. When they are attacked they withdraw into the shell by the contraction of a muscle in the abdomen, but often this does not save

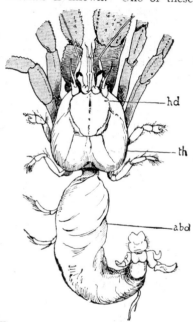

Fig. 531.—A hermit crab withdrawn from its shell. The anterior legs are cut short.—From Thomson.

hd., Head ; *th* , thorax ; *abd.*, abdomen.

them from being eaten by fishes, of which they are a very favourite food. They are very active, and are constantly travelling in search of food, dragging about their shells with them. Sea-anemones are, as we have seen, polyps related to *Hydra*, but more complicated in their internal structure. Owing to their nematocysts they are distasteful to fishes, as is shown by the fact that when alive they will not serve for bait. They cannot pursue food, but must wait till it comes within reach of their tentacles. Now certain kinds of sea-anemones are found on the shells of hermit crabs. Here they are never molested by the owner of the shell, and benefit by the constant change of feeding ground and by fragments of food which are let fall by the hermit crab, to obtain which some of them stand with the mouth on the lower side of the shell, which their base enwraps. In return the crab obtains protection

FIG. 532.—Sea-anemones on the shell of a hermit crab.—After Andres.

from fish, which are kept from eating it by the stinging powers of the anemone. Within the shell there is often found a species of *Nereis* which with its horny jaws steals the food out of the very pincers of the crab, without, so far as can be seen, conferring any benefit in return, and must therefore be regarded as a parasite.

Upon the exploitation by animals of the means of living that the world affords, two further com-

Adaptive Radiation. ments may be made. First, that the more highly organised do not always oust the lower. *Amœba* and Man still exist upon the same planet, though they make very different jobs of life. Secondly, we may

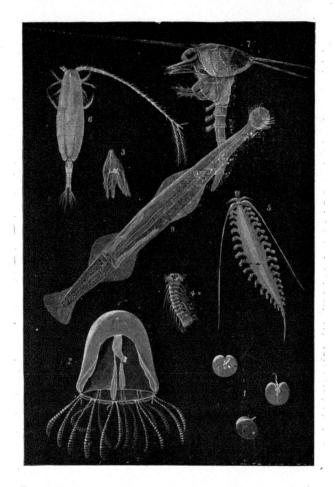

FIG. 533.—Members of the pelagic fauna, considerably magnified.

The animals shown here belong to the plankton or drifting fauna, so called
because its powers of swimming are insignificant compared with the
strength of the currents of the sea. They derive their food from minute
floating plants, and in turn serve to feed larger pelagic animals, such as
the great jelly-fish, herrings, and whales.

1, *Noctiluca*, a large, phosphorescent flagellate : 2, medusa of a hydroid ; 5, a
worm related to *Nereis* ; 6, a crustacean related to *Cyclops* ; 8, the Arrow
worm (*Sagitta*) ; 3, 4, 7, larvæ of a sea-urchin, a worm related to *Nereis*,
and a crustacean related to the lobsters. Many other bottom-living forms
are distributed in larval phases such as these (see p. 385).

note that often, whether by increased complexity or merely by diversity of organisation, there are from a given situation more ways of advance than one. This leads to what is known as *adaptive radiation.* The classification of any group of animals, which in another aspect is its genealogical tree, is an expression of this. Among mammals, for instance, there are tree-climbing, forest and marsh, and plain dwelling, burrowing, aquatic, and flying groups, and in most of these we find carnivorous and herbivorous members. In each such mode of life the species that adopt it come into relations, as devourers, or competitors, or prey, with members of other groups— reptiles, birds, fishes, insects—which have taken the same course.

Faunas. The assemblage of animals which dwells in any given locality or kind of locality—its *fauna*—is, as will be gathered from the foregoing pages, no collection of independent units, but a complex system of beings in constant interaction with one another and with their surroundings, both living and lifeless. We may recognise *geographical faunas*, which belong to localities, and *œcological faunas*, which belong to kinds of locality. These, of course, are cross divisions, for most local areas have parts of different kinds—as an island may have mountains, plains, and streams—and most kinds of local conditions turn up again and again in different places— as, for instance, do those of fresh-water ponds. The kinds of animals which make up a geographical fauna are determined by the past history of the locality (see p. 692) —as, for instance, by causeways of land which in earlier ages allowed the immigration of certain animals but disappeared before others were evolved—and such a fauna has no features which are common to all its members except in so far as it may happen to be also an œcological fauna, which it will be when the locality is throughout of one type. But an œcological fauna has usually well-marked common features which appear in different forms in all its members, however unrelated they be in evolution, and enable them to live in the conditions which are common to them all. Thus, we may divide œcological faunas into those of the *land* and the *water*, and it then appears that land animals have means of breathing in air, internal fertilization, a covering which hinders the loss of water from the body, an absence of special swimming organs, and usually strong skeletons in correspondence with their life in a medium which does not support them as water would. Differences of colour, clothing, shape of limbs, etc., distinguish the faunas of mountains, deserts, snowfields (see *Frontispiece*), marshes, and so forth. Again, the œcological subfaunas of the sea— the *shallow-water fauna*, the *deep-sea fauna*, and the *free-water or pelagic fauna*—have each their own character-istics. The pelagic fauna, for instance, consisting of animals whose life is passed in independence of any solid substratum, usually shows in its members great buoyancy, attained either by extreme delicacy of tissues, as in the jelly-fish, or by air-bladders and like arrangements. It has also a curious and unexplained tendency to phosphores-cence, which at times causes it to light up the surface of the sea in a well-known and beautiful manner. The deep-sea fauna, living in darkness or half-darkness, where plant life is impossible (p. 26), is blind or has very powerful eyes, and is carnivorous, deriving all its food in the long-run from the falling bodies of pelagic animals. Its members also are often phosphorescent. The study of such faunas and their characteristics is one of the most fascinating chapters of Natural History.

We have already briefly considered the general relation in which living beings stand with their lifeless **Living and Lifeless Things.** surroundings. We have seen that the living being—that is, in the long-run, its protoplasm, which alone is active in it—delicate and un-stable though it is, by a purposive reaction maintains its existence in the face of the forces of inorganic nature. These forces are very powerful and unceasingly at work, and would surely destroy the organism but for its activity. Act-ing from without upon a lifeless object they find in it a toy or a passive victim ; but in the living being they set in action a machine of great efficiency which reacts upon them for its own benefit. In so doing it is engaged in the " struggle for existence." The result of this is, in the animal, ability to exist amid surroundings which would destroy it but for its life. In the world as a whole the result is a complication of the action of its forces which is a factor of enormous importance in the system of nature. By the living machine these forces bring about results which they could not otherwise accomplish. The history of this reaction is written large in the very substance of the earth. Enormous beds of chalk and limestone composed of the skeletons of minute marine animals, countless coral reefs and islands, vast areas covered with vegetable mould by the action of plants and earthworms, and great tracts of country whose face has been changed by human activity, bear witness to its existence ; and since the coming of Man it has progressed more and more rapidly till it promises to dominate every other terrestrial agent of change in nature.

In conducting this struggle the organism turns to its own use a part of the forces of nature, and that is what is happening in the circulation of matter and transference of energy through the bodies of organisms. Only by a continual change of its substance can the organism keep in being. It is thus, like a stream or a whirlpool, an object in nature which remains in existence in spite of a continual change of its substance ; but whereas the existence of the stream or the whirlpool is maintained by the action of external forces, the existence of the organism is mantained by a reaction in which energy is liberated and directed from within. As we saw at the outset of our studies, the organism is in this respect unique.

The question suggests itself whether this peculiarity of living beings be due to their possessing any property that is not found in the rest of nature—whether, that is, life differs fundamentally from the processes of the lifeless world, or, on the contrary, could, if we knew enough, be completely described in terms of those physical and chemical laws which suffice to describe the events which occur in inanimate objects. This is the ultimate problem of Biology.

In many respects the events in living beings are certainly not peculiar to them. Disintegration with evolution of energy is a common process in lifeless things. In them it may be started by stimuli which have no relation to its magnitude, or may be spontaneous. There is nothing unusual in the appearance of the energy as chemical work ; and even contraction, secretion, and conduction, though

46

FIG. 534.—*Stomias boa*, a phosphorescent fish taken at a depth of 1900 metres.   Less than half natural size.—From Hickson, after Filhol.

they present difficulties, will probably eventually prove capable of explanation. Absorption is common in lifeless nature and assimilation has at least suggestive analogies in what is known as " autocatalysis."

But when we regard the *direction* of living processes we are on different ground. The gross mechanism of the organs, and of the nervous and hormone systems by which they are regulated, is describable in physical and chemical terms. But the origin of these systems is not. Why does the solution of colloids and crystalloids which we call protoplasm, which makes and uses this coarser mechanism, conduct its traffic with its surroundings in such a way as to conduce to its survival ? To this question there is as yet no answer.

Two warnings, however, must be given lest the nature of these peculiarities be misunderstood. It
A Qualifica-
tion. must in the first place be recognised clearly that they do not dispense the bodily machine from the obligation to act, like other machines, in conformity with the principle of the conservation of energy. Like a steam-engine, the body can do nothing except in virtue of the energy which it obtains, in the long run, from the food which provides its fuel. Secondly, in the purposive direction of the processes of life we have a phenomenon which, though it is unique, is not necessarily incapable of explanation.

So far we have been dealing with matters of fact. The existence in living beings of the peculiarities
Mechanism
and Vitalism. we have just stated is indisputable. Over their explanation, however, rages the great controversy of Biology. The *mechanistic* school of biologists regards all the phenomena of life as due to the laws of physics and chemistry, and looks forward to the day when the extension of our knowledge will enable us to explain them all in terms of these sciences. The apparent exceptions to the laws of chemistry and physics are, for it, not real exceptions, but are due only to our ignorance of the details of the processes in which they occur. The purposive direction of the life processes is due to the structure of the living machine, though here again our ignorance does not allow us to see how it is brought about.

The *vitalistic* school believes that the present impossibility of understanding biological phenomena in the light of physical and chemical facts is due to the operation in living beings of a further factor or factors, without a knowledge of which life will never be explained. It is held that no machine can be conceived which would direct its own activity in the way in which the activity of a living being is directed—that, indeed, the word " machine " can only be used in a limited sense of a living organism. As to the nature of the factor in question, if it exist, nothing is known, though there is a tendency among vitalists to regard it as psychical, but it must in any case be able to direct the physical and chemical forces of life without increasing or diminishing their energy.

The problem of the peculiarities of life is bound up with that of its origin. If we understood how life arose we should know to what its peculiarities are due, though it is true that we might well know this without being able to reproduce it. Life, as we have seen, is found only in *organised bodies*, though not all organised bodies are alive. We may class material objects as follows :—

The Origin of Life : Organised Bodies.

$$\text{Organised} \quad \begin{cases} \text{Living} \\ \text{Dead} \end{cases} \Bigg\} \text{Lifeless.}$$
$$\text{Unorganised} \qquad \qquad \Bigg/$$

It is possible that if we knew how organised bodies first arose we might understand the origin of life, but this is by no means certain. The organised body is one thing. The life in it is quite another. On this point cases of suspended vitality (p. 145) are an interesting commentary.

Organised bodies are characterised by peculiarities of structure, of composition, and of origin. Their peculiarities of structure and composition we have already studied. We may now consider their origin. Here we are met at the outset by a difficulty. We are bound to believe that these complex structures have arisen from matter in its simpler unorganised form. The theories of special creation and of evolution agree in regarding the unorganised world as primary and organised bodies as derived from it. Yet

The Origin of Organised Bodies.

organised bodies, alive or lifeless, never, in the present
state of nature, arise from unorganised matter. Every such
body arises by the processs of fission from a previously
existing living body. In the case of the higher organisms
this is no more than a truism. We know that every
individual of the familiar kinds of animals and plants
had a parent from whose body is has arisen. But there
are cases in which parentage is not so obvious. If the
dead body of any organism be heated strongly, so as to
kill any living things that
may be in it, and placed in
an apparently clean vessel,
closed so as to prevent the
entry of living organisms,
it will nevertheless putrefy,
and microscopical examination will show that putrefaction is accompanied by the
appearance of innumerable
minute " micro-organisms "
of various kinds (p. 713),
some of which are indeed
the cause of the putrefaction. Have not these been
developed from the sub-
stance of the dead organism
without the intervention of
life ? The answer to this
question has not been easily
reached. One of the hardest-
fought controversies in the

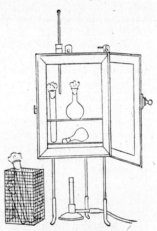

FIG. 535.—A hot-air steriliser.—
From Muir and Ritchie.
Note the plugs of cotton wool in the
mouths of the vessels.

history of science has been between the supporters on the
one hand of the theory of *Abiogenesis* or *Spontaneous
Generation*—the origin of living from lifeless matter—
and on the other of the rival and now victorious theory of
Biogenesis, which maintains the aphorism *omne vivum e
vivo*. Finally, however, it has been demonstrated that
organic matter will not develop micro-organisms if,
after being properly sterilised by heat, it be placed
while it is still hot into a sterilised vessel to which
only filtered air has access, or if it be sterilised in

such a vessel.[1] The explanation of the appearance of such organisms in other circumstances is that they give rise to minute germs or " spores " which are capable of existing in a dried state, and in that state are carried by the air, to germinate when they fall on suitable ground ; and that such spores were present either in the substance which putrefies or, if that has been rendered sterile, in the vessel which contains it, or in air which has access to it. The micro-organisms are killed both in the organic matter and in the vessel by sterilisation, and their germs are filtered out from the air which enters as the vessel cools. In this, as in every other instance which has been carefully investigated, it is proved to be the case that organised bodies arise only from living bodies of their own kind. The first organised bodies must have arisen from unorganised matter, and it may be that the conditions in which this happened will some day be discovered and perhaps even reproduced. But at present it is true that living organised bodies are necessary for the reproduction of their kind.

It will be seen that there are two distinct ways in which life is necessary for its own continued occurrence. It alone can provide the kind of body in which it occurs, and such a body cannot live unless the life of its parent be continued in it. Thus all life is part of a single, self-continued process. This, however, is no more than might be expected. If, as we have seen to be the case, life requires substances which do not arise in lifeless nature, and involves processes which lifeless things cannot carry out, it is not likely to arise spontaneously amid lifeless surroundings. It may well be that a process so peculiar required for its starting conditions which existed in a former state of the earth, but cannot now be brought about. These conditions, whatever they may have been, must have included the presence of a factor that endowed the first living beings with some degree of that purposiveness without which they could not have survived. The

The Continuity of Life.

---

[1] The experiments are usually made with a broth or infusion of meat or hay which is kept in test tubes whose mouths are plugged with cotton wool, put in while the contents are boiling, to serve as a filter.

circumstances which brought into being protoplasm in a state of metabolism must also have brought into being a rudimentary capacity for purposive reaction. It is interesting to speculate whether this could arise by a fortuitous arrangement of unorganised matter, or must be regarded as the development of some latent tendency in the lifeless universe. In any case purposive reaction has evolved to greater complexity as living things themselves have evolved, and that presumably by variation and selection, if we accept this as the method of evolution of organisms. However that may be, the facts that we have here considered give a new importance to that ceaseless activity by which living beings maintain their existence amid their lifeless surroundings. If that activity failed or were overborne, life, so far as we can see, would cease for ever.

APPENDIX

PRACTICAL WORK

A. GENERAL INSTRUCTIONS

IT is absolutely imperative that the student should make a careful personal examination of each of the animals about which **Practical Work.** he reads, and should verify to the utmost extent possible the statement made in his text-books. However clearly he may seem to have understood these statements, he will never really comprehend any organism until he has handled it himself, nor will he by any other means realise that his subject-matter is the living animal and not what is said about it. In the following pages certain instructions are given to facilitate this practical work, but they must not be considered as exhaustive, and the student should follow out any lines of investigation which his own ingenuity can suggest to him.

The following apparatus, etc., will be needed :—

1. Some *dissecting instruments*, including two or three dissecting knives or *scalpels* of various sizes, a large and a small **Apparatus.** pair of *forceps*, a large and a small pair of fine-pointed dissecting *scissors*, a blunt probe or *seeker*, and some *needles* mounted in handles. A box of such instruments can be bought for about £1, 5s.

2. A *dissecting dish* for dissecting under water. A shallow pie-dish with a sheet of cork weighted with lead on the bottom will serve this purpose.

3. A *magnifying glass* with a stand and arm to hold it over the dish while both hands are used for dissection.

4. Some stout pins, a sponge, and a duster.

5. Some wide-mouthed jars with corks or stoppers to keep specimens for dissection or from day to day while they are being dissected. A 2 per cent. solution of formalin in water is the best preserving fluid in most cases, but 70 per cent. methylated spirit may be used.

6. Plenty of clean water.

7. Glass pipettes. Some of these should be drawn out to a fine opening : others should have wider mouths.

8. Chloroform for killing, and various other reagents for staining, etc., which will be mentioned later.

9. A microscope with the apparatus and reagents necessary for its use (see below).

In all cases in which it is possible, the animal should be *examined alive* before dissecting, staining, etc. The shape and attitudes, movements, mode of feeding, respiratory movements, and so forth, should be carefully noted. It must then be *killed* for detailed examination, which will generally include both dissection and microscope work. Small organisms may be killed with a drop of some poisonous fluid, such as alcohol, or solutions of corrosive sublimate or osmic acid (see below). Crayfishes are best killed by sudden immersion for a few seconds in boiling water. For most other animals the best method is the use of chloroform either by placing them in a closed vessel with a bit of sponge soaked in the liquid, or by holding a cloth similarly soaked over the nostrils. Care should be taken that the exposure is long enough to kill.

General Instructions: Killing.

Dissection is an art that must be acquired by practice. The following rules will be of use to the beginner :—

Dissection.

1. *Never start till you are sure what you are looking for.*

2. *Never cut anything till you know what it is.*

3. *Fasten down the animal* with pins to the bottom of the dissecting dish or with nails to a dissecting board (according to size) *and keep the organs well stretched.*

4. *Dissect along, not across,* such structures as nerves and blood vessels.

5. *Keep your dissecting instruments sharp.* They should be scrupulously cleaned and dried before being put away, and fine instruments should never be used for coarse work.

6. Small animals, including the frog, should be dissected under *water,* which *should be changed as soon as it becomes cloudy* from the presence of blood, etc. The water supports and keeps apart the organs, prevents their surfaces from glistening, as they would do if they were merely damp with blood, etc., and helps to keep them clean. You will find it of no advantage to take the animal out of the water with the object of seeing parts of it more clearly.

Careful *drawings* should be made at all stages of the examination. They *should never be copied* from books or lecture diagrams. The use of coloured chalks in these drawings is not desirable, as it enables you to represent an organ by a mass of colour without realising its outline. The drawings should be of a good size in order to show detail clearly. It is easier to draw a symmetrical object after making a faint line upon the paper for the middle of the object.

The use of a compound *microscope* also requires practice. Such a microscope consists of a *stand* bearing a horizontal *stage* for the object, a *mirror* to throw light through the object from below by way of a hole in the stage, a *diaphragm* to vary the amount of light, a vertical *tube* through which the object is viewed from above, and combinations of *lenses* which are placed at the ends of the tube. Two such combinations must be used—an *objective or object glass* which screws into the lower end of

The Microscope.

the tube, and an *ocular or eye-piece* which slips into the upper end. Objectives and oculars are of various powers, and an objective of high power may be used with an eye-piece of low power, or *vice versa.*

The lowest magnification obtainable in a student's microscope is usually about 50–80 diameters, the highest about 250–300. The object is placed upon the stage and brought into focus by raising and lowering the tube. *Coarse adjustment* is effected by sliding the tube, either directly or by a rack and pinion; *fine adjustment* by raising or lowering the arm which holds the tube. This is done by a screw which works against a concealed spring. With the high power the objective is closer to the object, when it is in focus, than with the low. An object may be viewed either by *reflected* light falling upon it from above, or, if it be transparent, by *transmitted light* cast through it from below by the mirror. The object is placed or *mounted* upon a glass *slide.* Usually it is immersed in some medium which is either temporarily or permanently fluid (see p. 732). In this case it must be protected by a *coverslip* of thin glass.

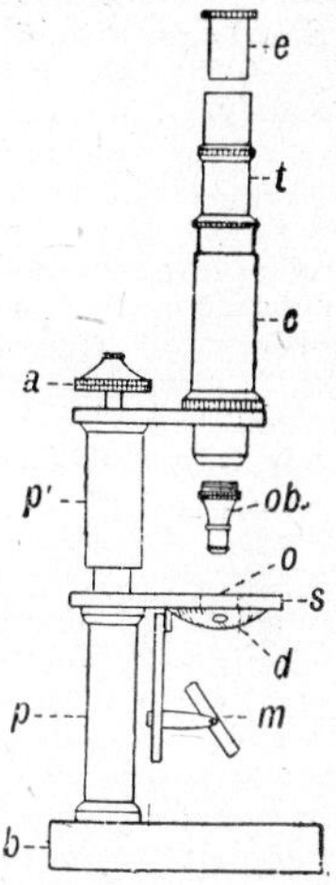

In many cases it is desirable to stain the object. A few re-agents, such as *methylene blue,* will stain living objects; for most it is necessary that the animal or tissue should be killed. This is done with a *fixing agent,* a strong poison that kills rapidly and so allows only the minimum of change to take place in the object. Saturated solution of *corrosive sublimate* in water, 2 per cent. solution of *osmic acid* in water, 1 per cent. solution of *glacial acetic acid* in water, *absolute alcohol,* and other substances, are used for this purpose. Osmic acid is useful for small animals; for tissues, a mixture of nine parts cor-

Staining.

FIG. 536.—Side view of a compound microscope, with detached eye-piece and objective.

a., Milled rim of screw of fine adjustment; *b.,* base of stand; *c.,* collar; *d.,* diaphragm which can be turned to bring between the mirror and the object holes of various sizes, one of which is shown; *e.,* eye-piece or ocular. above the end of the tube into which it slides; *m.,* mirror; *o .,* position of opening in stage; *ob.,* objective, below the end of the tube into which it screws; *p.,* portion of pillar fixed to base; *p'.,* movable portion, raised or lowered by fine adjustment; *s.,* stage; *t.,* tube.

rosive sublimate solution and one part glacial acetic acid is a good reagent. The specimen must be thoroughly washed to rid it of all traces of the fixative before staining. *Carmine,* and *logwood* or *hæmatoxylin* are common stains. Various preparations of each of these are in use for different purposes; they can be bought ready made, and directions for preparing and using them may be found in books, such as Marshall and

Hurst's *Practical Zoology*. *Borax carmine* and *hæmatoxylin* are alcohol stains. *Picrocarmine* is a water stain containing picric acid. After staining, the object must be washed with dilute alcohol (for an alcohol stain) or water (for a water stain) to remove the excess of stain.

Mounting. Small aquatic animals may be mounted alive in water ; parts of the tissues of larger animals which are to be examined in the living condition must be mounted in *normal salt solution*— a ·75 per cent. solution of common salt in distilled water. This approximates more nearly to the natural fluids of the body, and has not the injurious effect of pure water. Objects which are intended for a prolonged examination should be mounted either in *glycerine* or in some solid medium, such as *glycerine jelly*, which becomes solid when cold, or *Canada balsam*, which becomes solid when dry. An object may be placed direct from water into glycerine ; to be mounted in Canada balsam it must first be dehydrated by soaking in absolute alcohol, then steeped in *oil of cloves* or in *xylol* till the alcohol is removed, and then placed in a drop of balsam upon the slide and covered. The object should not be placed direct from water into absolute alcohol, lest the diffusion currents set up by this strong dehydrant should injure it, but 30, 50, 70, and 90 per cent. solutions of alcohol should be used successively for a period varying with the size and density of the object. Thus the complete process for staining and mounting in Canada balsam involves the successive use of : stain, 30 per cent. or 50 per cent. alcohol to wash, 70 per cent., 90 per cent., and absolute alcohol, xylol or oil of cloves, and Canada balsam. A very small object is best submitted to these processes on the slide, either under a coverslip (p. 731) or not, but for most they are performed in *watch-glasses*.

It is often important to study slices or *sections* of animals, organs, or tissues. This may sometimes be done by placing the object (after *hardening* in absolute alcohol, corrosive sublimate, or other hardening agent) between two pieces of pith or carrot, and slicing off sections *freehand* with a sharp razor. More often, however, it is necessary to use a section-cutting machine or *microtome*. The **Section-cutting.** object is embedded before cutting in some fluid which solidifies, such as paraffin wax. The technique of this process should be learnt in the laboratory. It is described in Marshall and Hurst's *Practical Zoology* and other books.

The following hints will be of service in using the microscope :—

Hints on the use of the Microscope.
1. Examine every object first with the low power, using the high power afterwards if necessary.
2. Focus roughly with the coarse adjustment, and only then use the fine.
3. Use the utmost care to prevent the objective from getting dirty. It is damaged by cleaning. Never use the high power without a cover glass. The eye-piece and objective may be cleaned if necessary with chamois leather or silk. Canada balsam may be removed by the *very* careful use of benzol or xylol, but in the laboratory it is better to leave this to the demonstrator.
4. The object may appear indistinct owing to the presence of dirt on the coverslip, the objective, or the ocular. If the dirt be

upon the coverslip the dimness will be affected by moving the slide ; if it be upon the ocular, by turning the latter ; if neither of these be in fault the objective is dirty. In a wet preparation a dirty coverslip must be replaced ; a dry one may be cleaned in the same way as the objective.

5. If the tube will not slide freely, it or the inside of the collar tube which holds it is dirty. They may be cleaned by careful but vigorous rubbing with a dry duster.

6. Keep both eyes open in looking through the microscope.

The following is an outline of the procedure which should be followed in the practical examination of an animal :—

How to Examine an Animal.

1. Examine alive, as recommended above.

2. Make a drawing of the external features. These are generally best shown in a side view.

3. Make separate drawings of parts, such as limbs, the mouth, etc., which are not fully shown in your first drawing. In the case of the crayfish and cockroach this will involve several drawings of appendages.

4. If the animal have a perivisceral cavity in which the organs lie free, open this cavity and make a drawing of the organs *in situ* without disarrangement. Vertebrates should be opened on the ventral side, invertebrates on the dorsal. If the body-wall be hard, as in the crayfish and cockroach, it may be removed as a single piece after two lateral incisions ; if it be soft, a median incision should be made, and the body-wall turned back or *reflected* to each side and pinned out. In a vertebrate the skin and the muscular body-wall must generally be turned over separately. The thorax of a mammal should not be opened till a later stage, and the relation of the organs and cavities should be observed carefully during the process.

5. Remove the alimentary canal by cutting through its ends, and the mesentery if there be one. Draw (*a*) the removed canal, (*b*) the body cavity with the organs left behind. In the crayfish, the endophragmal skeleton must be cut away in order to show the nerve cord.

6. In a vertebrate, make a special dissection of the heart, the great vessels entering and leaving it, and the respiratory organs. Make a drawing.

7. In a vertebrate, make a dissection of the organs of the neck and throat from the ventral side. Draw.

8. Expose the brain or cerebral ganglia, and examine it *in situ* with its nerves. Draw. Remove, and draw dorsal and ventral views. Ninety per cent. alcohol is useful in whitening and hardening the nervous system.

9. In a vertebrate, make a series of drawings of the parts of the skeleton. Skeletons may be prepared by removing most of the flesh and boiling or macerating (*i.e.* placing in water and allowing the flesh to rot). They should then be washed thoroughly and bleached in sunlight. Cartilaginous skeletons, however, should not be rotted or allowed to dry, but dipped into hot water for a few minutes and cleaned with a brush.

10. Examine under a microscope and draw : (*a*) some of the blood ; (*b*) if possible the sperm ; (*c*) in the case of at least one of the vertebrate animals studied, portions of the tissues fresh and stained ; (*d*) in the case of small animals, transverse and longitudinal sections of the whole body.

11. Examine and draw any larval stages that the animal may have.

The following pages contain directions for observing and dissecting, according to the instructions given above, a number of animal types. After working through these in two or three cases, the student should be able to apply the same general directions to the examination of other animals which he may wish to study.

B. INSTRUCTIONS FOR OBSERVING AND DISSECTING CERTAIN ANIMALS

The numbers of the items refer to the General Instructions on pp. 733, 734.

FROGS are easily found in damp places during a great part of the year,

The Frog. but in late autumn and in winter they can most conveniently be obtained from persons who have a stock of them,[1] or from those who are skilled in finding them during their hibernation.

1. Observe how the animal sits, crawls, jumps, and swims ; the movement of the floor of the mouth in breathing ; and if possible the feeding. At the breeding season look for pairs coupled.

Kill by enclosing in a vessel with a little chloroform.

2. In a side view, note : head and trunk (no neck or tail) ; fore and hind limbs ; mouth, nostril, eye, tympanic membrane (pierce and pass seeker through Eustachian tube to mouth) ; sacral prominence (Fig. 12).

Find cloacal opening.

3*a*. In hand and foot, number the digits. Note : palmar and plantar surfaces ; absence of claws or nails ; web of foot ; pad on first (really second) digit of hand in male (Fig. 13).

b. Open the mouth widely. If the gullet rise, press it back with the handle of a scalpel. Note : maxillary and vomerine teeth ; posterior nares ; eyeballs ; Eustachian tubes ; tongue ; its attachment ; glottis (Fig. 537).

4*a*. Lay the frog on its back under water in a dissecting dish ; pin through hands, feet, and tip of jaw ; cut the skin along the mid-ventral line, thus opening the ventral lymph sac ; free the skin where it is held down on the breast, turn it outwards, and pin. Note : rectus abdominis, pectoral, and

[1] All the animals ordinarily studied in the laboratory can be obtained from dealers, whose advertisements are usually to be found in the pages of *Nature*.

submaxillaris muscles ; xiphoid cartilage ; anterior abdominal and cutaneous veins ; hypoglossal nerves (Fig. 26).

b. Cut through the muscles of the ventral body-wall, and through the pectoral girdle, on one side of the middle line. Ligature doubly the anterior abdominal vein near the liver ; cut between the ligatures ; carefully cut through the muscles which still hold down the pectoral girdle ; turn back the body-wall, and pin it. Arrange the viscera for drawing to show as much as possible, noting : heart ; lungs, liver, gall bladder, stomach, small intestine (duodenum and ileum), rectum, bladder, pancreas, hepato-pancreatic duct ;

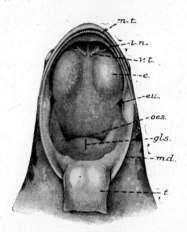

FIG. 537.—The mouth of a frog.

e., Protuberance caused by eyeball ; *eu.*, Eustachian tube ; *gls.*, glottis ; *i.n.*, internal narial opening ; *m.t.*, maxillary teeth ; *md.*, lower jaw ; *t.*, tongue ; *v.t.*, vomerine teeth.

spleen ; ovaries or testes, fat bodies, and, in female, oviducts (Fig. 32).

5*a.* Remove the alimentary canal by cutting through the œsophagus, mesentery, and rectum. Cut open the intestine, wash, and note folds of wall.

b. In the abdominal cavity, note : fat bodies, testes or ovaries, kidneys ; kidney ducts ; in male, vesiculæ seminales and vasa efferentia ; cloaca, bladder ; and the following veins— femoral (traced backwards for a short distance by carefully snipping through connective tissue and parting muscles at back of thigh), renal-portal, sciatic, pelvic, vesical, and anterior abdominal (cut) (Figs. 43, 45).

6 and 7a. In another frog, or before doing number 5, open the pericardium, turn the heart forwards, and cut the ligament which
connects the ventricle dorsally with the pericardium.   Note:
glossopharyngeal, vagus, and hypoglossal nerves; ventricle,

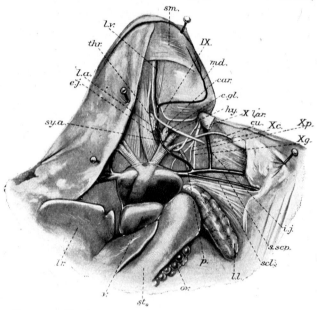

FIG. 538.—The forepart of a frog's body dissected from the ventral
side, and stretched to display the organs.

c gl., Carotid gland; *car.*, common carotid artery; *cu.*, cutaneous artery;
e j., external jugular vein; *hy.*, hypoglossal nerve; *i.j.*, internal jugular
vein; *l.a.*, lingual artery; *l.l.*, left lung; *l.v.*, lingual vein; *lr.*, liver;
md., mandibular vein; *ov.*, part of ovary; *p.*, pulmonary artery; *s.scp.*,
subscapular vein; *scl.*, subclavian vein; *sm.*, submaxillaris or mylohyoid
muscle; *st.*, stomach; *sy.a.*, systemic arch; *thr.*, thyroid gland; *v.*, ventricle; *IX.*, glossopharyngeal nerve; *Xc., Xg., Xlar., Xp.*, cardiac, gastric,
laryngeal, and pulmonary branches of vagus nerve.

auricles, and sinus venosus; inferior vena cava and hepatic
veins; superior venæ cavæ, external jugular, innominate,
internal jugular, subscapular, subclavian, musculo-cutaneous,
and brachial veins; pulmonary veins (Fig. 538; but in
this figure the heart is in its normal position and the
pericardium unopened).

The heart will sometimes be beating when the body is opened, though the animal is dead. If not, it may often be stimulated to beat by a prick. In the beating heart, note the successive phases of the beat (p. 68).

7*b*. Turn the heart back, cut through one superior vena cava, and remove its branches. Wash the dissection. Note: auricles, ventricle, truncus. Trace: carotid, systemic, and pulmonary arches: lingual (external carotid) artery, carotid gland, and internal carotid artery; subclavian and cœliaco-mesenteric arteries; dorsal aorta (Fig. 40).

8*a*. Remove the kidneys and generative organs without injuring the aorta. Note: vertebral column; dorsal aorta and

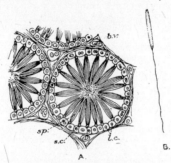

FIG. 539.—*A.*, A diagram of part of a section of the testis of a frog, showing one ripe seminiferous tubule and portions of two others, with connective tissue binding them together, and blood vessels (*b.v.*). *B.*, A ripe spermatozoon.

i.c., Cells of the lining epithelium. Some of these are undergoing the divisions by which they form the spermatocytes from which in turn spermatozoa arise; *s.c.*, supporting cells, carrying *sp.*, bundles of spermatozoa.

iliac arteries; spinal nerves, with calcareous concretions; ganglia and commissures of sympathetic chains; rami communicantes; sciatic plexus (Fig. 47; see p. 86).

b. Remove the roof of the skull and the neural arches. Harden the central nervous system by pouring on two or three changes of 90 per cent. alcohol. Note: olfactory lobes, cerebral hemispheres, thalamencephalon, optic lobes, medulla oblongata, fourth ventricle, spinal cord (Fig. 50, I).

c. Remove the central nervous system and observe its ventral side. Note: olfactory lobes, cerebral hemispheres, optic chiasma, infundibulum, pituitary body (if not torn away), crura cerebri, spinal cord (Fig. 50, II).

9. Examine and draw the skeleton in the following divisions:

backbone and pelvic girdle in dorsal view (Fig. 15) ; skull in dorsal (Fig. 15) and in ventral view (Fig. 17) ; hyoid (Fig. 21) ; fore-limb (Fig. 15) ; hind-limb (Fig. 15) ; pectoral girdle in ventral view (Fig. 22) ; pelvic girdle in side view (Fig. 23).

10*a*. Examine a drop of the blood diluted with normal (75) salt solution (Fig. 81, *A*).

   b. Tease in normal salt solution a piece of testis. Note spermatozoa (Fig. 539, *B*).

   c. Examine in normal salt solution the following : pigment cells in web of foot (Fig. 72, B) ; striped muscle fibres, frayed apart (Fig. 77) ; unstriped muscle fibres, in wall of bladder spread out (Fig. 76) ; connective tissue, in thin sheet as found among leg muscles (Fig. 79) ; fatty tissue, from fat body (Fig. 80) ; cartilage, from edge of xiphisternum scraped clean (Fig. 78) ; nerve fibres, obtained by fraying out a large nerve with needles (Fig. 70).

   d. Examine the following sections prepared by an expert : bone (Fig. 7) ; nerve (Fig. 71) ; spinal cord (Fig. 49) ; intestine (Figs. 58, 59) ; testis (Fig. 539, *A*).

   e. Pith a frog (*i.e.* cut through the backbone just behind skull, and pass a seeker through the wound forwards into the skull to destroy the brain and backwards into the neural canal). Arrange the animal so that one foot lies with the web spread out under the objective of a microscope. With the low power note the circulation in the capillaries (Fig. 38).

   f. Skin the leg of the same frog. Stimulate the gastrocnemius muscle (Fig. 26)—(1) by pinching, (2) by touching with a hot needle, (3) by a drop of dilute acid. Note contraction of the muscle in consequence of these mechanical, thermal, and chemical stimuli.[1] Dissect out the sciatic nerve (which may be traced back from the abdominal cavity) and apply to it the same stimuli. Note contraction of muscles.

11. In the spring, obtain some spawn and preserve a portion of it in 2 per cent. formalin solution or 70 per cent. alcohol. Keep the rest in a large vessel of water with living water weeds. Watch the hatching and growth of the tadpoles, preserving some at every stage. Examine carefully and note : cleavage (Fig. 469) ; gastrulation (Fig. 471) ; and the history of the neural folds, sucker, mouth, gill-clefts, gills, operculum, limbs, and tail (Figs. 11, 473, 475, 476, 478).

Amœba proteus may be bred from the surface layer of clean pond-mud which contains its minute food-plants. This is allowed to stand in tap water. A brown scum arises and is poured off with the upper water and a few wheat grains added to it. Minute amœbæ

---

[1] This experiment does not prove the irritability of the muscle fibres independent of the nerve endings upon them unless the latter have first been numbed, as by the injection of the poison *curare* into a lymph sac of the frog.

appear, grow, and divide.   The species of *Entamœba* which is most
convenient for laboratory purposes is *E. blattæ*, found among the

**Amœba Entamœba,
Polytoma, Euglena,
Chlamydomonas, Opalina
Parameculum, Balantidium,
Nyctotherus, Vorticella,
Monocystis.**

contents of the rectum of the cockroach.
In cold weather, the cockroach should be
obtained from some warm place, such as a
bakehouse.   *Polytoma* occurs with allied
organisms in water which is very foul with
decaying animal matter, as in the macerating
tub in which bones are prepared for mounting as skeletons ;   *Euglena*
in the green water which sometimes fills small ponds and hoof-prints ;
Chlamydomonas in water butts and ponds where the water is greenish ;
Opalina, Balantidium, and *Nyctotherus* in the upper part of the
rectum of the frog ;   *Paramecium* in hay infusions or similar solutions
of decaying vegetable matter (p. 161).   *Vorticella* may be found
plentifully growing on objects in ponds and streams, as, for instance,
on willow roots.   *Monocystis* will generally be found on opening the
vesiculæ seminales of a well-grown earthworm, the large species
hanging on to the funnels of the vasa deferentia as white threads
visible to the naked eye, the smaller more often free in the contents
of the vesiculæ, which must be mounted and examined, to find also
the cysts, with various stages of conjugation and spore formation.

1.   Examine each of these Protozoa alive, (*a*) with the naked eye,
    if possible, to note the true size, (*b*) with low power, (*c*)
    with high power.   Free living forms should be mounted in
    water ; parasites and *Polytoma* in the fluids in which they
    live, diluted with a drop of normal salt solution.   *Para-
    mecium* may be made to move more slowly by the addition
    of a little gum to the water in which it is mounted.
    Polytoma is quiet in the drying edges of a film of the fluid
    which contains it, mounted without coverslip.

2.   Kill by placing at one side of the coverslip a drop of osmic
    acid and drawing under with blotting-paper at the opposite
    side, taking care not to sweep away the animals.   Wash
    with water in same way, stain in same way with picrocar-
    mine, wash again, draw under coverslip glycerine, first
    dilute and then pure.   Flagella and trichocysts are best
    shown by using iodine solution, which both kills and stains.
    (*Polytoma* is best fixed with osmic vapour in a film on a
    coverslip, stained there, and subsequently mounted.)

In living and stained specimens, note : shape, changing in *Amœba*
and *Entamœba* by amœboid movement, in *Euglena* and *Monocystis* by
euglenoid movement ; pseudopodia, flagella, cilia, or absence of all these :
nucleus (nuclei in *Opalina*) ; micronucleus in Ciliata except *Opalina* ;
staining of nuclei ; ectoplasm, endoplasm, food vacuoles (not in *Chlamy-
iomonas, Polytoma, Euglena, Opalina,* or *Monocystis*) ; contractile
vacuole or vacuoles (none in *Monocystis* or *Entamœba*), whether simple
or complex ; trichocysts in *Paramecium* ; red spot and chloroplasts in
Euglena and *Chlamydomonas* ; gullet and vestibule in Ciliata other than
Opalina ;   feed these Ciliata with Indian ink ground up in water ;
stages of *Monocystis*.   (Figs. 10, 88, 90, 94, 96-98, 101, 110, 111, 128, 129.

Specimens of one or more species of *Hydra* may usually be obtained
by gathering weeds from a clean pond and allowing them
Hydra.   to stand in a vessel of water. Some of the polyps will
migrate to the wall of the vessel, where they can easily
be detected, gently pushed off, and sucked up with a pipette.

   1*a*. Note: extension, contraction on touching, spontaneous
movements.

   b. Place a brown specimen with a water-flea in a watch-glass
containing only a little water. Note that the water-flea is
numbed when it touches the tentacle of the *Hydra*.
Probably it will be seized and swallowed by the latter.

   2. With hand lens, note: body ; foot ; tentacles ; bud, testes,
and ovary, if present (Figs. 138, 146, 147).

   3. Mount in water, raising coverslip on two small strips of paper.
Note: with low power, oral cone and mouth ; with high
power, in tentacle, ectoderm, endoderm, batteries of
nematocysts, cnidocils (Fig. 140) ; after running 5 per cent.
salt solution under coverslip, threads of nematocysts
extruded (Fig. 143, D).

      Small organisms often found running over the body of the
Hydra are ciliate Protozoa.

   10. In stained and mounted sections (transverse and longitudinal),
note, under low power ; ectoderm, endoderm, jelly, enteron
(Figs. 142, 139) ; under high power, details of ectoderm
and endoderm (Fig. 144).

On rocky parts of the coast *Obelia* and other hydroids may be
found at low tide. They will travel alive in a vessel of
Obelia.   sea water.

   1. Note retraction of polyp heads when touched or
shaken.

   2. Kill a twig by dropping osmic acid suddenly on to it when it is
in a small quantity of water, with tentacles expanded. Stain
and mount. Note: hydranths, with tentacles and mouth,
cœnosarc, gonangia, peritheca, hydrothecæ (Figs. 149, 150).

   10. Examine a vertical section of a hydranth (Fig. 151).

   11. Examine a medusa, stained and mounted (Fig. 154).

Fresh specimens of the Liver Fluke can only be obtained when a
sheep infected with them is killed. Laboratory speci-
The Liver   mens are usually preserved in formalin.
Fluke.
   2. Note: mouth, ventral sucker, genital pore
(Fig. 165).

   2. Dry the surface of the body and under a lens note spicules.

   4. In a specimen which has been fixed while it was flattened
under pressure and mounted in balsam, note: pharynx,
intestinal cæca ; testes, cirrus sac ; ovary, yolk glands,
uterus, shell gland (Figs. 167, 169).

   5. In an injected specimen observe excretory systems (Fig. 167).

   10. Examine a transverse section through the region of the ovary
(Fig. 166).

   11. Stages of the life history should be examined if available
(Fig. 170).

Fresh Tapeworms are rarely obtainable. Laboratory specimens are preserved in formalin.

The Tapeworm. 2. Note : head, neck, proglottides (Fig. 173, 5).

3. In head, under magnification, note : suckers, hooks (Fig. 173, 4).

4*a*. In young proglottides, stained and mounted, note : excretory canals ; testes and vas deferens ; ovary, uterus, vagina (Fig. 174).

b. In old proglottis, note : large, branched uterus, with thick-shelled fertilised eggs (Fig. 173, 6).

10. In transverse section of a proglottis, note : cuticle, nuclei of ectoderm, withdrawn into deeper parts of cells, lying in superficial region of parenchyma ; longitudinal muscle fibres ; layer of transverse muscle ; excretory canals ; nerve cords ; testes, with developing spermatozoa ; uterus, with fertilised eggs ; yolk glands (Fig. 175).

11. In cysticercus, note : head with hooks and suckers, young proglottides ; bladder (Fig. 173, 3).

Fresh cysticerci of a tapeworm which infects the dog may often be found in the mesentery of the rabbit. On being placed in warm salt solution, some of them will evert the head.

If the Earthworm be studied during the winter, advantage should be taken beforehand of good weather for obtaining

The Earth-worm. specimens. They can be kept alive in damp leaves and earth for some weeks.

1. The movements and habits of earthworms are best studied in the field. Darwin's *Earthworms and Vegetable Mould* is an interesting work on this subject.

2. Note : in dorsal view, prostomium, peristomium, following somites, clitellum, anus (terminal) ; in ventral view, mouth, chætæ, genital pores (Fig. 178).

3. Extract a chæta with forceps and examine it under low power (Fig. 180).

4. Pin the worm ventral side downwards and stretch it well. Open it by a cut along the dorsal middle line from the prostomium to somite 25, turn the body-wall outwards, snipping through the septa, and pin. Note : septa ; nephridia ; suprapharyngeal ganglia ; mouth, pharynx, œsophagus, crop, gizzard, intestine ; vesiculæ seminales ; spermathecæ (these mark somites 9 and 10, and thus enable the other somites to be identified) ; dorsal blood vessel, hearts, contractions of these if the worms have been recently chloroformed (Figs. 184, 540, diagram).

5*a*. Cut through the gut just behind the gizzard, lift it with forceps, and working forwards separate it from the septa. In somite 13 note the ovaries before cutting the septum in front. Be careful not to remove the vesiculæ seminales. Cut through the pharynx behind the suprapharyngeal ganglia and remove the alimentary canal. Note the parts mentioned above, and also œsophageal glands and pouches.

b. In the worm, note the following structures exposed by removal of the alimentary canal : suprapharyngeal ganglia, circumpharyngeal commissures, subpharyngeal ganglia, ventral nerve cord ; spermathecæ, vesiculæ seminales, ovaries ; nephridia (Figs. 183, 193).

10*a.* Open another worm under normal salt solution.

Remove a nephridium with the part of the septum in front of it to which it is attached, mount it in salt solution, and examine it under the microscope. Note : nephrostome (Fig. 187) ; various portions of tube with capillaries (Figs. 186 and 188). Small, parasitic nematode worms will probably be seen.

Remove and mount an ovary (Fig. 192).

Mount contents of a vesicula seminalis. Examine alive, fix with a drop of absolute alcohol, stain with picrocarmine

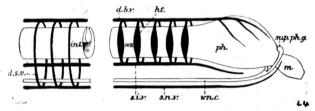

FIG. 540.—A diagram of the principal blood vessels of the earthworm.

d.b.v., dorsal blood vessel ; *d.s.v.*, dorso-subneural vessel ; *ht.*, one of the " hearts "; *int.*, intestine ; *m.*, mouth ; *œs.*, œsophagus ; *ph.*, pharynx ; *sup.ph.g.*, suprapharyngeal ganglion ; *s.i.v.*, subintestinal vessel ; *s.n.v.*, subneural vessel ; *v.n.c.*, ventral nerve cord.

(p. 732), and examine. Observe stages of development of spermatozoa (Fig. 191).

Mount and examine contents of a spermatheca. Examine and note ripe spermatozoa (Fig. 191).

b. Examine under low power a transverse section of the intestinal region. Note : in body-wall, cuticle, epidermis, and circular and longitudinal muscles ; cœlom ; in gut-wall, typhlosole chloragogen cells, muscular layer, endoderm ; nerve cord ; dorsal subintestinal, and subneural blood vessels ; nephridia ; chætæ (Fig. 181). Examine portions of the section under high power (Fig. 186).

Longitudinal sections of the earthworm are difficult to interpret because the worm is never quite straight when it is cut, and because the contents of the section vary with the distance from the middle line, but there may be found in them, besides the body-wall, some or all the regions of the alimentary canal, septa, vesiculæ seminales, and usually portions of the dorsal blood vessel, ventral nerve cord, and suprapharyngeal ganglia (Fig. 182, diagram).

Specimens of the Leech must be bought from a dealer.

The Leech.

1. Note the movements of the worm in swimming and looping. It is often difficult to induce it to feed. When it does so, it can be caused to relax its hold by salt sprinkled on its back, but the bleeding of the wound is sometimes difficult to stop. Kill with chloroform.

2. Note : in dorsal view, annuli, spots which mark the true somites, eyes, hinder sucker, anus ; in ventral view, oral sucker, mouth, penis (thrust out), female opening, hinder sucker (Fig. 198).

3. Examine the mouth and remove a jaw (after 5).

4. Pin the leech through the suckers, stretching well. Open it by a dorsal incision a little to one side of the middle line ; carefully dissect away the skin and pin it out. Wash. Note : dorsal sinus, lateral vessels ; pharynx, crop, cæca, stomach ; intestine (Fig. 199) ; nephridia.

5. Remove the alimentary canal. Note : nervous system ; nephridia ; generative organs (Fig. 198).

10. Examine a transverse section (Fig. 200).

Crayfish occur in streams in many parts of Britain, but are most conveniently obtained from dealers. Bought specimens

The Crayfish.

may be of the French species.

1. In the living animal note movements of limbs in locomotion and feeding. With a pipette place carmine at the bases of the legs and note that it is sucked under the branchiostegite and driven out below the antenna. Cut away the branchiostegite above the jaws, and note the movement of the scaphognathite.

Crayfish may be kept alive for a long time in running water. They should be killed with hot water, and may then be preserved in 70 per cent. alcohol (renew the spirit). Preserved specimens are only of use for examination of external features and of the nervous system.

2. Note : in dorsal view, cephalothorax, rostrum, cervical groove, branchiostegite, abdominal terga, telson ; eyes ; antennules, antennæ, scales of latter, great chelæ, walking legs, uropods (Fig. 201) ; in ventral view, limbs (working with list on p. 296), as individual jaws are difficult to identify for the first time until they are removed) ; sterna (Fig. 202).

3. Remove the telson. Note the sixth abdominal somite with its limbs.

Remove the sixth abdominal somite and view the fifth from behind. Note : tergum, sternum, pleura, limbs (Fig. 207).

Remove the limbs of one side from behind forwards, bringing away the podobranchiæ with the legs to which they belong. Arrange the limbs on a sheet of paper, and compare with Figs. 203–207, noting the parts of each limb.

Cut away a branchiostegite (Fig. 212) ; count gills (p. 307).

4. Cut away the median part of the carapace and of the abdominal terga. Note : heart, ostia ; ovary, or testes and vasa deferentia ; " stomach," muscles running from it to cara-

pace, " liver," " intestine " ; mandibular muscles, longitudinal muscles (Fig. 209).

In an injected specimen,[1] similarly opened, note : ophthalmic, antennary, gastric, and dorsal abdominal arteries (Fig. 209). Press apart organs and note : hepatic arteries, sternal artery (shown in Fig. 210).

5*a*. Remove the heart and genital gland. Cut through the œsophagus and hind gut and very carefully remove the alimentary canal under water. In the removed canal note : œsophagus, " cardiac " and " pyloric " regions, mesenteron, with cæcum, " liver," joining mesenteron by a short duct, hind gut (Figs. 208, 210).

　b. Examine the removed genital gland and its ducts (Figs. 218, 219).

　c. Remove carefully the longitudinal muscles, leaving the nerve cord behind. Cut through the false bottom of the thorax. Whiten the nerve cord with 90 per cent. alcohol. Note : green glands, with their sacs ; cerebral ganglion, circumœsophageal commissures, subœsophageal ganglion, ventral nerve cord, with its ganglia ; sternal artery (Fig. 215).

10. Examine under a microscope the contents of a vas deferens (spermatozoa, Fig. 220), and a muscular fibre (striped).

11. In a " berried " female, note how the eggs are attached. If possible find a female carrying young and examine them (Fig. 221).

Cockroaches are easily caught, in places they infest, with traps sold for the purpose. They should be killed with chloroform.

The Cockroach.　1. In a living specimen, note the mode of use of the legs and antennæ, the movements of the jaws in feeding, and those of the abdomen in respiration.

　2. Note : head, neck, thorax, abdomen ; segments of latter ; eyes, antennæ, wings, legs, and cerci, and in male styles ; terga and sterna ; stigmata (Figs. 227, 228).

3*a*. Note parts of head in side and front views (Fig. 229).

　b. Remove and examine head appendages (Fig. 230).

These are best seen after boiling in potash, to remove soft tissues, and mounting in balsam.

　c. Examine the parts of the hinder end of body in male and in female (Figs. 227, 240, 241).

4*a*. Cut off the wings. Fasten the animal down by pinning or (better) by embedding its under surface in melted paraffin wax and when cool pinning through the wax. Cut through the abdominal and thoracic terga and remove them carefully so as not to injure the heart. Note : heart in pericardium ; fat body ; tracheæ (Fig. 541).

4*b*. Free alimentary canal from fat body and tracheæ and unravel it. Note : œsophagus, crop, proventriculus, chylific

---

[1] The blood vessels of a freshly killed crayfish may be injected by removing carefully a small piece of carapace just over the heart, placing into one ostium the point of a fine pipette full of carmine, and pressing gently but steadily. The point of the pipette must not contain bubbles of air.

ventricle, ileum, colon, rectum ; salivary glands and receptacles ; pyloric cæca ; Malphigian tubes ; cerebral ganglion (Fig. 237).

4*c*. Remove stain, and mount in balsam a salivary gland and receptacle, and also remove and mount a portion of fat body with tracheæ.

5. Remove the alimentary canal. Note : cerebral, subœsophageal, thoracic, and abdominal ganglia ; and the commissure, connecting them ; in females colleterial glands, oviduct, spermatheca, ovarian tubes (Fig. 237) ; in immature male, testis, vas deferens, mushroom-shaped gland ; immature male, mushroom gland, its duct, accessory gland.

10. Examine under a microscope : the stained salivary gland ; the fatty tissue with tracheæ (Fig. 239) ; an ovarian tube (low power) ; contents of mushroom gland ; muscular fibre (striped).

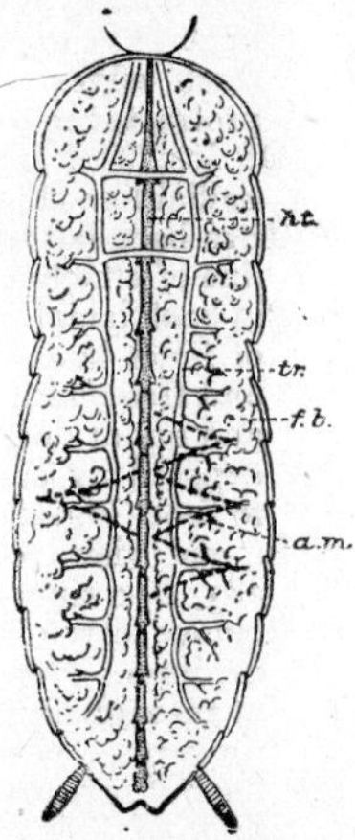

The most convenient source from which to obtain specimens **Ascaris.** of *Ascaris* is the pig, which is infested by a species closely similar to, if not identical with, *A. lumbricoides*. The related but larger *A. megalocephala* from the horse is also often available. The worms should be preserved in formalin.

2. Note, in specimens of the two sexes : smooth cuticle, anterior and hinder ends, "excretory" pore, genital pore (Fig. 259).

3. Examine under a lens the ends of the body. Note : lips, papillæ ; curved tail of male, with penial setæ ; tail of female merely convex, without setæ (Fig. 260).

4. Cut open the worms a little to one side of the middle line, and pin out the body-wall. Unravel the genital organs. Note : pharynx, intestine, rectum ; lateral lines ; dorsal and ventral lines ; in male, testis, vas deferens, penial setæ in sheaths ; in female, ovaries, oviducts, uteri, vagina (Figs. 264, 265).

10. In a transverse section of the intestinal region, note : cuticle, epidermis, muscle layer ; lateral lines ; dorsal and ventral lines ; intestine ; ovary or testis ; uterus or vas deferens (Fig. 261).

Observe a muscle fibre under high power (Fig. 262).

FIG. 541.—The heart and neighbouring structures of a cockroach : somewhat diagrammatic.

a.m., Areas marked by dotted lines to show the position of alary muscles below the fatty body ; *f.b.*, fatty body ; *ht.*, heart ; *tr.*, tracheæ.

Mussels may easily be found by searching the shallow part of ponds
and streams, usually partly buried in the mud.

The Swan   1. Note protrusion of foot, and current through
Mussel.   siphons (Fig. 276, A).

     2a. Note : in side view, umbo, lines of growth, position
of hinge, ends, of shell (Fig. 276, A) ; in dorsal view, umbo,
lines of growth, ligament (Fig. 277).

   b. Remove left valve of shell by separating it from edge of mantle
and cutting through attachment of adductor muscles (keep
edge of scalpel close to shell). Note : mantle lobes, their
thick edges, siphons, two adductor, two adductor, and
protractor muscles (Fig. 278, left mantle lobe cut away).

   c. On inside of shell, note : marks of attachment of muscles,
pallial line (Fig. 276, B).

   d. Turn back left mantle-lobe. Note : foot ; labial palps ; gills,
line of attachment of outer gill to mantle, siphons (Fig. 278).

   e. Pin back labial palps and gills of left side. Note : attachment
of inner lamella of inner gill ; seeker passed between foot
and free middle part of inner gill into epibranchial chamber
and out at dorsal siphon. Left kidney and genital openings
exposed by cutting through attachment of inner gill plate
to foot (Fig. 279).

   3. In end views of animal note : mouth, labial palps (Fig.
283, B) ; siphons, cloaca, anus.

   4. Remove carefully dorsal wall of body, thus opening pericardium. Note : rectum ; ventricle, auricles (Fig. 282).

   5. Cut through auricles and hinder end of rectum and turn latter
forwards. Note : renopericardial openings. Cut through
floor of pericardium on one side, thus opening non-glandular
limb of kidney. Note : opening to exterior ; glandular
limb of kidney ; visceral nerve-commissures.

      The alimentary canal should be studied in a specimen in
which it has been injected and dissected out (Fig. 285).

   8. Find nerve ganglia—cerebral by gently scraping skin behind
anterior adductor, pedal by cutting vertically through
muscular part of foot and separating the halves,
parieto-splanchnic on ventral surface of posterior adductor.

10a. Remove from its shell a spirit-preserved specimen. With a
sharp scalpel make the following sections : (1) through
middle of foot, (2) through hinder part of foot, (3) behind
foot. Note : attachments of gills (Fig. 281) ; internal
organs in transverse section (Fig. 284. The first section
will probably not show the heart).

   11. Examine larvæ if present (Figs. 287, 288).

The edible snail (*Helix pomatia*) occurs in many parts of England,
and may be obtained from dealers. It is larger than
The Snail.   the common snail (*H. aspersa*). Snails are best killed
by drowning, since they then die extended.

   1. Observe alive. Note : mode of walking, etc.

   2a. Note : shell, lines of growth, umbilicus (opening of columella) ; head, anterior tentacles, posterior (oculiferous)

tentacles, mouth ; foot, pore of pedal gland ; genital pore ; collar (edge of mantle) ; opening of lung (Fig. 290,, A).

2b. Carefully cut away shell. Note : opening of lung ; anus ; columellar muscle ; roof of lung ; visceral hump, liver, albumen gland, kidney, pulmonary vessels (seen through skin).

3a. Pin the snail down under water. Open the lung by a transverse incision behind the collar and an incision along the left side of the roof. Turn back the mantle roof and pin it down. Note : floor of lung, rectum, kidney duct, roof of lung, pulmonary vessels, kidney, pericardium, auricle, ventricle.

3b. Open pericardium, find renopericardial opening (near the middle of the renal side), and pass a bristle through it.

4a. Cut along the right side of the roof of the lung, leaving the rectum on the roof. Turn back the roof. Make a median incision from the head to the visceral hump, thus opening the hæmococlic perivisceral cavity. Turn back and pin the flaps thus made. Carefully remove the thin skin of the visceral hump. Unravel the contained organs, pinning out the genital organs to the animal's right, the alimentary canal to the left. Note : hermaphrodite gland, hermaphrodite duct, albumen gland, common duct with passages for ova and sperm, free oviduct and vas deferens, vagina, mucous glands, dart sac, spermatheca, spermathecal duct (with appendix in *H. aspera*), penis, retractor muscle of penis, flagellum of penis (Fig. 290, C, diagrammatic).

4b. Remove dart from dart sac and examine it.

5a. In alimentary canal, note : buccal mass, œsophagus, crop, stomach, intestine, rectum, salivary glands, salivary ducts, liver, liver ducts ; nerve collar (Fig. 290, C, diagrammatic).

5b. Cut open buccal mass, remove radula, mount it, and examine it under low power.

8a. Observe nerve collar *in situ*. Note : cerebral ganglion, with nerves to buccal ganglia and tentacles, infracœsophageal mass of ganglia, with nerves to viscera and foot.

8b. Dissect away connective tissue around infracœsophageal mass. Note : pedal, pleural, and visceral ganglia.

Starfishes may be found almost everywhere upon the British coast. They may be obtained from the Marine Biological **The Starfish.** Station at Plymouth.

1. In a living specimen, note the movements of the tube-feet, spines, and pedicellariæ, and watch the animal walking. Observe the dermal gills and the eyes. Lay the animal upon its back and note how it rights itself. While it is in that position, observe the organs in a widely opened ambulacral groove. Touch the bottom of groove with a seeker, and watch the contraction of the groove and its protection by the adambulacral spines (Fig. 292).

The starfish may be preserved in formalin or 70 per cent.

alcohol. Openings should be made at the sides of the
arms to admit the fluid.

2. Make drawings of the oral and aboral sides, showing the mouth,
ambulacral grooves, tube-feet, adambulacral and other
spines, and madreporite (Figs. 291, 292).

3a. Find the nerve cord at the summit of the ambulacral groove.
   b. Examine under a lens a small portion of the aboral surface.
Note : spines, cushions, pedicellariæ, gills (Fig. 291).
   c. Note the pedicellariæ upon the adambulacral spines, between
the spines of the aboral surface, and on the cushions at the
base of the spines. Remove, mount, and examine pedicellariæ from each of these positions (Figs. 291, 292).

4 & 5. Cut through the body-wall along the outline of the animal, so
as to divide it into oral and aboral halves. Cut through
œsophagus, stone canal, and retractor muscles, and remove
the aboral half of the body-wall with the alimentary canal.
Note and draw : in oral half, axial sinus with stone canal and
axial organ, nerve ring, position of water vascular ring,
Tiedemann's bodies, ambulacral ossicles, and ampullæ of
tube-feet (Fig. 297) ; in aboral half, stomach, pyloric sac,
pyloric cæca, rectal cæca, and generative organs (Fig.
294).

10. Examine and draw a transverse section of the decalcified arm of
a small specimen, cut by an expert. Note : body-wall, spines,
gills, ambulacral ossicles, nerve cord, radial water vessel,
ampullæ, tube-feet, body-cavity, pyloric cæca (Fig. 296).

11. If possible, examine and draw larvæ (Fig. 298, simplified).
Specimens of *Amphioxus* may be obtained from dealers.

The Lancelet.

2a. In a left side view, note : mouth, oral cirri ; anus ;
atriopore ; myotomes ; dorsal, caudal, and anal
fins (Fig. 302).

   b. In a ventral view, note : ventral groove ; metapleural folds ;
mouth, etc., as before (Fig. 303).

4. In a specimen which has been macerated for twenty-four hours
in 20 per cent. nitric acid, remove on the right side the wall of
the atrial cavity, the muscles dorsal to it, and the oral hood.
Note : velum, enterostome, oral cirri, pharynx, gill slits,
liver, intestine, anus ; notochord ; spinal cord ; fin rays ;
generative organs.

5. Remove and stain the hind end of the pharynx, slitting it open
dorsally and flattening it. Note : primary and secondary
bars, skeletal bars, synapticulæ, developing slits (Fig. 307).

8. Remove the spinal cord by shaking the macerated specimen in
a test tube with water, stain, and mount. Note : eye spot ;
first pair of nerves ; dorsal and ventral nerves ; cerebral
vesicle, central canal (Fig. 314).

10. In transverse section, note : in the pharyngeal region, myotomes ; notochord and its sheath ; spinal cord ; pharynx,
gill-slits, endostyle, dorsal groove ; ventral aorta and suprabranchial arteries ; atrial cavity ; cœlom ; gonads ; liver ;
metapleural folds ; dorsal fin (Fig. 308) ; in the intestinal

region, myotomes, notochord, and spinal cord ; intestine ; dorsal aorta, subintestinal vessel ; anal fin (Fig. 310).

11. Examine either specimens or wax models illustrating the development (Figs. 461–466).

The Dogfish will usually not be procurable alive.

It can sometimes be observed in an aquarium.

The Dogfish.[1]

 2*a*. In ventral view of specimen (whose belly may have been opened to let in preserving fluid) note : nasal openings, oronasal grooves. mouth ; cloacal opening ; pectoral fins, pelvic fins, with claspers in male ; anal and caudal fins (Fig. 326).

 b. In side view, note : head, trunk, and tail ; eye, mouth. spiracle, gill-clefts ; lateral line ; pectoral, pelvic, dorsal, caudal, and anal fins (Fig. 315).

3*a*. Strip off a small portion of skin to show myomeres (Fig. 317).

 b. Examine scales under lens (Fig. 316).

 c. Examine teeth.

4. In a ventral view of the contents of the abdominal cavity, note : suspensory ligament, with internal opening of oviducts in female and vestige of same in male ; bilobed liver, gall bladder, bile duct ; cardiac and pyloric divisions of stomach, bursa entiana, intestine, rectum ; pancreas and its duct ; rectal gland ; spleen (Fig. 326).

5*a*. Turn the liver forward and alimentary canal to the left, and note in addition : cœliac artery, portal vein, testis or ovary, vas deferens or oviduct.

 b. Remove the alimentary canal and its appendages, cut open the cloaca, remove the dorsal peritoneum on one side. Note : in male, testes, vasa efferentia, vas deferens, vesicula seminalis, sperm sac ; kidney ; cloaca, anus, urinogenital papilla, abdominal pouches ; in female, ovary, oviduct, its internal and cloacal openings, shell gland ; kidney, its duct and bladder ; urinary papilla ; abdominal pores (Figs. 328, 329).

 c. Cut open the intestine, wash out, and examine the spiral valve.

6*a*. Open the pericardium. Note : sinus venosus, auricle, ventricle, conus, ductus Cuvieri (Figs. 326, 331).

 b. Pass a seeker, behind the heart, through the pericardio-peritoneal canal.

 c. Cut open sinus venosus and ductus Cuvieri and find openings of : hepatic, posterior cardinal, and anterior cardinal sinuses.

7*a*.[2] Skin the throat and dissect away underlying sheet of muscles. Note thyroid gland lying between two great strands of

---

[1] The Piked Dogfish (*Acanthias vulgaris*), sometimes used for dissection, differs from the rough hound only in comparatively unimportant points. It is rather smaller, and more slender, and has a sharp spine in front of each dorsal fin. Its oronasal grooves are closed, the gall-bladder is more and the thyroid less conspicuous, the pancreas is variable in size, and both ovaries are present. The fourth and fifth afferent branchials have a common root. The ophthalmic branch of the fifth nerve passes ventral to the superior oblique muscle and is therefore probably the *ophth. profundus*, and the maxillary and mandibular branches separate earlier.

[2] Parts of the arterial system missed in the dissection owing to lack of blood in preserved specimens should be identified in injected specimens.

muscle. Remove thyroid and muscle strands ; note ventral
aorta ; trace afferent branchial arteries (Fig. 331).

b. Cut through the jaw and branchial arches on one side, turn
the floor of the mouth outwards, and remove mucous membrane of roof of mouth. Note gill-clefts. Find : gills and
pseudobranch ; efferent branchial and epibranchial
arteries ; dorsal aorta ; carotid arteries, and point of origin
of orbital (" external carotid ") arteries ; subclavian and
cœliac arteries (the latter found by tracing back dorsal
aorta) (Fig. 332).

8*a.* Cut through the skin round the eye and pull the eyeball
outwards. Note, in orbit : eyeball ; internal, superior, and
external recti muscles ; superior oblique ; optic nerve,
fourth nerve (Fig. 339).

b. Remove the eye by cutting through the six muscles and the
optic nerve, close to the eyeball. Note : four recti muscles,
two obliques ; second, third, and fourth nerves, maxillary,
mandibular, and ophthalmic branches of fifth nerve, hyomandibular, prespiracular palatine, and ophthalmic branches
of seventh (Fig. 340).

c. Cut away roof of cranium and neural arches. Note : olfactory
lobes, cerebrum, thalamencephalon, optic lobes, cerebellum,
medulla oblongata, restiform tracts, fourth ventricle, spinal
cord roots of all cranial nerves except sixth, spinal nerves
(Fig. 336).

d. Slice horizontally through the auditory capsule until nerves
passing through it are exposed ; then slit open the anterior
cardinal sinus and trace distribution of these nerves. Note :
semicircular canals ; roots of ninth and tenth cranial nerves ;
ninth passing to first branchial arch, with branch to hyoid
arch ; branches of tenth to branchial arches 2–5, each with
branchlet to preceding arch, other branches of same nerve
to lateral line, and to heart and viscera (Fig. 321).

e. Cut through nerves and remove the brain. In ventral view,
note : olfactory lobes, cerebrum, optic nerves and chiasma,
infundibulum, lobi inferiores and sacci vasculosi, crura
cerebri, medulla oblongata, restiform tracts ; roots of third
and of fifth to tenth cranial nerves (Fig. 337).

9. Draw the skeleton in the following sections : cranium (side,
dorsal and ventral views) ; jaws and branchial arches ;
vertebral column (side view of portions of trunk and tail
regions, longitudinal section) ; pectoral girdle and fin ;
pelvic girdle and fin (Figs. 319, 320, 322, 323).

In order to obtain these fish in inland places with the viscera
The Cod[1] **(or** intact a special order must be given to a fishmonger.
Haddock or 1. It will usually not be possible to observe the
Whiting. animal alive, but a study of the habits of a bony

[1] The student who has not already studied the dogfish or some other fish is recommended to read the paragraph which begins at the bottom of p. 420, and also to
note the following facts :—

In the cod, haddock, and whiting, the body is coated with scales which are thin,

fish can conveniently be made by watching a goldfish.
Note : the respiratory movements, and the use of the tail
and fins.

2. In side view, note : the same parts as in the dogfish, with which
   make a comparison (p. 750 footnote). Note also : the absence
   of eyelids ; and of spiracle ; the gill cover, consisting of the
   operculum proper and the expansible branchiostegal membrane ; the double nostril on each side ; the separate anal,
   genital, and urinary openings ; the scales (Figs. 348, 347 D).
3a. Lift the gill cover and observe the gills.
  b. Dissect away the skin on one side of the body and note :
     myomeres ; lateral line branch of vagus, starting under the
     operculum ; the cutaneous branch of the trigeminal (peculiar
     to Actinopterygii), starting on the head and branching to
     supply sense organs on the fins.
  c. Open the mouth, and examine the teeth.
4. Make a flap of the right wall of the abdominal cavity by an
   incision passing in front of the anus, and turn this flap back.
   Note : œsophagus, stomach, pyloric cæca, intestine, rectum ;
   liver (three lobes), gall bladder, bile duct ; spleen ; air
   bladder ; cœliac artery, portal vein, hepatic veins ; testis or
   ovary, vas deferens or oviduct ; ureter. Pass a secker into
   genital duct and into ureter (Fig. 542).
5. Open the air bladder. Note : vascular plexus from which gas
   is secreted into bladder ; dorsal aorta. Remove dorsal wall
   of air bladder and note kidneys.

flat plates of bone, completely covered by skin and overlapping backwards; it is
shaped for cleaving the water. The mouth is at the front end; in life it is
continually opening and taking in gulps of water, which passes into the pharynx
and outward on the sides of the head through five gill-clefts that open under a gill-
cover or operculum on each side. Above the mouth lie the nostrils, which have no
internal openings. A shallow ventral depression in which lie the anal, genital, and
urinary openings is placed midway underneath. The widest part of the body
contains the body cavity, which reaches some way behind the vent. The narrower
hinder region or tail contains only muscle and backbone, and ends in two equal
flukes, which are used in propelling the fish (p. 423). The two pairs of limbs
or fins, used in steering, balancing, and backing, are quite unlike the corresponding
members of a frog or a man, and the pelvic or true hinder pair lies forward under
the throat. They and the dorsal and ventral fins by which the body is kept upright
are strengthened by rays. There is no neck. The body is stiffened by the backbone, composed of a row of bony rings or vertebræ, which runs along the upper
side of its whole length except in the head, where it is continued by the skull. In
the middle region ribs arch outwards from the backbone in the body-wall. There
is no breastbone. As in all Vertebrata, the central nervous system lies in the
hollow of the skull and backbone, the body cavity below the latter, containing the
stomach, coiled intestine, and other viscera, and the heart in a part of the body
cavity known as the pericardial cavity, which here stands in front of the rest and is
cut off from it. From the heart, a ventral arterial system, consisting of a median
ventral aorta and an afferent branchial artery in each of the " branchial arches "
which separate the gill-clefts, conveys blood to the gills, which stand upon the
arches, whence it passes, oxygenated, to the body by means of a dorsal arterial
system. In returning to the heart, most of it passes either through a hepatic portal
system in the liver or through a renal portal system in the kidneys. The latter are
dark brown strips of tissue lying under the backbone above the body cavity, from
which they are separated by a large, closed air-bladder. The genital ducts are
continuous with the gonads in both sexes, and have no connection with the
kidneys.

6. Cut through girdles and note : heart in pericardium, its parts (Fig. 349).

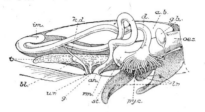

FIG. 542. — A semi-diagrammatic view of the contents of the abdominal cavity of a male cod which has been opened on the right-hand side.

a.b., Air bladder ; *an.*, anus ; *bl.*, bladder ; *d.*, duodenum ; *g.*, genital opening ; *g.b.*, gall-bladder ; *im.*, ileum ; *kd.*, kidney duct ; *lr.*, liver ; *œs.*, œsophagus ; *py.c.*, pyloric cæca ; *rm.*, rectum ; *st.*, stomach ; *t.*, testis ; *ur.*, urinary opening.

7a. Dissect away muscles, etc., in front of the heart, and trace ; ventral aorta and afferent branchial arteries (Fig. 349).

b. Cut away the floor of the mouth, and on its roof dissect out the efferent branchial system (Fig. 350).

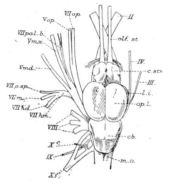

FIG. 543.— The brain and its nerves in a cod.

c.str., Corpora striata, two large masses or ganglia of grey matter which lie at the base of the cerebrum of vertebrata and are here exposed because the roof of the cerebrum, which in the cod is thin and non-nervous, has been torn away ; *cb.*, cerebellum ; *l.i.*, right lobus inferior ; *m.o.*, medulla oblongata ; *olf.st.*, stalk of olfactory lobe ; *op.l.*, optic lobes ; *II.-X.*, cranial nerves ; *V.md.*, *V.mx.*, *V.op.*, mandibular, maxillary, and ophthalmic branches of the fifth nerve ; *VII.hd.*, *VII.hm.*, *VII.m.*, *VII.op.*, *VII.p.sp.*, *VII.pal.b.*, hyoidean hyomandibular, mandibular, palatobuccal, and ophthalmic branches of seventh nerve ; *X.c.*, cutaneous branch of the vagus nerve, from which the lateral line is innervated The cutaneous branch of the fifth nerve is not shown.

8*a*. Cut away the roof of the cranium and expose the brain. Note its regions and trace out the nerves. The ophthalmic is the superficial one (Fig. 543).

b. Cut through the auditory capsule. Note labyrinth, with large otolith in vestibule.

9*a*. In skull, note the following bones : in cranium, basioccipital, exoccipitals, supraoccipital, parietals, alisphenoids, frontals, parasphenoid ; in auditory capsule of one side, epiotic, pterotic, opisthotic, prootic, sphenotic ; in either orbit lacrymal, suborbitals ; in nasal region, nasals, vomer, mesethmoid, parethmoids ; in either upper jaw palatine,

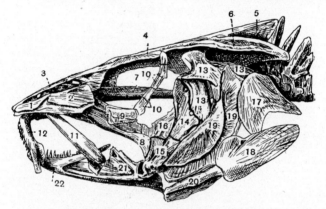

FIG. 544.—The skull of a cod, from the left side.—From Reynolds.

1 and 2, Lacrymal ; 3, median ethmoid ; 4, frontal ; 5, supraoccipital ; 6, pterotic ; 7, orbit ; immediately below is the parasphenoid ; 8, pterygoid ; 9, suborbital ; 10, bones of orbital ring ; 11, maxilla ; 12, premaxilla ; 13, hyomandibular ; 14, symplectic ; 15, quadrate ; 16, metapterygoid ; 17, opercular ; 18, sub-opercular ; 19, preopercular ; 20, interopercular ; 21, articular ; 22, dentary.

pterygoid, mesopterygoid, metapterygoid, quadrate, premaxilla, maxilla ; in either lower jaw, articular, angular, dentary ; in either hyoid arch, hyomandibular, symplectic, epihyal, ceratohyal, hypohyals, urohyal, brachiostegal rays ; in either operculum, opercular, preopercular, subopercular, interopercular (Fig. 544).

b. Note the parts of the vertebræ.

c. In the shoulder girdle and fore-fin skeleton, note : post-temporal, supracleithrum, cleithrum ("clavicle"), post-cleithrum, scapula, coracoid, brachial ossicles, fin rays (Fig. 545).

a. In the pelvic girdle note that each half consists of a single bone, in which iliac, ischial, and pubic regions are not distinguishable.

48

Lizards are found in various parts of England, but it will usually be
most convenient to obtain specimens from a dealer.

The Lizard.   1. The animal should be kept under observation
alive. Kill with chloroform.

2. Note: head, neck, trunk, tail, limbs, mouth, nostril, eye,
with three lids; shallow depression for ear; vent; scales
(Fig. 359 A).

3*a*. Hand and foot. Count the digits.

  b. Open the mouth. Note teeth. tongue, glottis, nares.

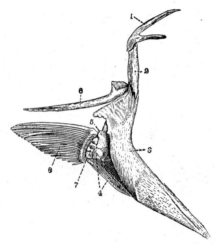

FIG. 545.—The right half of the pectoral girdle and right pectoral
fin of a cod.—From Reynolds.

1, Post-temporal; 2, supracleithrum; 3, cleithrum; 4, coracoid; 5, scapula;
6, post-cleithrum; 7, brachial ossicles; 8, dermal fin rays.

4. Pin the animal on its back. Cut through the abdominal body-
wall to one side of middle line (note that skin adheres to
muscles) and through the pectoral girdle, and turn back.
Note: anterior abdominal vein on body-wall; heart in
pericardium, aortic arches, inferior vena cava; lungs;
liver and gall bladder; stomach, duodenum, ileum, rectum,
cloaca, bladder; pancreas; fat bodies in hinder part of
body-wall (Fig. 546).

5. Cut through the liver on the left side of the animal. Turn the
viscera to left, and spread them out. Note: course of
alimentary canal; and principal blood vessels (Fig. 548);

testes or ovaries, epididymides, vasa deferentia, or oviducts,
kidneys, Cut open cloaca and note openings of rectum,
bladder, ureters, and generative ducts (Fig. 547).
6. Open the pericardium and note parts of heart and roots of
great vessels (Fig. 548).

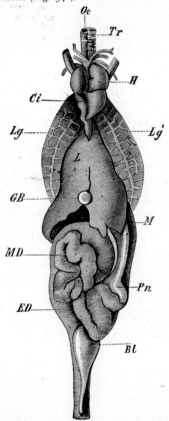

FIG. 546.—The viscera of the Sand Lizard (*Lacerta agilis*), in
their natural relations.—From Weidersheim.

Bl., Bladder ; *Ci.*, inferior vena cava ; *ED.*, rectum ; *GB* ., gall bladder ;
H., heart ; *Lg.*, *Lg'.*, lungs ; *M.*, stomach ; *MD.*, small intestine
Oi., œsophagus ; *Pn.*, pancreas ; *Tr.*, trachea.

7. Dissect up throat and trace trachea, gullet, jugulars.
8. Break away the roof of the skull and observe dorsal view of brain. Remove brain and observe ventral view. Note that it resembles that of the frog in general features, but has larger cerebral hemispheres and twelve nerves.
9. In the skull of the common lizard the supratemporal fossa is bridged by bones. For this reason, and because of the small size of the animal, it is convenient to study instead of its skeleton that of some other and larger kind (e.g. *Uromastix*). In the skull (Fig. 549) note the following bones : in the

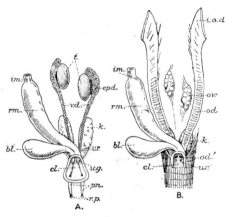

FIG. 547.—The urinary and genital organs of a lizard (*Lacerta*).

A, Male ; *B*, female.

bl., Bladder ; *cl.*, cloaca ; *epd.*, epididymis ; *i.o.d.*, internal opening of the oviduct ; *im.*, ileum ; *k.*, kidney ; *od.*, oviduct ; *od'.*, external opening of oviduct ; *ov.*, ovary ; *pn.*, penes ; *r.p.*, retractor muscles of the penes ; *rm.*, rectum ; *t.*, testes ; *ug.*, urinogenital opening ; *ur.*, ureter ; *ur'.*, opening of ureter ; *v.d.*, vas deferens.

cranium, supraoccipital, exoccipitals, basioccipital ; parietal,[1] epipterygoids, basisphenoid ; frontal ; [1] parasphenoid ; at the sides of the cranium, squamosals, supratemporals, postfrontals, prefrontals, lacrymals ; in either auditory capsule, prootic ; in nasal region, vomer [1] and nasals ; in either upper jaw, premaxilla,[1] maxilla, jugal, palatine, transpalatine, pterygoid, quadrate ; in either lower jaw. dentary, Meckel's cartilage, angular, splenial, supra-angular, coronoid. Examine also the other parts of the skeleton (Fig. 550 for shoulder girdle).

[1] Two fused.

1. The student should not fail to make himself acquainted with

the many interesting facts which may be learnt from

The Pigeon. watching pigeons, concerning, for instance, the nesting

care of the young, and their feeding ; the use of the

oil gland ; moulting ; the use of the wings and of the tail

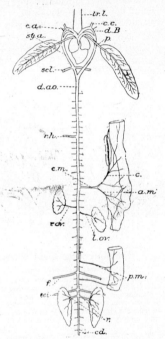

FIG. 548.—The principal arteries of a lizard.

a.m., Anterior mesenteric; *c.,* cœliac; *c.a.,* carotid arch; *c.c.,* common carotid; *c.m.,* cœliaco-mesenteric; *cd.,* caudal; *d.ao.,* dorsal aorta; *d.c.* ductus caroticus; *f.* femoral or external iliac; *l.ov.,* left ovarian: *p.,* pulmonary; *p.m.,* posterior mesenteric; *r.,* renal; *r.h.,* right hepatic; the left hepatic is a branch of the cœliac; *r.ov.,* right ovarian; *scl.,* subclavian; *sci.,* sciatic or internal iliac; *sy.a.,* systemic arch; *tr.l.,* tracheo-lingual.

in flight and gliding, steering and alighting ; courting ;

challenging, and fighting with beak and wing.

2. Of external features, note the head, neck, trunk, very short

tail ; beak, cere, nostrils ; eyes, with three eyelids ; ear openings ; vent ; wings and legs ; reptile-like scales on latter (Figs. 369, 370).

3*a*. Pluck the bird. In so doing note arrangement of feathers, especially on wings (Figs. 369, 370, 375).

   b. Note parts of wing, alar membranes, bastard wing (Fig. 370).

   c. Examine the various kinds of feathers (Fig. 372).

   d. Note pterylæ and apteria (Figs. 369, 370).

4*a*. Skin the ventral surface of thorax, abdomen, and neck. Note

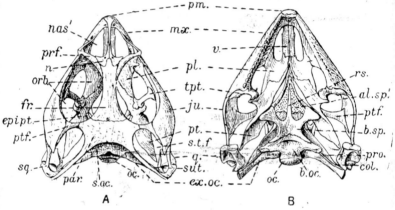

FIG. 549.—The skull of the lizard *Uromastix*.

A, Dorsal view ; *B*, ventral view

al.sp′., Cartilage representing alisphenoid ; *b.oc.*, basioccipital ; *b.sp.*, **basisphenoid ;** *col.*, columella auris ; *epipt.*, epipterygoid ; *ex.oc.*, exoccipital ; *fr.*, frontal ; *ju.*, jugal ; *mx.*, maxilla ; *n.*, nasal ; *nas′.*, region from which cartilaginous nasal capsule has been removed ; *oc.*, occipital condyle ; *orb.*, orbit ; *par.*, parietal ; *pl.*, palatine ; *pm.*, premaxilla ; *prf.*, prefrontal and lachrymal, fused ; *pro.*, prootic ; *pt.*, pterygoid ; *ptf.*, postfrontal and postorbital, fused ; *q.*, quadrate ; *rs.*, rostrum ; *s.oc.*, supraoccipital ; *s.t.f.*, supratemporal foramen ; *sq.*, squamosal ; *sut.*, supratemporal bone (very small) ; *tpt.*, transpalatine ; *v.*, vomer (" prevomer ")

on the underpart of the neck the crop. Separate the large superficial muscle of the breast (pectoralis major) of one side from the keel of the sternum and from the entire length of the clavicle. Turn the muscle forwards, taking care not to injure the blood vessels of the armpits. Observe close to these vessels the axillary air sacs (branches of the inter-clavicular). Note the deeper muscle of the breast (pectoralis minor) still attached. Cut through its origin, turn it for-wards and make out the insertion of both breast muscles and their mode of action. Dissect away the pectoral muscles of the other side in the same way ; open the abdomen and

raise the hind end of the sternum, cut through the attachment of the sternum to ribs and coracoid on each side, and remove the sternum. Note: gullet, crop; thymus; trachea, muscles of syrinx; heart in pericardium, roots of arteries; liver, gizzard, duodenum, pancreas, ileum; thoracic and abdominal air sacs (Fig. 385).

b. Displace viscera and examine them. Note, in addition to

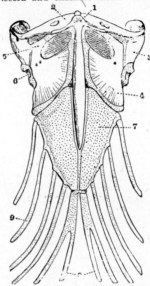

FIG. 550.—A ventral view of the shoulder girdle and sternum of *Loemanctus longipes*, a lizard.—From Shipley and MacBride.

1, Interclavicle; 2, clavicle; 3, scapula; 4, coracoid; 5, precoracoid, 6, glenoid cavity; 7, sternum; 8, sternal bands; 9, sternal portion of a rib.
The dotted regions are cartilage.

parts already seen, proventriculus, rectum and its cæca, cloaca; pancreatic and bile ducts; spleen, lungs, portal, epigastric (anterior abdominal) and coccygeomesenteric veins.

5. Remove the alimentary canal. Note: kidneys, ureters; testes or ovary, vasa deferentia or oviducts (right oviduct small) (Figs. 386, 387); veins (Fig. 390), arteries (Fig. 389).

6. Remove the pericardium. Note great vessels entering and leaving heart (Fig. 389).

7a. Displace the gullet and windpipe and trace the carotid arteries and jugular veins along the neck.

7*b*. Trace the brachial and pectoral arteries and veins to the wings.

8. Sking the top of the head and very carefully remove the roof of the skull. Note the parts of the brain in dorsal, and after its removal in ventral view (Fig. 391).

9. The skeleton of the Common Fowl is often studied instead of that of the pigeon. Its parts should be examined with the aid of the figures and description on pp. 497–503.

In buying rabbits for dissection, avoid those that are likely to be very fat.

The Rabbit.

1. Wild rabbits can be watched if the observer will keep still. Feeding and breeding habits are better observed in tame ones.

2. Note : head, neck, trunk, tail, limbs, the proportions of the parts of the latter ; nostrils, lips, teeth ; eyes, their lids ; whiskers ; ears ; anus ; urinogenital opening.

3*a*. Skin the face. Note: masseter muscle, facial nerve, parotid gland.

b. In the orbit, find lacrymal and infraorbital glands.

c. Cut through muscles at sides of mouth and open it widely. Note : teeth (count), hard palate, soft palate, posterior nares, pharynx, beginning of œsophagus, glottis, epiglottis, tongue. Slit open soft palate and find Eustachian tubes.

4*a*. Fasten the animal on its back. Skin the abdomen and turn flaps of skin outward. Make a median and a transverse cut through abdominal muscles and turn flaps outwards. Note : xiphisternum ; falciform ligament ; liver ; stomach ; small intestine, cæcum, colon, rectum ; urinary bladder (Fig. 411).

b. Turn up the liver and spread out the duodenum. Note : liver, gall bladder, bile duct ; portal vein, hepatic artery ; œsophagus, cardiac and pyloric regions of stomach, duodenum ; pancreas, its duct (Fig. 412) ; spleen.

c. Turn the stomach and intestine to the animal's right. Note : kidney ; adrenal body ; dorsal aorta, cœliac, hepatic, lieno-gastric, anterior mesenteric, left renal, and posterior mesenteric arteries ; inferior vena cava, left renal vein ; left vagus on œsophagus, solar plexus, left splanchnic nerve (Fig. 426).

5*a*. Doubly ligature the portal vein and cut between the ligatures, ligature œsophagus and cut above ligature, ligature and cut rectum, cut through mesentery, remove alimentary canal, and spread out. Note : œsophagus, stomach, pyloric sphincter, duodenum, ileum, sacculus rotundus, cæcum, vermiform appendix, colon, rectum (Fig. 413).

b. In the abdomen, note : muscular portion and central tendon of diaphragm ; œsophagus ; kidneys ; suprarenal bodies ; ureters, bladder ; dorsal aorta, cœliac, anterior mesenteric, renal, genital, posterior mesenteric, and common iliac arteries ; inferior vena cava, renal, genital, and external and internal iliac veins (Figs. 416, 420) ; in male, testis (pulled out of scrotal sac), epididymis, vas deferens, uterus masculinus, spermatic cord (Fig. 416) ; in female, ovaries, oviducts, internal openings of same, uteri, vagina.

   c. Cut away the ventral part of the pelvic girdle. Note : in male, rectum, bladder, ureter, vas deferens, uterus masculinus, prostrate, perineal gland (Fig. 417, A) ; in female, rectum, bladder, ureter, vagina, vestibule, perineal gland (Fig. 417, B).

6*a.* Cut through the ribs and remove the sternum. Note : ribs, intercostal muscles ; thymus gland ; heart ; lungs ; phrenic nerves ; diaphragm ; pleural cavities (Fig. 414, thymus removed).

   b. Remove the thymus and pericardium and turn the heart to animal's right. Note : left auricle, left ventricle, parts of right auricle and ventricle ; pulmonary arteries ; arch of aorta ; innominate, right subclavian, right common carotid, left common carotid and left subclavian arteries ; dorsal aorta, passing through diaphragm ; left superior vena cava, left subclavian, external jugular, and pulmonary veins ; inferior vena cava, œsophagus (Fig. 414, lower part).

   c. After doing No. 7, cut through great vessels at some distance from the heart and remove the latter. Note in dorsal and ventral views of it the chambers and vessels mentioned above.[1]

   d. Cut open the right side of the heart. Note thin wall of auricle, thick wall of ventricle, columnæ carneæ, flaps of tricuspid valve, chordæ tendineæ and papillary muscles, semilunar valves, openings of veins (Fig. 418).

7. Remove the skin of the neck and underlying muscles. Note and trace : posterior cornu of hyoid ; tendon of mandibular muscle ; larynx, trachea ; thyroid gland ; œsophagus ; common, external, and internal carotid arteries ; external and internal jugular, anterior and posterior facial veins ; submaxillary and parotid glands ; main vagus, superior and recurrent laryngeal, depressor, hypoglossal, and cervical sympathetic nerves ; vagus and superior cervical sympathetic ganglia (Fig. 414).

8. Remove the brain. Note : in dorsal view, olfactory lobes, cerebral hemisphere, cerebellum, medulla oblongata, fourth ventricle. Pull outwards, one cerebral hemisphere, and note : corpus callosum, optic thalami, corpora quadrigemina (Fig. 423). In ventral view, olfactory, temporal, and pyriform lobes ; infundibulum ; pituitary body ; corpus albicans ; crura cerebri ; pons Varolii ; medulla oblongata ; roots of second, third, and fifth to twelfth cranial nerves (Fig. 424).[2]

9. Examine the several parts of the skeleton, taking the following vertebræ as examples of their series : atlas, axis, third cervical, fourth thoracic, second lumbar, sacrum (Figs. 397–409).[3]

---

[1] The heart of a sheep is often dissected instead of that of the rabbit. The chief difference between the two is that, like those of man, the two superior venæ cavæ (innominate veins) of the sheep unite before entering the auricle.

[2] The brain of the sheep is often examined instead of that of the rabbit. Its features will readily be followed from the description of the rabbit's brain, but it will be noted that the cerebral hemispheres are much better provided with convolutions.

[3] The skull of the dog is often studied in preference to that of the rabbit. See the footnote on p. 528 (Figs. 446 and 447).

10*a*. Examine under the microscope a drop of blood. Compare
       the red corpuscles (i) with those of the frog, which you have
       already seen (Fig. 81) (ii) with those in a drop of your own
       blood (Fig. 82).

   b. If possible, sections prepared by an expert from the principal
       organs (liver, lungs, pancreas, salivary glands, small in-
       testine, testis, etc.) of a mammal should be examined, with
       the aid of some work on mammalian histology.

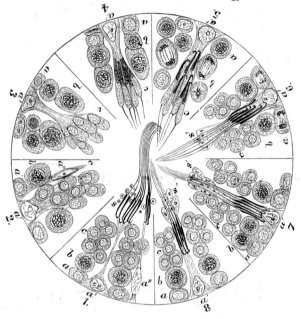

FIG. 551.— A diagrammatic representation of the spermatogenesis
of the Rat.—After Schafer.

Each of the numbered sections of the diagram represents a portion of the circumference of a seminiferous tubule at a certain stage of the process.   In (1) the cells
(spermatids) which result from the two successive maturation divisions of the
spermatocytes, and eventually become spermatozoa, are seen in their earliest
condition.   In (2) they have become attached in groups to supporting cells
(cells of Sertoli).   In (3) to (8) they are becoming spermatozoa, of which their
nuclei constitute the heads.   In (1) again, they are ready to be set free.
a, and *a′*, Lining epithelium cells of the tubules ; *a* are " spermatogonia," which by
division (seen in 6) throw off spermatocytes ; *a′* are cells of Sertoli, which
support the spermatids ; *b*, spermatocytes.   These undergo the two maturation
divisions (indicated in 5) whose ultimate products are *c*, the spermatids.   The
latter, in the process of development into spermatozoa, which they undergo
after attachment to cells of Sertoli, throw off *s′*, portions of their cytoplasm
which disintegrate (*s*).

INDEX

Numbers in heavy type refer to pages with illustrations of the structure in question.

Separate references are not given to each mention of an organ in the section on practical work.

49

Wood louse - lice
Small terrestrial
crustacean w. greyish
segmented body
7 prs legs Damp conditions
Oniscus and other
genera
Order Isopoda